GARDENS OF ENGLAND AND WALES
1987

D0543028

A guide to over 2,300 gardens,
the majority of which are not normally open to the public

CONTENTS

THE NATIONAL GARDENS SCHEME
CHARITABLE TRUST

57 LOWER BELGRAVE STREET, LONDON SW1W 0LR
(01-730 0359)

FOREWORD

The Diamond Jubilee of the National Gardens Scheme is an important milestone for all gardeners. This important charity deserves the warmest congratulations of all who have watched its remarkable growth over sixty years, during which it has raised nearly £4 million. The pioneering work of the National Gardens Scheme has attracted worldwide attention and schemes modelled on it now exist in many other parts of the world.

The Royal Horticultural Society is proud of its long and close relationship with the National Gardens Scheme at a time when interest in gardening has never been greater, nor so widely spread. The role played by the National Gardens Scheme in generating this interest cannot be underestimated. Furthermore, the joy of sharing a common love of plants with friends is one of the delights of gardening and the opportunity to visit gardens throughout England and Wales has undoubtedly created for both visitors and garden owners many new and lasting friendships. Our wholehearted admiration for their achievements must go not only to national Headquarters for their leadership, but equally to each County Organiser whose tireless energy and dedication has encouraged and helped garden owners, often diffident and self-effacing, to receive and welcome visitors. The grass roots organisation in the counties provides 'the sap' which enables the national Scheme to flourish.

The ability of an organisation to adapt to change is often a fine test of its quality. The many economic and social changes of the last sixty years seem to have acted as a positive stimulus to the National Gardens Scheme to find new ways of combining garden visits with the raising of ever-increasing funds for charity. What began as an opportunity to assist District Nurses has now become a major fund raiser, not only for elderly nurses but also for the training of Macmillan Nurses to care for the terminally ill. Gardens and gardeners also benefit from the promotional work of the National Gardens Scheme. Since 1949, an annual contribution has been made to the National Trust Gardens Fund to help maintain gardens of special historic or horticultural importance, and more recently elderly gardeners and their dependants have been added to the long list of those assisted. Many smaller local charities also benefit now that garden owners can donate a share of the proceeds to an additional charity of their own choice.

The Diamond Jubilee edition of *Gardens of England and Wales* lists a record number of well over 2,300 gardens, that are open to the public. The choice of which garden to visit has never been more difficult so the obvious solution must be to visit as many as possible. You will not be disappointed and will have the satisfaction of knowing that your contribution will provide for the continuity and expansion of work that helps both people in need and our environment.

ROBIN HERBERT
President, The Royal Horticultural Society

THE FIRST SIXTY YEARS

'The Gardens Scheme' was started at the suggestion of Miss Elsie Wagg, a member of the Council of the Queen's Nursing Institute, as part of a national memorial to Queen Alexandra whose deep and sympathetic interest in District Nursing was well known.

Although this country was renowned for its gardens, few people had the opportunity to see them, so that when 600 were opened in 1927 the response was such that the experiment became an English institution. The Scheme, now called the **National Gardens Scheme Charitable Trust,** has continued and expanded ever since, until in 1986 it comprised over 2,000 gardens.

The National Gardens Scheme helps many deserving causes, the chief call on its funds being in support of its original beneficiary, the **Queen's Nursing Institute** for the relief of District and other nurses in need – be this caused by old age, difficulties through illness or the stress and pressure of their work.

Since 1949 a contribution has been made to the **National Trust** to help maintain gardens of special historic or horticultural interest. In 1984 the increasing popularity of the Scheme made it possible to further extend its charitable work by assisting the **National Society for Cancer Relief** with funds for training **Macmillan Nurses** in the continuing care of the terminally ill. In 1986 the Scheme took on the charitable work previously organised by Gardeners' Sunday in aid of the **Gardeners' Royal Benevolent Society** and the **Royal Gardeners' Orphan Fund.**

Many other national and local charities also benefit from the Scheme, since garden owners may, if they so wish, allocate an agreed proportion of the proceeds of an opening for the National Gardens Scheme to another charity. The names of these additional charities are published in the descriptive entries for the gardens.

The Chairman and Council wish to express their deep gratitude to all those whose generous support of the National Gardens Scheme makes it possible to help these most worthwhile charities. Please help us by visiting as many gardens as you can, in this, our **Diamond Jubilee Year.**

THANK YOU FOR YOUR SUPPORT.

1927 'PIONEER' GARDENS OPENING IN 1987

The National Gardens Scheme will have much pleasure this year in offering a tree to the owners of each of the gardens which played such a very important role in establishing the Scheme in 1927, and which are supporting the Scheme in this, the Diamond Jubilee year. The National Gardens Scheme acknowledges with gratitude Notcutts Nursery, whose generosity has helped to make this gesture possible. The 'pioneer' gardens are as follows:

SANDRINGHAM (Norfolk)

ABBOTSBURY GARDENS (Dorset)
ABBOTSWOOD (Gloucestershire)
ALDERMASTON COURT (Berkshire)
ARLEY HALL (Cheshire)
ASCOTT (Buckinghamshire)
BAYFIELD HALL (Norfolk)
BENINGTON LORDSHIP (Hertfordshire)
BERKELEY CASTLE (Gloucestershire)
BIDDICK HALL (Durham)
BITTESCOMBE MANOR (Somerset)
BLENHEIM PALACE (Oxfordshire)
BLICKLING HALL (Norfolk)
BORDE HILL GARDEN (Sussex)
BRICKWALL (Sussex)
BROUGHTON CASTLE (Oxfordshire)
BULWICK PARK (Northamptonshire)
BURWARTON HOUSE (Shropshire)
CARCLEW GARDENS (Cornwall)
CHETTLE HOUSE (Dorset)
CIRENCESTER PARK (Gloucester)
COLESBOURNE PARK (Gloucestershire)
COMPTON ACRES GARDENS (Dorset)
CRANBORNE MANOR (Dorset)
DROVE HOUSE (Norfolk)
ERDDIG PARK (Clwyd)
FAULKBOURNE HALL (Essex)
FONTHILL HOUSE (Wiltshire)
FORDE ABBEY (Dorset)
GARNONS (Herefordshire)
GLOUCESTER COLLEGE OF AGRICULTURE
GRAYTHWAITE HALL (Cumbria)
GUNBY HALL (Lincolnshire)
GWYSANEY HALL (Clwyd)
HACKWOOD PARK (Hampshire)
HALL BARN (Buckinghamshire)
HESTERCOMBE HOUSE (Somerset)
HIGHDOWN (Sussex)
HIGHWOOD GARDEN (Dorset)
HOLDENBY HOUSE (Northamptonshire)
HODNET HALL GARDENS (Shropshire)
HOLKER HALL (Cumbria)
HOLLAND HOUSE (Worcestershire)
HURST LODGE (Berkshire)
ICOMB PLACE (Gloucestershire)
KINGSTON MAURWARD (Dorset)
KNOLE (Kent)
LANHYDROCK (Cornwall)
LEA GARDENS (Derbyshire)
LEVENS HALL (Cumbria)

LILFORD PARK (Northamptonshire)
LINGHOLM (Cumbria)
LOCKO PARK (Derbyshire)
MADRESFIELD COURT (Worcestershire)
MAESLLWCH CASTLE (Powys)
THE MANOR HOUSE, SUTTON
   COURTENAY (Oxfordshire)
MELBURY HOUSE (Dorset)
MILTON LODGE (Somerset)
MINTERNE (Dorset)
MOCCAS COURT (Herefordshire)
NORTH LUFFENHAM HALL (Rutland)
NOTTINGHAMSHIRE COLLEGE OF
   AGRICULTURE
NUNEHAM PARK (Oxfordshire)
OAKLANDS (Avon)
OTELEY (Shropshire)
PARNHAM (Dorset)
PEOVER HALL (Cheshire)
PINBURY PARK (Gloucestershire)
PITCHFORD HALL (Shropshire)
PLAS HEATON (Clwyd)
PYLEWELL PARK (Hampshire)
RABY CASTLE (Co. Durham)
RAMSTER (Surrey)
RHUAL (Clwyd)
RIVERHILL HOUSE (Kent)
ST. NICHOLAS (Yorkshire)
SANDLING PARK (Kent)
SEZINCOTE (Gloucestershire)
SHERBORNE PARK (Gloucestershire)
SHUGBOROUGH (Staffordshire)
SOMERLEY (Hampshire)
SOMERLEYTON HALL (Suffolk)
SOUTHILL PARK (Bedfordshire)
SPETCHLEY PARK (Worcestershire)
STANWAY HOUSE (Gloucestershire)
SUDELEY CASTLE (Gloucestershire)
TRELISSICK (Cornwall)
WALCOT HALL (Shropshire)
WASING PLACE (Berkshire)
WAYFORD MANOR (Somerset)
WESTONBIRT SCHOOL (Gloucestershire)
WELBECK (Nottinghamshire)
WELFORD PARK (Berkshire)
WILLEY PARK (Shropshire)
WROXTON ABBEY (Oxfordshire)

The above are known to be 1927 gardens; but the records for that year are incomplete and if anyone is aware of any additional gardens open for the National Gardens Scheme in 1927, the Administrator at Headquarters would be grateful to hear.

GENERAL INFORMATION AND KEY TO SIGNS USED IN THIS BOOK

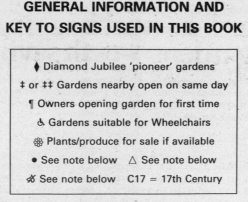

♦ Diamond Jubilee 'pioneer' gardens

‡ or ‡‡ Gardens nearby open on same day

¶ Owners opening garden for first time

& Gardens suitable for Wheelchairs

❀ Plants/produce for sale if available

● See note below △ See note below

✘ See note below C17 = 17th Century

Children: All children must be accompanied by an adult.

✘ No Dogs: but otherwise dogs are usually admitted, *provided they are kept on a lead*. Dogs are not admitted to houses.

● Gardens marked thus, which open throughout the season, give a guaranteed contribution from their takings to the National Gardens Scheme.

△ **Where this sign appears alongside dates in the** *descriptive* entry for a garden it denotes that this garden will be open in aid of the National Gardens Scheme on the dates shown, but that this garden *is also open* regularly to the public *on other days too.* Details about the regular opening of such gardens can be found in *Historic Houses, Castles and Gardens* obtainable from booksellers; see page x. (In the case of National Trust gardens details can also be found in their *Handbook for Members and Visitors*; see page x.)

Additional Charities nominated by Owner: Where the owners of 'private' gardens (not normally open to the public) have nominated some other charity to receive an agreed share from an opening for the National Gardens Scheme, the name of the other charity is included in the descriptive entry.

Distances and sizes: In all cases these are approximate.

Open by appointment: Owners who open their gardens by appointment will welcome individuals as well as parties, unless the information given in the details about the gardens specifies parties only.

Coach parties: Please, by appointment only unless stated otherwise.

Houses are not open unless this is specifically stated; where the house or part-house is shown an additional charge is usually made.

Tea: When this is available at a garden the information is given in capitals, e.g. TEAS (usually with home-made cakes) or TEA (usually with biscuits). There is, of course, an extra charge for any refreshments available at a garden. Any other information given about tea is a guide only to assist visitors in finding somewhere in the area for tea.

Buses: Continuance of many bus services, and particularly in rural areas, is a matter of considerable uncertainty and especially on SUNDAYS. It is strongly recommended that details should be checked in advance.

National Trust Members are requested to note that where a National Trust property has allocated an opening day to the National Gardens Scheme which is one of its normal opening days members can still gain entry on production of their National Trust membership card (although donations to the Scheme's charities will be welcome). Where, however, the day allocated is one on which the property would *not* normally be open, then the payment of the National Gardens Scheme admission fee will be required.

Professional photographers: No photographs taken in a garden may be used for sale for reproduction without the prior permission of the garden owner.

RELEVANT ORGANISATIONS AND
THEIR PUBLICATIONS

Historic Houses, Castles and Gardens in Great Britain and Ireland, 1987 edition. Published by British Leisure Publications, a division of Information Services Ltd, Windsor Court, East Grinstead House, East Grinstead, West Sussex. Price £3.25 at W. H. Smith and all leading booksellers in Great Britain and Ireland. Published annually in January, gives details of over 1,300 houses, castles and gardens open to the public.

The National Trust. Certain gardens owned by the National Trust are opened in aid of the National Gardens Scheme on the dates shown in this book. Information about the regular opening of these gardens is given in the 1987 *Handbook for Members and Visitors* (issued free to Members), published by the National Trust (£2.95 plus 50p for postage; subject to alteration) and obtainable from 36 Queen Anne's Gate, London SW1H 9AS, or from any National Trust property.

Scotland's Gardens Scheme raises funds through the opening of gardens for the Queen's Nursing Institute (Scotland), the Gardens Fund of the National Trust for Scotland and over 100 other charities nominated by the garden owners. Handbook with all details of openings published mid-March. Tours: three six-day coach tours. Free brochure available. Handbook (£1.30 inc. p & p) from Scotland's Gardens Scheme, 31 Castle Terrace, Edinburgh EH1 2EL. Tel. 031-229 1870.

The National Trust for Scotland was established in 1931. In its care are over 100 properties including, as well as gardens and castles, cottages, mountains, islands and historic sites. The National Trust for Scotland, 5 Charlotte Square, Edinburgh EH2 4DU.

Ulster Gardens Scheme. A list of the private gardens open to the public under the Ulster Gardens Scheme can be obtained from: The Regional Information Officer, The National Trust, Rowallane, Saintfield, Co. Down. Tel. Saintfield 510721.

The Automobile Association Guide to *Stately Homes, Museums, Castles and Gardens in Britain* gives details of around 2,000 places of interest in England, Wales, Scotland and the Channel Islands. Available from AA bookshops and all good booksellers. Price £5.95.

Historic Houses Association represents over 1,200 private owners of historic houses and outstanding gardens. The HHA is particularly concerned with the problem of funding gardens. It administers a training scheme for young gardeners in the private sector; runs the Christie's/ HHA Garden of the Year Award; co-operates on a biannual gardens management course at Wye College, Kent, and organises periodic seminars. A quarterly magazine is available to Members and Friends of the Historic Houses Association and on subscription. HHA, 38 Ebury Street, London SW1W 0LU. Tel. 01-730 9419.

Historic Irish Tourist Houses & Gardens Association publishes annually an illustrated leaflet with information about nearly 50 properties. Available free from HITHA, c/o Dalkey Travel, 3a Castle Street, Dalkey, Co. Dublin.

The Automobile Association has kindly arranged for information on gardens open for the Scheme to be available from their local offices.

The Royal Automobile Club has kindly arranged that their Patrols will direct motorists to gardens in the locality when asked.

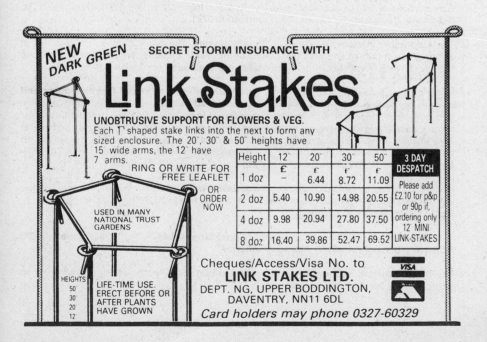

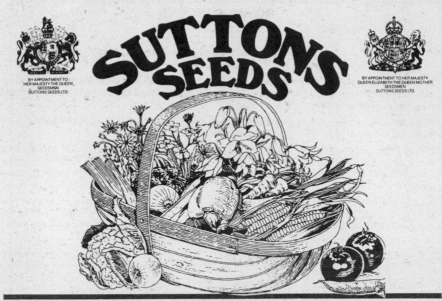

ROYAL GARDENS

SANDRINGHAM HOUSE AND GROUNDS
(Norfolk)

By gracious permission of Her Majesty The Queen, the House and Grounds at Sandringham will be open (except when Her Majesty The Queen or any members of the Royal Family is in residence) on the following days:

April, May, June, July, August and September from April 19 until Thursday September 24 inclusive every Sunday, Monday, Tuesday, Wednesday and Thursday.

Please note that the HOUSE ONLY will be closed to the public from July 20 to August 8 inclusive and that the House and Grounds will be closed from July 24 to August 5 inclusive. Coach drivers and visitors are advised to confirm these closing and opening dates nearer the time.

Hours: Sandringham House: 11 (12 noon on Sundays) to 4.45; Sandringham Grounds: 10.30 (11.30 on Sundays) to 5. **Admission Charges:** House and Grounds: Adults £1.80, OAPs £1.40, Children £1.00; Grounds only: Adults £1.30, OAPs £1.00, Children 70p. It is not possible to purchase a ticket to visit the House only. Admission to the Museum is free.

Advance party bookings will be accepted during April, May and September only, except on Bank Holidays and Sundays. There are no reductions in admission fees for parties. Picnicking is not permitted inside the Grounds. Dogs are not permitted inside the Grounds. Free car and coach parking.

Sandringham Church will be open as follows, subject to Weddings, Funerals and Special services: when the Grounds are open as stated above, Monday to Thursday inclusive 11-5 (Sundays 2-5 April to Sept.). At other times of the year, the Church will be open from 11-12.30 and 2-5, but the Church is always closed on Fridays and Saturdays throughout the year.

Enquiries: Mr. R.S. French, Estate Office, Sandringham or by telephone 9-1, 2-4.30 Monday to Friday inclusive at King's Lynn 772675.

Sandringham Flower Show will be held on Wednesday July 29. Full details may be obtained from the Flower Show Secretary, Mr. J. Annison, The Dene, West Newton, King's Lynn (telephone Dersingham 40575).

FROGMORE GARDENS
(Berkshire)

By gracious permission of Her Majesty The Queen, the Frogmore Gardens, Windsor Castle, will be open from 11-7 on the following days:

Wednesday May 6 and Thursday May 7

Coaches by appointment only: apply to the National Gardens Scheme, 57 Lower Belgrave Street, London SW1W 0LR (Tel. 01-730 0359) stating whether May 6 or 7, and whether morning or afternoon. Admission 80p, Children 15p. Dogs not allowed. Royal Mausoleum also open, free of charge, both days. Entrance to Gardens and Mausoleum through Long Walk gate. Visitors are requested kindly to refrain from entering the grounds of the Home Park. Light refreshments will be available at the car park (near the outer gate to the Gardens).

BARNWELL MANOR
(Northamptonshire)

By kind permission of Their Royal Highnesses Princess Alice Duchess of Gloucester and the Duke and Duchess of Gloucester, the gardens at Barnwell Manor will be open from 2.30-6 on:

Sundays May 3 and 31: Admission 60p, Children 10p

THE ROYAL HORTICULTURAL SOCIETY
FLOWER SHOWS IN 1987

Chelsea Flower Show
will be held in the Royal Hospital Grounds, Chelsea

Admission:

Tuesday, 20 May	8 am to 8 pm	to holders of Private View tickets
Wednesday, 21 May	8 am to 8 pm	£14.00 until 4 pm, then £8.00
Thursday, 22 May	8 am to 8 pm	£12.00 until 4 pm, then £6.00
Friday, 23 May	8 am to 5 pm	£9.00

Westminster Shows
organised by the RHS at their Halls at Vincent Square/Greycoat Street

Opening Shows: January 27/28; February 24/25
Spring Shows: March 17/18; April 7/8; April 28/29
Summer Shows: June 16/17; July 14/15; August 11/12
Great Autumn Show: September 15/16/17
Autumn Shows: October 6/7; October 27/28; November 24/25

Other Flower Shows at the RHS Halls

British Orchid Growers Association Show: March 14/15
National Dahlia Society: September 2
Royal National Rose Society: September 7/8
National Chrysanthemum Society: September 7/8; November 6/7

THE SOCIETY'S GARDEN AT WISLEY

The famous garden at Wisley is twenty miles south-west of London, between Cobham and Ripley in Surrey, on the west side of the London-Portsmouth road (A3).

Wisley is a wonderful garden. At every season there is something to delight and to teach the gardener. Daffodils, rhododendrons, and rock plants, roses and herbaceous plants, orchards, the heather garden and the glasshouses.

The garden is open every day except Christmas Day

February to October:
Weekdays: 10 am to 7 pm or sunset (whichever is earlier)
Sundays: from 10 am for members; after 2 pm for the public until 7 pm or sunset (whichever is earlier)

November to January:
Weekdays: 10 am to 4.30 pm
Sundays: from 10 am for members; after 2 pm for the public until 4.30 pm

Admission: free with 2 friends per member's ticket; £2.00 for the public.
Sundays: April-October £2.50

———

Further details about the Flower Shows and Wisley Garden available from
The Secretary, Royal Horticultural Society,
Vincent Square, London SW1P 2PE
Tel. 01-834 4333

MARION SMITH

LIFE SIZE BRONZE RESIN SCULPTURES ALL LIMITED
EDITIONS DESIGNED FOR GARDENS AND INTERIORS

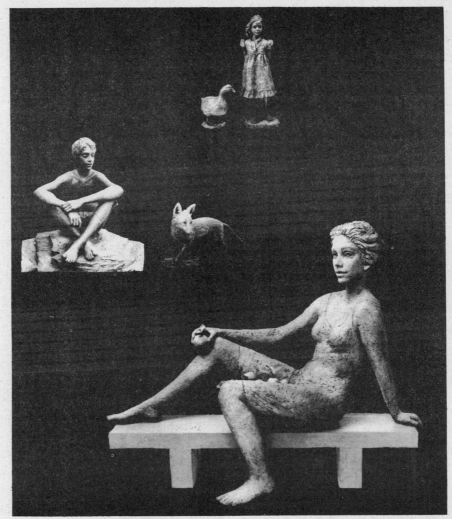

Brochure from:
**MARION SMITH, THE STUDIO, FARM COTTAGE,
PUTTENHAM, NR. GUILDFORD, SURREY GU3 1AJ
TELEPHONE: GUILDFORD (0483) 810352**

EXHIBITING ANNUALLY AT THE CHELSEA FLOWER SHOW

The Gardens

AVON

Hon County Organiser:
MRS M.G. THOMPSON, 33 Old Sneed
  Avenue, Stoke Bishop,
  Bristol, BS9 1SD
Assistant Hon County Organiser:
MRS R.L PHILLIPS, Wreyland, The Green,
  Tockington BS12 4LG

DATES OF OPENING

BY APPOINTMENT ONLY for dates see text:
  ESTATE YARD HOUSE, Dyrham
REGULAR OPENINGS for dates see text:
  THE MANOR HOUSE, Walton-in-Gordano

MARCH Sunday 29
  OAKLANDS, Almondsbury
APRIL Sunday 5
  GROVE COTTAGE, Flax Bourton
APRIL Sunday 12
  ABBOTS LEIGH GARDENS, Abbots Leigh
APRIL Easter Sunday 19
  VINE HOUSE, Henbury
APRIL Easter Monday 20
  ALGARS MANOR, Iron Acton
  VINE HOUSE, Henbury
APRIL Saturday 25
  TOCKINGTON GARDENS
APRIL Sunday 26
  BURWALLS, Leigh Woods
  COLEY COURT & THE LITTLE MANOR, nr
    Bristol
  CROWE HALL, Widcombe
  LYEGROVE, Badminton
  TOCKINGTON GARDENS
MAY Sunday 3
  COOMBE DINGLE GARDENS, nr Bristol
MAY Monday 4 (Bank Hol)
  COOMBE DINGLE GARDENS, nr Bristol
MAY Saturday 9
  BRACKENWOOD NURSERIES, Portishead
  GOLDNEY HOUSE, Bristol
MAY Sunday 10
  BRACKENWOOD NURSERIES, Portishead
  GOLDNEY HOUSE, Bristol
  SEVERN VIEW, nr Thornbury
MAY Wednesday 13
  ORCHARD HOUSE, Claverton
MAY Sunday 17
  SEVERN VIEW, nr Thornbury
MAY WEDNESDAY 20
  ORCHARD HOUSE, Claverton
MAY Saturday 23
  PARSONAGE FARM, Publow
MAY Sunday 24
  ALGARS MANOR & ALGARS MILL, Iron
    Acton
  PARSONAGE FARM, Publow
  SEVERN VIEW, nr Thornbury
  VINE HOUSE, Henbury

MAY Monday 25 (Bank Hol)
  ALGARS MANOR & ALGARS MILL, Iron
    Acton
  PARSONAGE FARM, Publow
  VINE HOUSE, Henbury
MAY Wednesday 27
  ORCHARD HOUSE, Claverton
MAY Saturday 30
  SEVERN VIEW, nr Thornbury
MAY Sunday 31
  SEVERN VIEW, nr Thornbury
JUNE Wednesday 3
  ORCHARD HOUSE, Claverton
JUNE Saturday 6
  SEVERN VIEW, nr Thornbury
JUNE Sunday 7
  CLIFTON GARDENS, Bristol
  CROWE HALL, Widcombe
  SEVERN VIEW, nr Thornbury
JUNE Wednesday 10
  ORCHARD HOUSE, Claverton
JUNE Saturday 13
  BRACKENWOOD NURSERIES, Portishead
JUNE Sunday 14
  BRACKENWOOD NURSERIES, Portishead
  HILL HOUSE, Wickwar
JUNE Wednesday 17
  ORCHARD HOUSE, Claverton
JUNE Sunday 21
  DOYNTON HOUSE, Doynton
  HARPTREE COURT, East Harptree
JUNE Wednesday 24
  ORCHARD HOUSE, Claverton
JUNE Saturday 27
  CHURCH FARM, Lower Failand
  PEAR TREE HOUSE, Litton
JUNE Sunday 28
  BADMINTON VILLAGE
  CHURCH FARM, Lower Failand
  PEAR TREE HOUSE, Litton
JUNE Monday 29
  BADMINTON VILLAGE
JULY Wednesday 1
  ORCHARD HOUSE, Claverton
JULY Sunday 5
  LYEGROVE, Badminton
JULY Sunday 12
  THE HOLMES GARDEN, Bristol
  KELSTON ROAD GARDENS, nr Bath
  LITTLETON HOUSE, West Littleton
  UNIVERSITY OF BRISTOL, BOTANIC
    GARDEN
  WICK MANOR, Wick
JULY Monday 13
  WICK MANOR, Wick
JULY Wednesday 15
  COMBE HAY MANOR, Bath
JULY Sunday 19
  HAZEL COTTAGE, Lower Hazel
  SPRINGFIELD BARN, Upton Cheyney
JULY Sunday 26
  STANTON PRIOR GARDENS, nr Bath
JULY Wednesday 29
  COMBE HAY MANOR, Bath

SEPTEMBER Sunday 6
UNIVERSITY OF BRISTOL, BOTANIC GARDEN
SEPTEMBER Saturday 19
TOCKINGTON GARDENS
SEPTEMBER Sunday 20
BURRINGTON GARDENS
TOCKINGTON GARDENS
OCTOBER Saturday 10
PEAR TREE HOUSE, Litton
OCTOBER Sunday 11
PEAR TREE HOUSE, Litton

DESCRIPTIONS OF GARDENS

Abbots Leigh Gardens. 2m W of Bristol. From Bristol take A369 to Portishead; opp George Inn turn into Church Rd. From M5 take exit 19 (Gordano Services) A369 to Bristol, 3m. TEAS. *Combined adm 80p Chd 25p. Sun Apr 12 (2-5.30)*
    Abbots Leigh House ⚘ (Mr & Mrs R. Gallannaugh) 1½-acres; lawns, herbaceous borders, shrubs, trees, specimen cedar of Lebanon, lily ponds, formal rose garden. 200-yr old Dower House (not open)
    Glebe House ⚘ (Prof & Mrs Peter Bromhead) Church Rd; 1st on left after village green and church. Park in school or by village green. 1-acre garden of former Victorian vicarage; spring bulbs, shrubs and trees. Views over Severn Estuary

Algars Manor & Algars Mill, Iron Acton 9m N of Bristol. 3m W of Yate Sodbury. Turn S off Iron Acton bypass B4059, past village green, 200yds, then over level Xing (Station Rd). TEAS Algars Manor. *Combined adm £1 Chd 20p. Sun, Mon May 24, 25 (2-6)*
    Algars Manor ⚘ (Dr & Mrs J. M. Naish) 3-acre woodland garden beside R. Frome; mill-stream; native plants mixed with azaleas, rhododendrons, camellias, magnolias, eucalyptus. Picnic areas. Early Jacobean house (not open) and old barn. *Adm 50p Chd 20p. Mon April 20 (2-6) Also by appt (Tel 045422 372)*
    Algars Mill (Mr & Mrs J. Wright) entrance via Algars Manor. 2-acre woodland garden beside R. Frome; spring bulbs, shrubs; early Spring feature of wild Newent daffodils. 300-400 yr old mill house (not open) through which mill-race still runs

Badminton Village ⚘ 5m E of Chipping Sodbury. TEA Village Hall on Sun. *Combined adm £1.50 Chd 20p (Share to GTNC). Sun, Mon June 28, 29 (2-6)*
    Essex House ⚘ (Mr & Mrs James Lees-Milne) Small garden redesigned and maintained by present tenants since 1976; old shrub roses, topiary
    The Old Vicarage ⚘ (Mrs Guiness) Pretty walled garden in picturesque setting

Brackenwood Nurseries' Woodland Walk ⚘ ⚘ (John Maycock Esq) 131 Nore Rd (coast rd) Portishead. From Bristol A369 (10m). M5 Junc 19 or Bus No 359. Walk lies behind Brackenwood Garden Centre (open daily 9-5.30, Tel 0272 843484), ¾m from Portishead on coast rd to Clevedon. 5-acre steeply sloping woodland garden overlooking Bristol channel; rhododendrons, azaleas, camellias, pieris, embothriums, rare trees and shrubs; water lily pools, bog garden. Waterfowl enclosure, swan pool, aviaries, parakeets. TEAS. *Adm 60p Chd 30p. Sats, Suns May 9, 10, June 13, 14 (9-5)*

¶**Burrington Gardens** ⚘ 12m S of Bristol; 1m off A38 (3m S of Bristol Airport); ¼m off A368, N of Burrington Village. TEAS at Burrington Combe Cafe (1m). *Combined adm £1 Chd 25p. Sun Sept 20 (2-6)*
    Bourne House ⚘ (Mr & Mrs Christopher Thomas) 8-acres inc 2 paddocks, stream with waterfalls, waterlily pool. Mature trees, shrubs, autumn flowering cyclamen; bulbs; herbaceous; roses
    Tankards (Mr & Mrs Neil Revie) Burrington ½-acre garden; island beds, herbaceous borders. Mixture of unusual shrubs and perennials; small pond; variety of ground cover; autumn colour

Burwalls ⚘ (University of Bristol) 2m W of Bristol. Take B3129; immediately after crossing Clifton Suspension Bridge, entrance on left through small wooden door in wall behind lay-by, just beyond main entrance to Burwalls House. 4-acre terraced garden on edge of gorge; spring flowers and shrubs; also woodland containing Iron Age Fort. Ground floor of Burwalls House (former home of Sir George A. Wills Bt) also open. *Adm 50p Chd 20p (Share to Cancer Research Campaign). Sun April 26 (2-6)*

Church Farm ⚘ ⚘⚘ (Mr & Mrs N. Slade) Lower Failand, 6m SW of Bristol. Take B3128 out of Bristol to Cleveland Rd. Via Clerk-Combe Hill, turn right down Oxhouse Lane opp garage; left past Church then right into private road, house is 1st right; or turn off M5 Junc 19 towards Bristol. Through Portbury, turn left into Failand Lane. Parking adjacent to church. 3-acre small holding overlooking Severn Estuary. Garden started in 1974; run on organic principles with partial self sufficiency and livestock. TEAS. *Adm 50p Chd 25p (Share to Failand Church Fund). Sat, Sun June 27, 28 (2-6)*

Clifton Gardens ⚘⚘ Bristol. From Blackboy roundabout 1st left after Bristol Zoo, College Rd, 1st right Cecil Rd, 2nd left Canynge Rd. *Combined adm £1.25 Chd 25p. Sun June 7 (2-6)*
    45 Canynge Rd ⚘ (John & Georgiana Nye) ⅓-acre garden; mostly shrubs, Mulberry tree and pool backed by yew hedge. Rec-

tangular design recently made less formal

15 The Paragon & (D. Pamment Esq) Below Avon Gorge Hotel, opp Royal York Crescent. Formal and informal garden, unusual rock garden and old fashioned roses; view over Avon Gorge, Cumberland Basin and Dundry

9 Sion Hill & (Mr & Mrs R.C. Begg) Turn left just before bridge. Small walled town garden, densely planted; climbing and herbaceous plants; herb garden; old roses

17 Sion Hill & (Mrs P.Stock) Turn left just before bridge. Small town garden with trees and shrubs. TEAS

Coley Court && (Mrs M.J. Hill) East Harptree, 8m N of Wells. A39 at Chewton Mendip take B3114 2m signed Coley, follow lane 400yds to white house on left before bridge. 1 acre; open lawn, stone walls, spring bulbs; 1 acre old Somerset orchard. Early Jacobean house (not open). Also open **The Little Manor** & (Lt-Col & Mrs K.P.P. Goldschmidt) Farrington Gurney on A39. Turn E in village to A362, then left up lane. ¾-acre spring garden; many varieties of bulbs, flowering trees, many rare shrubs; rose garden. Early C17 house with attractive courtyard. TEAS. *Combined adm £1 Chd 20p (Share to Avon Red Cross). Sun April 26 (2-6)*

Combe Hay Manor (Mr & Mrs N. Robertson) 4m S of Bath signed off A367. Small C18 park with lake, temple and Chinese bridge. *Adm 60p Chd 25p. Weds July 15, 29 (2-6)*

Coombe Dingle Gardens 4m NW of Bristol centre. From Portway down Sylvan Way, turn left into the Dingle and Grove Rd. From Westbury-on-Trym, Canford Lane sharp right at beginning of Westbury Lane. From Bristol over Downs, Parrys Lane, Coombe Lane; turn left and sharp right into the Dingle and Grove Rd. TEA Hillside. *Combined adm 80p Chd under 10 free, 10-16yrs 40p (Share to Friends of Blaise) Sun, Mon May 3, 4 (2-6)*
Hillside && (Mrs C.M. Luke) 42 Grove Rd. 2-acres; late Georgian lay-out, Victorian rose garden; fine trees, shrubs, walled kitchen garden
Pennywell (Mr & Mrs D.H. Baker) Grove Rd. 2 acres; varied collection trees and shrubs inc 50ft span flowering cherry; fritillaries, rockery, organic kitchen garden. Views over adjoining Blaise Castle Estate, Kingsweston Down and the Trym Valley

Crowe Hall (John Barratt Esq) Widcombe, 1m SE of Bath. Left up Widcombe Hill, off A36, leaving White Hart on right. Large varied garden; fine trees, lawns, spring bulbs, walled gardens etc; on steep hillside with Italianate terraces; Victorian grotto contrasting with English landscape; summer display of flow-

ers in tubs. DOGS welcome. *Adm 50p Chd 25p. Suns April 26, June 7 (2-6)*

Doynton House && (Mrs C.E. Pitman) Doynton. 8m E of Bristol, ¾m NE of A420 at E end of Wick. Mature, old-fashioned 2-acre garden with herbaceous borders, shrubs and lawns TEAS. *Adm 50p Chd 20p. Sun June 21 (2-6)*

Estate Yard House && (Mr & Mrs Samuel Rowley) Dyrham 8m N of Bath, 12m E of Bristol. 2¼m S of M4 Junc 18 on A46; follow signs to Dyrham and Doynton; 1st right. ¾ acre in delightful setting; wall plants, spring bulbs, shrubs, roses, varied planting, mature trees. *Adm 50p. Some Sats & Suns by appt (Tel Abson 2509)*

Goldney House & (University of Bristol) Lower Clifton Hill, Bristol. At top of Constitution Hill, Clifton. 9-acre historic garden, developed 1731-68 by Thomas Goldney, Bristol merchant; fine period grotto; terrace, bastion, tower, orangery and parterre; old-world garden with many species of the period. Cream TEAS in orangery. *Adm £1 OAPs/Chd 50p (Share to Goldney Restoration Fund). Sat, Sun May 9, 10 (2-5)*

Grove Cottage & (Mr & Mrs A.J. Hills) Church Lane, Flax Bourton 6m S of Bristol. Take A370 to Weston. At end of Long Ashton bypass after Jubilee Inn turn right into B3129 (parking). 1 acre; gradually replacing grass with paved areas and larger borders with new planting of trees, shrubs, herbaceous and silver leaved plants; many varieties narcissi. TEA. *Adm 40p Chd 20p. Sun April 5 (2-6)*

Harptree Court && (Mr & Mrs Richard Hill) East Harptree, 8m N of Wells via A39 Bristol Rd to Chewton Mendip; then B3114 to East Harptree, gates on left. From Bath via A368 Weston-super-Mare Rd to West Harptree. Large garden; fine old trees in lovely setting; woodland walks; handsome stone bridge; lily pond and new paved garden. TEAS. *Adm 70p Chd free (Share to Imperial Cancer Research) Sun June 21 (2-6)*

¶**Hazel Cottage** & (Dr & Mrs Brandon Lush) Lower Hazel ¼m W of Rugeway on A38; 10m N of Bristol. 2nd house on left. ½-acre cottage garden with wide variety of herbaceous plants and shrubs, inc many alpines. *Adm 40p Chd 20p (Share to Friends of Age Research, Bristol). Sun July 19 (2-6)*

Hill House & (Sally, Duchess of Westminster) 4m N of Chipping Sodbury on B4060. Through Wickwar, left by wall signed to M5, then 200yds on left. Medium-sized garden; tree and shrub paddocks; gold/silver planting in gravel; wild flowers, grasses; flowering cherries, bulbs. 2 aviaries of foreign birds, flock of Welsh mountain sheep. *Adm 60p Chd 25p (Share to GTNC). Sun June 14 (2-6)*

The Holmes Garden &⚘ (University of Bristol) Churchill Hall, Stoke Park Rd, Bristol. Follow signs to Stoke Bishop; Stoke Park Rd is off Stoke Hill. 3½-acre plantsman's garden begun 1879; wide range of trees and shrubs inc fine magnolias; rock-garden; dell with acid-loving plants; small arboretum nr Churchill Hall also open, planted 1961 with recent additions (all trees labelled). TEAS. *Adm 50p Chd 20p. Sun July 12 (2-6)*

Kelston Road Gardens ⚘⚘ 3m NW of Bath on A431 to Bitton. Please observe parking advice. TEA. *Combined adm 80p Chd 20p (Share to All Saints Church, Weston). Sun July 12 (2-6)*
  23 Kelston Road (Mr & Mrs W.B. Williams) ⅓-acre terraced plantsman's garden on 4 levels; replanted since 1982; rockery, herbaceous, old fashioned roses, vegetables; acid beds; greenhouse; good views
  Cleeve Hill (Mr & Mrs C.H. Hayes) 1-acre terraced garden; roses, herbaceous borders; walled garden with white border; view over small wood to R. Avon

Littleton House ⚘ (Capt Francis Burne) West Littleton. 9m N of Bath, 9m NW of Chippenham, 2m S of M4 Exit 18 off A46 1m. Delightful and typical recently planted Gloucestershire walled garden surrounded by historic scheduled buildings dating from C16. TEA. *Adm 50p Chd 20p (Share to Theatre Royal, Bath). Sun July 12 (2-6)*

Lyegrove &⚘ (Christopher Selmes Esq) Badminton, 4m E of Chipping Sodbury. Turn off A46 at Cross Hands Inn onto B4040, garden left between Old Sodbury and Badminton. 4 acres; lawns, yew hedges, herbaceous borders, old roses, mature trees and shrubs; spring garden; lily pond; old walls. Laid out in 1920s by the late Countess of Westmorland and architect, Kitchin. *Adm 60p Chd 30p. Suns April 26, July 5 (2-6)*

The Manor House &⚘⚘ (Mr & Mrs Simon Wills) Walton-in-Gordano, 2m NE of Clevedon. Entrance by last house nearest Clevedon on N side of B3124 at Walton-in-Gordano. Clevedon-Portishead buses stop in Village. 4 acres; plantman's garden, mainly shrubs and fine trees, much new planting inc bulbs, alpines, and herbaceous plants, mostly labelled. Coaches by appt only. TEAS (April 20, May 4,25 Aug 31) *Adm 75p Chd free (Share to St Peter's Hospice, Bristol). April 1-Sept 17 every Mon, Wed, Thurs (10-4); Suns April 12, May 10, June 14, July 12, Aug 9, Sept 13 (2-6). Mons April 20 May 4, 25 (10-6); Sun, Mon Aug 30, 31 (2-6); also by appt all year (Tel Clevedon 872067)*

♦**Oaklands (Elderly Persons' Home)** & (The County of Avon) By courtesy of the Social Services Cttee, the Officer-in-charge and staff of the Social Services and Estates Services Depts. Almondsbury 7m N of Bristol. Off A38 on Almondsbury side, 100yds past A38-M5 roundabout junc. 12-acre well-maintained garden with carpet of spring flowers. House and grounds owned by the County of Avon for an Elderly Persons' Home; originally property of Hiatt Baker family who planted many rare trees, shrubs and plants; in recent years tended by one gardener (in contrast to the number employed in pre-war years); TEA. *Collecting box (Share to Oaklands Comfort Fund). Sun March 29 (2-4.30)*

Orchard House ⚘⚘ (Rear-Adm & Mrs Hugh Tracy) Claverton, 3½m from Bath on A36; follow signpost to Claverton Village. Or ½m down hill from American Museum. Bus stop Claverton. 2½-acre plantsman's garden; botanical interest combined with attractive and informal layout; collections of herbs, alpines, ground-cover, silver plants; rock gardens, herbaceous borders, lawns, shrubs, views. Small (wholesale) Nursery. *Adm 60p Chd 30p (Share to RNLI). Weds May 13, 20, 27, June 3, 10, 17, 24 July 1, (2-6)*

Parsonage Farm &⚘⚘ (Mr & Mrs Andrew Reid) Publow, 9m S Bristol. A37 Bristol-Wells; at top of Pensford Hill, almost opp B3130 to Chew Magna, take lane which runs down side of row of houses; 250yds on right. 3½-acre woodland garden with large collection of trees and shrubs inc rhododendrons, azaleas and conifers; tuffastone rockery and heather garden. Flower Festival in village. TEAS in aid of All Saints, Publow. *Adm 60p OAPs/Chd 25p. Sat, Sun, Mon May 23, 24, 25 (2-5)*

Pear Tree House (Mr & Mrs John Southwell) Litton, 15m S of Bristol, 7m N of Wells. On B3114, Litton Harptree; ½m past Ye Olde Kings Arms. 3-acre plantsman's garden; developed from fields since 1963; pinetum, acers, birches, hollies, species roses; giant grasses; 3 ponds, as seen on TV 'Gardeners World'. TEA. *Adm 50p Chd 20p. Sats, Suns June 27, 28, Oct 10, 11 (10-to dusk)*

Severn View ⚘⚘ (Mr & Mrs Eric Hilton) Grovesend, 1½m E of Thornbury. On A38 on Bristol side of Severn Vale Nurseries. (Grovesend is postal address, but ignore signpost to it) 1-acre; notable for large rock garden with wide range of alpine plants, many rare, grown in screes, raised beds, troughs, rock walls, peat beds etc. Also shrubs, herbaceous borders; 3 alpine houses and many frames. Fine views of Severn Valley. *Adm 50p Chd free (Share to GTNC). Suns May 10, 17, 24, Sats, Suns May 30, 31, June 6, 7 (2-6)*

Springfield Barn ⚘⚘ (Mr & Mrs H. Joseph Woods) Upton Cheyney, Bitton, 5m NW of Bath; 8m SE of Bristol. A431 Bath-Bristol, turn off for Upton Cheyney. Please observe parking advice. 1 acre garden, started 1960, designed and planted with up to six hundred species, many from own propagation, by present owners. Pool and water feature fed by spring. TEA. *Adm 60p Chd 25p. Sun July 19 (2-6)*

¶**Stanton Prior Gardens** &❀ 6m from Bath on A39 Wells Rd; from The Globe Inn through Corston to Wheatsheaf Inn turn left to Stanton Prior; gardens either side of Church. TEAS. *Combined adm 75p Chd 20p (Share to MENCAP). Sun July 26 (2-6)*

> **Church Farm** (Mr & Mrs L. Hardwick) Herbaceous borders, open lawn, rock garden, wild area with ¼-acre pond; ducks and geese
> **The Old Rectory** ✗ (Col & Mrs P.D.B. de Mesquita) 1-acre garden inc medieval pond. Landscaped and re-planted in 1983 with unusual shrubs and plants

Tockington Gardens &❀ On B4461 10m N of Bristol; 2m N of M4/M5 intersection. A38 N towards Thornbury; 1m after intersection with M5 left along B4461. In Tockington bear right and up Old Down Hill; at top go over Xrds into Foxholes Lane. TEAS. *Combined adm 75p OAPs/Chd 30p (Share to St Peter's Hospice) Sats, Suns April 25, 26; Sept 19, 20 (2-6)*

> **Old Down House** (Mr & Mrs Robert Bernays) 5 acres divided into small formal and informal gardens by hedges and walls; topiary, shrubs; azaleas, rhododendrons, camellias; extensive lawns; fine trees (cedars, weeping beeches etc); herbaceous borders, semi-wild areas, fine views to Severn and Welsh Hills
> **The Brake** (Mrs R.H. Bernays) Vicarage Lane. 1½ acres made almost entirely since 1978; with superb views of Severn Estuary, the Welsh Mountains and Forest of Dean. Long herbaceous borders, interesting ground cover, woodland garden; bulbs, roses, some climbing up ancient fruit trees

University of Bristol Botanic Garden & ✗❀ Bracken Hill, North Rd, Leigh Woods, 2m W of Bristol. From Bristol via Clifton cross suspension bridge North Rd is 1st right. 5 acres garden with about 4,000 species illustrating diversity of the plant kingdom; special collections of hebe, cistus, ferns, sempervivum; etc many British plants; 5,000sq ft of glass; large rock garden. *Adm 50p Chd 20p. Suns July 12 Sept 6 (2-5)*

Vine House & (Prof & Mrs T.F. Hewer) Henbury, 4m N of Bristol. Bus stop: Salutation Inn, Henbury, 50yds. 2 acres; trees, shrubs, water garden, bulbs, naturalised garden landscaped and planted by present owners since 1946. Subject of article in *West Country Gardens,* 1980. *Adm 50p OAPs/Chd 25p (Share to Friends of Blaise). Suns, Mons April*

19, 20; May 24, 25 (2-7); also by appt all year (Tel Bristol 503573)

Wick Manor & ✗❀ (Mr & Mrs Kenneth Bishop) Wick, 5m NW of Bath. Signed from Wick Church on A420. 2-acre garden; formal walls protect herbaceous borders and lawns; young specimen trees in 9-acre parkland; river. Georgian ecclesiastical folly. Medieval house extended in C18 (not open). TEAS. *Adm 50p Chd 20p (Share to Wick Village Hall). Sun, Mon July 12, 13 (2-6)*

BEDFORDSHIRE

Hon County Organiser:
MRS S. WHITBREAD, The Mallowry, Riseley, Bedford MK44 1EF

DATES OF OPENING

MAY Sunday 3
  CARDINGTON GARDENS, nr Bedford
MAY Sunday 17
  ODELL CASTLE, nr Bedford
MAY Sunday 24
  APSLEY GUISE GARDENS, nr Bletchley
  WOODBURY HALL, Everton
MAY Sunday 31
  SOUTHILL PARK, nr Biggleswade
  TODDINGTON MANOR, Toddington
JUNE Sunday 14
  TODDINGTON MANOR, Toddington
  WESTFIELD HOUSE, Oakley
JUNE Sunday 21
  HOWBURY HALL, nr Renhold
JUNE Sunday 28
  CARDINGTON GARDENS, nr Bedford
  MAULDEN GRANGE, Maulden
JULY Sunday 5
  LUTON HOO GARDENS, Luton
  THE RECTORY, Barton-le-Cley
JULY Sunday 12
  ODELL CASTLE, nr Bedford
AUGUST Sunday 9 & Sunday 16
  TODDINGTON MANOR, Toddington
AUGUST Sunday 30
  THE RECTORY, Barton-le-Cley

DESCRIPTIONS OF GARDENS

Aspley Guise Gardens ✗ 2m W of M1 (Exit 13) via B557, towards Bletchley. Entrance from Church Rd. *Combined adm £1.50 or 50p each; Chd ½ price. Sun May 24 (2-6)*
> **Aspley House** & (Mr & Mrs C.I. Skipper) House on E side of village. 5 acres; shrubs and lawns. William and Mary house (not open). TEAS

¶The Dove House ᕗᚋ (Mr & Mrs N.A. Slocock) The Avenue. 1-acre around converted C18 dovecote and barns. Box hedges and paved gardens are features. **Manor Close** (Sir Kenneth & Lady Allen) Small garden next to church **The Rookery** (C.R. Randall Esq) 5 acres; rhododendrons and woodland

Cardington Gardens ᕗ 2m SE of Bedford. Tea Bedford. *Combined adm 50p Chd 25p. Suns May 3, June 28 (2-6.30)*
Howard's House (Humphrey Whitbread Esq) Walled and flower gardens; flowering cherries and clematis
Trinity House (Peter Inskip Esq) Beside Church, small garden surrounding old vicarage built 1781

Howbury Hall ᕗᚋ (Mr & Mrs A.N. Polhill) nr Renhold, 4m E of Bedford. Via A428 Bedford-St Neots, drive is 400yds from roundabout on left. Large garden with lawns, herbaceous borders, rose garden and pleasant woodland. TEAS. *Adm 50p Chd 25p. Sun June 21 (2-6)*

Luton Hoo Gardens ᚋ (The Wernher Family) Luton; entrance at Park St gates. Bus: Green line 707,717,727 London-Luton Garage: London Country 321 Watford-Luton via St Albans to Luton Garage. Landscape garden by Capability Brown. House built by Robert Adam in 1767. NO DOGS. Tea Wernher Collection Restaurant. *Adm gardens only £1 Chd 50p. △ Sun July 5 (2-6)*

Maulden Grange ᕗᚋ (Sir Ronald & Lady Stewart) Maulden. On A507 1m E of Ampthill, 9m S of Bedford, 9m from Luton. Entrance to Drive, Church Rd by Village School. Walled garden and tropical greenhouse. Beautiful trees inc one of the largest copper beech. Elizabethan house(not open). Exhib at C13 church, 300 yds from House. TEAS in Church Hall. *Adm 50p Chd 25p. Sun June 28 (2.30-6.30)*

Odell Castle (The Rt Hon Lord Luke) NW of Bedford. From A6 turn W through Sharnbrook; from A428, N through Lavendon and Harrold. Station: Bedford 10m. Terrace and lower garden down to R. Ouse. House built 1962 on old site, using original stone. TEAS. *Adm 50p Chd 25p. Suns May 17, July 12 (2-7)*

The Rectory ᕗ (Revd Ian Graham Orlebar) Barton-le-Cley 6m N of Luton. From A6 turn E on to B655, then into Church Rd. Bus: Bedford-Luton. 2 acres with background of Chilterns; moat, rockery, mature trees, lawns; overlooked by C12 Church. TEAS. *Adm 50p Chd 25p. Suns July 5, Aug 30 (2-6)*

♦**Southill Park** ᕗᚋ (Mr & Mrs S.C. Whitbread) 5m SW of Biggleswade. Large garden, rhododendrons, renovated conservatory. TEAS. *Adm 80p Chd 50p. Sun May 31 (2-6)*

Toddington Manor ᕗᚋ (Sir Neville & Lady Bowman-Shaw) 1m NW of Toddington, 1m from M1 (exit 12); 1st right in village (signed Milton Bryan); house ½m on right. 5 acres; restored since 1979 from total neglect; 2 ponds; stream running through garden; lake in woods; Wellingtonias; pleached lime walk; walled garden with original greenhouses; interesting shrubs and trees. Rare breeds of cattle and sheep. Vintage tractor collection. Private cricket pitch in front of house (usually a match on open days). TEAS in walled garden. *Adm £1 Chd 20p (Share to Local Charities). Suns May 31, June 14, Aug 9, 16 (2-7)*

Westfield House ᚋ (Mrs Davison) Oakley. 5m NW of Bedford; via A6 turn to W marked Oakley Station. Medium-sized; formal and informal garden; roses, glades, shrub walk; herbaceous borders. TEAS. *Adm 50p Chd 25p. Sun June 14 (2-7)*

Woodbury Hall (Mrs Astell) Everton, 3½m NE of Sandy. Large garden; rhododendrons, lawns, views. (Tetworth Hall, Cambs) open same day. *Adm 50p Chd 25p. Sun May 24 (2-6.30)*

BERKSHIRE

Hon County Organiser:
MRS M.A. HENDERSON, Ridings, Kenton Road, Wargrave, RG10 8P8
(Tel. 073522 2523)
Asst Hon County Organisers:
(Central) MRS A.P.D. SMYTH, Rye House, Silchester, Reading, RG7 2HJ
(West) MRS G. ELMES, Stable Cottage, Donnington Grove, Newbury, RG14 2LA
Hon County Treasurer:
MICHAEL PAYNE, Scotlands Farm, Cockpole Green, nr Wargrave, RG10 8QP

DATES OF OPENING

FEBRUARY Wednesday 25
THE OLD RECTORY, Burghfield
MARCH Wednesday 25
THE OLD RECTORY, Burghfield
MARCH Sunday 29
WELFORD PARK, nr Newbury
APRIL Sunday 5
FOXGROVE, Enborne, nr Newbury
APRIL Sunday 12
BUSSOCK MAYNE, Snelsmore Common
BUSSOCK WOOD, Snelsmore Common
OLD RECTORY COTTAGE, Tidmarsh

APRIL Easter Sunday 19
    INKPEN & WEST WOODHAY GARDENS,
    nr Newbury
APRIL Sunday 26
    ELCOT PARK HOTEL, nr Newbury
    ENGLEFIELD HOUSE, nr Theale
    FOLLY FARM, Sulhamstead
    FOXGROVE, Enborne, nr Newbury
    FOX STEEP, Henley-on-Thames
    ODNEY CLUB, Cookham
    SCOTLANDS, Cockpole Green, nr
      Wargrave
    SHINFIELD GRANGE, nr Reading
APRIL Wednesday 29
    THE OLD RECTORY, Burghfield
MAY Sunday 3
    ELCOT PARK HOTEL, nr Newbury
    SIMMS FARM HOUSE, Mortimer
MAY Wednesday 6 & Thursday 7
    FROGMORE GARDENS, Windsor
MAY Sunday 10
    SONNING-ON-THAMES GARDENS
    STONE HOUSE, Brimpton
MAY Sunday 17
    BEENHAM HOUSE, Beenham
    BUSSOCK WOOD, Snelsmore Common
    THE COACH HOUSE, Bradfield
    GREENBANKS, Cold Ash
    HURST LODGE, nr Twyford
    JASMINE HOUSE, Hatch Bridge, nr
      Windsor
MAY Sunday 24
    ALDERMASTON COURT, Aldermaston
    BOWDOWN HOUSE, Newbury
    COLNBROOK COTTAGE, Inkpen, nr
      Hungerford
    LITTLE BOWDEN, Pangbourne
    OLD RECTORY COTTAGE, Tidmarsh
    THATCHED LODGE, Crookham Common,
      nr Newbury
    WALTHAM PLACE, White Waltham
MAY Monday 25 (Bank Hol)
    FOLLY FARM, Sulhampstead
    FOXGROVE, Enborne, nr Newbury
MAY Wednesday 27
    THE OLD RECTORY, Burghfield
MAY Sunday 31
    ENGLEFIELD HOUSE, nr Theale
    SWALLOWFIELD PARK, nr Reading
JUNE Sunday 7
    WASING PLACE, Aldermaston
JUNE Saturday 13
    LUXMOORE'S, PROVOST'S & FELLOWS'
      GARDENS, Eton
JUNE Sunday 14
    BEAR ASH, Hare Hatch, nr Wargrave
    THE OLD RECTORY & THE COTTAGE,
      Peasmore
    THE PRIORY, Beech Hill, nr Reading
    STONE HOUSE, Brimpton
JUNE Sunday 21
    FOXGROVE, Enborne, nr Newbury
    ST MARY'S FARM, Beenham
    WALTHAM PLACE, White Waltham
JUNE Monday 22
    ST MARY'S FARM, Beenham

JUNE Wednesday 24
    THE OLD RECTORY, Burghfield
JUNE Saturday 27
    BASILDON PARK, nr Reading
JUNE Sunday 28
    BRADFIELD & BUCKLEBURY GARDENS,
      nr Theale
    FOUDRY HOUSE, Mortimer
    HAZELBY HOUSE, North End, nr Newbury
    OLD RECTORY COTTAGE, Tidmarsh
    THE OLD RECTORY, Farnborough
JULY Sunday 5
    THE OLD RECTORY, Farnborough
    WASING PLACE, Aldermaston
    WOOLEY PARK, nr Wantage
JULY Sunday 12
    CHIEVELEY GARDENS, nr Newbury
    FOLLY PARK, Sulhampstead
    LITTLE BOWDEN, Pangbourne
    THE OLD MILL, Aldermaston
    STANFORD DINGLEY VILLAGE GARDENS
    STONE HOUSE, Brimpton
JULY Sunday 19
    FOXGROVE, Enborne, nr Newbury
    GRAZELEY COURT FARM & HAWTHORNE
      COTTAGES, Grazeley
    ORCHARD COTTAGE, Cookham
    WALTHAM PLACE, White Waltham
JULY Sunday 26
    OLD RECTORY COTTAGE, Tidmarsh
    SCOTLANDS, Cockpole Green, nr
      Wargrave
    SHINFIELD GRANGE, nr Reading
JULY Wednesday 29
    THE OLD RECTORY, Burghfield
AUGUST Sunday 9
    ORCHARD COTTAGE, Cookham
AUGUST Sunday 16
    ORCHARD COTTAGE, Cookham
    PLANT SCIENCE LABORATORIES,
      Reading
SEPTEMBER Sunday 6
    COLNBROOK COTTAGE, Inkpen, nr
      Hungerford
    HURST LODGE, nr Twyford
    OLD RECTORY COTTAGE, Tidmarsh
SEPTEMBER Sunday 13
    THE COACH HOUSE, Bradfield
SEPTEMBER Sunday 27
    FOLLY FARM, Sulhampstead
    SHINFIELD GRANGE, nr Reading
SEPTEMBER Wednesday 30
    THE OLD RECTORY, Burghfield
OCTOBER Sunday 4
    SCOTLANDS, Cockpole Green, nr
      Wargrave
OCTOBER Wednesday 28
    THE OLD RECTORY, Burghfield

DESCRIPTIONS OF GARDENS

♦¶**Aldermaston Court** ✳ (Blue Circle Indus-
tries plc) Newbury 10m W; Reading 10m E;
Basingstoke 8m S. 137 acres, surrounding
Victorian Mansion (1849) with modern

offices making interesting contrast of architecture. Fine trees, specimen rhododendrons and shrubs, large lawns, lakeside restaurant with TEAS. *Adm £1 Chd free (Share to other charities). Sun May 24 (10-4)*

Basildon Park (Lord & Lady Iliffe; The National Trust) Lower Basildon, Reading. Between Pangbourne and Streatley, 7m NW of Reading on W of A329. Colourful shrub roses and specimen trees in grass, lovely view across Thames Valley. Private garden of old roses and old-fashioned plants also open. *Adm House & garden £1.80 Chd 90p. Grounds only 60p Chd 30p. Sat June 27 (2-6)*

Bear Ash ✿❀ (Lord & Lady Remnant) Hare Hatch, 2m E of Wargrave. ½m N of A4 at Hare Hatch, between Reading and Maidenhead. 2 acres; charming garden overlooking parkland; silver and gold planting; shrub and specie roses; mini-vineyard. Swimming pool. TEAS. *Adm 75p Chd free. Sun June 14 (2-6)*

Beenham House (Prof & Mrs Gerald Benney) Beenham. ½-way between Reading and Newbury, 1m N of A4; entrance off Webbs Lane. 21 acres of grounds and garden; old Lebanon cedars, oaks, hornbeams; recent plantings. Good views of park and Kennett Valley. Regency house (not open). Coach parties by appt. TEAS. *Adm 80p Chd 25p (Share to St Mary's Church, Beenham). Sun May 17 (2-6)*

Bowdown House & (M. Dormer Esq) 3m Newbury, Greenham Common N. On Bury's Bank Rd 2m past Greenham Golf Club. Lutyen's parterre gardens in style of Gertrude Jekyll; fine trees and rare shrubs. 50 acres of ancient woodland, now a nature reserve in care of BBONT. House by Sir Oswald Partridge Miln. TEAS at Thatched Lodge. *Adm 50p Chd 10p (Share to BBONT). Sun May 24 (2-6)*

Bradfield & Bucklebury Gardens 7m W of Reading. From Theale (M4 exit 12) take A340 towards Pangbourne and then turn off W to Bradfield. *Sun June 28 (2-6)*

    Mariners ❀ (Mr & Mrs W.N. Ritchie) 1st right after War Memorial in Mariners Lane. 1-acre charming well designed garden, owner-maintained; made from heavy clay field since 1973; large variety plants, herbaceous and shrub borders, roses, clematis, silver-leaved plants. TEAS & ice-cream. *Adm 40p Chd 10p*

    The Village House (Mr & Mrs P.A.McN. Boyd) opp Church. 3½-acre informal garden on mixed soils from chalk to neutral. Large variety shrubs; collection shrub roses; mixed borders; lawns sloping to R. Pang (with foot-bridge); many young trees; fine specimen winter flowering cherry of great size. Queen Anne village house (not shown). DOGS on leads. *Adm 50p Chd 20p*

¶**Roselands** (Rear Adm & Mrs H.W. Hollins) The Avenue, Bucklebury. 2-acres lawns; camellias; roses, specimen trees. Attractive period wisteria-clad house. Pond garden with trout. TEAS. *Adm 50p Chd 20p (Share to Sea Cadets)*

Bussock Mayne &✿ (Mr & Mrs D. Trotman) Snelsmore Common, 3m N of Newbury on B4494. Medium-sized garden; shrubs, borders, rock garden. Swimming pool. Tea Newbury. *Adm 50p Chd 10p. Sun Apr 12 (2-6)*

Bussock Wood (Mr & Mrs W.A. Palmer) Snelsmore Common, 3m N of Newbury. On B4494 Newbury-Wantage rd. Daffodils, bluebells, rhododendrons; fine trees and views; sunken garden with lily pond. Early Briton Camp. *Adm 50p Chd 10p (Share to BRCS, Berkshire). Suns April 12, May 17 (2-6)*

Chieveley Gardens &✿ 5m N Newbury. Take A34 N pass under M4, then left to Chieveley. After ½m left up Manor Lane. TEAS Chieveley Manor. *Combined adm 60p Chd 30p (Share to St Mary's Church, Chieveley). Sun July 12 (2-6)*

    Chieveley Manor (Mr & Mrs C.J. Spence) Large garden with fine view over stud farm. Walled garden containing herbaceous borders; shrubs and rose garden. Listed House (not open)

    Maypole Cottage (The Misses B & R Hartas Jackson) Attractive small garden, owner maintained with shrubs and plants of botanical interest

The Coach House &✿❀ (Mr & Mrs G.F. Harrison) Horse Leas, Bradfield. 7m W of Reading. From Theale M4 Exit 12 take A340 towards Pangbourne; turn W at Xrds to Bradfield ½m past Bradfield College Xrds on right of road to Southend & Bucklebury; house on right. Unusually interesting and attractive small garden created by owners from difficult N facing slope with heavy clay soil; skilful layout makes the area seem much larger than it is; wide variety plants grown; rock garden; pond. *Adm 50p Chd 10p (Share to The Samaritans of Reading)). Suns May 17, Sept 13 (2-6)*

Colnbrook Cottage ✿❀ (Mr & Mrs R. Skotzen) Inkpen, 3m S of Hungerford. 3½-acres surrounded by woodland; partly on long steep bank; variety of trees, shrubs, rhododendrons; herbaceous plants, bulbs. Work started autumn 1975 enlarging a neglected cottage garden. Please park in rd (unless unable to walk 100 yds). TEA. *Adm 40p Chd 10p (Share to Inkpen Parish Church). Suns May 24, Sep 6 (2-6)*

Elcot Park Hotel & (H.P. Sterne Esq) 5m W of Newbury. From A4 midway between Newbury and Hungerford, turn N at sign to Elcot Park. 16 acres overlooking Kennet Valley with extensive views; mainly lawns and woodland; laid out by Sir William Paxton in 1848; magnificent display of daffodils, rhododendrons and other shrubs. TEAS. *Adm 50p Chd 5p.* △*Suns April 26; May 3 (2-6)*

Englefield House ↻⚥❀ (Mr & Mrs W.R. Benyon) nr Theale. Entrance on A340. 7 acres of woodland garden with interesting variety of trees; shrubs; stream and water garden; terrace with borders. Commercial garden in village. Deer park. TEAS Long Gallery. Open every Mon all year, 10-dusk. *Adm £1 Chd free. (Share to St Mark's Church). Suns April 26, May 31 (2-6)*

Folly Farm ↻⚥❀ (The Hon Hugh & Mrs Astor) Sulhamstead, 7m SW of Reading. A4 between Reading/Newbury; (2m W of M4 exit 12); take rd marked Sulhamstead at Jack's Booth 1m after Theale roundabout; entrance 1m on right. One of the few remaining gardens where the Lutyens architecture remains intact. Garden, laid out by Gertrude Jekyll, has been planted to owners' taste, bearing in mind Jekyll and Lutyens original design. Raised white garden, sunken rose garden; spring bulbs; herbaceous borders; ilex walk; avenues of limes, yew hedges, landscaped lawn areas, formal pools. Some recent simplifications and new planting. House (not open) by Lutyens. TEAS. *Adm £1 Chd free (Share to West Berkshire Marriage Guidance Council). Suns April 26, Mon May 25, Suns July 12, Sept 27 (2-6)*

Foudry House ↻⚥ (Mr & Mrs J.G. Studholme) Mortimer, 6m SW of Reading; 4m from M4 exit 11 via Grazeley. At T-junc on edge of village, from Grazeley, turn right; 100yds. 4 acres, mainly trees, unusual shrubs and shrub roses. TEAS (In aid of Church of England Children's Society). *Adm 50p Chd 10p. Sun June 28 (2-6)*

Foxgrove ❀ (Miss Audrey Vockins) Enborne, 2½m SW of Newbury. From A343 turn right at 'The Gun' 1½m from town centre. Bus: AV 126, 127, 128; alight Villiers Way PO 1m. Small family garden; interesting foliage plants, troughs, spring bulbs, orchard with shrubs; vegetable garden; double primroses, snowdrop species and varieties; peat bed; alpine house; adjoining Nursery. TEAS. *Adm 50p Chd free (Share to NCCPG). Suns April 5, 26; Mon May 25, Suns June 21; July 19 (2-6.30); also by appt in Feb & March (Tel Newbury 40554)*

Fox Steep ↻⚥ (Judmonte Farms) Crazies Hill. Midway between Henley-on-Thames and Wargrave. 2m E of Henley on A423; take turning at top of hill to Cockpole Green. From Knowl Hill on A4 and Wargrave follow Cockpole Green signs. Old well-established 4-acre garden provides pretty setting for Elizabethan timbered house, formerly an Inn; associated with Gertrude Jekyll. TEAS Scot-

land's Farm. *Adm 75p Chd free Sun Apr 26 (2-6)*

Frogmore Gardens ↻⚥ (by gracious permission of Her Majesty The Queen) Windsor Castle; entrance via Park St gate into Long Walk (follow AA signs). Visitors are requested kindly to refrain from entering the grounds of the Home Park. Station and bus stop; Windsor (20 mins walk from gardens); Green Line buses 704,705,718 from London. Limited parking for cars only. Large garden with lake and lovely trees. The Royal Mausoleum, within the grounds, will also be open free of charge. Refreshment tent in car park on Long Walk(from where there is a 5 min walk to the gardens). **Coaches by appointment only** (apply to NGS, 57 Lower Belgrave St, London SW1W 0LR. Tel 01-730-0359 stating whether May 6 or 7; am or pm). *Adm 80p Chd 15p. Wed May 6, & Thurs May 7 (11-7; last adm 6.30)*

¶**Grazeley Court Farm** ↻⚥ (Mr & Mrs J.H.Bullingham) Grazeley. 3m S of Reading. M4 junc 11; take A33 to Basingstoke; at roundabout take 3rd exit to Grazeley 'Mortimer'; 1½m turn right signed 'Grazeley Green'; house ½m on right by bungalow. Woodland; interesting trees, lawns and mixed borders. Nearby gardens **Hawthorne Cottages** (Mr & Mrs A. Clarke; Mr & Mrs J. Lee; Mr & Mrs G. Grant)** small colourful gardens. TEA. *Combined adm 80p Chd 20p (Share to Holy Trinity Church, Grazeley). Sun July 19 (2-6)*

Greenbanks ⚥ (Mr & Mrs B.J. Pinnock) The Ridge, Cold Ash. N of Thatcham. Turn right at bottom of Cold Ash Hill, up Collaroy Rd, left at top, first house on left. 1⅓ acres. Beautifully planned with large variety shrubs and conifers. Lovely view. TEA. *Adm 50p Chd 5p. Sun May 17 (2-6)*

Hazelby House ↻⚥❀ (Mr & Mrs M.J. Lane Fox) North End, 6m SE of Newbury. From A343 Andover rd just outside Newbury, take turning to Ball Hill; approx ¼m beyond Ball Hill on rd to Kintbury. 4 acres; many interesting plants and trees; herbaceous borders, shrub borders, rose garden; white garden; lake. Subject of special article in Sunday Telegraph. NO DOGS. *Adm 80p Chd 40p (Share to St Martins Church, East Woodhay). Sun June 28 (2-6.30)*

◆**Hurst Lodge** ↻❀ (Lady Ingram) 7m E of Reading. From M4, Exit 10 to Reading on A329(M) exit to Winnersh; left at roundabout towards Wokingham on A329; left at lights Xrds on B3030 for Hurst and Twyford; follow 'Garden open' signs; garden in Hurst Village on A321 Twyford-Wokingham rd. An old 3-acre garden; spring flowers, shrubs; bulbs; late flowering shrubs. TEAS. Free car park. *Adm 50p Chd 5p. Suns May 17, Sept 6 (2-5.30)*

Inkpen & West Woodhay Gardens SW of Newbury. Turn S off A4 Bath Rd; on 2½m through Kintbury. *Sun April 19 (2-6)*

Kirby House & (The Hon John Astor) From Kintbury towards Inkpen and then Combe. 4 acres in beautiful setting with many varied mature trees, daffodils, narcissi and blossom. C18 brick house (not open). *Adm 50p Chd free*

West Woodhay House & ❀ (J. Henderson Esq) From Kintbury follow signs to West Woodhay. Large garden with fine views over parkland to downs; bulbs, roses, shrubs, lake, lawns, woodland garden. Beautiful Inigo Jones house 1635 (not open). TEAS garden room. *Adm 75p Chd 25p (Share to West Woodhay Church).*

Jasmine House ⚘ (Mr & Mrs E.C.B. Knight) Hatch Bridge, 3m W of Windsor. On A308 Windsor-Maidenhead opp Windsor Marina; follow signs from new roundabout by Willows Garden Nurseries. ⅓-acre garden designed for all-year interest with conifers (over 150 different), dwarf rhododendrons, heather beds; sink gardens; trees notable for decorative bark; ornamental pools; collection of Bonsai. Garden featured in RHS Journal (March 1979); 'The Gardens of Britain' & 'Mon Jardin et Ma Maison' (Feb 82). Tea Windsor or Maidenhead. *Adm 70p Chd 10p. Sun May 17 (2-6)*

Little Bowden & (Michael Verey Esq) 1½ m W of Pangbourne on Pangbourne- Yattendon Rd. Large garden with fine views; woodland walk, azaleas, rhododendrons, bluebells. Heated swimming pool 15p extra. TEA. *Adm 50p Chd 10p. Suns May 24 & July 12 (2.30-6)*

Luxmoore's Garden: also **Provost's & Fellows' Gardens** &⚘ (Provost Fellows of Eton College) Eton College, Windsor. Stations: Windsor ¾ Eton ½m. Bus: Green Line 704 & 705 London-Windsor 1m. Luxmoore's Garden is an island garden created by a housemaster about 1880; views of college and river. Provost's and Fellows' Gardens adjoin the ancient buildings on N and E sides. Parking in Cannon Yard, New School Yard and Parade Ground. Tea shops in Eton High St. *Combined adm 70p Chd 30p. Sat June 13 (2-6)*

Odney Club & (John Lewis Partnership) Cookham. Bus: A4094 or B4447 from Maidenhead. Car park in grounds. 120 acres; daffodils; lawns, garden and meadows on R. Thames; specimen trees. Cream TEAS River Room. *Adm 75p Chd 25p (Share to Help the Aged). Sun April 26 (2-6)*

The Old Mill &⚘ (Mrs E.M. Arlott) Aldermaston. On A4 between Reading and Newbury, take A340 then follow signs. 7 acres; lawns; walks; flower beds; shrubs; R. Kennet flows through with sluices and hatches. Fine Old Mill House (not open). TEA. *Adm 50p Chd 10p. Sun July 12 (2.30-6)*

Old Rectory Cottage ⚘❀ (Mr & Mrs A.W.A. Baker) Tidmarsh, ½m S of Pangbourne, midway between Pangbourne and Tidmarsh turn E down narrow lane; left at T-junc. Medium-sized garden; wild garden, small lake, unusual plants, early spring bulbs, shrubs, lilies, roses, autumn colour and berries; sorbus avenue, rose hedge. Featured in An Englishman's Garden, RHS The Garden (June 83), Homes Gardens (June 84). *Adm 50p Chd free (Share to BBONT). Suns April 12, May 24, June 28, July 26, Sept 6 (2-6)*

The Old Rectory, Burghfield &⚘❀ (Mr & Mrs R.R. Merton), 5m SW of Reading. Turn S off A4 to Burghfield village; right after Hatch Gate Inn; entrance on right. Medium-sized garden; herbaceous and shrub borders; roses, hellebores, lilies, many rare and unusual plants collected by owners from Japan and China; old-fashioned cottage plants; autumn colour. Georgian house (not open). *Adm 50p Chd 30p (Share to Save the Children & NCCPG) Weds Feb 25, March 25, April 29, May 27, June 24, July 29, Sept 30, Oct 28 (10.30-4); also by written appt*

The Old Rectory, Farnborough &⚘❀ (Mrs Michael Todhunter) 4m SE of Wantage. From B4494 Wantage-Newbury rd, 4m from Wantage turn E at sign for Farnborough. Outstanding garden with unusual plants: fine view; old-fashioned roses; herbaceous borders. Beautiful house (not open) built c.1749. *Adm 75p Chd free (Share to All Saints, Farnborough) Suns June 28, July 5 (2-6)*

The Old Rectory, Peasemore ❀ (Mr & Mrs I.D. Cameron) 7m N of Newbury. Turn right (E) off B4494. Georgian house with fine trees in lovely setting. Shrub roses, peonies, large rose border and herbaceous border. TEAS. Also **The Cottage** (Mr & Mrs M.R. Telfer) Traditional garden, slowly developed since 1982, in pictureaque cottage setting. Formal gravel garden; old-fashioned shrub roses, mixed borders. *Combined adm 60p Chd 15p. Sun June 14 (2-6)*

Orchard Cottage &⚘❀ (Mrs Reginald Samuel) Sutton Rd, Cookham, 3m A4094 N of Maidenhead. 1 acre; 500 roses, 400 dahlias; water garden; herbaceous and shrub borders, soft fruit, herb garden, large greenhouses, many varied and unusual plants. Wide range horticultural subjects (the late Mr Samuel was Chairman of Windsor Rose Society & Vice-President of National Dahlia Society). TEA. *Adm 50p Chd 10p. Suns July 19 Aug 9, 16 (2-6)*

Plant Science Laboratories, Botanical Garden &⚘❀ (University of Reading) White Knights, Reading. From A327 Reading-Shinfield rd, left into Pepper Lane, then left into University grounds. From A329 Wokingham-Reading; left at Earley traffic lights; right fork; then right into University grounds,

Whiteknights. 12 acres; teaching and research collection concentrating on plants of Europe, with selection from Asia and N America; secondary interest concerns plants of southernmost S America and other Austral continents and islands; a developing garden set in parkland of c.1800-1860; woodland walk; fern garden, rose border; pelargonium collection; pond; virtually every plant labelled; information sheet available. TEA *Adm 60p Chd free (Share to British Assoc. of Myasthenics). Sun Aug 16 (2-6)*

The Priory ⚘❀ (O.W.Roskill Esq) Beech Hill, 9m S of Reading. Turn off at Spencers Wood PO Bus: 411, 412 from Reading. C14 Benedictine priory largely rebuilt 1648. Branch of Loddon flows through garden. Probably laid out in C17. Lawns, herbaceous borders, shrubs; kitchen garden. *Adm 50p Chd 20p. Sun June 14 (2-6)*

St Mary's Farm ⚘❀ (C.W.L. Keen Esq) Beenham, 8m W of Reading. Turn off A4 N for Beenham. Planted since 1976; formal herb garden; vegetable garden with cottage flower borders; fine trees. 1820 parsonage; views. TEAS. *Adm 50p Chd 10p (Share to St Mary's Church). Sun, Mon June 21, 22 (2-6)*

Scotlands ♿⚘❀ (Mr Michael & the Hon Mrs Payne) Cockpole Green. Midway between Henley on Thames and Wargrave. 2m E of Henley on A423; take turn at top of hill to Cockpole Green. 4 acres; clipped yews; shrub borders; grass paths leading through trees to woodland; pond-garden with Repton design rustic summer house. House (not open) converted from C17 chalk and flint barn. TEAS April, July. *Adm 75p Chd free Suns April 26, July 26 (2-6), Oct 4 (2-5)*

Shinfield Grange ♿⚘❀ (University of Reading, Department of Horticulture) Cutbush Lane, Shinfield, 3m SE of Reading. From A327 going S, Cutbush Lane is 1st turn left, after M4 Motorway and Black Boy. Bus: No. 8, alight between Weather Centre and Shire Hall, ½m. 15 acres teaching garden with plant collections grouped in formal and informal situations: summer borders, annual borders, herbaceous border, shade garden; glade, small lake and wild flower areas. TEA (3.30-5) *Adm 80p OAPs 50p Chd 30p. Suns Apr 26, July 26, Sept 27 (2-6)*

Simms Farm House ⚘❀ (H.H. Judge Lea & Mrs Lea) Mortimer, 6m SW of Reading. At T-junc on edge of village, from Grazeley, turn right uphill; left by church into West End Rd; at next Xrd left down Drury Lane; right at T-junc. 1-acre garden with mixed shrub borders, small rockery; unusual plants. Lovely view. TEA. *Adm 50p Chd 20p. Sun May 3 (2-6)*

Sonning-on-Thames Gardens ⚘ 3m SW Wargrave, 2m E of Reading. Exceptionally attractive Thames-side village with gardens close together. Fine Church. TEAS. *Combined adm £1 Chd free. Sun May 10 (2-6)*

   Thatched Cottage ♿ (Dr Grenfell Bailey) 3 acres attractively laid out; lawns, specimen trees, herbaceous border; swimming pool

   ¶**Uppfield** (Mr & Mrs Mark Bodley Scott) Charvil Lane. Informal garden; orchard; geese, ducks and stream

   Pool House (Dr & Mrs John Glyn) 2 acres; well planted; wide variety trees and shrubs; rockery. Beautiful views of Thames and Chilterns

¶**Stanford Dingley Village Gardens** ⚘ Between Reading and Newbury. TEAS. *Combined adm £1 Chd free. Sun July 12 (2-6)*

   The Garden House (Sonia, Lady Fairfax) Queen Anne house (not open) fronting village rd. Lawns, formal lay-out; herbaceous borders; roses. TEA on terrace behind house

   Roman Way (Mr & Mrs Peter Trentham) Attractive Tudor House. Wide variety plants, shrubs and trees. Kitchen garden

   Ducarts (Mr & Mrs Hugo Johnson) Black and white Elizabethan Cottage. Garden recently restored

   Bradfield Farm (Mrs Christopher Newton) Interesting and unusual plants

   Ingle Spring (Mrs K.O.Jeakes) 2 acres; lawns and borders sloping down to R. Pang; small lake; attractive views

Stone House ♿❀ (Mr & Mrs Nigel Bingham) Brimpton, 6m E of Newbury. Turn S off A4 at junc by Coach & Horses, signed Brimpton and Aldermaston. ½m W of T-junc by War Memorial signed Newbury. Medium-sized garden in attractive park; naturalised bulbs; rhododendrons; water garden; extensive collection plants and shrubs; walled kitchen garden; picnic area. TEA. *Adm 50p Chd 10p (Share to Brimpton Church May & June; The NT Newbury, July). Suns May 10, June 14, July 12 (2-6)*

Swallowfield Park ♿⚘ (Country Houses Association Ltd) 5m S between Reading and Wokingham on A33 under M4; 2m then left to Swallowfield. Entrance by Village Hall. Landscaped garden, exceptionally fine trees including cedars; ancient yew tree walk, small lake; massed rhododendrons; distinguished house built 1689 (not open). TEA. *Adm £1 Chd 50p (Share to Country House Assn Ltd). Sun May 31 (2-5.30)*

¶**Thatched Lodge** ⚘ (Messrs Terry Adnams & Robert Burchi) Bury's Bank Rd, Crookham Common, 3m Newbury. 2m past Greenham Golf Club. 3½ acres; rhododendrons and flowering shrubs; attractive dell, 2 ponds with carp and golden orfe, water plants; orchid collection. TEAS. *Adm 50p Chd 10p (Share to BBONT). Sun May 24 (2-6)*

Waltham Place ♿❀ White Waltham. 3½m S of Maidenhead. Exit 8/9 on M4, then A423(M) and follow signs. 40 acres woodland and gardens with magnificent trees, bluebells, rhododendrons; interesting long borders; walled garden; kitchen garden; glasshouses. Plants well labelled. TEAS. *Adm £1 Chd free. (Share to Macmillan Nurses). Suns May 24, June 21, July 19 (2-6)*

♦**Wasing Place** ♿❀ (Sir William Mount Bt) Aldermaston, SE of Newbury. Turn S off A4 at Woolhampton; or 3m E take A340 to Aldermaston. ½m drive. Large garden; unusual shrubs and plants, rhododendrons, azaleas; lawns, walled and kitchen garden; greenhouses, herbaceous borders, magnificent cedars. C12 church. TEA (in aid of Wasing Church). *Adm £1 Chd free. Suns June 7, July 5 (2-6)*

♦**Welford Park** (Mrs J.L. Puxley) 6m NW of Newbury. Entrance on Newbury/Lambourn Rd (fine gates with boot on top). Spacious grounds; snowdrops, daffodils, crocuses; walk by R. Lambourn. Queen Anne house (not open). *Adm 75p Chd 25p (Share to Welford Church). Sun March 29 (2-5)*

Woolley Park ♿⚘ (Mr & Mrs Philip Wroughton) 5m S of Wantage on A338 turn left at sign to Woolley. Large park and lawns fine trees and views. Walled garden in process of restoration. NO DOGS. TEAS. *Adm 50p. Sun July 5 (2-6)*

BUCKINGHAMSHIRE

Hon County Organiser:
MRS PETER TOYNBEE, The Old Vicarage, Brill, Aylesbury HP18 9RP
Hon County Treasurer:
PETER TOYNBEE, ESQ.

DATES OF OPENING

BY APPOINTMENT ONLY for dates see text:
HALL BARN, Beaconsfield

MARCH Sunday 22
GREAT BARFIELD, Bradenham, nr High Wycombe
APRIL Sunday 12
ASCOTT, Wing, nr Aylesbury
APRIL Easter Sunday 19
QUOITINGS, Marlow
APRIL Easter Monday 20
GREAT BARFIELD, Bradenham, nr High Wycombe
SPINDRIFT, Jordans, nr Beaconsfield

APRIL Sunday 26
CAMPDEN COTTAGE, Chesham Bois
CHETWODE MANOR, nr Buckingham
HAMBLEDEN MANOR GARDENS, nr Henley-on-Thames
NETHER WINCHENDON HOUSE, nr Aylesbury
MAY Sunday 3
HAREWOOD, Chalfont St Giles
TURN END, Haddenham
MAY Sunday 10
CLIVEDEN, nr Taplow
GREAT BARFIELD, Bradenham, nr High Wycombe
MAY Sunday 17
ASCOTT, Wing, nr Aylesbury
WEXHAM SPRINGS, nr Slough
MAY Sunday 24
CAMPDEN COTTAGE, Chesham Bois
DORNEYWOOD GARDEN, Burnham
THE MANOR HOUSE, Little Marlow
MAY Monday 25 (Bank Hol)
GARDEN COTTAGE, Farnham Royal
MAY Wednesday 27
MARTINS, Lee Common, nr Great Missenden
MAY Sunday 31
LITTLE PASTON, Fulmer, nr Gerrards Cross
JUNE Sunday 14
ASCOTT, Wing, nr Aylesbury
LITLE PASTON, Fulmer, nr Gerrards Cross
THE OLD FARM, Bishopstone
THE OLD RECTORY, Cublington, nr Leighton Buzzard
PAUL END, Penn, Beaconsfield
TERRICK HOUSE, Terrick, nr Aylesbury
TURN END, Haddenham
WINSLOW GARDENS, nr Buckingham
JUNE Monday 15
WINSLOW GARDENS, nr Buckingham
JUNE Sunday 21
CAMPDEN COTTAGE, Chesham Bois
EAST & BOTOLPH CLAYDON GARDENS, nr Winslow
HILLESDEN HOUSE, nr Buckingham
WEIR LODGE, Eythrope, nr Stone
JUNE Saturday 27
THE WHITE COTTAGE, Chalfont St Peter
JUNE Sunday 28
‡BRILL GARDENS, nr Thame
HADDENHAM GARDENS, nr Thame
HAMBLEDEN MANOR GARDENS, nr Henley-on-Thames
HAREWOOD, Chalfont St Giles
THE MANOR HOUSE, Bledlow
NAPHILL HOUSE, Naphill, nr High Wycombe
OLD INN COTTAGE, (see Oxfordshire)
SPINDRIFT, Jordans, nr Beaconsfield
WEST WYCOMBE PARK, High Wycombe
THE WHITE COTTAGE, Chalfont St Peter
JULY Wednesday 1
THE WHITE COTTAGE, Chalfont St Peter
JULY Saturday 4
THE WHITE COTTAGE, Chalfont St Peter

JULY Sunday 5
GREAT BARFIELD, Bradenham, nr High Wycombe
PADBURY GARDENS, Buckingham
TYTHROP PARK, Kingsey, nr Thame
THE WHITE COTTAGE, Chalfont St Peter
JULY Wednesday 8
THE WHITE COTTAGE, Chalfont St Peter
JULY Sunday 12
ASCOTT, Wing, nr Aylesbury
BARNFIELD, Northend Common, nr Henley-on-Thames
COURT FIELD HOUSE, Little Hampden, Great Missenden
LONG CRENDON GARDENS, nr Thame
QUAINTON GARDENS, nr Aylesbury
WHITCHURCH GARDENS, nr Aylesbury
JULY Saturday 18
WATERCROFT, Penn, nr High Wycombe
JULY Sunday 19
CAMPDEN COTTAGE, Chesham Bois
WATERCROFT, Penn, nr High Wycombe
AUGUST Sunday 2
THE MANOR FARM, Little Horwood, nr Winslow
NETHER WINCHENDON HOUSE, nr Aylesbury
AUGUST Sunday 30
HERON PATH HOUSE, Wendover
AUGUST Monday 31 (Bank Hol)
HERON PATH HOUSE, Wendover
SPINDRIFT, Jordans, nr Beaconsfield
SEPTEMBER Sunday 6
CLIVEDEN, nr Taplow
MANAWATU, Beaconsfield
PAUL END, Penn, Beaconsfield
QUOITINGS, Marlow
SEPTEMBER Sunday 20
CAMPDEN COTTAGE, Chesham Bois
HAREWOOD, Chalfont St Giles

DESCRIPTIONS OF GARDENS

♦**Ascott** ✗✿ (E. de Rothschild Esq; The National Trust) Wing, 2m SW of Leighton Buzzard, 8m NE of Aylesbury via A418. Bus: United Counties 141 Aylesbury-Leighton Buzzard. Beautiful surroundings and layout. Garden part formal, part natural; many specimen trees, shrubs, sunken garden; lily pond. Tea Mentmore Village. *Adm £1.40 Chd 70p. △Suns April 12; May 17; June 14; July 12 (2-6)*

Barnfield ✿ (Mr & Mrs John Annan) Northend Common, 7m N of Henley-on-Thames. From Henley via A423; turn right on to B480 to Stonor then follow signs to Northend; or from M40, leave by junc 6 on to B4009 to Watlington; follow sign to Northend. Medium-sized garden; shrub roses; wandering paths and views. TEAS. *Adm 50p Chd 10p (share to Riding for the Disabled). Sun July 12 (2-6)*

Brill Gardens ✗ 7m N of Thame. Turn off B4011, Thame-Bicester; or turn off A41 at Kingswood; both marked to Brill. TEAS Leap Hill. *Combined adm £1 Chd free. Sun June 28 (2-7)*

Commoners (Mrs Ruth Wickenden) Tram Hill. Under ¼ acre; low walled old cottage garden; alpines, shrubs, herbaceous, some vegetables, small bog garden. Views in all directions

Leap Hill ᕕ (Mrs Gillian Morris-Adams) Thame Rd. 2 acres developed since 1963; herbaceous border and shrubs; vegetables; roses of special interest to flower arrangers; conservatory. Extensive views towards Chilterns. Adjoining cottage patio also on view

¶**56 Windmill Street** (Mr & Mrs C.D. Elliott) Pocket handkerchief walled garden featuring imaginative use of space; shrubs, herbaceous and alpines. Pergola, patio, raised beds, many containers

Campden Cottage ✗✿ (Mrs P. Liechti) 51 Clifton Rd, Chesham Bois, N of Amersham. From Amersham-on-the-Hill take A416; after 1m turn right (E) at Catholic Church. From Chesham take A416; and first turning left after beech woods. ½-acre derelict garden, restored by present owner since 1971; plantsman's garden of year-round interest; fine collection of unusual and rare plants. Featured on TV "Gardeners' World". Please use car park signed on main road. Teas Old Amersham. No push chairs. *Adm 50p Chd free. Suns April 26, May 24, June 21, July 19, Sept 20, (2-6); parties by appt (Tel Amersham 6818)*

Chetwode Manor ᕕ✗ (Mrs Collins) 5m SW of Buckingham via A421. Turn E by Newton Purcell railway bridge; after 1½m turn left at T-junc; turn right in 100yds; garden 200yds on right. Medium-sized garden, large mixed borders, shrubs; ground-cover plants; spring bulbs, fine osmarea hedge; spectacular white wisteria. C17 Manor House (not open). TEA. *Adm 50p Chd 10p. Sun April 26 (2-6)*

Cliveden ᕕ✗ (The National Trust) 2m N of Taplow. B476. Bus: AV 63 Slough-Maidenhead. Bus stop: Feathers Inn, Cliveden ¼m. One of the most beautiful places in England. Water garden; grand view of R. Thames. Suitable for wheelchairs only in part. TEAS. *Adm grounds only £2 (Mon to Wed £1.50); Chd ½-price. △Suns May 10; Sept 6 (11-6)*

Court Field House ᕕ (Sir Leonard & Lady Figg) Little Hampden. 2½m Gt Missenden/Prestwood. From Gt Missenden follow signs Butlers Cross and Princes Risborough, 2m turn right signed Cobblers Hill, then ½m on left. 3-acre pleasant secluded garden in pretty surroundings; shrubs, herbaceous, bedding plants; greenhouse; woodland walks; large well-kept walled kitchen garden. *Adm 50p Chd 20p (Share to Little Hampden Church). Sun July 12 (2-6)*

Dorneywood Garden ⚭❀ (The National Trust) nr Burnham. 1½m N of Burnham village. Between B476 and B473. Bus: Alder Valley 63 (Slough-Dropmore-Maidenhead). Natural garden. TEAS. *Adm 60p Chd 30p. Sun May 24 (2-6.30)*

East & Botolph Claydon Gardens ⚭ 2½m SW of Winslow. Follow signs to Claydons. TEAS Pond Cottage. *Combined adm £1.50 Chd 20p. Sun June 21 (2-6)*

    Beech House ❀ (Mr & Mrs D. Dow) ¼-acre walled garden, derelict in 1977; mixed borders, shrubs, flowers; paved features; small alpine beds. Views of C17 cottage and church (featured in Arthur Mee's 'Buckinghamshire')

    ¶**The Corner House** (Mr & Mrs R. Allen) ¼-acre semi-formal garden from an all grass garden in 1982; roses; shrubs; small fish pond; herbaceous, rockery

    The Emerald (Dr & Mrs N.W. Shephard) 1 acre; mixed shrubs, herbaceous borders; pond; bog garden, well; herbs

    ¶**7 Orchard Way** �&. (Mr & Mrs T. Crawley) Small 6 yr old labour-saving garden on clay designed for year-round interest. Conifers, heathers in peat bed. Conservatory.

    Pond Cottage (Mr & Mrs B.W. Kay) ⅓-acre productive and decorative garden between C17 cottage and C19 barn; thickly planted with foliage, fruit trees, shrubs, herbaceous plants and shrub roses since 1975; vegetables, soft fruit

Garden Cottage �&⚭❀ (Mr & Mrs L.M. Brockwell) Farnham Royal. 3m NW of Slough; on A355 turn W at Farnham Royal along Farnham lane towards Burnham; then 2nd right and 1st left into East Burnham Lane. Informal 1-acre country garden. Wide range of plants particularly herbaceous. Year round colour, form and foliage. Yew hedges, mixed borders, raised beds, heather garden. Many choice plants inc euphorbias, geraniums, epimediums etc. Nursery adjoining. Morning coffee and TEAS in aid of The Thames Valley Hospice *Adm 60p Chd free; parties welcome. Mon May 25 (11-5); also daily by appt (Tel 02814 2243)*

Great Barfield �&⚭❀ (Richard Nutt Esq) Bradenham, 4m NW of High Wycombe 4m S of Princes Risborough. From A4010 at Red Lion turn into village; at bottom of village green turn right; walk down 'no through rd'. 1½ acre plantsman's garden, reflecting inimitable Chiltern valley. Full of colour shape and form throughout year; *March*; bulbs, hellebores, salix, stems and pussy. *April*; more bulbs, narcissus species and cultivars rarely

seen, flowering shrubs. *Mid May; Anemone nemorosa, Pulmonaria* and *Ranunculus ficaria* forms; *July*; old fashioned shrub roses; species roses and roses climbing up trees. A place to sit and absorb views and plants. Holder on behalf of NCCPG of the National collections of *Iris Unguicularis Ranunculus ficaria* and *Leucojum*. Owner feels strongly that many unusual plants should be more frequently grown and are grown here. Unusual plants are for sale. Home-made TEAS. *Adm £1 Chd under 16 10p, 3 or more free (Share to Bradenham Church Restoration Fund). Sun March 22, Mon April 20, Suns May 10, July 5 (2-6)*

Haddenham Gardens 3m NE of Thame. Off A418. Gardens signed in village. TEA and home-made biscuits 59 The Gables. *Combined adm 80p Chd free. Sun June 28 (2-6)*

    59 The Gables �&❀ (Mrs A.M. Johnstone) Off Churchway. Small garden begun in 1982, still developing. Ferns, Bonsai and interesting herbaceous plants and shrubs suitable for small gardens. All year interest.

    The Patch (Mr & Mrs Brian Andrews) Skittles Green Gibson Lane. Small walled cottage garden; herbaceous plants, shrubs, trees. Thatched C18 cottage (not open)

◆**Hall Barn** (Lt. Col. the Lord & Lady Burnham) Lodge gate 300 yds S of Beaconsfield Church in old town centre. One of the original gardens opening to the public in 1927 under the National Gardens Scheme, still owned by the Burnham family. A unique landscaped garden of great historical interest, laid out in the 1660's. Vast 300 yr old curving yew hedge. Very fine collection of trees, including the third largest beech in Buckinghamshire. Formal lake. Long avenues through the Grove, each terminating in a temple, classical ornament or statue, Obelisk with fine carvings in memory of Edmund Waller's grandson who completed the garden about 1730. Garden open by written appointment only. Applications to Lady Burnham, Hall Barn, Beaconsfield, Buckinghamshire HP9 2SG

Hambleden Manor Gardens �&. (The Viscount Hambleden) NE of Henley-on-Thames. 1m N of A4155. Spring bulbs and daffodils; conservatory, shrubs and old-fashioned rose garden. TEAS Hambleden Church. *Adm 80p Chd 10p. Suns April 26, June 28 (2-6)*

Harewood �&⚭❀ (Mr & Mrs John Heywood) Harewood Rd, Chalfont St Giles. Chalfont and Latimer Met Line tube station ¾m. From A404 Amersham-Rickmansworth rd, at mini roundabout in Little Chalfont village turn S down Cokes Lane, Harewood Rd is 200yds on left. 1 acre; fine yew and box hedges; established conifers; wide variety unusual shrubs and hardy plants; old shrub roses; many climbers inc roses, clematis, wisterias; new pool, sink gardens; unusual primulas and violas; planted for year round interest. Emphasis on foliage and colour contrast. All woody plants labelled; list available. Cream TEAS. *Adm 70p Chd free (Share to Arthritis & Rheumatism Council). Suns May 3, June 28, Sept 20 (2-6); also by appt (Tel Little Chalfont 3553)*

¶**Heron Path House** ✿❀ (Mr & Mrs Bryan C.Smith) Chapel Lane. ½m S of Wendover on A413. Chapel Lane 2nd turn on left; house at bottom. 2½-acre garden on old farm site. Lawns, terraces, shrub borders, bedding plants inc geraniums and fuchsias. Large rockery; pond under construction. Greenhouse. *Adm £1 Chd 30p. Sun & Mon Aug 30 & 31 (2-6)*

Hillesden House ﴾✿❀ (Mr & Mrs R. M. Faccenda) Hillesden, 3m S of Buckingham via Gawcott. Follow Hillesden signs after Gawcott on Calvert Rd. 6 acres developed since 1978 from virgin land on site of C16 Manor House by superb Perpendicular Church "Cathedral in the Fields"; large lawns, shrubberies; rose, alpine and foliage gardens; conservatory; 3 lakes; commanding views over countryside. TEAS. *Adm 80p Chd free (Share to Hillesden Church). Sun June 21 (2-6)*

Little Paston ﴾ (David R. Allen Esq) Fulmer Common Rd, Fulmer. Fulmer is in triangle formed by A40, A412, A332, N of Slough (map ref 160/999849). 10-acre woodland garden with lawns, beautiful pond, picturesque water garden; kitchen garden; rhododendrons. TEA. *Adm 50p Chd 25p. (Share to Multiple Sclerosis Research & Cancer Research). Suns May 31, June 14 (2-6)*

Long Crendon Gardens. 2m N of Thame B4011 to Bicester. TEAS. *Combined adm £1.50 Chd free. Sun July 12 (2-6.30)*
　¶**Barrys Close** ﴾ (Mr & Mrs Richard Salmon) Lower End. 2 acres. Interesting collection of trees and shrubs; herbaceous border. Spring-fed pools and water garden. Good views
　Croft House (Cdr & Mrs Peter Everett) Thame Rd. In Square, white wrought iron railings. ½-acre walled garden; plants and shrubs of botanical interest esp to flower arrangers
　48 High Street (Mr & Mrs John Allerton) ¼-acre village garden; colourful herbaceous borders, shrubs, old-fashioned roses; vegetables
　Manor House ﴾ (Mr & Mrs William Shelton) turn right by church; house through wrought iron gates. 6 acres; lawns sweep down to 2 ornamental lakes; much planting in progress; fine views towards Chilterns. House (not open) 1675
　Old Post House ❀ (Mr & Mrs Nigel Viney) In High Street on left at corner of Burts Lane. Small cottage garden in pictures-

que village street. Interesting shrubs, small produce stall
　Windacre ﴾❀ (Mr & Mrs K. Urch) 62 Chilton Rd. 1 acre; trees, roses, shrubs, orchard, main features sunken lawns and trees

Manawatu ﴾❀ (Mr & Mrs Bernard C. Frost) 24 Burkes Rd, Beaconsfield, S of railway bridge on B474 in centre of New Town, 400yds from mini roundabouts to Burkes Rd. Park in rd or shopping centre. Disabled park in drive. 3-acre semi-formal garden; interesting collection of trees, flowering shrubs; rock garden; waterfall, pool; herbaceous borders; fine yew hedge walk; woodland dell; herbs; greenhouses. TEAS. *Adm £1 Chd free. Sun Sept 6 (2-6)*

¶**The Manor Farm** ﴾✿❀ (Mr & Mrs Peter Thorogood) Little Horwood 2m NE Winslow off A413. 5m E Buckingham off A421. Hilltop farmhouse garden on acid clay, newly laid out and replanted 1986. Wide range of plantsman's plants for year round interest in colour, form and foliage. Many plans for future. Cream TEAS in aid of 'Little Horwood Recreation Ground Trust'. *m 70p Chd free. Sun Aug 2 (2-6)*

The Manor House, Bledlow ✿❀ (The Lord & Lady Carrington) ½m off B4009 in middle of Bledlow village. Station: Princes Risborough, 2½m. Medium-sized garden on chalk; paved gardens, shrub borders, old roses. House (not open) C17 & C18. Also village garden scheme with water and species plants. TEAS. *Adm £1 Chd free. Sun June 28 (2-6); also by appt May to Sept (2-4.30)*

The Manor House, Little Marlow ﴾ (Sir Eric & Lady Weiss) 2m NE of Marlow. Off A4155, midway between Bourne End and Marlow. 5 acres; water features; walled garden; heather and woodland garden. Free-flight nun doves. TEA. *Adm 80p Chd free. Sun May 24 (2-6)*

¶**Martins** ﴾✿❀ (Dr & Mrs Michael Whitehead) Lee Common. 3m Gt Missenden. From A413 take B485 for 500yds, turn L (Frith Hill), 2m turn L to Lee Common, 300yds on to Crocketts Lane which runs beside house. ⅓-acre garden planted for year round interest. Unusual plants. Small collection of alpines; heathers and mixed borders. Teas Gt Missenden Wendover or Amersham. *Adm 50p Chd 10p. Wed May 27 (1-5)*

¶**Naphill House** ﴾✿ (Mrs F. Broom-Smith) 5m S Princes Risborough. 2½m N of High Wycombe on A4128; 1st left after Hughenden Church up Coombe Hill to Hunts Hill Land. 2-acre mature garden. Roses; delphiniums, kitchen garden. Queen Anne farmhouse (not open). Sculpture exhibition (some for sale). TEAS. *Adm 50p Chd 10p (Share to NSPCC). Sun June 28 (2-6)*

Nether Winchendon House &⚘ (Mrs J.G.C. Spencer Bernard) Nether Winchendon, 5m SW of Aylesbury; 7m from Thame. Picturesque village, beautiful church. 5 acres; fine trees, variety of hedges; naturalised spring bulbs; shrubs; herbaceous borders; newly-planted avenue. Tudor manor house (not open) home of Sir Francis Bernard, Governor of Massachusetts. *Adm £1 Chd 25p. △Suns April 26, Aug 2 (2.30-6)*

The Old Farm & (Mrs Delap) Bishopstone, 3m SW of Aylesbury. From A418 Thame-Aylesbury, at Stone Church turn off right for Bishopstone. Medium-sized garden; flowering shrubs, borders, trees, pond. *Adm 60p Chd 10p. Sun June 14 (2-6); also by appt (Tel 0296 748236)*

The Old Rectory, Cublington &⚘ (Mr & Mrs J. Naylor) 7m SW of Leighton Buzzard. From Aylesbury via A418 towards Leighton Buzzard; after 4½m turn left (W) at Xrds. Follow signs to Aston Abbotts, then Cublington. 2-acre country garden with herbaceous border, rosebeds, shrubs and mature trees; vegetables; ponds, climbing plants. TEAS. *Adm 75p Chd 10p (Share to Multiple Sclerosis Society). Sun June 14 (2-5)*

Padbury Gardens &⚘⚘ 2m S of Buckingham on A413. In Padbury village follow signs to gardens. TEA. *Combined adm £1 Chd free (Share to League of Friends of Buckingham Hospital). Sun July 5 (2-7)*
  The Old Vicarage (Mr & Mrs H. Morley-Fletcher) 2½ acres on 3 levels; flowering shrubs and trees; rose garden. Growing collection of hebes; pond and sunken garden. Fine views across Buckinghamshire countryside
  Padbury Lodge (Adrian Hornsey Esq) 2 acres; mature trees, inc mulberry; lawns, herbaceous borders, terrace round house; pond with waterfall; walled vegetable garden; greenhouse

¶**Paul End** ⚘ (The Misses Anderson) Paul's Hill, Penn. 2m NW of Beaconsfield on B474. Access through churchyard of historically interesting Penn Church. Medium-sized garden on clay. Several levels, 500ft up with extensive views. Wide variety of shrubs inc arbutus, griselina, pieris and callicarpa, giraldii; herbaceous border; roses. *Adm 80p Chd free (Share to Penn Parish Church Fund). Suns June 14, Sept 6 (2-6)*

¶**Quainton Gardens** 7m NW of Aylesbury. Turn N off A41, 1m E or W of Waddesdon. TEA. *Combined adm £1 Chd free. Sun July 12 (2-6)*
  Brudenell House ⚘ (Dr & Mrs H.B. Wright) Church St (opp. Church). 2-acre garden surrounding old rectory. Interesting mature trees, large herbaceous borders; rose garden, fruit and vegetables

Cross Farmhouse & (Mr & Mrs Elliott Viney) House at top of green facing S. 1-acre garden created in 1979; large bank and rough pond. Shrubs, ground cover and climbers chosen for extended interest and minimum care throughout year. Old fruit trees; open view to Quainton Hills

Hatherways ⚘⚘ (Mr & Mrs D. Moreton) 1-acre picturesque cottage garden. Many old fashioned roses and clematis; shrubs, trees, bog garden

Quoitings &⚘ (Kenneth Balfour Esq) Oxford Rd, Marlow, 7m E of Henley, 3m S of High Wycombe; at Quoiting Sq, turn N out of West St (A4155); garden ¼m up Oxford rd on left. 2½-acre secluded garden with fine trees inc pomegranate, tulip and various conifers; colourful herbaceous borders, bedding; lawns; ha-ha; vistas. C17/C18 house (not open) formerly home of Histiographer Royal to William IV and Queen Victoria. TEAS. *Adm 70p Chd free. Suns April 19 (12-5), Sept 6 (2-7)*

Spindrift ⚘ (Mr & Mrs Eric Desmond) Jordans, 3m NE of Beaconsfield. From A40, midway between Gerrards Cross and Beaconsfield turn N into Potkiln Lane; after 1m turn left into Jordans village; at far side of green turn right to cul-de-sac. Unusual garden on different levels. Sunken rockery; pond; herbaceous and shade borders; mature trees; wide variety of foliage plants. Holly and yew hedges. Model terraced fruit and veg garden. Greenhouse and vines. Member of Nat Vegetable Research Station. TEAS, coffee, lunches, (home-made). *Adm 60p Chd 25p. Mon April 20, Sun June 28. Mon Aug 31 (11-6); also by appt for parties (Tel Ch St Giles 3172)*

Terrick House &⚘ (Mr & Mrs Geoffrey Gomme) 4½m S of Aylesbury on A4010. About 2-acres; mature and unusual trees; very fine herbaceous borders; large rock garden and pool. TEA. *Adm 80p Chd free. Sun June 14 (2-6.30)*

Turn End ⚘⚘ (Peter Aldington Esq) Townside, Haddenham. 3m NE of Thame. From A418 turn to Haddenham between Thame (3m) and Aylesbury (6m). From Thame Rd turn at Rising Sun into Townside. Bus: Ox. 280 Oxford-Aylesbury. Bus stop: The Crown. Interesting secluded ¾-acre walled garden containing 'outdoor rooms'; a garden of surprises; shade loving plants, bulbs, alpines, climbers, mature trees. Also open, award-winning house, designed and built by owners round small courtyard garden. Home-made TEAS in aid of Ambulance Service. *Adm 70p Chd 20p (Share to Aylesbury Hospitals Trust Fund). Sun May 3, June 14 (2-6)*

Tythrop Park &⚘ (Mr & Mrs Jeremy Cotton) Kingsey 2m E of Thame, via A4129; lodge gates just before Kingsey. 4 acres inc 2 walled gardens on clay being reinstated after decades of neglect; newly laid out court garden by Hon Robert Stonor; replanting of wilderness; unique walled kitchen garden; Muscat and Black Muscat d'Hamburg vine propagated from Hampton Court vine 150yrs ago in vine house; Carolean House (not open); stable block recently restored. TEAS. *Adm £1 Chd free (Share to The Lord Roberts Workshops). Sun July 5 (2-6)*

Watercroft and Watercroft Cottage &⊛ (Sir Barrie & Lady Heath) Penn 3m N of Beaconsfield on B474, ¼m E of Penn village centre. Medium-sized garden on clay concentrating on organic growing techniques, nature conservation and wildlife flowers; old roses; weeping Ash; pond; kitchen garden; herbs; bees. Honey for sale if available. C18 house, C19 brewhouse (not open). TEA if fine. *Adm 70p Chd 10p (Share to Three Counties Wildlife Appeal). Sat, Sun July 18, 19 (2-5.30)*

Weir Lodge &⊛ (Mrs Nigel Birbeck) Eythrope, nr Stone, 4m W of Aylesbury. From Stone Xrds (A418) turn N signed 'Eythrope only'; after ½m cross small bridge over river; follow signs. Medium-sized riverside garden; mature trees; flowering shrubs, borders, problem areas; ground-cover plants. TEAS. *Adm 60p Chd free. Sun June 21 (2-6)*

West Wycombe Park &⚸ (Sir Francis Dashwood, Bt; The National Trust). West Wycombe. 3m W of High Wycombe on A40. Bus: from High Wycombe and Victoria. Landscape garden; numerous C18 temples and follies inc Temple of the Winds, Temple of Venus, Walton bridge; Swan-shaped lake, Temple of Music; cascade. TEA Cave's Cafe. *Adm House & grounds £2 Chd £1; grounds only £1.40 Chd 70p. Sun June 28 (2-6)*

Wexham Springs & (Cement and Concrete Association) Framewood Rd 2½m Slough/Gerrards Cross. From Slough on A4 follow signs to Wexham Park Hospital, then 1m on right. From A40 turn S at French Horn PH, through Fulmer Village. 70-acre informal garden; mixed shrubs, fine trees; natural lake; formal areas; paved and planted courtyards; terraces; garden walks. *Adm 60p Chd 20p or £1.50 per car. Sun May 17 (2.30-6)*

¶**Whitchurch Gardens** ⚸ 4m N of Aylesbury on A413; TEAS at Crown & Thistle. *Combined adm £1 Chd under 12 free. Sun July 12 (2-6)*

    Fairings ⚸ (Mrs L. Wilkey) Castle Lane. Colourful cottage garden with many stone troughs, containers and vases
    Mullions (Dr & Mrs L.I. Holmes-Smith) Market Hill (entrance in Castle Lane). ⅓-acre picturesque cottage garden on three terraces. House built 1600 (not open). Garden entrance in Cantle Lane
    The Old Cottage (Mr & Mrs R. Gwynne-Jones) 41 High St. ¾-acre. Herbaceous

border; herb garden; veg; views across Vale of Aylesbury
Priory Court & (Mr & Mrs H. Bloomer) Opp. Pace garage, next to Pearsons shop. ½-acre; herbaceous borders pond, greenhouse with vine

¶**The White Cottage** &⚸⊛ (Mr & Mrs A.W. Pardey) 32 Nortoft Rd. 1¼m Chalfont St Peter. A413 to roundabout in Ch St Peter; E up Joiners Lane; at t-junc into Denham Lane; Nortoft Rd 2nd R; house 16 houses down on R. ⅓-acre garden of year round interest; heather and conifer beds; selection of old-fashioned roses, traditional cottage garden flowers and climbing plants. Small bog garden; mixed shrubs inc magnolia grandiflora. TEA. *Adm 50p Chd free (Share to Save the Children Fund). Sats, Suns, Weds June 27, 28; July 1, 4, 5, 8 (2-6); also by appt in April. Tel 02407 2520*

Winslow Gardens ⚸ On A413 10m N of Aylesbury, 6m S of Buckingham. Free public car park. TEAS Winslow Hall (June 14), TEA 26 High St (June 15). *Combined adm £1.50 Chd free. Sun, Mon June 14, 15 (2-6)*
    26 High Street ⊛ (Mr & Mrs D. Drakard) opp Church. Narrow walled garden developed since 1974 behind C17/C18 house (not open); mainly herbaceous; shrubs, climbers, many unusual plants
    32 Horn Street ⚸⊛ (Mrs Gwladys Tonge) Horn St runs from Bell Hotel to Granborough Rd. Small walled plantsman's garden on 3 levels; conservatory, fernery, pond. Small collections of alpines, ferns, ivies, shrubs, interesting and unusual herbaceous plants. Large variety of clematis. Unsuitable for pushchairs. Also by appt April 1 to Sept 30 (Tel 029671 2577)
    Winslow Hall & (Sir Edward & Lady Tomkins) 3 acres of lawn framed by large variety flowering shrubs and trees. Many unusual specimens inc Acers, a remarkable weeping Atlantic Cedar; roses of all sorts; clematis; contrasting colourful foliage from spring to autumn, starting with daffodils and ending with splendid colours in Oct; attractive walled vegetable garden. Unique Christopher Wren house, built for Sir William Lowndes in 1700, has survived without major structual alteration; early C18 English furniture; good collection Chinese art, particularly Tang period; fine clocks. Coaches by appt only. House and Gardens open all Bank Hols ex Dec 26 (2-5.30); July 15-Sept 15 daily ex Mons; July 1-14 & Sept 16-30 weekends only (2.30-5.30). *Adm £1.50 Chd free Groups £1.25. Gardens only Adm £1. Suns May-June (2-5); also by appt (Tel Winslow 3433) Catering by arrangement*

CAMBRIDGESHIRE

Hon County Organisers:
South: LADY NOURSE, North End House,
Grantchester CB3 9NQ &
THE HON MRS MARTIN BROWNE
Berghane Hall, Castle Camps CB1 6TN
North:(Huntingdon,I of Ely, Peterborough):
MRS JAMES CROWDEN, 19 North Brink,
Wisbech PE13 1JR

DATES OF OPENING

BY APPOINTMENT ONLY for dates see text:
BERRY CLOSE STUDIO, nr Great Gransden
REGULAR OPENINGS for dates see text:
THE CROSSING HOUSE, Shepreth
DOCWRA'S MANOR, Shepreth
DUXFORD MILL, nr Cambridge

APRIL Thursday 9 & Friday 10
ANGLESEY ABBEY, nr Cambridge
APRIL Sunday 12
TRINITY COLLEGE FELLOWS' GARDEN,
Cambridge
APRIL Easter Sunday 19
LONGSTOWE HALL, Longstowe
APRIL Friday 24
WIMPOLE HALL, nr Royston
APRIL Sunday 26
BARTLOW PARK, nr Linton
BARTON GARDENS, nr Cambridge
KING'S COLLEGE FELLOWS' GARDEN,
Cambridge
MAY Sunday 10
LECKHAMPTON, Cambridge
MAY Sunday 24
DUXFORD MILL, nr Cambridge
TETWORTH HALL, Sandy
MAY Monday 25 (Bank Hol)
DUXFORD MILL, nr Cambridge
MAY Sunday 31
SAWSTON HALL, nr Cambridge
JUNE Sunday 7
TETWORTH HALL, Sandy
JUNE Sunday 14
DOCWRA'S MANOR, Shepreth
THE LAURELS, Great Shelford
JUNE Sunday 21
THE BELL SCHOOL OF LANGUAGES,
Cambridge
FEN DITTON GARDENS, nr Cambridge
JUNE Sunday 28
GRANTCHESTER GARDENS, nr
Cambridge
MELBOURN BURY, nr Royston
MELBOURN LODGE, nr Royston
THE TICKELL ARMS, Whittlesford
JULY Sunday 5
ELTON HALL, nr Peterborough
THE MANOR HOUSE, Boxworth
WEST WRATTING PARK, West Wratting

JULY Saturday 11
EMMANUEL COLLEGE GARDEN &
FELLOWS' GARDEN, Cambridge
FEN VIEW, Waterbeach
JULY Sunday 12
ANGLESEY ABBEY, nr Cambridge
DUXFORD MILL, nr Cambridge
FEN VIEW, Waterbeach
GRANCHESTER GARDENS GROUP 11, nr
Cambridge
JULY Thursday 16
PECKOVER HOUSE, Wisbech
JULY Sunday 19
CLARE COLLEGE FELLOWS' GARDEN,
Cambridge
83 HIGH STREET, HARLTON
KING'S COLLEGE FELLOWS' GARDEN,
Cambridge
PAMPISFORD GARDENS
UNWINS SEED TRIAL GARDEN, Histon
AUGUST Sunday 30
DUXFORD MILL, nr Cambridge
LONGSTOWE HALL, Longstowe
AUGUST Monday 31 (Bank Hol)
DUXFORD MILL, nr Cambridge

DESCRIPTIONS OF GARDENS

Anglesey Abbey &% (The National Trust) 6m
NE of Cambridge. From A45 turn N on to
B1102 through Stow-cum-Quy. 100 acres
surrounding an Elizabethan manor created
from the remains of an abbey founded in
reign of Henry I. Garden created during last
50 years; avenues of beautiful trees; groups
of statuary; hedges enclosing small intimate
gardens; daffodils and 4,400 white and blue
hyacinths (April); magnificent herbaceous
borders (July). TEAS. △ *Adm garden only £1
Chd 50p. Thurs, Fri April 9, 10; Sun July 12
(1.30-5.30)*

Bartlow Park (Brig & Mrs Alan Breitmeyer)
1½ m SE of Linton. 6m NE of Saffron Walden;
12m SE of Cambridge; from A604 at Linton
turn SE for Bartlow. Bus: Cambridge-
Haverhill; alight Bartlow Xrds, 300yds.
Medium-sized new garden around recently
built house; spring bulbs, flowering shrubs,
roses, lawn, ornamental trees, set in fine
natural landscape of mature trees. *Adm 80p
Chd 20p (Share to Bartlow Parish Church)
Sun April 26 (2-6)*

Barton Gardens ❀ 3½m SW of Cambridge.
Take A603, in village turn right for Comber-
ton Rd. TEA. *Combined adm 40p Chd 5p
(Share to GRBS). Sun April 26 (2-5)*
    The Seven Houses & (GRBS) Small bun-
    galow estate on left of Comberton Rd.
    1½-acre spring garden; bulbs naturalised
    in orchard. Gift stall.
    The Gables % (P.L. Harris Esq) 11 Com-
    berton Rd. 2-acre old garden, mature
    trees, ha-ha, spring flowers

The Seasons & (Dr Coslett) 31 Comberton Rd. ½-acre rock garden, bulbs
¶**Townend** (B. Overton Esq) 15a Comberton Rd. 1 acre; lawns, trees, pond; extensive views
¶**King's Tythe** (Maj. C.H. Thorne) Comberton Rd. Mixed domestic
¶**Garden House** (Mrs Pamela Wheeldon) Comberton Rd. Mixed domestic
¶**3 Hines Close** (L. Pratt Esq) Mixed domestic; easy to run. TEA

The Bell School of Languages & Red Cross Lane, Hills Rd, Cambridge. In SE Cambridge close to new Addenbrooke's Hospital on A604. Car park. Bus: Eastern Counties 185, 186, 193 to Hospital island; 113 passes gates (Haverhill bus). Large garden; herbaceous borders; summer bedding plants; fine trees and view. TEA. *Adm 60p Chd free. Sun June 21 (2-5.30)*

Berry Close Studio (Stanley Anderson Esq) Great Gransden. Cambridge 15m; St Neots 7m between Great Gransden/ Little Gransden on B1046; look for showcase and sign 'Berry Close Studio'. 3-acre contoured landscape garden; interesting forms and shapes; all-year-round garden. Studio contains permanent exhibition of landscape paintings of English Countryside. Tea in village. *Collecting box. By appt only (Tel Gt Gransden 304)*

Clare College, Fellows' Garden && (Master & Fellows) Cambridge. The Master and Fellows are owners of the Fellows' Garden which is open; the Master's garden (nearby) is not open to the public. Approach from Queen's Rd or from city centre via Senate House Passage, Old Court and Clare Bridge. 2 acres; one of the most famous gardens on the Cambridge Backs. Free leaflet. TEAS. *Adm 60p Chd free. Sun July 19 (2-6)*

The Crossing House & (Mr & Mrs Douglas Fuller) Meldreth Rd, Shepreth, 8m SW of Cambridge. ½m W of A10. King's Cross-Cambridge railway line runs alongside garden. Small cottage garden with many old-fashioned plants grown in mixed beds in company with modern varieties; shrubs, bulbs, etc, many alpines in rock beds and alpine house. *Collecting box. Visitors welcome any day of the year (Tel Royston 61071)*

Docwra's Manor &&& (Mrs John Raven) Shepreth, 8m SW of Cambridge. ½m W of A10. Cambridge-Royston bus stops at gate in Shepreth. 2 acres of choice plants in series of enclosed gardens. TEAS June 14 only. *Adm £1 OAPs 50p Chd free. Suns April 5, May 3, June 7, July 5, Aug 2, Sept 6, Oct 4 (2-6); Mon May 4; Weds, Fris April 1 to Oct 9 (10-5); also by appt (Tel Royston 60235 & 61473). For NGS (Share to Cambs & Isle of Ely Naturalists Trust) Sun June 14 (2-7)*

Duxford Mill && (Mr & Mrs Robert Lea) 9m S of Cambridge. Close to Duxford village, on Bl379,off A505 and 1½m from Junc 10, M11 (Cambridge by-pass). Bus: Eastern Counties 112 Cambridge-Saffron Walden. Lawns and borders of modern roses beside the R. Cam. Gardens landscaped to include vistas of Mill Pool, Regency Stone Temple; sculpture by Wiles; ornamental water fowl and water garden. Old water mill and miller's house mentioned in Domesday survey l080; much visited during Protectorate by Oliver Cromwell. Charles Kingsley stayed for long periods and is reputed to have written parts of *The Water Babies* here. Free car park. TEAS (in aid of local charities). *Adm 50p Chd 10p. Suns, Mons May 24, 25; Aug 30, 31 & Sun July 12 (2-6); by appt for coach parties (June-Sept)*

Elton Hall &&& (Mr & Mrs William Proby) 8m W of Peterborough, 5m N of Oundle on A605. 8 acres under restoration; rose garden, 1000 roses replanted; new herbaceous borders; arboretum planted 1983. House (open). TEAS. *Adm £2.20 Chd £1.10. △Sat July 5 (2-5)*

Emmanuel College Garden & Fellows' Garden && in centre of Cambridge. Car parks at Parker's Piece and Lion Yard, within 5 mins walk. One of the most beautiful gardens in Cambridge; buildings of C17 to C20 surrounding 3 large gardens with pools; also herb garden; herbaceous borders, fine trees inc Metasequoia glyptostroboides. On this date access allowed to Fellows' Garden with magnificent Oriental plane and more herbaceous borders. Teashops in Cambridge. *Adm 60p Chd free. Sat July 11 (2.30-5.30)*

Fen Ditton Gardens &&& 3½m NE of Cambridge. From A45 Cambridge-Newmarket rd turn N by Borough Cemetary into Ditton Lane; or follow Airport sign from by-pass. TEAS Church Hall. *Combined adm £1 Chd 40p (Share to Ely Cathedral Restoration Fund). Sun June 21 (2-6)*
    The Rectory (Revd & Mrs L. Marsh) Garden with mature trees in process of reconstruction; interesting collection of plants, herbs and shrubs have been planted to restore garden to its former standard; vegetable plots organically managed. House (not open) late C17
    The Old Stables (Mr & Mrs Zavros) Large informal garden; old trees, shrubs and roses; many interesting plants, herbs and shrubs have been introduced. House (not open) converted by owners in 1973 from C17 stables
    Hardwicke House & (Mr L. & Mr J. Drake) 2 acres designed to provide shelter for plants on exposed site; divided by variety of hedges; species roses; rare herbaceous plants; home of national collection of aquilegias, collection of plants grown in this country prior to 1650

Fen View ⚘✿ (Mr & Mrs R.L. Guy) 90 Bannold Rd, Waterbeach. 7m N of Cambridge on E of A10, well signed. Small garden on edge of village; views over countryside on popular walk to R. Cam; new herbaceous border; fish pond; bog garden; bulbs; raised beds; conifers; heathers; model vegetable garden; fruit. TEAS. *Collection box. Sat, Sun July 11, 12 (2-6)*

Grantchester Gardens. ✿ 2m SW of Cambridge. Al0 from S, left at Trumpington (Junction 11, M11). M11 from N, left at Junc 12. Tractor rides through village. Palestrina Singers will be performing at the Old Vicarage; Exhibition of garden paintings by Helen Herbert at North End House. Craft Fair at Manor Farm, Quality handmade goods; wooden toys; pottery, stained glass; glass blowing demonstration; Honey and demonstrations of Beekeeping. TEAS. *(Share to Grantchester Church). Sun June 28 (2-6)*

    The Old Mill (Jeremy Pemberton Esq) ½-acre on both sides of Mill Race in attractive rural setting. The Old Mill, mentioned in Rupert Brooke's poem 'Grantchester', was burnt down in 1928.

    The Old Vicarage ⚘✿ (Mr & Mrs J.H. Archer) 2½ acres; house dating from C17; informal garden laid out in mid C19; lawn with fountain; ancient mulberry tree; many other interesting trees inc cut-leaf beech; beyond garden is wilderness leading to river bank bordered by large old chestnut trees immortalised by Rupert Brooke, who lodged in the house 1910-1912.

    Balls Grove ✿ (Mr & Mrs R.H. Barnes) 3½ acres; lawns with perennial beds and shrubs; 2 ponds, small copse with large trees.

    Grape House (Miss V. James) ¾-acre, partly old-fashioned, partly newly developed; planned for easy maintenance

    Home Grove ⚘✿ (Dr & Mrs C.B. Goodhart) 1-acre informal, orchard-type garden with shrub roses. Specimen trees and lawns and carefully planned kitchen garden

    North End House ⚘✿ (Sir Martin & Lady Nourse) 1-acre, newly laid out; shrub and herbaceous borders; old-fashioned roses; water garden and rockery. Small conservatory.

Grantchester Gardens Group 11. For directions and description see above. In centenary year of Rupert Brooke's birth a one-man play written by Mark Payton (NT player) will be performed at The Old Vicarage at 2.30 and 5.30. The following gardens will also be open. *Sun July 12 (2-6)*

    The Old Mill (Jeremy Pemberton Esq)
    The Old Vicarage (Mr & Mrs J.H. Archer)
    North End House (Sir Martin & Lady Nourse)

83 High Street Harlton ⚘✿✿ (Dr Ruth Chippindale) 7m SW of Cambridge. A603 (toward Sandy); after 6m turn left (S) for Harlton. Garden on left in Haslingfield direction. ⅓ acre; for all-the-year interest with mixed borders, rockery and small herbaceous border; foliage interest. TEAS 100 High Street. *Adm 50p Chd 20p (Share to Harlton Church Restoration Fund). Sun July 19 (2-6)*

King's College Fellows' Garden, ⚘✿ Cambridge. Bulbs. Tree leaflets available. *Adm 30p Chd free. Suns April 26, July 19 (2-6)*

The Laurels ⚘✿ (The Misses Collett) Great Shelford, 4m S of Cambridge. A1301, fork right at War Memorial if coming from Cambridge. Medium-sized, mature garden; large trees; yew hedge; lawns and herbaceous borders. TEA. *Adm 50p Chd 5p. Sun June 14 (2-7)*

Leckhampton ⚘✿ (Corpus Christi College) 37 Grange Rd, Cambridge. Grange Rd is on W side of Cambridge and runs N to S between Madingley Rd (A1303) and A603; drive entrance opp Selwyn College. 8 acres; originally laid out by William Robinson as garden of Leckhampton House (built 1880); George Thomson building added 1964 (Civic Trust Award); formal lawns, rose garden, small herbaceous beds; extensive wild garden with bulbs, cowslips, prunus and fine specimen trees. TEAS. *Adm 50p Chd 15p Sun May 10 (2-6)*

Longstowe Hall ⚘✿ (M.G.M Bevan Esq) 10m W of Cambridge. Nr junc of A14 and B1046. Very large garden with extensive lawns; 2 lakes; attractive woodland walks; many fine specimen trees; daffodils and oxlips; formal rose garden and 2 long herbaceous borders. TEAS. Free car park. *Adm 60p Chd 30p. Suns April 19, Aug 30 (2-6)*

The Manor House ⚘ (Lt-Col E.B. Thornhill) Boxworth. 6½m W of Cambridge. 1m S of A604 turn S at sign to Boxworth, after 1m take turn left at sign marked Public Bridle Path to Lolworth down Manor Lane for 300 yds. Medium garden; roses, herbaceous border, clipped trees, yew hedge, shrubs. Picnic area; TEA & soft drinks. *Adm 50p Chd 20p. Sun July 5 (2-6)*

Melbourn Bury ⚘✿✿ (Mr & Mrs Anthony Hopkinson) 2¼m N of Royston; 8m S of Cambridge; off the A10 on edge of village, Royston side. 5 acres; small ornamental lake and river with wildfowl; large herbaceous border; fine mature trees with wide lawns and rose garden. TEAS. *Combined adm with Melbourn Lodge 80p OAPs 40p Chd free. Sun June 28 (2-6)*

Melbourn Lodge ⚘ (J.R.M. Keatley Esq) Melbourn 3m N of Royston, 8m S of Cambridge. House in middle of Melbourn village on A10.

2 acre garden maintained on 20 hrs work in season. C19 grade II listed house (not open). *Combined adm with Melbourn Bury 80p OAPs 40p Chd free (Share to Local Charities). Sun June 28 (2-6)*

Pampisford Gardens 8m S of Cambridge on A505. TEAS at The Old Vicarage (in aid of RDA). *Combined adm £1 Chd 40p. Sun July 19 (2-6)*

¶**Beech Corner** ⚿ (Mr & Mrs B.E. Bridgland) 22 Church Lane. Small new garden; well laid out with interesting plants
¶**Cornerways** ⚿ (Mrs E.M.Godden) 14 Brewery Rd. Small well kept garden with mixed borders
¶**The Dower House** ⚿ (Dr & Mrs O.M. Edwards) 7 High Street. Medieval house surrounded by well designed and interesting garden
¶**Nos 3-6 Glebe Crescent.** ⚿ A row of pensioners houses with very colourful small gardens
The Old Vicarage ⚿❀ (Mr & Mrs Nixon) Next to Church in Village. 2 ½-acres; mature trees; shrub and herbaceous borders with good ground cover plants; small Victorian style conservatory planted with rare species

Peckover House ♿⚿ (The National Trust) Wisbech. In centre of Wisbech town, on N bank of R. Nene (B1441). Garden only open. 2-acre Victorian garden; rare trees, inc maidenhair (Ginkgo) tree. Orange trees growing under glass. TEAS 19 North Brink (adjoining Peckover House). *Adm 50p Chd 20p △ Thurs July 16 (2-6)*

Sawston Hall ♿ (The Cambridge Centre for Languages) 7m S of Cambridge. Between A11, A505 & A604; off A130, 2m from M11 (Cambridge by-pass) junc 10. In centre of Sawston turn off at War Memorial X. Bus: EC 183, 184 from Cambridge. Historic garden surrounding unspoilt Tudor Hall, home of Huddleston family and forebears for 600 yrs up to 1982 and refuge of Queen Mary Tudor in 1553. Interior courtyard, formal lawns, yew hedges, specimen trees, shrubs, climbers, roses, borders, moat with lilies and bull-rushes; 50-acres of attractive woodland walks, SSSI. Cream TEAS; picnic lunches may be eaten in restaurant (licensed). *Adm grounds only 60p Chd 20p (Share to Garden Restoration Fund). Sun May 31 (11-6)*

Tetworth Hall ❀ (Sir Peter & Lady Crossman) 4m NE of Sandy; 6m SE of St Neots off Everton-Waresley rd. Large woodland; bog garden; rhododendrons; azaleas, unusual shrubs and plants; fine trees. Queen Anne house (not shown). TEA. *Adm 50p Chd 20p (Share to Waresley Church). Suns May 24, June 7 (2-7)*

The Tickell Arms ♿ (J.H. De La Tickell & Siegfried Fisher) Whittlesford. 7m S of Cambridge

off A505 (junc 10, M11). Former small walled kitchen garden; now with pools, fountains, statuary; orangery. TEAS. *Adm 50p (Share to DGA). Sun June 28 (2.45-6)*

Trinity College, Fellows' Garden ⚿ Cambridge. Bulbs. *Adm 40p Chd free. Sun April 12 (2-6)*

Unwins Seed Trial Garden ⚿❀ Impington Lane, Histon, 3m N of Cambridge. Follow A45 to B1049 exit. From Cambridge via B1049; at traffic lights right into Impington lane; follow AA/RAC signs, 'Unwins Seed Trial Garden'. In centre of attractive small village. 4-acre trial garden; dazzling display of more than 30,000 flowers inc Unwins internationally famous sweet peas; over 1,000 varieties of vegetables, many of which can be seen for 1st time in this country. TEA. *Adm 40p Chd free. Sun July 19 (10-4)*

West Wratting Park ♿⚿ (Lady Ursula d'Abo) 8m S of Newmarket. From A11, between Worsted Lodge and Six Mile Bottom, turn E to Balsham; then N along B1052 to West Wratting; Park is at E end of village. Georgian house (orangery shown), beautifully situated in rolling country, with fine trees; rose and herbaceous gardens; walled kitchen garden. *Adm 50p Chd free. Sun July 5 (2-7)*

Wimpole Hall ♿⚿ (National Trust) Arrington. 5m N of Royston signed off A603 to Sandy 7m from Cambridge or off A14. Part of 350-acre park. Vivid show of many varieties of daffodils is main attraction in April; fine trees and marked walks in wood. Guided walks (40p extra) at 11, 12, 2 & 3. TEAS & lunches. *Adm 60p Chd 30p. △ Fri April 24 (11-4); Coach parties by appt*

CHESHIRE & WIRRAL
SOUTH MERSEYSIDE

Hon County Organisers:
MAJ & MRS J.A. READMAN, Mere House, Chester Rd, Oakmere, Northwich, CW8 2HB
Assistant Hon County Organiser:
MRS T. R. HILL, Salters Well House, Tarporley

DATES OF OPENING

BY APPOINTMENT ONLY for dates see text:
BELL COTTAGE, Vale Royal Abbey, nr Northwich
REGULAR OPENINGS for dates see text:
ARLEY HALL & GARDENS, nr Northwich
CAPESTHORNE, nr Macclesfield
CHOLMONDELEY CASTLE GARDENS, nr Malpas
PEOVER HALL, Over Peover, nr Knutsford

APRIL Saturday 25 & Sunday 26
  HAREBARROW, Prestbury
MAY Sunday 10
  NEWBOLD, Bruera, nr Chester
  TUSHINGHAM HALL, nr Whitchurch
MAY Sunday 17
  COOMBE DALE, Bickerton, nr Malpas
  HAUGHTON HALL, nr Bunbury
  POULTON HALL, Bebington
  HEATHERGATE, Heswall
MAY Saturday 23
  CAPESTHORNE, nr Macclesfield
MAY Sunday 24
  ALSAGER GARDENS, Alsager
  PENN, Alderley Edge
  TIRESFORD, Tarporley
MAY Monday 25 (Bank Hol)
  PENN, Alderley Edge
MAY Saturday 30
  PEOVER HALL, Over Peover, nr Knutsford
  THE QUARRY, Prenton
MAY Sunday 31
  HEATHERGATE, Heswall
  MANLEY KNOLL, Manley
  PEOVER HALL, Over Peover, nr Knutsford
JUNE Saturday 13
  ARLEY HALL & GARDENS, nr Northwich
JUNE Sunday 14
  ALSAGER GARDENS, Alsager
  POULTON HALL, Bebington
JUNE Sunday 21
  THE OLD HALL, Willaston, Wirral
JUNE Sunday 28
  CHERRY HILL, Malpas
JULY Saturday 11
  CHOLMONDELEY CASTLE GARDENS, nr
    Malpas
JULY Sunday 19
  PENN, Alderley Edge
JULY Sunday 26
  WOOD END COTTAGE, Whitegate, nr
    Northwich
AUGUST Monday 31 (Bank Hol)
  THORNTON MANOR, Thornton Hough

DESCRIPTIONS OF GARDENS

Alsager Gardens Alsager, Stoke-on-Trent.
From M6 junc 16; A500, signs to Alsager.
*Combined adm £1.50 Chd 75p. Each 50p Chd
25p. Suns May 24, June 14 (2-6)*
  ¶**35 Birch Avenue** (Mr & Mrs T.J.Peake)
  From centre of Alsager take Station Rd
  turn right at Manor Hotel. Approx 300 sq
  yds. Selection of conifers, heathers,
  alpines, dwarf and med size rhododendrons, azaleas, pieris etc. Fish
  pond; small bog; perennials inc irises and
  lilies, begonias and annuals. *(Share to
  Leukaemia Research Fund)*
  Orchard Villa ⚘❀ (Mr & Mrs J.Trinder) 72
  Audley Rd, Alsager. From Alsager centre
  take Station Rd, house on right past station. ⅓-acre with wide range of herbaceous perennials, groundcover,

alpines, specialist irises of plantsman's
interest. TEA. *(Share to Multiple Sclerosis)*
Parville ⚘ (Mr & Mrs S. Weatherby) 49
Ashmores Lane, Alsager. Off A50 at Law-
ton Cross Rd for Alsager B5077; 3rd left
into Ashmores Lane (one way). 1¼-acres
well established wall garden of particular
interest for the trees and shrubs inc many
rhododendrons, meconopsis, gentians;
wild garden adjoining. TEA. *(Share to
National Children's Home)*
117 Sandbach Rd(North) ⚘❀ (Mr & Mrs
J.M.Reeves) ¼m from town centre on
B5078 to Sandbach. Typical small suburban garden of about 150 sq yds. Over
600 species of alpines and dwarf bulbs
grown in 2 rockeries, a greenhouse and
assorted frames. Small area for peat-
loving plants. *(Share to RSPCA)*

◆**Arley Hall & Gardens** ⚘❀ (Hon M.L.W.
Flower), 6m W of Knutsford. 5m from M6 junc
19 & 20 & M56 junc 9 & 10. 8 acres; gardens
have belonged to 1 family over 500 yrs; great
variety of style and design; outstanding twin
herbaceous borders (one of earliest in England); unusual avenue of clipped Ilex trees,
walled gardens; yew hedges; shrub roses;
azaleas, rhododendrons; herb garden;
scented garden; woodland garden and walk.
Arley Hall and Private Chapel also open.
TEAS (in C16 converted barn adjacent to earlier 'Cruck' barn). Gift shop. Special rates and
catering arrangements for pre-booked parties. Tel Arley 353. *Adm Gardens only £1.45;
Hall & Chapel 85p extra; Chd 75p. April 5 to
Oct 4, every Tues-Sun inc & Bank Hols (April,
May, Sept, Oct 2-6; June, July, Aug 12-6; last
adm to gardens 5.30). For NGS Sat June 13
(12-6)*

Bell Cottage ⚘⚘❀ (J.W. Ellis Esq & G.K.
Armitstead Esq) Vale Royal Abbey, Whitegate, Northwich. Turn off A556 to Whitegate;
opp church follow drive for ¾m to Vale Royal
Abbey. Medium-sized garden of general interest; walled garden, wooded area, shrubs,
herbaceous, climbers and shrub roses. *Adm
50p Chd 25p. By appt only April-Sept (Tel
Sandiway 883495)*

Capesthorne ⚘⚘ (Sir Walter Bromley-
Davenport) 5m W of Macclesfield. On A34 7m
S of Wilmslow. Bus stop: Monks Heath
(1½m). Medium-sized garden; daffodil lawn;
azaleas, rhododendrons; flowering shrubs;
herbaceous border; lake and pool. Georgian
chapel built 1722 on view. Cheshire Conservation Trust Nature Trail (leaflet 5p) combined garden and woodland walk. Historic
parks and gardens. TEAS and LUNCHES.
Free car park. *Adm garden £1 Chd 50p Hall
extra £1 Chd 50p Suns April to Sept inc; Wed
& Sats May to Sept inc Tues & Thurs June to
Aug; also Good Fri & Bank hols. For NGS Sat
May 23 (12-6)*

Cherry Hill ⅋⊛ (Mr & Mrs Miles Clarke) 2m W of Malpas signed from B5069 to Chorlton. Massed bulbs in spring; walks through pine woods and rhododendrons to trout lake; walled garden, herbaceous borders, shrub roses. Home-made TEAS in attractive house overlooking Welsh mountains. *Adm 75p Chd 30p. Sun June 28 (2-6)*

Cholmondeley Castle Gardens ⊛ (The Marquess of Cholmondeley) Malpas 7m W of Nantwich off A49, RAC signposted. 30 acres; daffodils, azaleas, rhododendrons, rose garden, herbaceous borders, shrubs, trees; attractive water garden with island, temples, bridges laid out early C19. Ancient Private Chapel. Variety of farm animals. Lakeside picnic area. Gift Shop. TEAS. *Adm £1.50 OAPs £1 Chd 50p; reduced rate for coach parties. Suns & Bank Hols only from April 19 to Sept 27 (12-5.30); weekdays for groups by appt (Tel 082 922 383). For NGS Sat July 11 (12-5.30)*

Coomb Dale ⊛ (Mr & Mrs A. G. Barbour) Bickerton, Malpas. 10m SE of of Chester via A41. At Broxton roundabout turn E onto A534 towards Nantwich; next turn left after 'Copper Mine', public house on right. 5 acres. Rhododendrons, azaleas, shrubs and trees in woodland setting. Arboretum containing rare trees and conifers. TEAS. *Adm £1 Chd free (Share to Harthill & Burwardsley Churches). Sun May 17 (2-6)*

Harebarrow ⅋ (Mr & Mrs C.A. Savage) Chelford Rd, Prestbury 3m N of Macclesfield on A538. Leave A538 in village on minor rd signed Over Alderley/Chelford; garden 1m on left. 1 acre; planted with heathers (over 200 varieties giving year round colour) conifers and evergreen shrubs, designed for easy maintenance. Water garden, pond, extensive views of the Pennines. 2 acre paddock with registered flock of Jacob sheep and lambs. *Adm 50p Chd 20p. Sat, Sun April 25, 26 (2-6)*

Haughton Hall ⅋ (Geoffrey C. Dean Esq) nr Bunbury; 5m NW of Nantwich. 6m SE of Tarporley via Beeston Castle; N of A534 Nantwich-Wrexham rd. Medium-sized garden; species of rhododendrons, azaleas, shrubs, rock garden, lake with temple, waterfall. Bird garden with Cuban flamingoes, Stanley and E African Crown Cranes, black-necked swans, and some 30 species of water fowl. Dogs on leads only. TEAS. Free car park. *Adm £1 Chd 50p (Share to Bunbury Church) Sun May 17 (2-6); By appt for parties (Tel Bunbury 260251)*

Heathergate (Dr Anna Seager) Oldfield Rd, Heswall, Wirral. From Chester via A540; through Heswall; left at Quarry Rd Xrds; right at T-junc into Oldfield Rd. 1½ acres with azaleas, rhododendrons and other interesting flowering shrubs in peaty soil; open view across Dee estuary. TEAS. *Adm 50p Chd 10p (Share to Heswall Handicapped Boys' Camp), Suns May 17 & 31 (2-6)*

Manley Knoll ⅋ (D.G. Fildes Esq) Manley, NE of Chester. Nr Mouldsworth. B5393. Quarry garden; azaleas and rhododendrons. TEAS. *Adm 50p OAPs/Chd 20p. Sun May 31 (2-6.30)*

Newbold ⊛ (Maj J.N. Davies-Colley) 5m SE of Chester. From A41 Chester-Whitchurch; turn W at Hatton Heath towards Bruera; entrance on left after approx 1m. Old garden; rare trees; vistas. TEAS. *Adm 50p Chd 25p. Sun May 10 (2-6)*

The Old Hall ⅋⊛ (Dr & Mrs Wood) Hadlow Rd, Willaston S Wirral, 8m NW of Chester on village green. ¾-acre; mixed border, interesting plants. C17 house. TEAS. *Adm 50p Chd 25p (Share to Muscular Dystrophy Group). Sun June 21 (2-6)*

Penn ⅋ (Mr & Mrs R.W. Baldwin) Macclesfield Rd, Alderley Edge. ¾m E of Alderley Edge village, on B5087, Alderley Edge-Macclesfield Rd. Turn left into Woodbrook Rd for car parking. 2½ acres; rhododendrons (over 500 varieties of species and hybrids), azaleas, camellias, magnolias, summer shrubs on a hillside backing on to the Alderley Edge Nat. Trust property. *Adm 70p Chd 10p. Sun, Mon May 24, 25 Sun July 19 (2-6)*

◆**Peover Hall** ⅋⊛ (Mr & Mrs Randle Brooks) Over Peover. 3m S of Knutsford on A50, Lodge gates by Whipping Stocks Inn. 15 acres. 5 walled gardens: lily pond, rose, herb, white and pink gardens; C18 landscaped park, moat, C19 dell, rhododendron walks, large walled kitchen garden, Church walk, purple border, blue and white border, pleached lime avenues, fine topiary work. Dogs in park only. TEAS. *Adm £1 Chd 50p (Share to Over Peover Church Monuments Restoration Fund). Mons & Thurs (2-5) May to Oct. NOT Bank Hols. Other days by appt for parties. For NGS Sat, Sun May 30, 31 (2-5.30)*

Poulton Hall ⅋ (Dr & Mrs Roger Lancelyn Green) Poulton Lancelyn, 2m from Bebington. From M53, exit 4 towards Bebington; at traffic lights (½m) right along Poulton Rd; house 1m on right. 2½ acres; lawns, ha-ha, shrubbery, walled gardens in process of restoration and replanting. TEAS. *Adm 50p Chd 10p. Suns May 17, June 14 (2-6)*

The Quarry (Mrs Chris Jones) Burrell Rd (off Pine Walks), Prenton. Wirral Bus: Birkenhead Corp 84, 85 & 86, alight Mount Rd or Mendip Rd, 200 yds. 1¾ acres of unique design; advantage taken of former worked out quarry to make an alpine and rhododendron garden. Lily and fish pond. Unusual flowering trees and shrubs; Exbury strain azaleas, camellias, magnolias, heaths. *Adm 40p Chd 10p. Sat May 30 (11-5)*

Thornton Manor ❀ (The Viscount Leverhulme) Thornton Hough, Wirral. From Chester A540 to Fiveway Garage; turn right on to B5136 to Thornton Hough village. From Birkenhead B5151 then on to B5136. From M53, exit 4 to Heswall; turn left after 1m. Bus: Woodside-Parkgate; alight Thornton Hough village. Large garden of all year round interest. TEA. Free car park. *Adm £1 OAPs/Chd 40p. Mon Aug 31 (2-7)*

Tiresford ❀ (Mr & Mrs R.J. Posnett) Tarporley. A51 (½m S of Tarporley). Bus Nantwich-Chester, alight 100yds from garden. Medium-sized garden; water garden; rockery, roses, shrubs and azaleas, well-planted herbaceous border. Home-made TEAS. Free car park. *Adm 75p Chd 25p. Sun May 24 (2-7)*

Tushingham Hall &⚘ (F. Moore Dutton Esq) 3m N of Whitchurch. Signed off A41 Chester-Whitchurch Rd; Medium-sized garden in beautiful surroundings; bluebell wood alongside pool; ancient oak, girth 25ft. TEA. *Adm 50p Chd 20p (Share to St Chad's Church, Tushingham). Sun May 10 (2-6.30)*

¶**Wood End Cottage** ❀ (Mr & Mrs M.R. Everett) Grange Lane, Whitegate. Turn S off A556 (Northwich/Chester) to Whitegate village, opp school follow Grange Lane for 300 yds. ½-acre sloping to a natural stream being developed as a plantsman's garden. Mature trees, herbaceous, clematis, raised beds, small tufa bed. TEA. *Adm 50p Chd 25p (Share to British Epilepsy Assoc). Sun July 26 (2-6)*

CLWYD

Hon County Organisers:
MRS J.M.D. ALEXANDER, Wern Cottage, Tremostyn, Whitford CH8 9AR;
North: MRS RICHARD HEATON, Plas Heaton, Trefnant, Denbigh LL16 5AF.
South: MRS J. R. FORBES, Pen-y-Wern Pontblyddyn, nr Mold CH7 4HN

DATES OF OPENING

BY APPOINTMENT ONLY for dates see text:
TYNANT, nr Oswestry

APRIL Sunday 12
HAWARDEN CASTLE, Deeside
APRIL Sunday 26
GWAENYNOG, Denbigh
MAY Sunday 10
HARTSHEATH, nr Mold
PEN-Y-WERN, nr Mold
RUG, Corwen

MAY Sunday 17
BERTH, Llanbedr, nr Ruthin
DEE BANK, Overton-on-Dee
HARWARDEN CASTLE, Deeside
MAY Friday 22
ERDIGG PARK, Wrexham
MAY Saturday 23
CHIRK CASTLE, Chirk
MAY Sunday 31
GLYN ARTHUR, Llandyrnog
JUNE Saturday 6
LANGLANDS, Wrexham
JUNE Sunday 7
EYARTH HOUSE, nr Ruthin
JUNE Sunday 14
CEFN PARK & LLWYN ONN HALL, nr Wrexham
5B UPPER CLWYD STREET, Ruthin
JUNE Sunday 21
PLAS KINMEL, nr Abergele
JUNE Sunday 28
HAFOD-Y-COED, Tremeirchion
PLAS HEATON, Trefnant
JULY Friday 3
GLANABER, Llanasa
JULY Saturday 4
GLANABER, Llanasa
WELSH COLLEGE OF HORTICULTURE, Northop, Mold
WERN COTTAGE, nr Holywell
JULY Sunday 5
CUMBERS HOUSE, nr Whitchurch
MYNACHLOG, Northop, nr Mold
JULY Monday 6
GLANABER, Llanasa
JULY Saturday 11
NANTLYS, Tremeirchion
JULY Sunday 12
DONADEA LODGE, Babell
JULY Sunday 19
GWYSANEY HALL, nr Mold
9 HANDSWORTH CRESCENT, Rhyl
RHUAL, Mold
JULY Sunday 26
QUINTON, Worthenbury, nr Malpas
AUGUST Sunday 2
PLAS-YN-CEFN, St Asaph
AUGUST Sunday 9
CUMBERS HOUSE, nr Whitchurch
PLAS-YN-CEFN, St Asaph
SEPTEMBER Sunday 13
PLAS FFORDD DDWR, Llandynrog

DESCRIPTIONS OF GARDENS

Berth ⚘ (Mr & Mrs E.G.F. Davey) Llanbedr, 2m E of Ruthin. Off B5429 1m from Llanbedr. 2 acres; shrubs, herbaceous, pool. *Adm 80p Chd 20p (Share to St Peters Church, Llanbedr). Sun May 17 (2-6)*

Chirk Castle ⚘ (The National Trust) Chirk 7m SE of Llangollen. Off A5 in Chirk by War Memorial. 4½ acres trees and flowering shrubs, rhododendrons, azaleas, rockery, yew topiary. TEA. *Adm to garden £1 OAPs/ Chd 50p (Share to NT). Sat May 23 (12-6)*

Cefn Park (Mr & Mrs Roger Graham-Palmer) Cefn Rd, Wrexham. Take A525 from Wrexham; left at Kings Mills on to Abenbury Rd. Turn left into Cefn Rd, entrance on right. Or take Holt Rd(A534) to Rhosnesni roundabout, take Cefn Rd, entrance on left. Spacious lawns surround C18 house, semi enclosed rose garden with lily pond. Mature trees line 10 min walk down to walled vegetable garden from where you cross small field for tea at Llwyn Onn Hall. **Llwyn Onn Hall Hotel** C17 - 18 house, recently restored as Country House Hotel retaining original listed features. Visitors are invited to wander in garden inc walled water garden now being restored; fine trees; bog garden. TEAS. *Adm £1 Chd 10p. Sun June 14 (2-6)*

Cumbers House &※ (Lord & Lady Kenyon) Gredington, 7m W of Whitchurch. On A539 1m W of Hanmer 5m E of Overton-on-Dee. 2 acres some 100yrs old, being developed and replanted; further planting since 1980; most shrubs and trees are still in early stage; some unusual plants but visitors must not expect anything spectacular; small cold greenhouse; border with Laburnum screen planted 1985/6; ⅓ acre added for prospective small arboretum. TEAS. *Adm 50p Chd 25p (Share to St Chad's Church, Hanmer). Suns July 5, Aug 9 (2-6)*

Dee Bank &※ (Mr & Mrs D.B.Whitehouse) Overton-on-Dee, 7m SE of Wrexham, off A539 between Overton Bridge & Overton village. 1-acre garden and 2-acre wood; herbaceous beds; heather garden; small rock garden; spring shrubs and bulbs; woodland walk to river, woodland garden under development. Treehouse for children. Heated swimming pool. TEA. *Adm 60p Chd 30p (Share to Citizens Advice Bureau, Wrexham Branch). Sun May 17 (2-6)*

Dondea Lodge &※※ (Mr & Mrs Patrick Beaumont) Babell. Turn off A541 Mold-Denbigh rd at Afonwen, signed Babell; after 2m turn left; turn off A55 Holywell-St Asaph rd at B5122 to Caerwys; 3rd turning on left. 1½-acre garden developed since 1967; shrubs, shrub roses, clematis, ground cover plants. TEAS. *Adm £1 Chd 25p (Share to Distressed Gentlefolks Association). Sun July 12 (2-6)*

♦**Erddig Park** &※ (The National Trust) 2m S of Wrexham. Signed from A483/A5125 Oswestry Road; also from A525 Whitchurch Road. Garden restored to its C18 formal design inc varieties of fruit known to have been grown there during that period. TEAS. *Adm to garden only (house closed) £1 Chd 50p. △For NGS Fri May 22 (2-5)*

Eyarth House ※※ (Mr & Mrs J.T.Fleming) 2m S of Ruthin off A525. Bus:Ruthin-Corwen; Ruthin-Wrexham. Medium-sized garden; rock garden; shrubs and ornamental trees. TEA. *Adm 50p Chd 20p. Sun June 7 (2.30-6)*

Glanaber &※※ (Mrs J.M.P. Spiller) Llanasa, 3m SW of Prestatyn. Turn off A548 at Gwespyr or from A55 take A5151 turn off in Trelawnyd. 1 acre garden created from pastureland dominated by rare Maltese oak; large duck pond, fish/lily pond; bridges, arches, footpaths create pleasant walks; spring bulbs; herbaceous and bedding plants. C18 house. Old tools, machinery display. Garden and craft shops. Coffee, farmhouse lunch, cream TEAS. *Collection box. Open daily. For NGS Fri, Sat, Mon July 3, 4, 6 (10.30-5.30)*

Glyn Arthur ※ (Mr & Mrs Rowley Williams) Llandyrnog, 5m E of Denbigh, 6m N of Ruthin. A541 off B5429. 2 acres; azaleas, rhododendrons; short walk to landscaped trout pool. TEA. *Adm 70p Chd 25p (Share to Llangwyfan Church). Sun May 31 (2-6)*

Gwaenynog &※※ (Maj & Mrs Tom Smith) Denbigh. 1m W of Denbigh on A543, Lodge on left. 2-acre garden surrounding C16 house visited by Dr Samuel Johnson during his "Tour of Wales". Beatrix Potter wrote and illustrated "Flopsy Bunnies" here. TEA. *Adm £1 Chd 25p. Sun April 26 (2-6)*

♦**Gwysaney Hall** &※※ (Capt & Mrs P. Davies-Cooke) 1½m NW of Mold via A541; 400 yds after end of 30 mph limit, entrance on R (from Mold). 11 acres of pleasure grounds inc 1-acre of flowers, 2-acres lawn, 2-acres arboretum of specimen trees. TEA. *Adm 50p Chd 20p (Share to Girl Guides Assoc, Mold Branch). Sun July 19 (2-6)*

Hafod-y-Coed &※※ (Mr & Mrs M.W. Higgin) Tremeirchion, 3m E of St Asaph. 2 acres with shrubs, rock garden, roses and ornamental duckpond. TEA. *Adm 75p Chd 25p. Sun June 28 (2-6)*

¶**9 Hansworth Crescent** ※ (Mrs F.J..Cowx) Rhyl. Situated outskirts of town off Rhuddlan Rd. Suburban garden,75' x 30',lawns and flower borders, small greenhouse. TEA. *Adm 70p Chd 35p. Sun July 19 (2-6)*

Hartsheath ※ (Mrs H.M.C. Jones-Mortimer) Pontblyddyn. ½m S of intersection with A5104. Red brick lodge on E side of A541. Large woodland garden; many varieties of flowering cherries and crab apples. Tidy picnic lunchers welcomed. *Adm 50p Chd 10p (Share to Pontblyddyn Church). Sun May 10 (12-5.30)*

Hawarden Castle &※ (Sir William & Lady Gladstone) On B5125 just E of Hawarden village. Use Garden Centre entrance. Large garden and picturesque ruined castle. *Adm 50p Chd 25p. Suns April 12, May 17 (2-6)*

Langlands ✗ (Mr & Mrs C. L. Lacey) Maesydre Rd, Wrexham. From town centre take Chester Rd, at traffic lights take Penymaes Ave, 1st left into Maesydre Rd. Large town garden redesigned since 1981 to accommodate wide variety unusual plants; shrubs, perennials and bulbs grown in mixed borders in cottage garden style. *Adm 40p Chd 20p (Share to Dr Arthur's Terminal Care Fund). Sat June 6 (2-6)*

¶**Mynachlog** ✗ (Mr & Mrs J.Bankes) Northop, Mold. Leave Mold by Flint rd (A5119). Turn left at lights on X-rds of A5119 and A55, turn left after 100 yards towards Rhosesmor. Continue along winding lane uphill for about half a mile to entrance of drive. Welsh local stone farm house and buildings c. 1840. Garden, 2½ acres. large pond. Interesting variety of trees. Attractive situation. TEAS. *Adm 50p Chd 25p. Sun July 5 (2-6)*

Nantyls ✗ (Mr & Mrs A.D.H.Pennant) Tremeirchion, 6m NE of Denbigh. From A541 turn at Bodfari on to B5429 towards Tremeirchion; garden 1½m on left. From A55 turn at Rhuallt on to B5429 towards Bodfari, 1m S of Tremeirchion on right. 1-acre garden set among woods with views of Vale of Clwyd. Conducted tours of house containing items of interest concerning Dr Johnson, Mrs Thrale and Pennants of Downing. TEAS (in house or on lawn). *Adm garden only 50p, house £1 extra Chd 20p (Share to St Stephens Church, Bodfari). Sat July 11 (2-6)*

Pen-y-Wern ✗ (Dr & Mrs Forbes) Pontblyddyn, 5m SE of Mold, 7m NW of Wrexham. On E side of A541, ½ way between Pontblyddyn and Caergwrle. 2½-acre country-house garden with many spring flowers. Wild fowl and ponds. TEAS. *Adm 50p Chd 10p (Share to Hope Parish Church). Sun May 10 (2-6)*

Plas Ffordd Ddwr ✗ (Mr & Mrs D.J.Thomas) Llandyrnog. 2m E of Denbigh. Follow signs to Llandyrnog from roundabout at Ruthin end of Denbigh by-pass A525, house 2m on right. 3½-acre country garden, elevated position in Vale of Clwyd.Re-design in progress. Part newly established. Shrubs, lawns and mature trees. TEA. *Adm £1 OAPs 50p Chd free (Share to Arthritis & Rheumatism Council). Sunday September 13 (2-6)*

◆**Plas Heaton** ✗ (Mr & Mrs R.J.Heaton) 2½m N of Denbigh on B5428. From Denbigh take Henllan rd, then turn right. Medium-size garden. Flower arrangements in house. TEA. *Adm garden and part house £1 Chd 25p. Sun June 28 (2-6)*

Plas Kinmel ✗ (Mrs D.H.Fetherstonhaugh) 3m SE of Abergele. From Abergele take A547, after approx 2m turn right (signed St George); then 1st left. Or A55 from St Asaph, after 3 m take 1st slip rd signed Towyn & St

George; at T-junc turn right; then 2nd right private rd. 1 ½-acres; roses and herbaceous , shrubs, water garden. House (not open) built 1860, fine example of Nessfield's work. TEAS. *Adm £1 OAPs/Chd 50p. Sun June 21 (2-6)*

¶**Plas-Yn-Cefn** (D.W. Williams-Wynn) St. Asaph. Take A55 from St. Asaph 2m. 2-acre garden, C15 house situated in informal garden, with rose garden on high level to South. Pony rides. Garden produce for sale. TEAS. *Adm £1 Chd 20p (Share to Cefn Church Fund). Sun Aug 9 (2-6)*

Quinton ✗ (Lt Cdr & Mrs John Anderton) Worthenbury. B5069 Malpas to Bangor 5m, Wrexham 8m, A525 Wrexham to Whitchurch rd to Bangor-on-Dee; Overton-on-Dee 5m. 2¼-acre garden comprises a wooded dingle bordering river; divided by yew hedges; classical long walk; herbaceous border. shrubs, heaths (home propagated); kitchen garden and ponds. TEA. *Adm 60p Chd 20p (Share to Worthenbury Village Hall). Sun July 26 (2-6); also Suns by appt mid May to mid Sept (Tel. 094 881 633)*

◆**Rhual** ✗ (Maj & Mrs Basil Heaton) 1m from Mold. Beyond Mold Church fork left taking rd towards Gwernaffield. 4-acres; original C17 house set in formal walled court and rose garden with lawns, herbaceous border and shrubs. *Adm 50p Chd 20p. Sun July 19 (2-6)*

Rug ✗ (The Lord & Lady Newborough) Corwen. From Corwen via A5 over river bridge to traffic lights; about ¼m turn off A5 right by Lodge. 5-acres in early stages of development after reduction of C18 house to its original size 1972-1976; mainly shrubs, wild woodland garden with dog cemetary in shrubbery beyond house, restored Victorian conservatory with family crest on pillars; 7-acre lake; wrought iron gates into park from Glynllifon and Canon from Belan Fort; sundial from Bodfean Hall. TEAS. *Adm 50p Chd 25p (Share to RNLI). Sun May 10 (2-6)*

Tynant ✗ (Mr & Mrs D.J. Williams) Moelfre, 8m W of Oswestry. From Oswestry take B4580 to Llansilin, thence follow signs to Moelfre. Signs in Moelfre to Tynant. 5-acre cottagey garden with streams, pools, vegetable and fruit gardens. Areas of interesting trees and shrubs. Walk through wild woodland garden with stream below, in pretty Welsh valley. *Adm 50p OAPs/Chd 25p (Share to Horticultural Therapy). By appt all year (Tel Llansilin 381)*

¶**5B Upper Clwyd Street** ✗ (Mrs B.M.Gearey) Central Ruthin. Small walled garden in town. Several hundred unusual Alpines in sun and shade, rock gardens, troughs and containers. Shrubs and herbaceous plants in peat bed. Car park 100 yards. *Adm 45p Chd free. Sun June 14 (11.30-6.30)*

Welsh College of Horticulture. &%❀ Between Mold and Flint (each 3m) College located on A55 main Chester-Holyhead rd, ¼m W of Northop. Amenity area with specimen lawn, trees and island beds of shrubs and herbaceous plants; glasshouse unit with decorative plants and commercial section producing food crops, cut flowers and pot plants; fruit and vegetable areas. TEAS. *Adm pedestrians & coach parties 25p Chd 10p; cars inc occupants £1. Sat July 4 (10.45-5.30)*

Wern Cottage ❀ (Mrs J.M.D. Alexander) Tremostyn, 2½m W of Holywell. Off A55 through Whitford, bear right at tree in road then 1st left for 250yds. Small cottage garden. TEA Glanaber, Llanasa. *Adm 80p Chd 20p (Share to Vale of Clwyd MIND). Sat July 4 (12-6)*

CORNWALL

Hon County Organiser
MRS BRIDGET OKELY, St Neot,
Nr Liskeard PL14 6NG
Hon County Treasurer:
MRS V. CHALLINOR DAVIES, Chysbryn,
Bareppa, Mawnan Smith TR11 5EG

DATES OF OPENING

BY APPOINTMENT ONLY for dates see text:
CHYVERTON, Zelah
REGULAR OPENINGS for dates see text:
KEN CARO, Bicton, nr Liskeard
LONG CROSS VICTORIAN GARDENS,
Trelights

APRIL Sunday 5
TREMEER GARDENS, St Tudy
APRIL Sunday 12
BURNCOOSE NURSERIES & GARDEN,
Redruth
POLGWYNNE, Feock
TRELISSICK, Feock
APRIL Saturday 18
BOSLOE, Mawnan Smith
MAY Sunday 3
CARCLEW GARDENS, nr Truro
PENWARNE, Mawnan Smith
ST MICHAEL'S MOUNT, Marazion
MAY Sunday 10
COTEHELE HOUSE, St Dominick, Saltash
MAY Sunday 17
TREBAH, Mawnan Smith
MAY Saturday 23
ELIM COTTAGE, Mylor Downs
MAY Sunday 24
LANHYDROCK, nr Bodmin
MAY Saturday 30
HEADLANDS, Polruan-by-Fowey

MAY Sunday 31
BOCCONOC, Lostwithiel
JUNE Sunday 14
THE HOLLIES, Grampound
JUNE Thursday 18
INCE CASTLE GARDENS & GROUNDS,
Saltash
JUNE Sunday 21
BOSVIGO HOUSE, Truro
JUNE Sunday 28
PENPOL HOUSE, Hayle
JULY Sunday 12
MARY NEWMAN'S COTTAGE, Saltash
AUGUST Sunday 9
TRERICE, Newlyn East
SEPTEMBER Sunday 27
TREBARTHA, North Hill, Launceston
OCTOBER Sunday 25
TRELEAN, St Martin-in-Meneage

DESCRIPTIONS OF GARDENS

Boconnoc &❀ (Capt J.D.G. Fortescue) 4m NE of Lostwithiel; turn E off A390 Lostwithiel-Liskeard rd; signs between Lostwithiel and Taphouse. Large garden; flowering shrubs, trees, views. TEAS. *Adm 70p Chd 25p (Share to Boconnoc Church Window Fund). Sun May 31 (2-6)*

Bosloe & (The National Trust) Mawnan Smith, 5m S of Falmouth. Medium-sized garden; fine view of R Helford. *Adm 60p Chd 30p. Sat April 18 (2-5)*

¶Bosvigo House % (Mr Michael & Mrs Wendy Perry) Bosvigo Lane. ¾-m from Truro centre off Redruth Rd. Past County Hall, right down Dobbs Lane. 3-acre garden still being developed surrounding Georgian house (not open) and Victorian conservatory. Series of enclosed, walled gardens with old fashioned roses, clematis, herbaceous plants. Woodland walk with many rare and unusual plants. TEA. *Adm 50p Chd 25p (Share to Local Cancer Relief Macmillan Fund). Sun June 21 (2-6)*

¶Burncoose Nurseries & Garden ❀ (Mr C.H. Williams) Burncoose, Gwennap. 3m SE of Redruth on A393 Falmouth rd, ½m beyond Lanner. 30-acre woodland garden established at turn of century. Many original plants imported from China inc collection of rare bamboos. Nursery (formerly South Down Nurseries) extends over 7 acres; involved in production of over 1500 types of ornamental shrubs and trees. TEA. *Adm 75p Chd 25p. Sun Apr 12 (2-5)*

♦Carclew Gardens % (H.H. Robert Chope & Mrs Chope) Perran-ar-Worthal, nr Truro. From A39 turn E at Perran-ar-Worthal. Bus: alight Perran-ar-Worthal 1m. Large garden, rhododendron species; terraces; ornamental water. TEAS. *Adm £1 Chd 50p (Share to Barristers Benevolent Fund). Sun May 3 (2-5.30)*

Chyverton (Mr & Mrs N.T. Holman) Zelah, N of Truro. Entrance ¾m SW of Zelah on A30. Georgian landscaped garden with lake and bridge (1770); large shrub garden of great beauty; water garden; outstanding collection magnolias acers, camellias, rhododendrons, rare and exotic trees and shrubs. Visitors personally conducted. *Adm £1.50 (parties over 20 £1) Chd free (Share to BRC, Cancer Relief). By appt only weekdays March, April & May (Tel Zelah 324)*

Cotehele House ✻❀ (The National Trust) 2m E of St Dominick, 4m from Gunnislake (turn at St Ann's Chapel); 8m SW of Tavistock; 14m from Plymouth via Tamar Bridge. Terrace garden falling to sheltered valley with ponds, stream and unusual shrubs. Fine medieval house (one of the least altered in the country); armour, tapestries, furniture. Lunches and TEAS (closed Fri). *Adm house, garden & mill £3 chd £1.50; garden, grounds & mill £1.50 Chd 75p. △ Sun May 10 (11-6; last adm house & mill 5.30)*

Elim Cottage (Maj & Mrs N.A.H. Marsden) Mylor Downs, nr Mylor Bridge. A39 from Truro to Falmouth, turn left after Norway Inn; after 1m cross over 'stop' sign; take 1st right lane for ¼m. ½-acre cottage garden of rhododendrons, azaleas, camellias and magnolia. Home-made cream TEAS. *Adm 75p Chd 20p. Sat May 23 (2-6)*

Headland ✻ (Jean & John Hill) Battery Lane, Polruan. On E of Fowey estuary; leave car in public park; walk down St Saviour's Hill, turn left at Coast Guard office. Cliff garden with sea on 3 sides; mainly plants which withstand salty gales but inc sub-tropical. Spectacular views of Coast; cove for swimming. Cream TEAS. *Adm 50p. Sat May 30 (2-8)*

The Hollies ⬧✻❀ (Mr J. & Mrs N.B. Croggon) Grampound, nr Truro. In centre of village on Truro-St Austell rd. 1-acre garden of unusual design; unusual mixed planting of trees, shrubs and alpines. TEAS. *Adm 60p Chd 30p. Sun June 14 (2-5.30)*

Ince Castle Gardens & Grounds (Patricia, Viscountess Boyd of Merton) 5m SW of Saltash. From A38, at Stoketon Cross take turn signed Trematon, Elmgate. 5 acres with lawns and ornamental woods; shell house and dovecote. TEA. *Adm 60p Chd free. Thurs June 18 (2-6.30)*

●**Ken Caro** ✻❀ (Mr & Mrs K.R. Willcock) Bicton, Pensilva, 5m NE of Liskeard. From A390 to Callington turn off N at Butchers Arms, St Ive; take Pensilva Rd; at next Xrds take rd signed Bicton. 2 acres mostly planted in 1970; well-designed and labelled plantsman's garden; rhododendrons, flowering shrubs, conifers and other trees; herbaceous borders. Panoramic views. Cut material over last 10 yrs has won many medals and cultural commendation certificates. Collection of waterfowl and aviary birds. *Adm 75p Chd 35p. April 26 to June 28 every Sun & Wed, Weds only July, Aug, Sept (2-6)*

◆**Lanhydrock** ⬧✻❀ (The National Trust) Bodmin, 2½m on B3268. Station: Bodmin Parkway 1¾ m. Large-sized garden; formal garden laid out 1857; shrub garden with good specimens of rhododendrons and magnolias and fine views. Lunches and TEAS. *Adm house & garden £3 Chd £1.50; garden only £1.60 Chd 80p. △ Sun May 24 (11-6; last adm to house 5.30)*

Long Cross Victorian Gardens ⬧❀ (Mr & Mrs R.Y. Warrillow) Trelights, St Endellion. 7m N of Wadebridge on B3314, nr Port Isaac and Port Quin. Garden in process of restoration; amongst majestic pines with panoramic sea views. Beer Garden, coffee and refreshments under cover. Cream TEAS (3-5). *Collecting box for NGS. Easter to Oct daily (11-dusk)*

¶**Mary Newman's Cottage** ✻ (Tamar Protection Society) Culver Rd, ½m from Saltash town centre; park on waterfront. ½-acre cottage garden with herbaceous, annuals and herbs being developed. Overlooks R. Tamar and Bridges. Recently restored C15 cottage, former home of Sir Francis Drake's first wife. TEAS. *Adm 50p Chd 25p (Share to Tamar Protection Society). Sun July 12 (2-6)*

Penpol House ⬧✻ (Maj & Mrs T.F. Ellis) Hayle. From Foundry Square, Hayle, take left of White Hart Penpol Rd; then 2nd turning left into Penpol Av; turn right for car park. 3-acres; old Cornish garden of C16 house; delphiniums, roses, herbaceous, shrubs, lawns, wall garden and other pocket gardens; neutral/alkaline soil also favours iris; recent plantings of pockets of trees and use of cover crops to counter loss of many elms in surrounding area. TEAS. *Adm 70p Chd 30p (Share to Cancer Relief Macmillan Fund). Sun June 28 (2-6)*

Penwarne (Mr & Mrs H. Beister) 3¼m SW of Falmouth. 1½m N of Mawnan. Garden with many varieties of flowering shrubs, rhododendrons, magnolias, New Zealand shrubs, formal and informal garden; walled garden. Ornamental ducks. *Adm 80p OAP/ Chd 50p. Sun May 3 (2-5)*

Polgwynne ⬧✻❀ (Mr & Mrs P. Davey) Feock. 5m S of Truro via A39 and then B3289 to 1st Xrds: straight on ½m short of Feock village. 3½-acre garden and grounds. Fruit and vegetable garden, woodlands extending to shore of Carrick Roads; magnificent Gingo Biloba (female, 11'4" girth), other beautiful trees; many rare and unusual shrubs. Lovely view of Carrick Roads. TEAS. *Adm 80p Chd 40p. Sun April 12 (2-5.30)*

St Michael's Mount ⚄ (The Rt Hon Lord St Levan; The National Trust) Marazion. ½m from shore at Marazion; by Causeway (open from approx 12.30/1pm); otherwise by ferry. Flowering shrubs; rock plants, castle walls; fine sea views. TEAS *Adm Castle & gardens £2.20, Chd £1.10. △ Sun May 3 (10.30- 4.45)*

Trebah ✿ (Maj & Mrs A. Hibbert) Mawnan Smith. 4m S of Falmouth. 25-acre S facing breathtaking ravine garden running down to private beach on R.Helford. Wide collection of mature and rare rhododendrons, azaleas, camellias, magnolias, drymis, laurellia, pieris, etc. Many sub-tropical species inc dicksonia, cyatheas, woodwardias, beschornerias, echiums, dasylirion, aeoniums, etc; magnificent arboretum recently catalogued. New feature is extensive water garden with dramatic waterfall and rock pool with koi carp. TEA/Coffee and biscuits. *Adm £1.50 Chd 50p (Share to Army Benevolent Fund). Sun May 17 (11-5)*

Trebartha (The Latham Family) North Hill, SW of Launceston. Nr junc of B3254 & B3257; proceed to North Hill village then ask; ½m walk from car park. Wooded area with lake surrounded by walks of flowering shrubs; woodland trail through fine woods with cascades and waterfalls; American glade with fine trees. TEAS. *Adm £1 Chd 40p (Share to North Hill Parish Church Roof Fund) Sun Sept 27 (2-6)*

Trelean ✿ (Sqn-Ldr G.T. & Mrs Witherwick) St Martin-in-Meneage, 2½m E of Helston. From Helston take St. Keverne rd, B3293; after 1m turn left for Mawgan then follow signs. Medium-sized newly created valley garden with stream and woodland walk; fine views of R. Helford; exceptional planting of cornus, acers and shrubs for autumn colour. Autumn colour film show. TEAS. *Adm 70p Chd 30p. Sun Oct 25 (12-4)*

♦**Trelissick** ♿⚄✿ (The National Trust; R. Spencer Copeland Esq) Feock, 4m S of Truro, nr King Harry Ferry. On B3289. Large garden; superb view over Falmouth harbour. Georgian house (not open). TEAS. *Adm £1.60 Chd 80p. △ Sun April 12 (1-6)*

Tremeer Gardens St Tudy, 8m N of Bodmin; W of B3266. 7-acre garden famous for camellias and rhododendrons with water; many rare shrubs. *Adm 60p Chd 30p. Sun April 5 (2-6)*

Trerice ♿⚄✿ (The National Trust) Newlyn East 3m SE of Newquay. From Newquay via A392 and A3058; turn right at Kestle Mill (NT signposts). Small manor house, rebuilt in 1571, containing fine plaster ceilings and fireplaces; oak and walnut furniture and tapestries. Lunches & TEAS. *Adm house & garden £2.20 Chd £1.10. △ Sun Aug 9 (11-6; last adm house 5.30)*

CUMBRIA

Hon County Organiser:
MRS R. E. TONGUE, Parrock Cross, Cleabarrow, Windermere
Assistant Hon County Organiser:
JOHN ROBINSON ESQ, The Garth, Penrith

DATES OF OPENING

REGULAR OPENINGS for dates see text:
HOLKER HALL & PARK, Cark-in-Carmel
LEVENS HALL, nr Kendal
LINGHOLM, Keswick
MUNCASTER CASTLE, Ravenglass

APRIL Sunday 26
SCARTHWAITE, Grange-in-Borrowdale
MAY Sunday 3
DALLAM TOWER, Milnthorpe
HALECAT, Witherslack
MAY Saturday 9
CRISPIN COTTAGE, nr Kendal
MAY Sunday 10
CRISPIN COTTAGE, nr Kendal
PARROCK CROSS, nr Windermere
STAGSHAW, nr Ambleside
MAY Thursday 14
HUYTON HILL, nr Ambleside
MAY Sunday 17
‡CAIRN COTTAGE, Grasmere
‡POOL FOOT, Brathan, nr Ambleside
SCARTHWAITE, Grange-in-Borrowdale
MAY Wednesday 20
MUNCASTER CASTLE, Ravenglass
MAY Thursday 21
HUYTON HILL, nr Ambleside
MAY Saturday 23 & Sunday 24
THE GARTH, Penrith
MAY Sunday 24
FELLSIDE, nr Keswick
MAY Monday 25 (Bank Hol)
LINGHOLM, Keswick
MAY Thursday 28
HUYTON HILL, nr Ambleside
MAY Sunday 31
FERN COTTAGE, Holme, nr Milnthorpe
HAZEL MOUNT, nr Broughton-in-Furness
JUNE Saturday 6
GRAYTHWAITE HALL, Ulverston
JUNE Sunday 7
‡CARK MANOR, Cark-in-Cartmel
‡FLOOKBURGH LODGE, nr
  Cark-in-Carmel
GHYLLAS, Sedbergh
GRAYTHWAITE HALL, Ulverston
HAZEL MOUNT, nr Broughton-in-Furness
‡ROSTEAD, Cark-in-Carmel
SCARTHWAITE, Grange-in-Borrowdale
STAGSHAW, nr Ambleside
JUNE Sunday 14
ACORN BANK, nr Penrith

JUNE Sunday 21
ACORN BANK, nr Penrith
ASH HOUSE, Thwaite, Millom
HOLKER HALL & PARK, Cark-in-Carmel
JUNE Sunday 28
DALLAM TOWER, Milnthorpe
FERN COTTAGE, Holme, nr Milnthorpe
JULY Sunday 12
HALECAT, Witherslack
JULY Sunday 19
DALLAM TOWER, Milnthorpe
HIGH LEASGHYLL, Milnthorpe
JULY Sunday 26
EDEN PLACE, Kirkby Stephen
FERN COTTAGE, Holme, nr Milnthorpe
AUGUST Sunday 2
YEWS, Windermere
AUGUST Sunday 30
FERN COTTAGE, Holme, nr Milnthorpe
AUGUST Monday 31 (Bank Hol)
LINGHOLM, Keswick

DESCRIPTIONS OF GARDENS

Acorn Bank ᕼ (The National Trust), Temple Sowerby. 6m E of Penrith on A66; ½m N of Temple Sowerby. Bus: Penrith-Appleby or Carlisle-Darlington; alight Culgaith Rd end. Medium-sized garden; good herb garden; parkland. *Adm 70p Chd 35p. March to Oct daily 10-5.30. △ Suns June 14, 21 (10.30-5.30)*

¶**Ash House** ᕼ (Sir Alec & Lady Jardine) Thwaites, Millom. Broughton 2½m W on A595. 1-acre garden set on sunny bank; shrubs; rhododendrons and azaleas. Views towards Duddon Estuary. TEA. *Adm 50p Chd 25p. Sun June 21 (2-5)*

¶**Bank House** For details see Lancashire

¶**Cairn Cottage** (Miss Elizabeth Adam) Pye Lane, Grasmere. Ambleside 4m; follow signs to Grasmere. ¼-acre garden; alpines, shrubs, roses, island beds. Alpine greenhouse. TEA. *Adm 50p Chd 25p. Sun May 17 (2-5)*

¶**Cark Manor** ᕼ (Mr & Mrs A.J.Wallis) Cark-in-Cartmel. Grange-over-Sands 3m. From A590 follow signs for Holker Hall on B5278. In Cark follow rd through and 200 yds further on from Rose and Crown is the entrance to the house and garden. 1-acre cultivated garden; shrubs, trees, croquet lawn on several levels. Georgian cottage extended in mid Victorian time and again in 1900 (not open). *Adm 50p Chd 25p. Sun June 7 (2-5)*

Crispin Cottage ᕼ (Mr & Mrs R.G. Rothwell) Underbarrow, 4m W of Kendal. In centre of Underbarrow village, 150yds from Church. Typical lakeland cottage garden, ⅓-acre, on natural rock; alpine, spring bulbs. TEAS Parrock Cross Sun Only. *Adm 40p Chd 20p. Sat & Sun May 9 & 10 (2-5.30)*

Dallam Tower ᕼ (Brigadier & Mrs C.E. Tryon-Wilson) Milnthorpe, 7m S of Kendal. 7m N of Carnforth, nr junc of A6 and B5282. Station: Arnside, 4m; Lancaster, 15m. Bus: Ribble 553, 554 Milnthorpe-Lancaster via Arnside, alight lodge gates. Medium-sized garden; natural rock garden, waterfalls, fine display of rambler and polyanthus roses; wood walks, lawns, shrubs. Tea High Leasghyll, Heversham (Sun July 19). *Adm 50p OAPs, Chd 20p. Suns May 3, June 28, July 19 (2-6)*

¶**Eden Place** ᕼ (Mr John H. Strutt) ½m from Kirkby Stephen. On A685 at N boundary of town; from Brough turn off A66 follow signs to Kirkby Stephen. 1½-acres newly laid out garden paths and herbaceous borders. Goldfish-pond; summer house. Several species tropical birds with brilliant plumage flying free especially late afternoon/evening. *Adm 50p Chd 20p. Sun July 26 (3-7)*

Fellside ᕼ (Mr & Mrs C.D. Collins) Millbeck, 2m N of Keswick. Turn off A591 Keswick-Bassenthwaite rd opp sign to Millbeck (2m from Keswick); at T-junc in Millbeck village turn right; garden 300yds on left. 1-acre, informal, shrub garden; 250 varieties of rhododendrons, camellias, azaleas, on steep terraced site. Pretty glen with beck; magnificent views of Derwent Water and Bassenthwaite. Tea John Gregg, The Cottage, Millbeck or The Old Mill (Nat Trust) Mirehouse. *Adm 50p Chd 25p. Sun May 24 (2-5.30)*

Fern Cottage ᕼ (Mr & Mrs Clive Jones) Holme, 3m SE of Milnthorpe off A6, 5m N of Carnforth off A6070. On S side Holme village beside canal bridge. Garden featured in "The Gardener's Garden" and "Gardeners' World" Aug '86. ¾-acre garden for all seasons; mixed borders, wall plantings; collection of Japanese maples, American hybrid hostas, osteospermum and bonsai. TEAS. *Adm 50p Chd 20p. Suns May 31, June 28, July 26, Aug 30 (2-6)*

Flookburgh Lodge ᕼ (Dr & Mrs P.L.E. Wood) Station Rd, Flookburgh, Cark-in-Cartmel. 4m W of Grange-over-Sands. Entrance (next Church) 100 yds S of Village square and bus stop. Car park in square. 1-acre garden with shrub roses, meconopses and primulas. LUNCHES/TEAS Grain of Wheat Cafe (Lakeland Nurseries). *Adm 40p Chd 10p (Share to St John the Baptist Church). Sun June 7 (2-5)*

The Garth ᕼ (John Robinson Esq) Penrith Centre. From Beacon Edge St, skirt high side of town into Lowther St, 1st left Beacon St, drive at end on left. 1 acre; flowering shrubs; landscaped Koi pools, conifers, alpines and waterside plants; rhododendron species contained within evergreen hedge. *Adm 60p Chd 30p (Share to Penrith Girl Guides). Sat & Sun May 23 & 24 (1.30-5)*

¶**Ghyllas** ✗ (Mrs J.L.Spencer) 1½m from Sedburgh. A684 Kirkby Stephen rd on RHS nr Burnt Mill. 4-acres partly wild on natural rock slope; azaleas; rhododendrons; alpines. Views over Howgill Fells. Ancient woodland. Pool. TEA. *Adm 75p (inc Tea) Chd 40p. Sun June 7 (2.30-5.30)*

◆**Graythwaite Hall** ⅃ (Myles Sandys Esq) Ulverston, nr Hawkshead. Off A590 at Newby Bridge; take rd up W side of Windermere Lake for 4m. 6 acre spring garden; rhododendrons, azaleas, spring flowering shrubs. Designed by Thomas Mawson 1889 inc his Dutch Garden and original layout. *Adm 75p Chd free.* △ *Sat, Sun June 6, 7 (10-6)*

Halecat ⅃✗❀ (Mr & Mrs M.C. Stanley) Witherslack, 10m SW of Kendal. From A590 turn into Witherslack at start of dual Carriageway (signposted Witherslack); left in township and left again, signpost 'Cartmel Fell'; lodge gates on left (map ref. 434834). Medium-sized garden; mixed shrub and herbaceous borders, terrace, sunken garden; gazebo; daffodils and cherries in Spring, beautiful view over Kent estuary to Arnside. Nursery garden attached. TEA. *Adm 50p Chd 10p (Share to Leukaemia Campaign). Suns May 3 & July 12 (2-5)*

Hazelmount ✗❀ (Mrs J. Barratt) Thwaites, Millom, 2m from Broughton-in-Furness off A595 up hill after crossing Duddon River Bridge. 5-acre woodland garden, small lake with stream; spring display of species rhododendrons, azaleas and flowering shrubs. Mature trees and exceptional views of Duddon Estuary and sea. TEA. *Adm 50p Chd 25p (Share to NSPCC). Suns May 31, June 7 (2-5.30)*

High Leasghyll ❀ (Miss H. Drew) Heversham. Open same afternoon as Dallam Tower (short distance away) to provide TEAS in aid of NGS. (Directions for getting here will be available at Dallam Tower). TEAS. *Adm £1 Chd 50p (incs TEA). Sun July 19 (2.30-6)*

◆**Holker Hall & Park** ⅃ (Mr & Mrs Hugh Cavendish) Cark-in-Cartmel, 4m W of Grange-over-Sands. 12m W of M6 (exit 36); through Grange-over-Sands, along B5278 (towards Haverthwaite) for a further 4m 22-acre garden associated with Joseph Paxton; exotic flowering trees; daffodils; exceptional magnolias, rhododendrons and azaleas; rose garden, cherry and woodland walks. House dates from C16 with C19 additions. Also The Lakeland Motor Museum, Craft and Countryside Exhibition, Gift Shop, Cafeteria, Animal house and Adventure Playground. (Adm to Hall extra) Group charges and catering by prior arrangement. *Adm from £1.65 Chd from £1. April 12 - Nov 1 daily except Sats (10.30-6; last Adm 4.30)*

Huyton Hill ⅃ (I.G. Butler Esq) Pullwoods. 2m S of Ambleside on Hawkshead Rd. B5286. Entrance on left. Also approach from Waterhead or Bowness Bay by boat. Station: Windermere 6m. Bus: Ambleside-Hawkshead (infrequent), alight at lodge. Very fine views of Windermere lake and surrounding hills. Variety of trees and flowering shrubs. Parkland walks. House C19 but modelled on Bramall Hall (Tudor mansion in Cheshire). *Adm 30p. Thurs May 14, 21 & 28 (12-5.30)*

◆**Levens Hall** ⅃✗❀ (C.H. Bagot Esq) 5m S of Kendal on Milnthorpe Rd (A6); Exit 36 from M6. 10 acres inc famous topiary garden and 1st ha-ha laid out by M. Beaumont in 1692; magnificent beech circle; formal bedding; herbaceous borders. Elizabethan mansion, added to C13 pele tower, contains superb panelling, plasterwork and furniture. Steam collection illustrating history of steam 1830-1920. Easter Sun-Oct 11. House and garden, gift shop, tearooms, children's play area, picnic area. Sun, Mon, Tues, Wed, Thurs (11-5) steam collection (2-5). Closed Fri & Sat. *Adm House & Garden £2.20 Chd £1.10. Garden only £1.30 Chd 70p. Reduction for groups & OAPs*

◆**Lingholm** ⅃✗❀ (The Viscount Rochdale) Keswick. On W shore of Derwentwater; Portinscale 1m; Keswick 3m. Turn off A66 at Portinscale; drive entrance 1m on left. Ferry: Keswick to Nicol End, 10 mins walk. Bus: Keswick Bus Station to Portinscale, 1m; 'Mountain Goat' minibus service from town centre passes drive end. Formal and woodland gardens; garden walk 1m; rhododendrons, azaleas, etc. Exceptional view of Borrowdale. Shop. TEAS. Free car park. *Adm £1.25 (inc leaflet) inc VAT Chd free. April 1 to Oct 3l daily (10-5). For NGS Mons May 25, Aug 31*

Muncaster Castle ⅃❀ (Mrs Patrick Gordon-Duff-Pennington) 1m E of Ravenglass, 17m SW of Whitehaven on A595. 30 acres; famous large collection of species rhododendrons, azaleas and camellias, some unique in UK; arboretum; historic and scenic site at foot of Eskdale. Bird garden and bears. Giftshop. Coach parties and schools by appt.only. Special arrangements for disabled at front gate. TEASHOP. *Adm House & gardens £2.20 Chd £1.10; garden only £1.10 Chd 70p; Parties £2 Chd £1. Good Fri April 17 to Sept 30 daily except Mons (also open all Bank Hols). For NGS Wed May 20 (12-5); house (1.30-4.30). House & garden closed May 9, 10; June 5, 6, 7*

Parrock Cross ✗ (Mr & Mrs R.E. Tongue) Cleabarrow, 3m SE of Windermere. Off B5284 Crook-Kendal Rd, nr Windermere golf course. 1¾ acres; natural rock formations; rhododendrons, azaleas, rockery. TEAS. *Adm 50p Chd 25p. Sun May 10 (2-5)*

¶**Pool Foot** ✍❀ (Miss Laura Richardson) Brathay, Clappersgate. 1 ¼m from Ambleside on Coniston Rd. 1-acre woodland and river garden; river walks by rhododendrons, azaleas; spring bulbs. Unusual trees. *Adm 50p Chd 30p. Sun May 17 (2-5)*

¶**Rostead** ✍ (Lt Cdr & Mrs J.M.Gale) 1½m Cark-in-Cartmel. By village sign off rd running between Cark and Cartmel. Turn opp. Cark Hall; gate immediately on left. Victorian house (Lakeland Vernacular) in about 1½-acres of garden bordering R. Eea. Established trees and shrubs. Drive flanked by rhododendrons. Many wild birds inc Kingfisher, Dipper, Long-tailed Tit and Goldcrest. TEA: Grain of Wheat Cafe (Lakeland Nurseries) Flookburgh. *Adm 50p Chd 25p. Sun June 7 (2-5.30)*

Scarthwaite ✍ (Mr & Mrs E.C. Hicks) Grange-in-Borrowdale. From Keswick take B5289 to Grange; cross bridge; house ¼m on left. Cottage garden, on glacial moraine; ferns, alpines, bulbs, herbaceous and shrubs packed into ¼-acre. Sunday Express Magazines 1985 Garden of the Year. TEA Grange Bridge Cottage (100yds). *Adm 50p Chd 20p. Suns April 26, May 17, June 7 (2-5)*

Stagshaw ✍❀ (The National Trust) ½m S of Ambleside. Turn E off A591, Ambleside-Windermere rd. Bus: 555 Kendal-Keswick, alight Waterhead, Ambleside. Woodland garden inc fine collection rhododendrons and azaleas. Many other ericaceous trees and shrubs inc magnolias, camellias, embothriums. Views over Windermere. TEAS (May 10, June 7). Open March to end June daily 10-6.30; (July to Oct by appt please send s.a.e.) *Adm 70p Chd 35p.* △*For NGS Suns May 10, June 7 (10-6.30)*

Yews ঌ (Sir Oliver & Lady Scott) Windermere. Bus: Ulverston-Bowness, alight Middle Entrance Drive, 50 yds. Medium-sized formal Edwardian garden; fine trees, ha-ha, herbaceous borders. *Adm 50p Chd 30p. Sun Aug 2 (2-6)*

DERBYSHIRE

Hon County Organiser:
MR & MRS R. BROWN, 210 Nottingham Rd.
Woodlinkin, Langley Mill, Nottingham
NG16 4HG
Hon County Treasurer:
MISS JUDY MEAGER, 7 Claramount Rd,
Heanor, Derbyshire

DATES OF OPENING

BY APPOINTMENT ONLY for dates see text:
DARLEY HOUSE, nr Matlock
REGULAR OPENINGS for dates see text:
HIGH PARK GARDEN CENTRE, nr
Hathersage
LEA GARDENS, nr Matlock

APRIL Easter Sunday 19
FIR CROFT, Calver, nr Bakewell
APRIL Sunday 26
MEYNELL LANGLEY, Derby
RADBURNE HALL, nr Derby
MAY Sunday 17
DAM FARM HOUSE, Brailsford
FIR CROFT, Calver, nr Bakewell
MAY Sunday 24
210 NOTTINGHAM ROAD, Woodlinkin
QUARNDON HALL, nr Derby
JUNE Sunday 7
BRAMLEY HALL COTTAGE, Apperknowle
JUNE Sunday 21
BRAMLEY HALL COTTAGE, Apperknowle
FIR CROFT, Calver, nr Bakewell
PROSPECT HOUSE, Swanwick
SILVER BIRCHES, Moorend, nr Ashbourne
JUNE Sunday 28
5 WOOD LANE, Horsley Woodhouse
JULY Sunday 5
BRAMLEY HALL COTTAGE, Apperknowle
LOCKO PARK, Spondon
210 NOTTINGHAM ROAD, Wodlinkin
JULY Saturday 11
TISSINGTON HALL, nr Ashbourne
JULY Sunday 12
DAM FARM HOUSE, Brailsford
THE LIMES, Apperknowle
JULY Sunday 19
DOVE COTTAGE, Clifton, Ashbourne
FIR CROFT, Calver, nr Bakewell
HARDWICK HALL, Doe Lea
JULY Sunday 26
THE LIMES, Apperknowle
AUGUST Sunday 2
DOVE COTTAGE, Clifton, Ashbourne
AUGUST Sunday 30
FIR CROFT, Calver, nr Bakewell

DESCRIPTIONS OF GARDENS

Bramley Hall Cottage ❀ (Mr & Mrs G.G. Nicholson) Chapel Lane, Apperknowle. 5m N of Chesterfield, from Unstone turn E for 1m to Apperknowle. 1¼ acres, plantsman's garden with extensive view; wide range shrubs, roses, heathers and herbaceous plants. TEAS. *Adm 50p Chd 20p. Suns June 7, 21; July 5 (2-6)*

Dam Farm House ঌ✍❀ (Mrs S.D. Player) Yeldersley Lane Brailsford, 5m SE of Ashbourne on A52, opp Ednaston Village turn, gate on right 500 yds. 1 acre; mixed borders; shrubs, collection of 'old roses'; scree garden. TEA. *Adm 50p Chd 25p (Share to Leukemia Fund, May; BRC, July). Suns May 17; July 12 (2-5.30)*

Darley House ໕𝒜☸ (Mr & Mrs G.H. Briscoe) Darley Dale, 2m N of Matlock. On A6 to Bakewell. 1½ acres; originally set out by Sir Joseph Paxton in 1845; being restored by present owners; many rare plants, trees; balustrade and steps separating upper and lower garden, a replica of Haddon Hall. TEA. *Adm 50p Chd 20p. Special arrangements for private parties. By appt March 30 to Oct 31 (Tel Matlock 733341)*

¶**Dove Cottage** 𝒜☸ (Stephen & Anne Liverman) Clifton. 1½m SW of Ashbourne. ¾-acre garden by R. Dove extensively replanted and developed since 1979. Emphasis on establishing collections of hardy plants and shrubs inc. Alchemillas, alliums, artemesias, berberis sp., geraniums, euphorbias, hostas, lilies, variegated plants etc. Fruit and veg garden. Childrens (welcome) own garden. Interesting gooseberry cordon hedges est. over 25 yrs. TEA. *Adm 50p Chd 25p (Share to British Heart Foundation). Suns July 19, Aug 2 (1.30-5.30)*

¶**Fir Croft** 𝒜☸ (Dr & Mrs S.B. Furness) Froggatt Rd, Calver, Via Sheffield. 4m N of Bakewell; between filling station and junc of B6001 with B6054. Plantsman's garden; rockeries and water garden. Extensive collection (over 1000 varieties) of conifers and alpines inc Lewisias, gentians, saxifrages, sempervivums. *Collection box. (Share to Rare Breeds Survival Trust). Suns Apr 19, May 17, June 21, July 19, Aug 20 (10-6)*

Hardwick Hall ໕𝒜☸ (The National Trust) Doe Lea, 8m SE of Chesterfield. S of A617. Grass walks between yew and hornbeam hedges; cedar trees; herb garden; herbaceous borders. Finest example of Elizabethan house in the country; very fine collection of Elizabethan needlework, tapestry. Restaurant in Old Kitchens. TEA. *Adm house & garden £2.80 Chd £1.40; garden only £1.40 Chd 70p. △Sun July 19 (12-5.30)*

High Peak Garden Centre, Bamford, Hope Valley. A625 2m W of Hathersage, 4m E of Castleton. 7½ acres; aim to present complete horticultural service within the atmosphere of the garden. Trees, shrubs, roses, conifers, heathers, fruits, alpines. Cafe, shops. *Collecting box for NGS. Open daily, Suns from 10am*

♦**Lea Gardens** ໕☸ (Mr & Mrs Tye) Lea, 5m SE of Matlock off A6. A rare collection of rhododendrons, azaleas, alpines and conifers in a lovely woodland setting. Light lunches, TEAS, home-baking. Coaches by appt. *Adm season ticket £1 Chd 50p daily. Daily March 20-July 31 (10-7)*

The Limes ໕☸ (Mr & Mrs W.Belton) Crow Lane, Apperknowle, 6m N of Chesterfield; from A61 at Unstone turn E for 1m to Apperknowle; 1st house past Unstone Grange. Bus: Chesterfield or Sheffield to Apperknowle. 2½ acres with herbaceous borders, lily ponds with ornamental bridges, roses and flowering shrubs, geraniums and summer bedding plants; greenhouses with pelargonium displays. Putting green. Nature trail over 5 acres. Large natural pond with ducks and geese. Donkeys. Craft workshop with displays; Home-made TEAS. *Adm 50p Chd 20p. Suns July 12 & 26 (2-6)*

♦**Locko Park** ໕𝒜 (Capt P.J.B. Drury-Lowe) Spondon, 6m NE of Derby. From A52 Borrowash bypass, 2m N via B6001, turn to Spondon. Large garden; pleasure gardens; rose gardens. House by Smith of Warwick with Victorian additions. Chapel, Charles II, with original ceiling. TEAS. *Adm 60p Chd 30p. Sun July 5 (2-6)*

Meynell Langley ໕☸ (Godfrey Meynell Esq) N side of A52; ½m on Derby side of Kirk Langley. Green iron gate and railings; ¾m drive. Wild garden, daffodils, trees; view of lake. TEAS in late Georgian house. *Adm 40p Chd 20p (Share to RGOF & GRBS). Sun April 26 (2-6)*

210 Nottingham Rd ໕☸ (Mr & Mrs R.Brown) Woodlinkin, Langley Mill. 12m NW of Nottingham, nr Codnor; A610 Bypass. ½ acre; collections of old, modern shrub and climbing roses; geraniums; hellebores; shrubs; small trees and alpines. TEA. *Adm 50p Chd free. Suns May 24, July 5 (2-5)*

Prospect House ໕ (Mr & Mrs J.W. Bowyer) 18 Pentrich Rd, Swanwick; turn at traffic lights A61 to B6016 Pentrich. Park main rd. ¾ acre; conifers, shrubs, herbaceous plants, cordyline palms, carpet bedding with sedums, sempervivums, echeverias; collection cacti; succulents, shrub and leaf begonia, abutilons various; rock plants; geraniums; pelargoniums, hostas. Greenhouses; kitchen garden. TEA. *Adm 40p Chd 10p. Sun June 21 (1.30-6.30)*

Quarndon Hall ໕𝒜☸ (Mr & Mrs Paul Bird) Church Rd, Quarndon. Off A6 between Duffield and Allestree; car parking at Joiners Arms. 3-acre old established garden in process of replanting; emphasis on unusual shrubs, trees and rhododendrons. TEAS. *Adm 50p Chd free. Sun May 24 (2-5)*

Radburne Hall ໕𝒜 (Maj & Mrs J.W. Chandos-Pole) Kirk Langley, 5m W of Derby. W of A52 Derby-Ashbourne Rd; off Radburne Lane. Large landscape garden; large display of daffodils; shrubs; formal rose terraces; fine trees and view. Hall (not open) is 7-bay Palladian mansion built c1734 by Smith of Warwick. Ice-house in garden. *Adm 50p Chd 20p. Sun April 26 (2.30-6)*

¶**Silver Birches** ❀ (Mr & Mrs E.Asprey) Hadley Lane, Moorend. 2½m E of Ashbourne off A52 or A517 nr Hole-in-the-Wall Pub, Moorend. ⅓-acre. Old and modern shrub and climbing roses. Mixed shrub and herbaceous borders; conifers and heathers;small fish and lily pond. TEA. *Adm 40p Chd 20p. Sun June 21 (2-6)*

Tissington Hall ⅃ (Sir John FitzHerbert, Bt) N of Ashbourne. E of A515. Large garden; roses, herbaceous borders. Tea village. *Adm 50p Chd 5p. Sat July 11 (2-6)*

5 Wood Lane ⅃❀ (Mr & Mrs T.P. Booth) Horsley Woodhouse, 6m N of Derby, West of A608 Derby-Heanor Rd, turn by Rose and Crown, Morley into Woodside then right into Wood Lane. Rd side parking with care in Wood Lane. ¾-acre mixed country garden; wide variety conifers, shrubs, climbing and shrub roses, trees; herbaceous plants; kitchen garden. Home-made TEAS. *Adm 50p Chd free. Sun June 28 (2-5.30)*

DEVON

Hon County Organiser:
MERVYN T. FEESEY ESQ, Woodside, Higher Raleigh Rd, Barnstaple

DATES OF OPENING

BY APPOINTMENT ONLY for dates see text:
BLACKPOOL HOUSE, Stoke Fleming
CELLARS, Noss Mayo
CLEAVE HOUSE, nr Okehampton
FARRANTS, nr Axminster
FURZEHILL, Molland
THE OLD RECTORY, nr Kingsbridge
51 SALTERS ROAD, Exeter
SANDERS, Stoke Fleming
SETTS, Bovey Tracey
WEETWOOD, Offwell
REGULAR OPENINGS for dates see text:
BICKHAM HOUSE, Roborough
BURROW FARM GARDEN, nr Axminster
CLOVELLY COURT, Clovelly
CROSSPARK, nr Okehampton
THE DOWNES, nr Bideford
1 FEEBERS COTTAGE, Westwood
FERNWOOD, Ottery St Mary
THE GARDEN HOUSE, Buckland Monachorum
HEDDON'S GATE HOTEL, nr Lynton
MARWOOD HILL, nr Barnstaple
METCOMBE BRAKE, nr Ottery St Mary
MIDDLE HILL, nr Tiverton
MODEL VILLAGE, Babbacombe
NORTHAMPTON COTTAGE, nr Honiton

PAIGNTON ZOOLOGICAL & BOTANICAL GARDENS
PORTLEDGE HOTEL, nr Bideford
ROSEMORE GARDEN, nr Torrington
SHALLOWFORD LODGE, nr Torrington
STORMSDOWN, nr Bickington
TAPELEY PARK, Instow

MARCH Sunday 29
38 PHILLIPS AVENUE, Exmouth
THE PINES, Salcombe
APRIL Saturday 4
MORWENNA, Topsham
APRIL Sunday 5
MORWENNA, Topsham
38 PHILLIPS AVENUE, Exmouth
WOODLAND GROVE, Bovey Tracey
APRIL Saturday 11
1 THE PARADE, Chudleigh
WESTPARK, Yealmpton
APRIL Sunday 12
KILLERTON GARDEN, nr Exeter
LOWER COOMBE ROYAL, Kingsbridge
1 THE PARADE, Chudleigh
WESTPARK, Yealmpton
APRIL Saturday 18
1 THE PARADE, Chudleigh
APRIL Easter Sunday 19
ANDREW'S CORNER, nr Okehampton
DOCTON MILL, nr Hartland
HIGHER KNOWLE, nr Bovey Tracey
THE MOORINGS, nr Lyme Regis
1 THE PARADE, Chudleigh
38 PHILLIPS AVENUE, Exmouth
VICARS MEAD, East Budleigh
WEST HILL GARDENS, nr Ottery St Mary
APRIL Easter Monday 20
BUNDELS, Sidbury
DOCTON MILL, nr Hartland
HIGHER KNOWLE, nr Bovey Tracey
LEE FORD, Budleigh Salterton
THE MOORINGS, nr Lyme Regis
VICAR'S MEAD, East Budleigh
WEST HILL GARDENS, nr Ottery St Mary
APRIL Sunday 26
41 BEAUMONT ROAD, St Judes, Plymouth
BERRYNARBOR GARDENS
HARTLAND ABBEY, Hartland
HIGHER KNOWLE, nr Bovey Tracey
KNIGHTSHAYES COURT, nr Tiverton
LITTLE BROOKFIELD, nr Exeter
THE ORCHARD, Kenn
SALTRAM HOUSE, nr Plymouth
APRIL Thursday 30
GREENWAY GARDENS, Churston Ferrers
MAY Saturday 2
MOTHECOMBE HOUSE, nr Plymouth
MAY Sunday 3
ANDREW'S CORNER, nr Okehampton
DOCTON MILL, Hartland
HIGHER KNOWLE, nr Bovey Tracey
HILL HOUSE, Lanscove, nr Buckfastleigh
MEMBURY GARDENS, nr Axminster
THE MOORINGS, Rocombe, nr Lyme Regis

MOTHECOMBE HOUSE, Holberton
VICAR'S MEAD, East Budleigh
WIGGATON GARDENS, nr Ottery St Mary
MAY Monday 4 (Bank Hol)
DOCTON MILL, nr Hartland
HIGHER KNOWLE, nr Bovey Tracey
HILL HOUSE, nr Buckfastleigh
MEMBURY GARDENS, nr Axminster
THE MOORINGS, nr Lyme Regis
VICARS MEAD, East Budleigh
MAY Wednesday 6
BARTON HOUSE, East Anstey
MAY Thursday 7
BARTON HOUSE, East Anstey
GREENWAY GARDENS, Churston Ferrers
MAY Saturday 9
MEADOWCROFT, Plympton
MAY Sunday 10
COLETON FISHACRE, nr Kingswear
HIGHER KNOWLE, nr Bovey Tracey
HILL HOUSE, nr Buckfastleigh
KILLERTON GARDEN, nr Exeter
MEADOWCROFT, Plympton
38 PHILLIPPS AVENUE, Exmouth
WOODSIDE, Barnstaple
MAY Saturday 16
DARTINGTON HALL GARDENS, nr Totnes
MAY Sunday 17
CASTLE DROGO, Drewsteignton
DARTINGTON HALL GARDENS, nr Totnes
DELAMORE, Cornwood
HIGHER KNOWLE, nr Bovey Tracy
HILL HOUSE, nr Buckfastleigh
LOWER COOMBE ROYAL, Kingsbridge
THE MOORINGS, nr Lyme Regis
THE PINES, Salcombe
WOODLAND GROVE, nr Bovey Tracey
MAY Thursday 21
RESTHARROW, nr Ottery St Mary
MAY Saturday 23
HUNTERS GATE, nr Bovey Tracey
MAY Sunday 24
ANDREW'S CORNER, nr Okehampton
CASTLE HOUSE, nr Axminster
THE CHANTRY, Ivybridge
CLIFTON HAMPDEN, Rackenford (by appt)
HIGHER KNOWLE, nr Bovey Tracey
HILL HOUSE, nr Buckfastleigh
HUNTERS GATE, Bovey Tracey (by appt)
THE LODGE, Plymouth
MEMBURY GARDENS, nr Axminster
THE MOORINGS, nr Lyme Regis
PARK LODGE, nr Torrington
38 PHILLIPPS AVENUE, nr Exmouth
VICARS MEAD, East Budleigh
WEST HILL GARDENS, Ottery St Mary
MAY Monday 25 (Bank Hol)
CLIFTON HAMPDEN, Rackenford (by appt)
HIGHER KNOWLE, nr Bovey Tracey
HILL HOUSE, nr Buckfastleigh
MEMBURY GARDENS, nr Axminster
THE MOORINGS, Rocombe, nr Lyme Regis
VICARS MEAD, East Budleigh
WEST HILL GARDENS, Ottery St Mary
MAY Wednesday 27
REDLAP HOUSE, nr Dartmouth

MAY Thursday 28
RESTHARROW, nr Ottery St Mary
MAY Friday 29
FARDEL MANOR, nr Ivybridge
MAY Saturday 30
MEADOWCROFT, Plympton
THE OLD GLEBE, Eggesford
MAY Sunday 31
HIGHER KNOWLE, nr Bovey Tracey
HILL HOUSE, nr Buckfastleigh
LEE FORD, Budleigh Salterton
MEADOWCROFT, Plympton
THE OLD GLEBE, Eggesford
THE OLD RECTORY, Clayhidon
THE ORCHARD, nr Exeter
ROBIN HILL, Exeter
JUNE Saturday 6
HIGHER LUKESLAND, Harford
TOPSHAM GARDENS
JUNE Sunday 7
ANDREW'S CORNER, nr Okehampton
41 BEAUMONT ROAD, St Judes, Plymouth
CASTLE DROGO, Drewsteignton
COLETON FISHACRE, nr Kingswear
OVERBECKS, Sharpitor
PARK LODGE, nr Torrington
38 PHILLIPPS AVENUE, Exmouth
TOPSHAM GARDENS
VICAR'S MEAD, East Budleigh
WOODSIDE, Barnstaple
JUNE Saturday 13
1 THE PARADE, Chudleigh
JUNE Sunday 14
BERRYNARBOR GARDENS, nr Ilfracombe
CLIFFE HOUSE, Lynmouth
KEEPERS COTTAGE, nr Buckfastleigh
1 THE PARADE, Chudleigh
PARK LODGE, nr Torrington
SKERRATON FARM, nr Buckfastleigh
JUNE Saturday 20
1 THE PARADE, Chudleigh
WEST HILL GARDENS, Ottery St Mary
JUNE Sunday 21
ABBOTSKERWELL GARDENS, nr Newton
  Abbot
ANDREW'S CORNER, nr Okehampton
CLIFTON HAMPDEN, Rackenford
THE GLEBE HOUSE, Whitestone
KEEPERS COTTAGE, nr Buckfastleigh
1 THE PARADE, Chudleigh
PARK LODGE, nr Torrington
38 PHILLIPPS AVENUE, Exmouth
PUTSBOROGH MANOR, Georgeham
SKERRATON FARM, nr Buckfastleigh
UNDERHILL CLOSE, South Molton
VICARS MEAD, East Budleigh
WESTHILL GARDENS, Ottery St Mary
JUNE Friday 26
FARDEL MANOR, nr Ivybridge
JUNE Saturday 27
BUNDELS, Sidbury
JUNE Sunday 28
ABBOTSKERWELL GARDENS, nr Newton
  Abbot
BUNDELS, Sidbury

THE GLEBE HOUSE, Whitestone
SALTRAM HOUSE, nr Plymouth
JULY Wednesday 1
PUTSBOROUGH MANOR, Georgeham
JULY Saturday 4
FORE STOKE FARM, nr Ashburton
JULY Sunday 5
BERRYNARBOR GARDENS
DOCTON MILL, nr Hartland
FORE STOKE FARM, nr Ashburton
THE GLEBE HOUSE, Whitestone
LITTLE BROOKFIELD, nr Exeter
MEMBURY GARDENS, nr Axminster
OVERBECKS, Sharpitor
38 PHILLIPPS AVENUE, Exmouth
ROBIN HILL, Exeter
WOODSIDE, Barnstaple
JULY Monday 6
DOCTON MILL, nr Hartland
MEMBURY GARDENS, nr Axminster
JULY Sunday 12
ANDREW'S CORNER, nr Okehampton
ASH PARK, nr Kingsbridge
THE GLEBE HOUSE, Whitestone
KNIGHTSHAYES COURT, nr Tiverton
JULY Saturday 18
MORWENNA, Topsham
WEST HILL GARDENS, nr Ottery St Mary
JULY Sunday 19
CASTLE TOR, Torquay
EXMOUTH GARDENS
MORWENNA, Topsham
THE PINES, Salcombe
41 SPRINGFIELD CLOSE, Plymstock
VICAR'S MEAD, East Budleigh
WEST HILL GARDENS, nr Ottery St Mary
JULY Sunday 19 to Sunday 26
51 ROCKFIELD AVENUE, Plymouth
JULY Sunday 26
DEEPAVALLI, Plympton
EXMOUTH GARDENS
UNDERHILL CLOSE, South Molton
JULY Friday 31
FARDEL MANOR, Ivybridge
AUGUST Sunday 2
THE LODGE, Plymouth
38 PHILLIPPS AVENUE, Exmouth
AUGUST Wednesday 5 & Thursday 6
BARTON HOUSE, East Anstey
AUGUST Sunday 9
DEEPAVALLI, Plympton
41 SPRINGFIELD CLOSE, Plymstock
WOODSIDE, Barnstaple
AUGUST Tuesday 11
DEEPAVALLI, Plympton
AUGUST Sunday 16
CLIFTON HAMPDEN, Rackenford
AUGUST Sunday 23
ASH PARK, nr Kingsbridge
CASTLE TOR, Torquay
AUGUST Friday 28
FARDEL MANOR, nr Ivybridge
AUGUST Sunday 30
DOCTON MILL, Hartland
VICAR'S MEAD, East Budleigh

AUGUST Monday 31 (Bank Hol)
DOCTON MILL, Hartland
VICAR'S MEAD, East Budleigh
SEPTEMBER Sunday 6
CASTLE HOUSE, nr Axminster
MEMBURY GARDENS, nr Axminster
38 PHILLIPPS AVENUE, Exmouth
SEPTEMBER Sunday 13
FORE STOKE FARM, nr Ashburton
VICAR'S MEAD, East Budleigh
OCTOBER Sunday 11
THE PINES, Salcombe
OCTOBER Sunday 18 & Monday 19
MEMBURY GARDENS, nr Axminster
NOVEMBER Sunday 1
THE MOORINGS, nr Lyme Regis

DESCRIPTIONS OF GARDENS

Abbotskerswell Gardens ✄❀ 1½m SW of
Newton Abbot. Take Totnes rd from Newton
Abbot, signed Abbotskerswell 1½m. Both
gardens at bottom of village. Teas in village.
*Adm 40p each (Share to Abbotskerswell
Church). Suns June 21, 28 (2.30-5.30); also by
appt (Tel Newton Abbot 53506)*
Priors (Mrs Hunloke) Small enclosed colourful garden; long herbaceous border;
old shrub roses
1 Vicarage Rd (Capt Shaw Hamilton)
Small secluded picturesque village garden; dwarf conifers; troughs and borders

Andrew's Corner ♿✄❀ (H.J. & R.J. Hill) Belstone, 3m E of Okehampton. A30, signed to
Belstone. Plantsman's garden 1,000ft up on
Dartmoor, overlooking Taw Valley; wide
range unusual trees, shrubs, herbaceous
plants for year round effect inc alpines, rhododendrons, bulbs, dwarf conifers; well
labelled; fruit, vegetables, goats, chickens.
TEAS. *Adm 50p Chd 10p. Suns April 19, May
3, 24, June 7, 21, July 12 (2.30-6); also by appt
(Tel Okehampton 840332)*

Ash Park ❀ (The Hon R.D.L. & Mrs Urquhart)
East Prawle, 7m SE of Kingsbridge. A379 to
Dartmouth. After 5m take S at Chillington,
signed East Prawle. Through village, keeping
right downhill to sea. Entrance on right ¼m,
level parking in field. 3-acre coastal garden
with spectacular views of English Channel.
Garden created over 5 years with wide range
of plants, chosen for salt and wind tolerance.
Incorporates natural rock outcrops and
ponds with splendid colour all year. Ideally
situated also to visit famous rock pools of
East Prawle and to walk coastal path. TEA.
*Adm 60p Chd 30p (Share to Village Church).
Suns July 12, Aug 23 (2-6)*

Barton House ✄❀ (Mr & Mrs M. Perkins) East
Anstey. 2½m N of A361 Taunton-Barnstaple
rd, adjacent church. 1-acre garden on edge of
Exmoor; wide range of plants; greenhouse
for tender rhododendrons and camellias.

Adm 50p Chd 25p. Weds, Thurs May 6, 7; Aug 5, 6 (2-6)

41 Beaumont Road ⚘ (Mr & Mrs A.J. Parsons) St Judes, Plymouth. ½m from city centre, 100yds from Beaumont Park; take Ebrington St exit from Charles X roundabout in city centre. Parking in nearby side rds. Matchbox sized, walled town garden; intensive tub-culture of uncommon shrubs, small trees, climbers; compact and colourful with roses; pieris, camellias and clematis. 1985 and 1986 Winners 'Plymouth in Bloom', Patio Cup. TEA. *Adm 50p Chd 10p. Suns April 26, June 7 (2-7)*

Berrynarbour Gardens ⚘ 3m E of Ilfracombe. Off A399 coast rd. Gardens close to each other in beautiful Sterridge Valley. Cream Teas in village. *Combined adm 60p Chd 30p. Suns April 26, June 14, July 5 (2-5.30); also by appt. Tel Combe Martin 2377/3745*
>   **9 Cherry Tree Cottage** (Mr & Mrs Waldon) Beautiful rockeries, shrubs and trees
>   **Lee House** (Mrs W. Sanders) Stream, ponds, daffodils; azaleas and cherry trees

Bickham House ⚘ (The Lord Roborough) Roborough, 8m N of Plymouth. Take Maristow turn on Roborough Down, ½-way between Plymouth and Tavistock, then follow poster directions. Bus stop: Maristow sign on Roborough Down; posters at Maristow turning 1m from house. Shrub garden, camellias, rhododendrons, azaleas, cherries, bulbs, trees. Lovely views. Home-made TEAS. *Adm 50p. April 5-May 24 every Sun; also Mons April 20, May 4, 25; also Suns June 14, 28 (2-6); parties catered for by appt with home-made lunch or tea if required (Tel Yelverton 852478)*

Blackpool House (Lady A. Newman) Stoke Fleming, 4½m SW of Dartmouth. Opp car park at Blackpool Sands. Shrub garden, on steep hillside, containing many rare, mature and tender shrubs. Beautiful sea views. Tea Venus Tea House on sands. *Adm 30p Chd 10p. By appt only, spring & summer (Tel Stoke Fleming 770261)*

Bundels &⚘ (Mr & Mrs A. Softly) Ridgway, Sidbury. From Sidmouth B3175 turn L at free Car Park in Sidbury. From Honiton A375. Turn right. Garden 100yds up Ridgway on left. ¾-acre garden set round C16 thatched cottage (not open); 'old-fashioned rose' garden created 1985. Cottage garden with accent on preservation of wild life. Gift stall and exhibition. TEAS village. *Adm 50p Chd 10p (Share to DTNC April; RNIB June). Mon April 20 (2-6); Sat, Sun June 27 (10-5), 28 (2-6)*

Burrow Farm Garden &⚘⚘ (Mr & Mrs John Benger) Dalwood, 4m W of Axminster. A35 Axminster-Honiton Rd; 3½m from Axminster turn N near Shute Garage on to Stockland Rd; ½m on right. Secluded 4-acre garden

with magnificent views has been planned for foliage effect and includes woodland garden in a dell with rhododendrons, azaleas etc; large bog garden; pergola walk with rose/herbaceous borders. Cream TEAS (Suns only). *Adm £1 Chd 20p. April 1 - Sept 30 daily (2-7)*

Castle Drogo &⚘ (The National Trust) Drewsteignton. W of Exeter, S of A30. Medium-sized garden; shrubs, woodland walk overlooking Fingle Gorge. Wheelchairs available for disabled visitors. Restaurant. *Adm £1.20 Chd 60p. △ Suns May 17, June 7 (11-6)*

Castle House ⚘ (Rear Adm B.B. Mungo) Membury, 3½m N of Axminster on Membury Rd. House alongside Membury Castle at top of hill. 2-acre terraced garden; partly wooded at 600ft on S slope of Iron Age hill fort. Panoramic views across Axe Vale and Dorset. Rhododendrons, heathers, shrubs; colour most of the year. *Adm 50p Chd 20p (Share to SSA-FA). Suns May 24, Sept 6 (2-5.30)*

Castle Tor ⚘⚘ (Leonard Stocks) Wellswood, Torquay. From Higher Lincombe Rd turn E into Oxlea Rd. 200yds on right, entrance identified by eagles on gate pillars. Spectacular scenic listed garden superbly designed and laid out under the influence of Lutyens in mid-30s. Stepped terraces, orangery, paved work and ornamental water. TEAS. *Adm 50p Chd 25p (Share to Torbay Hospital Scanner Appeal). Suns July 19, Aug 23 (2-6)*

Cellars &⚘⚘ (Dr & Mrs Robert Blair) Noss Mayo, nr Plymouth. A379 to Yealmpton; B3186 to Noss Mayo via Newton Ferrers and Bridgend. Noss Mayo follow side of estuary 1m towards Cellars Beach. 1¾-acre cliff top garden with acid soil largely reclaimed from woodland since 1975. TEA. *Adm 50p Chd 25p. By appt only (Tel Plymouth 872771)*

The Chantry &⚘ (Mr & Mrs Michael Thomas) Ivybridge ¼m. From A38 take Ivybridge exit, 10m E of Plymouth. Turn off main rd in Ivybridge by war memorial into Erme rd, then Station rd. 3½-acre, south-facing, mature garden with young underplantings with wide range of interesting trees and shrubs. Rhododendrons, azaleas, primulas and bulbs provide blaze of colour through spring and early summer. TEA. *Adm 75p Chd 25p (Share to Ivybridge Parish Church). Sun May 24 (2-6)*

¶**Cleave House** (Ann & Roger Bowden) Sticklepath, 3½m E of Okehampton on A30 towards Exeter. Cleave House on left in village, on main road just past small right turn for Belstone. ½-acre garden with mixed planting for all season interest. Demonstration beds of Hosta varieties with about 45 varieties for sale. *Open only by appt April to Oct; Tel 083784 0481*

Cliffe House (Mr & Mrs A.G. Braunton) Lynmouth. From Lynmouth via A39 (E) to Minehead, after 600yds turn right. Limited parking at garden (visitors who leave cars at Lynmouth may walk to garden via zig-zag path through grounds of Tors Hotel) 3-acre garden in area of outstanding beauty; natural rock gardens and woodland walks. TEAS. *Adm 75p Chd 30p. Sun June 14 (2-7)*

Clifton Hampden & (Dr & Mrs M.O. Coulter) Rackenford. 8m NW of Tiverton. Take B3221 to South Molton, left at War Memorial; 200yds on left after Stag Inn. 1-acre rural garden overlooking Little Dart Valley, first cultivated 1981, with pool, heathers and shrubs. *Adm 50p Chd free. Suns June 21, Aug 16 (12-6); also by appt Sun, Mon May 24, 25 (Tel Rackenford 247)*

Clovelly Court & (The Hon Mrs Rous) Clovelly. 11m W of Bideford. A39 Bideford to Bude turn at Clovelly Cross Filling Station, 1m lodge gates and drive straight ahead; also 'Long Walk' pedestrian entrance 200yds from top of village (back rd) at large green gate shared with entrance to coastal footpath. 25-acres parkland with beautiful open views through woodlands towards sea. 1-acre walled garden with borders, fruit and vegetables. 500yds walk from village (through green gate) along path lined with ancient trees and rhododendrons. Medieval Manor adjacent C14 Church nr coastline. Free parking in drive. TEA at lodge entrance or in village. *Adm 60p Chd 20p (Share to All Saints Church & other Local Charities). May 1-Sept 4 every Thurs (2-5); Coach parties by appt*

Coleton Fishacre ⚘ (The National Trust) 2m NE of Kingswear. 18-acre garden planted and developed according to personal taste of the D'Oyly Carte family during 1926-1947 and unaltered by subsequent owners, now under restoration; wide range of tender and uncommon trees and shrubs in spectacular coastal setting. *Adm £1.20 Chd 60p △Suns May 10, June 7 (11-6)*

Crosspark ⚘❀ (Mrs G. West) Holstock Cross, Northlew, 8m NW of Okehampton. From Okehampton follow A30 to Launceston for 1m; turn right B3218, then 2nd right to Northlew; cross square diagonally; take Highampton Rd for 1m; past cottages turn right by postbox; House at top of hill. 2-acre plantswomans garden of interest throughout year; rock garden, herbaceous, bog garden; azaleas; variety conifers, heathers, pond, waterfall, white garden. Unusual plants for sale. TEAS. *Adm 40p Sun, Mon April 19, 20; Sats, Suns, Mons May 2, 3, 4 & 23, 24, 25; every Sat, Sun in June, July, Sept also Oct 3, 4; 10, 11; 17, 18 (2-6); also by appt (Tel Beaworthy 518)*

Dartington Hall Gardens & (Dartington Hall Trust) 2m NW of Totnes. Turn off A384 at church. Station: Totnes (1½m); then bus. Large landscaped garden with ornamental trees and shrubs laid out around C14 Hall (rest of house not shown); Tiltyard. Commercial shrub and tree nursery; garden shop. *Adm (donation) 50p recommended △Sat, Sun May 16, 17 (dawn to dusk)*

Deepavalli ⚘❀ (Mr & Mrs Bernard A. Hope-Inglis) 10 Litchfield Close, Chaddlewood, Plympton. 5m W of Plymouth. A38 Marshmills to Plympton St Marys bridge roundabout into Glen Rd, left at top of hill into Kingston Drive, 4th turn right. Bus No 21 to top of Glen Rd. Small garden, front and back both 50'x 30'; crammed full of fuchsias, geraniums and bedding plants; features inc 200yr old pump, grape vines and aviary. TEA. *Adm 30p Chd 15p (Share to Fire Service National Benevolent Fund). Suns July 26, Aug 9; Tues Aug 11 (2-7)*

Delamore &❀ (Maj & Mrs F.A.V. Parker) Cornwood, Ivybridge. A38; leave at turning for Lee Mill and Cornwood 6m E of Plymouth. 4 acre garden with flowering shrubs, lawns and mature trees. Swimming pool available. TEAS. *Adm 75p Chd 40p. Sun May 17 (2-6)*

Docton Mill ⚘ (Mr & Mrs N.S. Pugh) Hartland, W of A39, in Speke's Valley between Lymebridge and Milford; follow Elmscott signs from Hartland village or from West Country Inn on A39 from Bude. Extensive garden developed around working water mill with many water features; river crossed by footbridges, mill pond, leat and smaller streams in 7½ acres of wooded valley in Conservation Area of outstanding natural beauty 1500yds inland from Speke's Mill Mouth coastal waterfalls and beach. Rockery and outcrops, stream, bog gardens, island beds, roses, shrubs, specimen trees mixed with areas of wild woodland, extensive lawns, orchard, mown grassy banks. Picnics allowed. Parking in rd. Teas Hartland Quay. *Adm 60p Chd free. Suns, Mons April 19, 20; May 3, 4; July 5, 6; Aug 30, 31 (10-5). Also by appt (Tel Hartland 02374 369)*

The Downes ⚘❀ (Mr & Mrs R.C. Stanley-Baker) 4½m S of Bideford; 3m NW of Torrington. On A386 to Bideford turn left (W) up drive, ¼m beyond layby. 15-acres with landscaped lawns; fine views overlooking fields and woodlands in Torridge Valley; many unusual trees and shrubs; small arboretum; woodland walks. TEA. *Adm 50p Chd 10p. Suns April 19 to June 21; also Fri, Sat April 17, 18; Mons April 20; May 4, 25 (all day); also by appt April-Sept (Tel Torrington 22244)*

Exmouth Gardens & Collecting Boxes (Share to Cancer Research). Suns July 19, 26 (2-6)
    Barrowdale Close nos. 11, 12 & 14-22 A376 from Exeter to Exmouth; left into Hulham rd, B3180; 5th right into Marley rd, 5th left into Barrowdale Close. Eleven

gardens (Britain in Bloom winners 2yrs running); annual flower beds; hanging baskets. Cream TEAS

No 2-4 & 6-8 Morven Drive A376 to Exmouth; Morven Drive 2nd right after 'Welcome to Exmouth' sign. 6 gardens (Britain in Bloom Winners 1985); mostly annual flower beds and hanging baskets

17 Salterton Road (Mr & Mrs C. Monisse) Exmouth to Budleigh Salterton rd; garden ½m on left. ½ acre garden mostly annuals; Britain in Bloom Winner 1985

Fardel Manor ⚘※ (Dr A.G. Stevens) 1¼m NW of Ivybridge; 2m SE of Cornwood; 200yds S of Railway bridge. 5 acres: 2½-acres recently planted; stream, pond, lake; orangery, shrubs; small courts and walled yards around C14 Manor. Teas Endsleigh Garden Centre. *Adm 60p Chd 30p (Share to FRAME). Fris May 29, June 26, July 31, Aug 28 (11-4.30)*

Farrants ㊑※ (Mr & Mrs M. Richards) Kilmington. 2m W of Axminster. A35, turn S at Kilmington Cross into Whitford Rd; garden about ¼m on left. 1-acre garden with stream planted since 1963; mostly shrubs and ground cover for colour contrast around C16 cottage. *Adm 50p Chd 20p (Share to World Wildlife Fund). By appt only (Tel Axminster 32396)*

1 Feebers Cottage ⚘※ (Mr & Mrs M.J. Squires) Westwood. 2m NE of Broadclyst from B3181 (formerly A38) Exeter-Taunton, at Dog Village (Broadclyst) bear E to Whimple, after 1½m fork left for Westwood. ⅔-acre cottage garden on level site with wide variety of trees, shrubs, rock-plants, alpines, old-fashioned roses, small pond with water plants. Nursery. TEAS next door July 5. *Adm 40p Chd 20p. every Sat, Sun April 18 - July 26, Aug 29-Oct 25 (2-6); also by appt (Tel Whimple 822118)*

Fernwood ⚘ (Mr & Mrs H. Hollinrake) Toadpit Lane, 1½m W of Ottery St Mary; ¼m down Toadpit Lane (off B3174). 2-acre woodland garden; wide selection of flowering shrubs, conifers and bulbs, giving colour over long period; species and hybrid rhododendrons and azaleas special feature in spring. *Adm 50p. April 1 to Sept 30 daily (all day)*

Fore Stoke Farm ㊑⚘※ (Mrs Anne Belam) Holne, nr Ashburton. From Ashburton dual-carriageway; take rd to Holne; up hill to moors; over cattle grid, right over another cattle grid; park in top meadow. ½-acre garden at 900ft on edge of Dartmoor, outstanding view; developed since 1979 round bungalow and stables; old fashioned roses; variety of plants chosen as expression of what owners love best. Some different annuals in Sept. Well labelled. Cream TEAS £1, Tea 20p. *Adm 60p Chd free (Share to Holne Mother's*

Union, July). Sats, Suns July 4, 5; Sun Sept 13 (2-6). Parties by appt welcome April-Sept (Tel Poundsgate 394)*

Furzehill ⚘※ (Miss E.F. Warden) Molland, 4½m E of S Molton on A361 turn left to Molland (signed Black Cock). Ignore 1st turn left, take lane left by oak tree; gate marked after 200yds. Cottage garden, spring bulbs, roses, herbaceous borders, vegetables and fruit. Interesting livestock. TEA. *Adm 50p Chd 25p. By appt only all year round (11-5) (Tel Bishops Nympton 423)*

The Garden House ㊑⚘※ (The Fortescue Garden Trust) Buckland Monachorum, Yelverton. W of A386, 10m N of Plymouth. 8-acre garden of interest throughout year; inc 2-acre walled garden, one of finest in country; fine collections of herbaceous and woody plants. Coaches and parties by appt only. *Adm £1 Chd 50p (Share to N.G.S). April 1 to Sept 30 daily (12-5)*

The Glebe House (Mr & Mrs John West) Whitestone. 4m W of Exeter, adjoining Whitestone Church. (Narrow lanes, unsuitable for coaches). 2 acres; lawns, trees, heathers; roses (species, old-fashioned, modern shrub, and climbing); clematis. Outstanding views S from Exe estuary to Dartmoor. Former Rectory, part C14 with Georgian frontage (not open). C14 Tithe Barn (Ancient monument). Interesting C13/14 Church adjoins. Parking in lanes around Church. *Adm 50p Chd free (Share to Whitestone Church). Suns June 21, 28; July 5, 12 (2-5)*

Greenway Gardens ㊑※ (Mr & Mrs A.A. Hicks) Churston Ferrers, 4m W of Brixham. From B3203, Paignton-Brixham, take rd to Galmpton, thence towards Greenway Ferry. 30-acres; old-established garden with mature trees; shrubs; rhododendrons, magnolias and camellias. Recent plantings; commercial shrub nursery. Woodland walks by R. Dart. TEA & biscuits. *Adm 60p Chd 30p. Thurs April 30, May 7 (2-6)*

Hartland Abbey ⚘ (Sir Hugh Stucley & The Hon Lady Stucley) Hartland. Turn off A39 W of Clovelly Cross. Follow signs to Hartland through town on rd to Stoke and Quay. Abbey 1m from town on right. 2 woodland shrubberies with Camellias, rhododendrons etc; ½m walk to walled gardens; ¾m woodland walk to sea. No picnics please. TEAS. *Adm £1 Chd 50p (Share to St Nectan's Church, Hartland). Sun April 26 (2-5.30)*

Heddon's Gate Hotel ⚘ (Mr & Mrs R. De Ville) Heddon's Mouth. 4m W of Lynton on A39 turn N at 'Moorlands' (signed Martinhoe and Woody Bay), 1st left (signed Hunters Inn, light vehicles only) or from Hunters Inn steep hill to Martinhoe for ¼m); then follow sign to 'Heddon's Gate'. 2-acre garden in 18-acres of woods and grounds in designated area of outstanding natural beauty. Deliberate Victorian atmosphere; steeply terraced with wild indigenous plants encouraged, access to coastal footpath. Cream TEAS (4.30-6) *Adm 70p Chd 35p. Daily June 1 to 30 inc (2.30-5.30)*

Higher Knowle (Mr & Mrs D.R.A. Quicke) Lustleigh, 3m NW of Bovey Tracey A382 towards Moretonhampstead; in 2½m left at Kelly Cross for Lustleigh; in ¼m straight on at Brookfield for Manaton; in ½m steep drive on left. 3-acre steep woodland garden; rhododendrons, azaleas, magnolias in natural setting; good Dartmoor views. Teas in village. *Adm 50p Chd 30p. Suns April 19, 26; May 3, 10, 17, 24, 31; also Mons April 20, May 4, 25 (2-6)*

Higher Lukesland &※֍ (J. Howell) Harford, 1½m N of Ivybridge. Follow sign by London Hotel, in Ivybridge, to Harford, across new rd and railway for 1½m. White entrance gate on right just beyond high stone wall. Parking in field opp gates. Small secluded semi-wild garden in rural setting, on level ground around new bungalow; cottage planting at front, wide range unusual foliage shrubs at rear specially grown for floral decoration, some chosen for royal weddings etc. TEA. *Adm 50p Chd 25p (Share to Dr Barnado's). Sat June 6 (2-6)*

Hill House &֍ (Mr & Mrs R. Hubbard) Landscove. A38 signed Ashburton or Totnes-Buckfastleigh A384 via Staverton; beside church. 2½ acres under restoration inc 18,000sqft of modern glasshouses growing cut flowers and propagating material. Featured in Edward Hyams book "An Englishmans Garden". Listed house (not open) adjoining church both designed by architect of Truro Cathedral. TEAS. *Adm 50p Chd 20p (Share to St Matthews Church, Landscove). Suns May 3, 10, 17, 24, 31; Mons May 4, 25 (2-6)*

¶**Hunters Gate** ※ (Mr & Mrs D. J. Pearce) Colehayes Drive. Bovey Tracey. Take B3344 W of Bovey Tracey; 1m private drive to Colehayes Pk opp. Edgemoor Hotel; 1st bungalow on right. 1½-acres; semi-woodland garden with rhododendrons and azeleas. Park by Edgemoor Hotel. *Adm 50p Chd 25p. Sat, Sun May 23, 24 (9-5.30); also by appt (Tel Bovey Tracey 833351)*

Keepers Cottage ※֍ (Mr & Mrs Ambrose Baker) Deancombe, 1½m SW of Buckfastleigh. From A38 turn W at sign for Lower Dean; in village take rd signed Deancombe; turn left upstream over bridge; 1st house on left. ½-acre plantsman's garden, inc water garden with primulas, hostas, some unusual shrubs and trees; terrace with alpines. Cream Tea Skerraton (q.v.). *Adm 75p Chd 25p (Share to Dean Prior, St. George the Martyr Church). Suns June 14, 21 (2-6)*

Killerton Garden &※ (The National Trust) 8m N of Exeter. Via B3181 Cullompton Rd (formerly A38), fork left in 7m on B3185. Garden 1m follow NT signs. 15 acres of spectacular hillside gardens sweeping down to large open lawns. Delightful walks through fine collection of rare trees and shrubs inc magnolias, azaleas, cork oak and conifers. Restaurant. *Adm £1.50 Chd 75p △ Suns April 12, May 10 (all day)*

Knightshayes Court &※ (Lady Amory; The National Trust) 2m N of Tiverton. Via A396 Tiverton-Bampton; in Bolham, turn E; drive ½m on left. Large woodland garden; rhododendrons, azaleas, alpine plants, unusual shrubs. Formal garden. Wheelchairs available for disabled visitors (with access to woodland garden by prior arrangement). Restaurant. *Adm £1.50 Chd 75p △ Suns April 26, July 12 (11-6)*

Lee Ford ֍ (Mr & Mrs N. Lindsay-Fynn) Budleigh Salterton. Bus:DG, frequent service between Exmouth railway station (3½m) and Budleigh Salterton, alight Lansdowne corner. 40 acres parkland, formal and woodland gardens with extensive display of spring bulbs, camellias, rhododendrons, azaleas and magnolias. Adam pavilion. Picnic area. Car park free. Home made cream TEAS (3-5.30). *Adm 75p OAP 50p Chd 40p (Share to Budleigh Salterton Hospicecare; May). Mon April 20, Sun May 31 (1.30-6 Charity Fair); also by prior appt for parties only (Tel: 03954 5894)*

Little Brookfield &※֍ (P.D. Byrne Esq) Pinhoe. From Exeter follow signs for Pinhoe (2½m); in Pinhoe; right down Station rd; park here or over level Xing in car park on right (not at house); garden 30yds on left. Small secluded town garden; sub-tropical effect; palms, delphiniums, bamboos; Palm house. *Adm 50p Chd 20p (Share to Hospice Care, Exeter). Suns April 26, July 5 (11-7)*

The Lodge ֍ (Mr & Mrs M.H. Tregaskis) Hartley Ave, Mannamead. 1½m from City Centre via A386. Turn right at Henders Corner into Eggbuckland rd, 2nd right at tel kiosk to end of cul de sac. ½ acre S sloping aspect with variety of unusual shrubs, conifers, camellias and ground cover plants. Former L.A. Nursery with range of lean-to glasshouses for fruit and tender subjects. TEA. *Adm 50p Chd 25p. Suns May 24, Aug 2 (2-7); also by appt (Tel Plymouth 220849)*

Lower Coombe Royal ※֍ (Mr & Mrs H. Sharp) Kingsbridge. ½m N of Kingsbridge on Loddiswell Rd. Sign at gate. Historic woodland garden with rhododendrons, camellias, azaleas, magnolias and rare trees; terraces with tender and unusual shrubs; lawns, herbaceous borders; eucalyptas. (Commercial shrub nursery open daily.) *Adm 50p Chd 25p Suns April 12, May 17 (1-6)*

Marwood Hill ⬥✿❀ (Dr J.A. Smart) Marwood, 4m N of Barnstaple. In Marwood village, opp church. 12-acre garden with 3 small lakes. Extensive collection of camellias under glass and in open; daffodils, rhododendrons, rare flowering shrubs, rock and alpine garden in quarry, rose garden; waterside planting; bog garden; many clematis; Australian native plants. TEAS in Church Room (Suns & Bank Hols or by prior arrangement for parties). *Adm 50p Chd 10p. Daily except Christmas Day (dawn-dusk)*

Meadowcroft ⬥❀ (Dr & Mrs D. Thompson) 1 Downfield Way, Plympton. From Plymouth left at St Mary's Church roundabout, along Glen Rd, 3rd right into Downfield Drive; garden on right. 2 acres; stream; rhododendrons, azaleas, trees, flowering shrub borders. TEA. *Adm 40p Chd 20p. Sats, Suns May 9, 10 & 30, 31 (2-6)*

Membury Gardens ✿ 3m NW of Axminster. A35 to Honiton, ½m W of Axminster turn N signed Membury. TEA Sandbanks. *Adm each garden 50p Chd 25p. Suns (2-5.30) See individual gardens for dates*
>   **The Folly** (Sir Peter & Lady Bristow) 100yds S of Church on left. Attractive small, thatched cottage flower garden, N facing; landscaped orchard to S of cottage, mainly daffodils in spring, shrub roses, water garden in progress. *Suns May 3, July 5, Sept 6*
>   **Quakers** ✿❀ (Mr & Mrs T.J. Wallace) At left turning about 900yds S of The Folly. Interesting small terraced flower garden above cottage. Across lane a plantsman's new tree and shrub garden leading to woodland stream. *Suns, Mons May 3, 4; 24, 25; July 5, 6; Oct 18, 19*
>   **Sandbanks** ⬥❀ (Mrs A.C. Booth) At top of village, 500yds beyond Xrds to Chard. ¾ acre garden in the making of general interest. Good views. *Suns May 3, 24; July 5; Sept 6*

Metcombe Brake (Mr & Mrs J.S. Fielden) Higher Metcombe, SW of Ottery St Mary. From A30 turn S, signed Exmouth (or from A3052 turn N, signed Ottery St Mary), along B3180 for 2m to Tipton Cross; take turn E to Tipton St John, ¾m downhill at 1st Xrds right at White Cottage into Higher Broad Oak Rd; 200yds then left at T-junc, leads into drive. 6-acre woodland garden; massed bulbs in spring; extensive collection of camellias, rhododendrons, other ornamental and rare trees, shrubs. Tea Ottery St Mary. *Collecting box. Every Sun April, May (2-6); also by appt (Tel Ottery St Mary 3583)*

Middle Hill ✿❀ (Mr & Mrs E. Boundy) Washfield, 4½m NW of Tiverton. Via B3221 towards Rackenford, ½m from Tiverton (Kennedy Way), turn right signed Washfield; through village, pass church on right; house

1¼m on left. Enthusiast's cottage-style garden with clay soil, on almost level site. A wide variety plants growing in different situations. Seats. *Collecting box (Share to Marie Curie Memorial Foundation). Suns April 26 to Sept 6 (except May 3, July 5, Aug 9, 16); also by appt April 26 to Sept 6 (Tel Oakford 380)*

Model Village ⬥❀ (T.F. Dobbins Esq) Babbacombe. 3m N of Torquay. A380 to Torquay, then follow main sea rd to Babbacombe. 5 acres; unique layout of conifers, including over 800 varieties from tall-growing to dwarf, around lake with waterfall and streams. With 600 models the whole is laid out to represent a scale model of the English countryside. 3 teashops/hotels within 150yds. *Adm £1.60 Chd 90p. Daily (except Dec 25) (9-dusk)*

The Moorings (Mr & Mrs A. Marriage) Rocombe, Uplyme, 2m NW of Lyme Regis. A3070 out of Lyme Regis, turn right 150yds beyond The Black Dog; over Xrds, fork right into Springhead Rd; top gate to garden 500yds on left. From Axminster A35; in 2m, 200yds beyond Hunters Lodge (Esso garage on Xrds), fork right twice then straight on 1m, top gate to garden on right. 3-acre peaceful woodland garden, developed since 1965, on hillside with terraced paths, overlooking unspoilt countryside. Fine trees inc many species eucalyptus, unusual pines, nothofagus; flowering shrubs inc some rare; daffodils and other spring flowers, ground cover, autumn colour. *Adm 50p Chd free (Share to Oxfam). Suns, Mons April 19, 20; May 3, 4 & 24, 25; Suns May 17, Nov 1 (11-5); also by appt (Tel Lyme Regis 3295)*

Morwenna ⬥❀ (Alf & Sheila Crouch) 67 Newcourt Rd, outskirts of Topsham, 3m SE of Exeter. 1 acre; landscaped to display wide range of plants, many collected overseas; spring bulbs; fruit and vegetable garden. *Adm 40p Chd 10p. Sats, Suns April 4, 5; July 18, 19 (2-6)*

Mothecombe House ⬥✿ (Mr & Mrs A. Mildmay-White) Holbeton, SE of Plymouth. From A379, between Yealmpton and Modbury, turn S for Holbeton. Woodland walk to sea. Queen Anne house shown. English and Dutch pictures. English and French furniture, porcelain. Flower arrangements by Plymouth and District Flower Club. TEAS. *Adm garden 60p Chd 30p; house 60p Chd 30p extra. Sat May 2 (11-1 & 2-5), Sun May 3 (2-6)*

Northampton Cottage ⬥❀ (Mr & Mrs D. Rodway) Cotleigh, 4m NE of Honiton. Follow signs to Stockland off A30 at E end Honiton, after 3½m cross bridge at foot of steep hill, in 100yds turn left into narrow lane. Small mature garden around thatched cottage (not open); rock garden, stream, roses, herbaceous, shrubs and trees; further 1½-acres streamside paddock. TEAS. *Adm 40p Chd 20p. Every Sun June - Sept (2-5.30)*

The Old Glebe ✿❀ (Mr & Mrs Nigel Wright) Eggesford, 4m SW of Chulmleigh. Turn S off A377 at Eggesford Station (½-way between Exeter & Barnstaple), cross railway and River Taw, drive straight uphill (signed Brushford) for ¾m; turn right into bridle path. 5-acre garden of former Georgian rectory with mature trees and several lawns, courtyard and walled herbaceous borders; in process of being re-established with emphasis on species and hybrid rhododendrons and azaleas. TEAS. *Adm 50p Chd 25p (Share to The Abbeyfield Chulmleigh). Sat, Sun May 30, 31 (2-6)*

¶**The Old Rectory, Clayhidon** ❀ (Mr & Mrs K.J. Wakeling) 4m from Wellington via South St or M5 exit 26 for Ford St. House next to Half Moon Inn and Church. 3 acres being rescued from neglect. Woodland garden with new plantings amid mature native trees; large numbers of naturalized bulbs mainly daffodils and snowdrops. Walled garden with mixed borders and rockery. *Adm 40p Chd 20p (Share to Friends of St Andrews Church). Sun May 31 (2-6); also by appt tel (0823) 680534*

The Old Rectory, Woodleigh ✿ (Mr & Mrs H.E. Morton) nr Loddiswell. 3½m N of Kingsbridge E off Kingsbridge-Wrangaton rd at Rake Cross (1m S of Loddiswell). 1½m to Woodleigh. Garden on right in hamlet. C19 Clergymans garden partly enclosed by stone walls; restored and added to by present owners; mature trees with collection of rhododendrons, camellias and magnolias and other shrubs; large numbers of naturalised bulbs especially crocus and daffodils in early March. *Adm 50p Chd 10p. By appt only (Tel Kingsbridge 550 387)*

The Orchard ❀❀ (Mrs Hilda M. Montgomery) Kenn. Exeter 5m. A38 to Mercury Motel; 5 mins walk. ¾ acre; mostly trees; variety of conifers, azaleas, camellias, rhododendrons, many shrubs; fishponds and flowerbeds. *Adm 75p Chd 35p (Share to Redgate Bird Sanctuary, Exmouth). Suns April 26, May 31 (10.30-6); also by appt (Tel Exeter 832530)*

Overbecks (The National Trust) Sharpitor 1½m SW of Salcombe. From Salcombe or Malborough follow NT signs. 6-acre garden with rare plants and shrubs; spectacular views over Salcombe Estuary. *Adm £1 Chd 50p.* △*Suns June 7, July 5 (all day)*

Paignton Zoological & Botanical Gardens. ❀✿ 1m W of Paignton Town centre on Totnes Rd (A385). Third largest zoo in England. 75-acres; nature trail with mature shrubs, trees from all over the world; tropical and subtropical houses; large collection of animals in park surroundings. Restaurant, miniature train (summer only); aquarium; gift shop; plant shop (spring, summer). Coach parties

by appt. TEAS. *Adm £2.70 Chd £1.70. Open all year (10-5)*

1 The Parade ❀✿ (Dr & Mrs F. Hamilton) Chudleigh, 10m SW of Exeter. Leave A38 on B3344 for Chudleigh; garden is on main rd through village, 200 yds W of church, corner of Lawn Drive. ⅔ acre town garden lies mostly behind the house; variety of ornamental shrubs, herbaceous and foliage plants, inc old roses. Teas Chudleigh. *Adm 50p Chd 10p. Sats, Suns April 11, 12; 18, 19; June 13, 14; 20, 21 (2-6); also by appt April to June (Tel Chudleigh 852555)*

Park Lodge ✿❀ (Mr & Mrs Charles Cook) Stevenstone. B3227 from Torrington; 1m sign on right 'Private rd to Stevenstone'; garden ¼m on right. Modest, peaceful garden. 2 acres of park recently restored, once part of immaculate estate belonging to Rolle family. *Adm 50p Chd 10p. Suns May 24, June 7, 14, 21 (2-5)*

38 Phillipps Avenue ❀✿❀ (Mr & Mrs R.G. Stuckey) Exmouth. From Exeter, turn left into Hulham rd just before 1st set of traffic lights, 1st left into Phillipps Avenue (ample parking). Small, highly specialised alpine and rock garden containing extensive collection of rock plants and minature shrubs, many rare and unusual. Small alpine nursery. Teashops Exmouth. *Adm 30p. Suns March 29, April 5, 19, May 10, 24, June 7, 21, July 5, Aug 2, Sept 6 (2-6); also by appt (Tel Exmouth 273636)*

The Pines (Mr & Mrs R.A. Bitmead) Main Rd, Salcombe. 1m from Salcome at junc of Devon and Sandhills rds; bottom entrance and parking Sandhills rd. All seasons ¾ acre S facing garden; fine coastal views to Sharpitor Headland and N Sands Valley. Informal garden of surprises; many interesting and unusual shrubs, trees; bulbs, camellias, azaleas, heathers, hebes, conifers; water gardens. *Adm 50p Chd 25p (Share to Cancer Research, Salcombe Branch). Suns March 29, May 17, July 19, Oct 11 (11-5)*

Portledge Hotel ❀✿❀ (Col & Mrs T.J. Pine-Coffin) Fairy Cross, 3m W of Bideford on A39 to Bude. Lawns with prolific wild flowers; herb garden; roses; woodland with azaleas. Young tree plantings amid mature woodland, House part Norman, Elizabeth I, and 1760. Beautiful views. Designated area of outstanding natural beauty. Coaches by appt only. Lunch & Cream TEAS at Hotel. *Collecting Box. March to Nov daily (10-6)*

Putsborough Manor ❀❀ (Mr & Mrs T.W. Bigge) Georgeham, NW of Barnstaple. A361 Barnstaple-Braunton; B3231 to Croyde; ¾m N of Village in attractive setting; lawn with mixed rose, shrub and herbaceous borders, stream with waterside plantings; separate walled garden with rose and shrub walk in part kitchen with herb garden and other features. TEA. Sun only. *Adm 60p Chd 10p (Share to St George's House, Georgeham). Sun June 21 (all day); Wed July 1 (2-5.30); also by appt in summer (Tel Croyde 890484)*

¶**Redlap House** ⚥ (Mr & Mrs R.W. Gaskell) 2m from Dartmouth. Turn S at Redlap Cross on B3205. Park in NT carpark at end on left. 4 acres in sheltered combe down to cliffs. Stream and bog garden with variety of tender trees, shrubs in romantic coastal setting. *Adm £1 Chd 50p (Share to Guide Dogs for the Blind). Wed May 27 (2-5.30)*

Restharrow ᴰ⚥ (Mr & Mrs D. Harverson) Bendarroch Rd, West Hill, 2m SW of Ottery St Mary via B3177 (W), after 1¾m in West Hill. Fork right along Bendarroch Rd; garden on left 150 yds beyond school. ¾-acre on level ground; wide range unusual plants and shrubs giving all year round effect; mixed curved borders; rock plants, collection silver, gold and variegated foliage; most plants labelled. Tea Ottery St Mary. *Adm 60p Chd 30p (Share to Amnesty International). Thurs May 21, 28 (2.30-6)*

Robin Hill ᴰ⚥ (Dr & Mrs G. Steele-Perkins) Deep Dene Park, Exeter. From Barrack Rd turn W into Wonford Rd; entry to drive on left beyond Orthopaedic Hospital. ½ acre around house on level ground with variety of ornamental trees and shrubs; wall plants, ground cover and small pond. *Adm 50p Chd 30p. Suns May 31, July 5 (2-6); also by appt (Tel Exeter 72861)*

51 Rockfield Avenue ⚥❀ (Mr & Mrs D.R. Waterfield) Southway, Plymouth. 3m from city centre via A38 from Marsh Mills roundabout; take Tavistock rd; 1st left at traffic lights down Southway Drive; 2nd right; 2nd left past church; 2nd left again; house 2nd on left. Bus: 40 or 41 from Plymouth city centre. Small town garden with country look; max colour during summer; inc fuschia, begonias, geraniums and various annuals etc. Scree alpine area. Winners of Plymouth in Bloom & Evening Herald Trophy's for best garden overall for last 3yrs. Featured on TSW Gardens for all, Garden News Best Small Garden in SW Region '84. Runner up Sunday Express Gardener of the Year 1986. *Adm 50p Chd 30p (Share to St Lukes Hospice, Plymstock). Sun to Sun July 19 - 26inc (2-6); also by appt (Tel Plymouth 701413)*

Rosemoor Garden Charitable Trust ᴰ❀ (Lady Anne Palmer) Great Torrington. 1m SE of Great Torrington on B3220 to Exeter. Plantsman's garden started in 1959; rhododendrons (species and hybrid), ornamental trees and shrubs; dwarf conifer collection, species and old-fashioned roses, scree and raised beds with alpine plants, arboretum. Nursery with unusual plants always open inc weekends (8-5). TEAS. Suns,

Weds & Bank Hols (Prior booking by groups for any day). *Adm £1 OAPs 80p Chd 50p. Groups 80p. Daily all year for NGS; Sats in June & July*

51 Salters Road ⚥ (Mrs J. Dyke) Exeter. Typical small town garden; specialising in unusual plants inc primulas, auriculas and alpines (owner has for many years been Committee member of Exeter Branch of Alpine Garden Society). *Collecting box for NGS. By personal appt only (Tel Exeter 76619)*

Saltram House ᴰ⚥ (The National Trust) Plympton, 3m E of Plymouth, S of A38, 2m W of Plympton. 8 acres with fine specimen trees; spring garden; rhododendrons and azaleas. C18 orangery and octagonal garden house. George II mansion with magnificent plasterwork and decorations, inc 2 rooms designed by Robert Adam. Restaurant. *Adm gardens only £1 Chd 50p.* △*Suns April 26, June 28 (11-6)*

Sanders ᴰ⚥ (Sir Julian Gascoigne) Stoke Fleming, Dartmouth. 300yds S of Stoke Fleming church on Old rd. Medium-sized garden with outstanding sea views; flowering shrubs; fuchsia collection; woodland garden. *Collecting box. Open by appt any time (Stoke Fleming 341 or by letter)*

Setts ❀ (Mr & Mrs Jack Cutler) Haytor Rd, 1m W of Bovey Tracey. Take B3344 Bovey Tracy to Widecombe Rd, after ¼m fork left, garden ¼m on right on Haytor Rd, next to Edgemoor hotel. ⅔ acre garden; herbaceous borders; wood containing rhododendrons (species and hybrids), azaleas, camellias, acers etc. Teas Bovey. *Adm 50p Chd 25p. By appt only (spring, summer, autumn) (Tel 0626 833043)*

Shallowford Lodge ⚥❀ (Mr & Mrs P.J. Cull) Great Torrington. ½m E of Torrington on B3227; turn S down Borough rd; left at Junior School; ½m to bottom of hill; 'OS map ref 506185. Small woodland garden begun 1970, being extended and planted with rhododendrons, azaleas, magnolias. Some level ground with streams, bog plants, primulas, wild daffodils and other bulbs; peat garden with collection dwarf rhododendrons; small nursery specialising in dwarf rhododendrons and other rare or distinctive plants. *Adm 40p Chd 20p. Thurs, Fris, Sats, Suns March 26 to May 31; also Mons April 20, May 4, 25 (11-6)*

Skerraton Farm (Mr & Mrs M. Ogle) Dean Prior, 3m SW of Buckfastleigh. From A38, ½m W of Buckfastleigh, take turning to Lower Dean and follow signs to Skerraton 2½ m. 2-acre garden; interesting woodland area with azaleas, camellias, rhododendrons; stream with marginal plants; formal garden with island and mixed border; pool; terrace with alpines. 800' up on Dartmoor with views across South Hams to sea. Dartmoor ponies and foals in paddocks and stables by house; horse drawn vehicles. Cream TEAS. *Adm 60p Chd 30p (Share to Church of St George The Martyr, Dean Prior). Suns June 14, 21 (2-6)*

41 Springfield Close ✕❀ (Mr & Mrs Clem Spencer) Plymstock, 4m SE of Plymouth city centre. Leave A379 to Kingsbridge opp Elburton Hotel, follow Springfield Rd across Reservoir Rd, 1st right into Springfield Close. Small landscaped surburban garden (450sq yds) with country atmosphere; shrubberies, herbaceous border, colourful bedding, fuchsias, pond, waterfall; doves and artists studio. Featured in TVSW "Gardens For All" July '85. TEA. *Adm 50p Chd 20p. (Share to Stoke Damerel Church & St Luke's Hospice). Suns July 19, Aug 9 (2-6); also by appt (Tel Plymouth 41052)*

Stormsdown &✕❀ (Mrs U.M. Domar & Mr P. Hewitt) nr Bickington, Ashburton. 1m N of A38 on Newton Abbot-Widecombe rd. 1½-acre garden with choice rhododendrons, azaleas, flowering trees and rare shrubs. *Adm 50p Chd 25p. All year (Mon-Sat 11-4.30 closed 1-2; Sun 2-4); Evening parties by appt (Tel Bickington 362 & 507)*

Tapeley Park & (Miss Rosamond Christie) Instow, on A39 Barnstaple-Bideford rd. Beautiful Italian garden of horticultural interest in all seasons; ice house; shell house; walled kitchen garden; woodland walk to lily pond. Pets, putting. play areas, picnic places. Craftshop. Light lunches & cream TEAS in Queen Anne dairy. Tours of house when numbers permit. *Collecting box for NGS. Easter to Oct daily except Mons (10-6) but open Bank Hol Mons*

¶**Topsham Gardens** 4m from Exeter. Free parking in Holman Way, access to Monmouth Avenue via footbridge over Holman Way. TEA No. 20 *Adm each garden 30p Chd 15p. Sat, Sun June 6, 7 (2-6)*
  4 Monmouth Avenue (Mr & Mrs A. Vanstone). ⅓-acre, level garden, shrubbery, azaleas, unusual plants, mixed borders, herbaceous, shrubs, alpine scree, lily pond
  20 Monmouth Avenue &❀ (Mr & Mrs H. Lock) ⅓-acre, level garden, wide range unusual plants and shrubs giving year round effect; mixed curved borders, herbaceous, shrubs, bulbs; some old-fashioned roses

Underhill Close ✕ (Mr & Mrs John Turner) West St, South Molton. N outskirts of S Molton B3227 signed Torrington, last house on left in West St. before cottage hospital. 2 acres with small terraces, emphasis on labour-saving planting and informality with many trees and shrubs planned to give shelter to elevated site. *Adm 30p Chd 5p (Share to South Molton Community Centre). Suns June 21, July 26 (2-7)*

Vicar's Mead ✕❀ (Mr & Mrs H.F.J. Read) Hayes Lane, East Budleigh, 2m N of Budleigh Salterton. From A376, Newton Poppleford-Budleigh Salterton, turn off W for East Budleigh; Hayes Lane is opp 'Sir Walter Raleigh'; garden 100yds W of public car park. 3½-acres created since 1977 around a 500yr-old historic former vicarage; wide range of unusual and rare shrubs and plants displayed on and around long red sandstone escarpment; hostas and 4 national collections a feature. Tea in village, 200yds. *Adm 40p Chd free. Suns, Mons April 19, 20; May 3, 4 & 24, 25, 31; Suns June 19, 21; July 19, Sun, Mon Aug 30, 31; Sun Sept 13 (2-6)*

Weetwood ✕ (Mr & Mrs J.V.R. Birchall) Offwell, 2m from Honiton. Turn S off A35 (signed Offwell), at E end of Offwell. 1-acre all seasons garden; rhododendrons, azaleas, shrubs, ornamental pools, rock gardens, collection of dwarf conifers. Teashops Honiton. *Adm 30p Chd 5p. By appt only spring, summer & autumn (Tel Wilmington 363)*

West Hill Gardens Ottery St Mary. Follow signs to West Hill; after 3m left into Lower Broad Oak rd; TEAS Meadow Mead (May Onwards). *Adm 30p each garden Chd free. Suns, Mons April 19, 20, May 24, 25, Sats, Suns June 20, 21, July 18, 19 (2-5)*
  Salehurst ✕❀ (Mr & Mrs F. Morley) Lower Broad Oak rd. ⅔ acre all year garden; good range shrubs; azaleas; small trees, roses. *Also by appt (Tel Ottery St Mary 2589)*
  Bramble Cottage ✕❀ (Mr & Mrs Brian Norton) Lower Broad Oak rd. ¾ acre semi-woodland garden; natural ponds and bog area; interesting shrubs; primulas a special feature of late spring, *Also by appt (Tel Ottery St Mary 4642)*
  Kings Gatchell ✕❀ (Mr & Mrs Kenneth Adlam) Higher Metcombe ⅔ acre. Wide variety of species inc large collection of hebes, ferns, both hardy and tender, alpines, etc. *Also by appt (Tel Ottery St Mary 3944)*
  Meadow Mead &✕ (Mr & Mrs Peter Griffiths) Higher Metcombe. ⅔ acre; shrubs and herbaceous borders; fruit and vegetable gardens. TEAS May onwards

Westpark ✕❀ (Mr & Mrs D. Court), Yealmpton, A379 E of Plymouth; Xrds centre of village, turn S on Newton Ferrers rd; park end of Torr Lane (Disabled in drive). 1-acre garden in attractive country setting around Victorian house. Mixed plantings of mature trees, shrubs, roses, borders; variety of naturalised spring bulbs. Woodland with rocky outcrop. TEA. *Adm 50p Chd 25p (Share to Yealmpton Church). Sat, Sun April 11, 12 (2-6)*

Wiggaton Gardens ❀ 1m S of Ottery St Mary on B3176 in middle of village, 3 adjacent old cottage gardens. Off rd car park. COFFEE/ TEA. *Combined adm 50p Chd 20p (Share to Devon Historic Churches Trust). Sun May 3 (11-6)*

Orchard Lea (Air Cdre & Mrs C. Neville) Established secluded garden spring bulbs and flowering shrubs and herbaceous borders. COFFEE and TEA

Hollybrook (Miss Ayre) Interestingly raised bulb plantings, spring shrubs, troughs

Farthings (Miss Cook) Spring garden with rockeries, flowering shrubs and bulbs

¶**Woodland Grove** ☕❀ (Maj & Mrs R.A.W. Reynolds) Bovey Tracey, 2m W of Bovey Tracey, take B3344 W from Dolphin Square towards Manaton. In 1¾m right at Raddaford Water towards Lustleigh. Entrance 200yds on left. Carpark in field on left beyond house. 22-acre woodland garden with massed daffodils in spring. Many camellias, whilst rhododendron species and hybrids are special feature in May. Woodland walks with spectacular views of Dartmoor. Teas in Lustleigh village or Bovey Tracy. *Adm 50p Chd 30p. Suns April 5, May 17 (2-5.30)*

Woodside ❀ (Mr & Mrs Mervyn Feesey) Higher Raleigh Rd, Barnstaple. On outskirts of Barnstaple, A39 to Lynton, turn right 300yds above fire station. 2 acres, S sloping; intensively planted; collection of ornamental grasses, bamboos, sedges and other monocots; unusual and rare dwarf shrubs, rock plants and alpines; raised beds, troughs; variegated and peat-loving shrubs, trees and conifers; New Zealand collection. *Adm 75p Chd 25p. Suns May 10, June 7, July 5, Aug 9 (2-6)*

DORSET

Hon County Organiser:
MRS CHARLES BUDDEN, Wolfeton, Dorchester DT2 9QN (Tel Dorchester 64278)

Assistant Hon County Organisers:
MR & MRS STANLEY CHERRY, Highbury, Woodside Rd, West Moors, Wimborne BH22 0LY (Tel Ferndown 874372)
MRS JOHN GREENER, Langebride House, Long Bredy, Dorchester (Tel Long Bredy 257)
MRS G. D. HARTHAN, Russets, Rectory Lane, Child Okeford, Blandford (Tel Child Okeford 860703)

Hon County Treasurer:
MRS R. PATTERSON, 10 Herringston Road, Dorchester

DATES OF OPENING

BY APPOINTMENT ONLY for dates see text:
MOULIN HUET, West Moors
14 UMBERS HILL, Shaftesbury
REGULAR OPENINGS for dates see text:
ABBOTSBURY GARDENS, nr Weymouth
CATNAP COTTAGE, Hilton
CHETTLE HOUSE, nr Blandford
COMPTON ACRES GARDENS, Poole
DEANS COURT, Wimborne
FORDE ABBEY, nr Chard
HEATHERWOOD NURSERIES, Ashington, Wimborne
HIGHBURY, West Moors
LANKHAM HOUSE, Cattistock
MINTERNE, nr Cerne Abbas
PARNHAM, Beaminster
PINE COTTAGE ARBORETUM, nr Bridport
SMEDMORE, Kimmeridge
TURNPIKE COTTAGE, Wimborne Minster

MARCH Sunday 22
LANGEBRIDE HOUSE, Long Bredy
APRIL Sunday 5
CHIFFCHAFFS, Bourton
DOMINEYS YARD, Buckland Newton
NORTH LEIGH HOUSE, Wimborne
APRIL Wednesday 8
CHIFFCHAFFS, Bourton
APRIL Sunday 12
‡ALLER GREEN, Ansty
FRANKHAM FARM, nr Sherborne
‡IVY COTAGE, Ansty
STOUR HOUSE, Blandford
APRIL Friday 17 & Saturday 18
CATNAP COTTAGE, Hilton
APRIL Easter Sunday 19
CATNAP COTTAGE, Hilton
LANGBRIDE HOUSE, Long Bredy
LINDENS, Sturminster Newton
APRIL Easter Monday 20
CATNAP COTTAGE, Hilton
EDMONSHAM HOUSE, nr Cranborne
APRIL Sunday 26
‡BOVERIDGE FARM, Cranborne
‡BOVERIDGE HOUSE, Cranborne
‡‡6 HOLLANDS MEAD AVENUE, Owermoigne
‡‡SUNNYBROOK, Owermoigne
APRIL Thursday 30
KINGSTON MAURWARD, nr Dorchester
MAY Sunday 3
CHIFFCHAFFS, Bourton
‡CULEAZE, nr Wareham
FRANKHAM FARM, nr Sherborne
‡‡ST NICHOLAS CLOSE, Wimborne
‡STOCKFORD, East Stoke
‡‡112 UPLANDS ROAD, West Moors
MAY Monday 4 & Wednesday 6
CHIFFCHAFFS, Bourton
MAY Sunday 10
CHETTLE HOUSE, nr Blandford
CULEAZE, nr Wareham

DAPPLE GREY, Ashley Heath
6 HOLLANDS MEAD AVENUE,
  Owermoigne
KESWORTH, Wareham
‡NORTH LEIGH HOUSE, Wimborne
‡ST NICHOLAS CLOSE, Wimborne
MAY Sunday 17
KESWORTH, Wareham
52 ROSSMORE ROAD, Parkstone
MAY Sunday 24
‡ALLER GREEN, Ansty
BOVERIDGE FARM, Cranborne
CHIFFCHAFFS, Bourton
FIELD COTTAGE, Corfe Mullen
HIGHWOOD GARDEN, Wareham
‡IVY COTTAGE, Ansty
MOIGNE COMBE, nr Dorchester
52 ROSSMORE ROAD, Parkstone
STOCKFORD, East Stoke
TURNPIKE COTTAGE, Wimborne Minster
MAY Monday 25 (Bank Hol)
CHIFFCHAFFS, Bourton
MAY Wednesday 27
CHIFFCHAFFS, Bourton
MAY Sunday 31
‡CANNINGS COURT, Pulham
FRANKHAM FARM, nr Sherborne
HIGHWOOD GARDEN, Wareham
6 HOLLANDS MEAD AVENUE,
  Owermoigne
KIBBLESTONE, Ashley Heath
THE OLD RECTORY, Litton Cheney
‡THE OLD RECTORY, Pulham
JUNE Saturday 6
SHUTE HOUSE, nr Shaftesbury
JUNE Sunday 7
59 BRANKSOME WOOD ROAD,
  Bournemouth
37 THE GLADE, Ashley Heath
MAY COTTAGE, Sturminster Newton
MOIGNE COMBE, nr Dorchester
WINCOMBE PARK, nr Shaftesbury
JUNE Saturday 13
CRANBORNE MANOR GARDENS,
  Cranborne
JUNE Saturday 13 to JUNE Sunday 28
MELFORD HOUSE, nr Sherborne
JUNE Sunday 14
‡THE COBBLES, nr Blandford
DAPPLE GREY, Ashley Heath
MAY COTTAGE, Sturminster Newton
‡RUSSETS, nr Blandford
STOCKFORD, East Stoke
TARRANT RUSHTON GARDENS
112 UPLANDS ROAD, West Moors
JUNE Thursday 18
MELBURY HOUSE, nr Yeovil
JUNE Sunday 21
‡CANNINGS COURT, Pulham
CHETTLE HOUSE, nr Blandford
CHIFFCHAFFS, Bourton
CHILCOMBE HOUSE, nr Bridport
THE COBBLES, nr Blandford
FIELD COTTAGE, Corfe Mullen
37 THE GLADE, Ashley Heath
MAY COTTAGE, Sturminster Newton

‡THE OLD RECTORY, Pulham
73 TRAVELLER'S REST, nr Blandford
TURNPIKE COTTAGE, Wimborne Minster
JUNE Wednesday 24
CHIFFCHAFFS, Bourton
JUNE Thursday 25
KINGSTON MAURWARD, nr Dorchester
MELBURY HOUSE, nr Yeovil
JUNE Saturday 27
THE MANOR HOUSE, Hinton St Mary
JUNE Sunday 28
THE COBBLES, nr Blandford
DEANS COURT, Wimborne
6 HOLLANDS MEAD AVENUE,
  Owermoigne
KINGSTON MAURWARD, nr Dorchester
‡LINDENS, Sturminster Newton
‡THE MANOR HOUSE, Hinton St Mary
‡MAY COTTAGE, Sturminster Newton
73 TRAVELLER'S REST, nr Blandford
26 WESTERN AVENUE, Bournemouth
JULY Thursday 2
KINGSTON MAURWARD, nr Dorchester
JULY Sunday 5
CHILCOMBE HOUSE, nr Bridport
THE COBBLES, nr Blandford
THE OLD RECTORY, Seaborough
STEEPLE MANOR, nr Wareham
‡26 WESTERN AVENUE, Bournemouth
‡WESTERN AVENUE GARDENS,
  Bournemouth
JULY Thursday 9
MELBURY HOUSE, nr Yeovil
JULY Saturday 11
ACACIA COTTAGE, nr Shaftesbury
JULY Sunday 12
ACACIA COTTAGE, nr Shaftesbury
CHIFFCHAFFS, Bourton
COX HILL, Marnhull
‡DAPPLE GREY, Ashley Heath
‡37 THE GLADE, Ashley Heath
THE OLD RECTORY, Fifehead Magdalen
‡‡26 WESTERN AVENUE, Bournemouth
‡‡WESTERN AVENUE GARDENS,
  Bournemouth
JULY Wednesday 15
CHIFFCHAFFS, Bourton
JULY Sunday 19
DOMINEYS YARD, Buckland Newton
‡6 HOLLANDS MEAD AVENUE,
  Owermoigne
LONG ASH COTTAGE, nr Dorchester
‡THE MANOR HOUSE, Chaldon Herring
STURMINSTER NEWTON GARDENS
26 WESTERN AVENUE, Bournemouth
JULY Thursday 23
MELBURY HOUSE, nr Yeovil
JULY Saturday 25
73 TRAVELLER'S REST, nr Blandford
JULY Sunday 26
CHETTLE HOUSE, nr Blandford
FIELD HOUSE, Corfe Mullen
73 TRAVELLER'S REST, nr Blandford
26 WESTERN AVENUE, Bournemouth
AUGUST Sunday 2
37 THE GLADE, Ashley Heath

AUGUST Sunday 9
NORTH LEIGH HOUSE, nr Wimborne
WOODLANDS, Talbot Woods,
Bournemouth
AUGUST Sunday 16
STOUR HOUSE, Blandford
WOODLANDS, Talbot Woods,
Bournemouth
AUGUST Sunday 23
FIELD HOUSE, Corfe Mullen
6 HOLLANDS MEAD AVENUE,
Owermoigne
AUGUST Sunday 30
‡ALLER GREEN, Ansty
‡IVY COTTAGE, Ansty
LINDENS, Sturminster Newton
RUSSETS, nr Blandford
SMEDMORE, Kimmeridge
AUGUST Monday 31 (Bank Hol)
RUSSETS, nr Blandford
SEPTEMBER Thursday 10
MELBURY HOUSE, nr Yeovil
SEPTEMBER Sunday 20
‡CANNINGS COURT, Pulham
LINDENS, Sturminster Newton
‡THE OLD RECTORY, Pulham
SEPTEMBER Sunday 27
‡ALLER GREEN, Ansty
DEANS COURT, Wimborne
‡IVY COTTAGE, Ansty
OCTOBER Sunday 4
DOMINEYS YARD, Buckland Newton

DESCRIPTIONS OF GARDENS

♦●**Abbotsbury Gardens** ▲※ (Strangways Estate) 9m NW of Weymouth. 9m SW of Dorchester. From B3157 Weymouth-Bridport, turn off 200yds W of Abbotsbury village, at foot of hill. 20 acres; uniquely mild Mediterranean-type climate, started in 1760 and considerably extended in C19; much replanting during past few years; very fine collection of rhododendrons, camellias, azaleas; wide variety of unusual and tender trees and shrubs. Peacocks. TEAS. *Adm £1.50 OAPs £1 Chd 50p (for party rate tel 0305-871387). March 15-Oct 18 daily (10-6)*

Acacia Cottage ▲※※ (The Misses Haslam & McTrusty) 46 Twyford, 4m SW of Shaftesbury. Signed to Twyford on A350 in Compton Abbas. ⅔-acre garden on greensand; shrubs and herbaceous plants. Tea Compton Abbas (Milestones Tearooms). *Adm 40p Chd free. Sat, Sun July 11, 12 (2-6)*

Aller Green ※ (A.J. Thomas Esq) Ansty, 12m N of Dorchester. From Puddletown take A354 to Blandford; after Blue Vinney Inn, take 1st left signed Dewlish/Cheselbourne; through Cheselbourne to Ansty then 1st right before Fox Inn. 1 acre typical Dorset cottage garden; unusual trees, shrubs and perennials in old orchard setting. *Combined adm with Ivy Cottage 75p Chd 20p. Suns April 12, May 24*

(Share to RNLI); Aug 30, Sept 27 (Share to GRBS & RGOF) (2-5.30)

Boveridge Farm ※※ (David Dampney Esq) Cranborne. Leave Cranborne on Martin rd unclass, thence take 2nd right Boveridge Farm, and park in farmyard. A plantsman's garden of 2 acres on 3 levels, part chalk and part acid; with lawns around old farmhouse, formerly manor house of the Hooper family; in rural surroundings with fine views. Many rare and interesting trees and shrubs. Specimen Acer 'Brilliantissimum', Prunus 'Shidare Yoshino', Prunus 'Pendula Rubra'. *Adm 50p Chd 20p (Share to Cranborne Church Organ Fund). Suns April 26, May 24 (2-6)*

Boveridge House ▲※ (Miss P. Harper) 1¼m E of Cranborne on B3078 turn N into main entrance. Country house garden surrounded by parkland, originally designed by Gertrude Jekyll in 1920, now being restored; lawns; ornamental pools; balustraded terrace, pergola; long grass walks with herbaceous borders; many spring bulbs; specimen Lebanon cedars, maples, fern-leaved beech. TEA. *Adm 50p Chd 25p (Share to School Swimming Pool Fund). Sun April 26 (2-6)*

¶**59 Branksome Wood Road** ※ (Mr & Mrs R.Butler) Bournemouth. ⅓-acre garden made by owners over 7 years ago, designed to utilise a steeply inclined site, and featuring a series of waterfalls and pools. Mature trees provide a setting for ericaceous plants and ferns against a woodland background. *Adm 40p Chd 20p. Sun June 7 (2-6)*

Cannings Court ▲※※ (Mr & Mrs J.D. Dennison) Pulham on B3143, turn E at Xrds 13m N of Dorchester. Sherborne and Sturminster Newton both 8m. 2 acres; large variety of interesting plants and shrubs; herbaceous border, stone walls; terrace; old farmyard. TEAS. *Adm 60p Chd 10p (Share to The Wessex Medical School Trust). Suns May 31, June 21, Sept 20 (2-6)*

Catnap Cottage ▲※ (Mrs M. J. Phillips) Hilton, 10m S of Blandford. Turn off Blandford-Dorchester rd (A354) at Milborne St Andrew for Milton Abbas and Hilton. 1¼ acres; trees, shrubs, perennials; grassy walks, vistas, conifers and ground cover; attractive setting, views; herb and shade gardens; all-the-year garden for plantsmen as shown on TV. Tea Milton Abbas. *Adm 40p Chd 20p (Share to Help The Aged). Fri, Sat, Sun, Mon April 17, 18, 19, 20 (10-5); Suns April 26-Sept 27 (1-5); also by appt (Tel Milton Abbas 880538)*

♦**Chettle House** ▲※※ (Mr & Mrs Patrick Bourke) Chettle. 6m NE of Blandford Forum on A354 turn left to Chettle, left at tree in village, up hill past church; car park past drive gates. Coach parties. Garden only suitable for wheelchairs. 3 acres with lawns, herbaceous and shrubs. Small vineyard and nursery. Queen Anne house. *Adm 75p Chd free. April 4-Oct 24 daily ex Tues. For NGS Suns May 10, June 21, July 26 (10.30-5.30)*

Chiffchaffs ✻❀ (Mr & Mrs K.R. Potts) Chaffeymoor; 3m E of Wincanton off A303 at W end of Bourton village, lane signed Chaffeymoor. Well-stocked garden; interesting plants, bulbs, shrubs, herbaceous border, shrub roses. An area of woodland now being cleared and planted. TEAS at weekends. *Adm 50p Chd 25p (Share to St Michael's Church, Penselwood). Sun, Wed April 5, 8; Sun Mon Wed May 3, 4, 6, 24, 25, 27; Suns, Weds June 21, 24; July 12, 15 (2-6)*

Chilcombe House ❀ (Caryl & John Hubbard) Chilcombe, 5m E of Bridport. 1m S of Askerswell; turn off A35 Dorchester-Bridport, 1m W of Askers Motel off dual carriageway. 2-acre hillside garden, in beautiful setting with magnificent views; wild areas, courtyards and walled garden divided into smaller sections with mixed planting shrubs, flowers, herbs, vegetables, fruit trees and many old roses. TEAS. *Adm 80p Chd free (Share to Common Ground). Suns June 21, July 5 (2-6.30)*

The Cobbles ✻❀ (Mr & Mrs A.P. Baker) Shillingstone, 5m NW of Blandford. In middle of village opp Old Ox Inn, Shillingstone. 1-acre cottage garden on chalk; mixed borders, ground cover; unusual plants; stream. Teas in village. *Adm 40p Chd free. Suns June 14, 21, 28; July 5 (2.30-5.30); also by appt June & July (Tel 0258 860335)*

♦●**Compton Acres Gardens** ❦✻❀ Canford Cliffs Rd, Poole. From Poole-Bournemouth Rd turn on to Canford Cliffs Rd, few yds from Canford Cliffs village, nr Sandbanks. Buses: Wilts & Dorset 147,150, 151 from Bournemouth & Poole; stop at entrance; yellow buses 11, 12 nearby. Reputed to be finest gardens in Europe, overlooking Poole Harbour inc Japanese, Italian, rock and water gardens; heather; woodland; sub-tropical glen; bronze and marble statuary. Large selection of plants for sale. TEAS. Free car/coach park. *April 1-Oct 31 daily (10.30-6.30; dusk if earlier)*

¶**Cox Hill** ✻❀ (Capt & Mrs J.R.Prescott) 3m N of Sturminster Newton, turning left at Walton Elm; 3m E of Stalbridge via Stour River Bridge at Kings Mill. Approx 2-acre garden and paddock (Jacob sheep). Outstanding views over Blackmore Vale, to Bullbarrow and Dorset Gap. Small water garden, trees, roses, herbaceous, orchard; interesting plants maintained within original victorian plan. TEA. *Adm 50p Chd 20p. Sun July 12 (2-6)*

♦**Cranborne Manor Gardens** ❦✻❀ (The Viscount & Viscountess Cranborne) Cranborne. 10m N of Wimborne on B3078. Beautiful and historic gardens laid out in C17 by John Tradescant and enlarged in C20, featuring several gardens surrounded by walls and yew hedges: white garden, herb, mount and knot garden with Elizabethan flowers. water and wild garden. Many interesting plants, with fine trees and avenues. *Adm £1.30 OAPs £1. Sat June 13 (12-5)*

Culeaze ❦❀ (Col & Mrs Barne) 1½m S of Bere Regis off Wool Rd; take 2nd left, signposted Culeaze; then right. Medium-sized garden; walled garden, rhododendrons, rare trees, flowers and shrubs; greenhouse and conservatory with mimosa. Tea Woodbury side, opp Garage in West St. Bere Regis. *Adm 40p Chd 10p. Suns May 3, 10 (2-6)*

Dapple Grey ✻❀ (Mr & Mrs Dennis Cole) 40 Lions Lane, Ashley Heath. Lions Lane at either end joins Woolsbridge Rd, which meets A31 at roundabout 3m W of Ringwood, and the Ringwood-Horton rd (unclass) at Ashley Heath. A delightful ½-acre garden made and maintained by owners, now coming to maturity, with the accent upon foliage plants, many unusual, for decorative effect and all year interest; Mrs Brenda Cole is a Chelsea Medallist in flower arrangements; this is reflected in the garden, incorporating on open days, flower arrangements in the garden setting as an additional attraction. Tea Three Legged Cross Garden Centre 2½m. *Adm 50p Chd 10p (Share to Macmillan Cancer Care Unit, Christchurch). Suns May 10; June 14; July 12 (2-5)*

Deans Court ❦✻❀ (Sir Michael & Lady Hanham) Wimborne. Just off B3073 in centre of Wimborne. 13 acres; partly wild garden; water, specimen trees, free roaming peacocks and other birds; kitchen garden with serpentine wall, selling organically produced plants and produce as available. House (open by written appt) originally the Deanery to the Minster. Herb garden; Henry Doubleday Research Assn sanctuary for threatened vegetable species. Wholefood TEAS; also morning coffee on Bank Hols. *Adm 60p Chd 30p. Suns, Mons April 19, 20; May 24, 25; Sun July 26; Sun, Mon Aug 30, 31 (Suns 2-6, Mons 10-6). For NGS Suns June 28, Sept 27*

¶**Domineys Yard** ✻❀ (Mr & Mrs W.Gueterbock) Buckland Newton, 11m from Dorchester and Sherborne 2m E of A352 or take B3143 from Sturminster Newton. Take 'no through rd' between church and 'Gaggle of Geese' Pub next to phone box. Entrance 200 metres on left. Park in lane. 2-acre garden on chalk, clay and green sand surrounding C17 thatched cottage. Developed over 25 years with unusual plants, shrubs and trees inc camellias, clematis, roses, lilies and other bulbs. Autumn colour making it a garden for all seasons. TEAS. *Adm 75p Chd 25p (Share to Cheshire Foundation Dorset Family Support Service). Suns April 5, July 19, Oct 4 (2-6)*

Edmondsham House ⅅ⚹֎ (Mrs Michael Smith) Edmondsham, nr Cranborne. B3081, turn at Sixpenny Handley Xrds to Ringwood and Cranborne; thereafter follow signs to Edmondsham. Large garden; spring bulbs, trees, shrubs; walled garden; walled vegetable garden; grass cockpit. Early church nearby. *Adm 50p Chd 20p (Share to Christian Aid). Mon April 20 (2.30-5); also by appt*

Field Cottage (Mr & Mrs Brian Sellers) Blandford Rd, Corfe Mullen. Leave A31 at Church 2m W of Wimborne on to B3074. After 1m garden is adjacent to Lockyers School. 1-acre garden of considerable charm surrounding C15 thatched cottage. Of special interest are the landscaping and 100yds shrubbed drive itself forming part of the collection. Other features are 100 year old pear tree, pools and lawns, and flowers grown especially for drying, one of the interests of the owners. Parking in School car park (by kind permission of the Headmaster). Dogs on leads. *Adm 40p Chd 20p (Share to Church Knowle Animal Sanctuary, MGFT). Suns May 24, June 21, July 26, Aug 23 (2-6)*

◆●**Forde Abbey** ⅅ (M.Roper Esq) 4m SE of Chard. 7m W of Crewkerne; well signed off A30. 30 acres; many fine shrubs and some magnificent specimen trees inc post-war arboretum; herbaceous borders, rock and kitchen gardens; in bog garden one of larger collections Asiatic primulas in SW. TEAS. *Adm charges not available as going to press. April-Oct weekdays (11-5) Suns (2-6) Closed Sats*

Frankham Farm ⅅ⚹ (Mr & Mrs R.G. Earle) Ryme Intrinseca. A37 Yeovil-Dorchester; 3m S of Yeovil turn E at Xrds with garage; drive ¼m on left. 1½-acres started in 1960s; shrubs, trees, spring bulbs, clematis, roses. TEAS. *Adm 50p Chd free (Share to Ryme Church). Suns April 12, May 3, 31 (2-6)*

37 The Glade ⚹֎ (Mrs Sally Tidd) Ashley Heath. 3m W of Ringwood, leave A31 at roundabout into Woolsbridge Rd; after ¾m left into The Glade. From N may be approached from Ashley Heath PO and Lions Lane. Colourful ⅓-acre garden in a pleasing setting designed, built and maintained by owner. Flower arranger's garden containing a varied collection of foliage plants, climbing plants, shrubs for decorative effect and year-round interest. As additional feature an exhibition of unusual floral collage, a hobby of the owner, will also be shown. Tea Three Legged Cross Garden Centre, 2m. *Adm 40p Chd 5p. Suns June 7, 21, July 12, Aug 2 (2-6)*

¶●**Heatherwood Nurseries** ⚹֎ (Mr & Mrs Ronald Squires) 1m S of Wimborne. Leave A349 Wimborne-Poole rd at Merley Bridge, signed Ashington, into Merley Park Rd. Thence garden is ¾m on left. ½-acre garden created by present Owners from original woodland. Main theme of the garden is heathers (800 in 50 vars.), conifers (300 in 30 vars.), azaleas and acers. Large lawn with ornamental pool and rockery. A wide selection of the plants shown is available for sale in the adjacent nurseries. Large car park. *Collection box. Daily except Dec 25, 26, Jan 1 (9-5, Suns 9-12)*

Highbury ⚹֎ (Mr & Mrs Stanley Cherry) West Moors, 8m N of Bournemouth. In Woodside Rd, off B3072 Bournemouth-Verwood rd; last rd at N end of West Moors village. Garden of ½-acre in mature setting. First opened to the public in 1910 and now restored and since 1970 again open as below. Many rare and unusual plants, shrubs and conifers in specialist collections; botanical and horticultural interest with everything labelled. Herb borders. Weather station and Information Centre. Much thought has been given to planting and designing with visitors in mind, (A.G. 1980). TEAS in orchard when fine. *Adm 40p Chd 20p. April 5-Sept 6 every Sun & Bank Hol (2-6); parties at other times by appt (Tel Ferndown 874372)*

◆**Highwood Garden** ⚹ (H.W. Drax Esq) Charborough Park, Wareham, 6m E of Bere Regis. Enter park by any lodge on A31; follow signpost to Estate Office, then Highwood Garden. Large garden with rhododendrons and azaleas in woodland setting. *Adm 60p Chd 30p. Suns May 24, 31 (2.30-6)*

6 Hollands Mead Avenue ⚹֎ (Mr & Mrs P.E. Baxter) Owermoigne. 6m E of Dorchester on A352, left at sign to Owermoigne village; 2nd left. Delightful ⅕ acre garden made and maintained by owners; planned for year-round colour; good herbaceous perennials, shrubs, collections of heaths, hostas, ferns and alpines. TEAS. *Adm 40p (Share to West Dorset Hospice). Suns April 26, May 10, 31; June 28; July 19; Aug 23 (2-6)*

Ivy Cottage ⚹֎ (Anne & Alan Stevens) Ansty, 12m N of Dorchester. A354 from Puddletown to Blandford; after Blue Vinney Inn take 1st left signed Dewlish/Cheslebourne; through Cheslebourne to Ansty then 1st right before Fox Inn. 1½-acre excellent plantsman's garden specialising in unusual perennials, moisture-loving plants; specimen trees and shrubs. TEAS. *Combined adm with Aller Green 75p Chd 20p. Suns April 12, May 24; (Share to RNLI) Aug 30; Sept 27 (Share to GRBS & RGOF) (2-5.30). Also every Thurs April - Sept 30 (10-5). Parties by appt only (Tel Milton Abbas 880053)*

Kesworth (H.J.S. Clark Esq) 1½m N of Wareham. Turn off A351 almost opp school at Sandford, down Kesworth Drive to level Xing. Grounds inc 600 acre wildlife sanctuary at W end of Poole Harbour suitable for picnics, birdwatching, walks through unspoilt woods and marshes amongst fine wild scenery; herd of Galloway cattle. Elegant and colourful small garden round house. Tea Wareham. *Adm £1 Chd free (Share to Sandford Church). Suns May 10, 17 (12.30-7)*

Kibblestone ✗ (Mr & Mrs Raymond Fitzgerald) Horton Rd, Ashley Heath. Leave A31 1m SW of Ringwood into Horton Rd unclass. After 100yds, right into the former Horton Rd now cul de sac, garden in 50yds. Relatively new, designed, built and maintained by owners; accent on interesting features, paved paths through colourful plantings and large rock garden, demonstrating maximum utilisation of ½ acre with wooded area, no lawns or grass. Features inc Moon Garden, pagoda, Ishi-doro (stone lanterns). Teas Ringwood. *Adm 30p Chd 10p. Sun May 31 (2-6); also by appt (Tel Ringwood 5056)*

◆**Kingston Maurward** ⅋✗❀ (Dorset County Council) Dorset College of Agriculture and Horticulture, E of Dorchester turn right 1m from Dorchester on A35. Bus alight Stinsford ¼m. Formal and teaching gardens; herbaceous border; shrubberies; rose gardens; Japanese garden; lake walk; plant houses, fruit and vegetable plots; educational plots in walled garden. Only walled area suitable for wheelchairs. Lunches on weekdays. Tea in nearby village (Suns only). *Adm £1 Chd free. Thurs April 30, June 25; Sun June 28, Thurs July 2 (2-6)*

Langebride House ✗❀ (Maj & Mrs John Greener) Long Bredy. ½-way between Bridport and Dorchester, 8m from each; S off A35, well signed. Old rectory garden modernised since 1966 for easier management; 200- yr-old beech trees; young flowering trees, shrub border, yew hedges, alpine garden. TEAS (April). *Adm 50p (March) 75p (April). Suns March 22, (2-4.30), April 19 (2-6)*

Lankham House ✗❀ (Sue & John Willows) Cattistock 10m NW of Dorchester. From A37 turn W at sign to Cattistock. From A356 1m NW of Maiden Newton. Please park at bottom of lane. ⅓-acre cottage garden. Ground cover and variegated plants; unusual perennials and shrubs; planted for year-round interest. Teas Evershot. *Adm 40p. Every Fri & Sat May to Sept (10-5)*

Lindens ❀ (Lady Morshead) Sturminster Newton. Follow signs from Blandford Forum, Shaftesbury or Gillingham. Turn down tiny lane opp island shop in market place. Ample parking at house. Garden with unusual plants and shrubs. TEAS. *Adm 50p Chd 20p (Share to GRBS & RGOF). Suns April 19, June 28, Aug 30, Sept 20 (2-6)*

Long Ash Cottage ✗❀ (Mr & Mrs A. Case) Milton Abbas. 10m From Blandford/Dorchester on A354, 3m from Milbourne St Andrew on Ansty Rd not Milton Abbas Rd. ½-acre cottage garden with many unusual and old

fashioned flowers, also a collection of rare poultry. TEAS. *Adm 50p Chd 25p. Sun July 19 (2-5.30)*

The Manor House, Chaldon Herring ✗❀ (Dale & Alice Fishburn) 9m E of Dorchester, mid-way between Dorchester/ Wareham on A352, turn S at sign to East Chaldon. 2 acres in valley in chalk hills, blends into surroundings; plantsman's garden with many perennials and climbers; small but fine kitchen garden. Home-made TEAS. *Adm 75p Chd free (Share St. Nicholas Church, Chaldon Herring). Sun July 19 (4-8)*

The Manor House, Hinton St Mary ⅋✗❀ (Mr & Mrs A. Pitt-Rivers) 1m NW of Sturminster Newton on B3092. Next to Church in Hinton St Mary. C17 house, C15 tithe barn set in 5-acre garden in heart of Blackmore Vale; trees, shrubs; lawns; yew hedges; collection of species and shrub roses. TEAS. *Adm £1 Chd 20p (Share to NSPCC). Sat, Sun June 27, 28 (2-6)*

May Cottage ⅋ (Mr & Mrs R.M. Hall) Fiddleford. Off A357 1m W of Shillingstone, 1m E of Sturminster Newton Bridge. ¾-acre garden surrounding thatched cottage, unusual trees, shrubs, perennials, alpines, clematis collection. *Adm 50p Chd free (Share to Save the Children African Appeal). Suns June 7, 14, 21, 28, (2-5.30)*

◆**Melbury House** ⅋✗❀ (Lady Teresa Agnew) 6m S of Yeovil. Signed on Dorchester-Yeovil Rd. 13m N of Dorchester. Large garden; very fine arboretum; shrubs and lakeside walk; beautiful deer park. Garden only. TEAS. *Adm £1 OAPs/Chd 50p (Share to Macmillan Trust). Thurs June 18, 25; July 9, 23, Sept 10 (2-6)*

Melford House ✗ (Rodney & Pamela Russell) High Street, Yetminster, 5m SW of Sherborne and A30; 5m SE of Yeovil off A37. Lovely small Elizabethan house, 1½ acres set amid picturesque Dorset village; designed and planted by owners. On different levels reminiscent of Italian garden with ponds, stone arches, balustrades and sculpture; mostly shrubs, herbaceous and roses with variety of greenery, soft colours; sloping down to orchard and river below. A peaceful setting for these well-known Wessex artists; Jubilee exhibition of their work on view in studio and house. Coach parties by appt only. Morning coffee, LUNCHES & home-made TEAS house or garden. *Adm £1 OAPs/Chd 80p (Share to Cancer Relief Macmillan Nurses). Daily June 13-28 inc (11-5.30)*

◆●**Minterne** (The Lord Digby) Minterne Magna, (A352). Important rhododendron and shrub garden landscaped in C18 with lakes, cascades and many fine and rare trees. *Adm £1 Chd and parking free. Open daily April 1 to Oct 31 (10-7)*

Moigne Combe (Maj-Gen H.M.G. Bond) 6m E of Dorchester. 1½m N of Owermoigne turn off A352 Dorchester-Wareham Rd. Medium-sized garden; wild garden and shrubbery; heathers, azaleas, rhododendrons etc; woodland paths and lake walk. Tea Galton Garden Centre Owermoigne. *Adm 50p Chd 20p. Suns May 24, June 7 (2-5.30)*

Moulin Huet ✗❀ (Harold Judd Esq) 15 Heatherdown Rd, West Moors. 7m N of Bournemouth. Leave A31 at West Moors Garage into Pinehurst Rd, take 1st right into Uplands Rd, then 3rd left into Heatherdown Rd. ⅓-acre garden of considerable botanical interest; large collection of 90 dwarf conifers; many plants and shrubs rare in cutivation; alpines, sink gardens, bonsai, rockeries, wood sculpture. Featured on TV 'Gardeners World' 1982. *Garden News* Gardener of the Year Award 1984. Tea Haskin's Garden Centre, Tricketts Cross ½m (on A31). *Adm 40p Chd 20p. By appt only April-Sept. Parties welcome (Tel Ferndown 875760)*

North Leigh House ❀ (Mr & Mrs Stanley Walker) Colehill, 1m NE of Wimborne. Leave B3073 (formerly A31) nr Sir Winston Churchill PH into North Leigh Lane, thence 5 acres of informal parkland with fine trees, rhododendrons; ornamental shrubs; specimen magnolia grandiflora and Green Brunswick fig; banks of wild orchids and naturalised spring bulbs in lawns; Victorian features include balustraded terrace, fountain pool, walled garden and conservatory, all being restored and maintained by owners. April opening daffodils; May wild orchids. Dogs on leads welcome. TEAS. *Adm 45p Chd 20p (Share to Animal Aid, April & May; Bournemouth & District Animal Ambulance Service Aug). Suns April 5, May 10, Aug 9 (2-6)*

¶**The Old Rectory, Fifehead Magdalen** ❀ (Col & Mrs J.H. Lidsey) 5m N of Gillingham. Small garden with interesting shrubs and perennials. *Adm 50p Chd free. Sun July 12 (2-6)*

¶**The Old Rectory, Litton Cheney** ✗ (Mr & Mrs H.Lindsay) 1m S of A35, 10m Dorchester. 6m Bridport. Park in centre of village and follow signs. Greatly varied garden with walled area, collection of herbaceous geraniums, shrub roses, 4 acres beautiful natural woodland garden on steep slope with streams and ponds (stout shoes recommended). TEAS in aid of church. *Adm 60p Chd 10p. Sun May 31 (2.30-6)*

The Old Rectory, Pulham ✗✗❀ (Rear Adm & Mrs John Garnier) on B3143 turn E at Xrds. 13m N of Dorchester. Sherborne and Sturminster Newton both 8m. 3 acres with mature trees and beautiful view; many trees, shrubs and borders planted since 1975. TEAS. *Adm 60p Chd 10p (Share to The Rebekah Fund). Suns May 31, June 21, Sept 20 (2-6)*

Old Rectory, Seaborough ❀ (Mr & Mrs C.W. Wright) 3m S of Crewkerne. Take B3165, after derestriction sign 1st left, 1st right, then after 2½m second left in village. 2-acre garden constructed since 1967; splendid views; rare trees, conifers, magnolias, flowering shrubs, roses, Himalayan plants, bulbs throughout the year, ferns; over 1000 species and cultivars, many rare and unusual. TEAS in aid of church. *Adm 50p Chd 20p. Sun July 5 (2-6)*

◆●**Parnham** ❧ (Mr & Mrs John Makepeace). ¾m S of Beaminster on A3066; 5m N of Bridport. 14 acres extensively reconstructed early this cent; variety of form and interest; riverside walk; picnic area; Yew Terrace comprising topiary of 50 clipped yews; spring-fed water channels cascading beside steps to Great Lawn; balustraded Ladies Terrace; formal East Court; Italian garden, glade and Woodland. House (Grade 1 listed building dating from 1540 with additions by John Nash) also open inc John Makepeace Furniture Workshops. Light lunches & TEAS. *Adm to whole site £2.20 Chd 10-15 £1 under 10 free. April 1-Oct 31 every Wed, Sun & Bank Hol (10-5); also by prior appt on Tues & Thurs for parties (Tel Beaminster 862204)*

Pine Cottage Arboretum ❀ (Mr & Mrs C.J.B. Lane) Gibbs Lane, Morecombelake, 4m W of Bridport. Take A35 4m turn right 50yds past PO; 1st house on right. Medium-sized garden; collection of over 800 rare and dwarf conifers; camellias, heathers; magnificent sea view. *Adm 50p Chd free. Thurs April-July inc (10-6); also by appt (Tel Chideock 89455)*

52 Rossmore Road ✗❀ (Mr & Mrs W.E. Ninniss) Parkstone, Poole. From A348 Poole-Ringwood rd turn SE into Rossmore Rd, thence ¼m. ⅓-acre interesting town garden designed in rooms; containing many rare and unusual plants; small knot garden; alpine lawn; herb garden. TEA. *Adm 40p Chd 10p. Suns May 17, 24 (2-6)*

Russets ❧❀ (Mr & Mrs G.D. Harthan) Rectory Lane, Child Okeford. 6m NW Blandford via A357 and turn off N at Shillingstone; or from A350 turn W at sign for Child Okeford. Parking space in Rectory Lane (ask nr centre of village). ½-acre plantsman's garden; many unusual shrubs, perennials, shrub roses and growing collection of clematis. TEAS. *Adm 50p Chd free. Suns June 14, Aug 30; Mon Aug 31 (2.30-5.30) also by appt (Tel Child Okeford 860703)*

St Nicholas Close ✗(Mr & Mrs Arthur Thorne) 38 Highland Rd, Colehill, Wimborne. Leave B3073 (formerly A31) at traffic lights turn N into St John's Hill, after small roundabout turn into Rowlands Hill, after ¼m turn right into Highland Rd and park. The garden is approached on foot, please, by short lane. ⅓-acre created by owners, with specialist collections of unusual species: cultivars of rhododendrons, azaleas, camellias against mature trees, inc eucalypts. *Adm 40p Chd 10p. Suns May 3, 10 (2-6)*

Shute House & (Lady Anne Tree) Donhead St Mary, 4m E of Shaftesbury. From A30 turn N. 3 acres; water, bog gardens and box gardens designed by Sir Geoffrey Jellicoe. Soft drinks available. Tea Blinking Owl on Salisbury-Shaftesbury rd or Grosvenor Hotel. *Adm £1 OAPs/Chd 50p (Share to Internat League for the Protection of Horses). Sat June 6 (2.30-5.30)*

Smedmore &❀ (Maj & Mrs John Mansel) Kimmeridge, 7m S of Wareham. Turn W off A351 (Wareham/Swanage) at sign to Kimmeridge. 2 acres; colourful herbaceous borders; display of hydrangeas; interesting plants and shrubs; walled flower gardens; vegetable garden; herb courtyard. C17/C18 manor house; marquetry furniture; Dresden china, doll collection etc. Tea Kimmeridge PO (1m), Corfe Castle (5m) or Wareham. *Adm house & garden £1.30 Chd 65p; garden only 65p Chd free. June 3-Sept 9 every Wed. For NGS Sun Aug 30 (2.15-5.30)*

Steeple Manor ✖ (Mr Julian & the Hon Mrs Cotterell) Steeple, 5m SW of Wareham in Isle of Purbeck. Take Swanage rd from Wareham, right in Stoborough. Garden designed by Brenda Colvin 1920's round C16/17 Purbeck Stone Manor House (not open); Restored and replanted by owners since 1980; walls, hedges, enclosed gardens, collection old roses; many interesting and tender plants and shrubs. Parts garden suitable for wheelchairs, which are welcome. *Adm 75p OAPs/Chd 30p (Share to Cancer Relief Macmillan Nurses). Sun July 5 (2-6)*

Stockford & (Mrs A.M. Radclyffe) East Stoke, 3½m W of Wareham on A352. Drive marked Stockford almost opp Black Dog. 3-acres of woodland and walled gardens. Very old thatched house. *Adm 50p Chd 25p. Suns May 3, 24; June 14 (2-7)*

Stour House &❀ (T.S.B. Card Esq) East Street, Blandford. On 1-way system, 100yds short of market place. 2½-acre town garden, half on a romantic island in R. Stour; bulbs; borders; river views. TEAS. *Adm 50p Chd 20p. Suns April 12; Aug 16 (2-6)*

Sunnybrook ✖ (Mr & Mrs A.N. Woodhall) Owermoigne, 6½m E of Dorchester. Take A352, turn to Owermoigne village, thence ¾m towards Crossways, garden on right. ¾-acre delightful spring garden, created and maintained by owners. Truly wild garden with accent on plants which attract butterflies and insects. *Adm 40p (Share to Dorset Hospice Trust). Sun April 26 (2-5.30)*

Sturminster Newton Gardens &✖ off A357 between Blandford and Sherborne take turn opp Nat West Bank. Park in car park or opp St Mary's Church. Walk down Penny St or through churchyard. TEAS. *Combined adm £1 Chd free. Sun July 19 (2-6)*
  Ham Gate (Mr & Mrs H.E.M. Barnes) Informal 2-acre garden with shrubs; trees; lawns running down to R. Stour; pleasant woodland views across water meadows
  Tanyard (Lt-Col & Mrs Peter Molloy) ½-acre walled garden; shrubs, perennials, roses, colourful patio with fuchsias, geraniums and clematis

Tarrant Rushton Gardens &✖ 3m SE of Blandford Forum; B3082 from Blandford to Wimborne, fork left at top of hill; right at T-junc; 1st left to Tarrant Rushton. TEAS Village Hall. Interesting church nearby in village. *Combined adm £1 Chd 50p (Share to Dorset Historic Churches Fund). Sun June 14 (2-5.30)*
  Tarrant Rushton House (Dr B.K. Blount) 3-acre garden with box-edged kitchen garden, brick walls; herbaceous borders; lawns bordering R. Tarrant
  River House (Drs A & P Swan) Adjacent to Tarrant Rushton House (no fence between); stream; willows; shrub roses
  Charlton Cottage (The Hon Penelope Piercy) 400yds S down Village Street. Thatched cottage in ¾-acre on both sides of lane; herbaceous borders, shrubs, views of Tarrant Valley and Downs

73 Traveller's Rest ✖❀ (Miss A. Chapman) Durweston 4m NW of Blandford. Take A350, turn over bridge at traffic lights signed Durweston and Shillingstone; 1st left opp village shop, then up narrow lane for 2m. Informal cottage garden in beautiful chalk downland; many fragrant cottage plants; collection of old roses; pool. Garden featured in BBC South programme 'Come into the Garden' in spring. *Collecting box (Share to Margaret Green Animal Sanctuary, Church Knowle). Suns June 21, 28, Sat, Sun July 25, 26 (2-5)*

Turnpike Cottage ✖❀ (Lys de Bray) 8 Leigh Rd, Wimborne. Listed Georgian thatched cottage 100yds E B3073 (Ex-A31)-A349 junc, itself 200yds E of Minster. (Due to town centre one-way system, by car garden may only be approached from E). Free public car park at rear. The garden is the 'living library' of botanical artist Lys de Bray FLS. ⅙-acre walled town garden on 2 levels; pond, waterfalls, rockery and raised beds, with alpines, old-fashioned perennials, roses, rare plants and foliage contrasts. The owner is a RHS Gold medalist whose botanical drawings and paintings are on permanent exhibition in her working studio which is open throughout year at weekends. *Adm 50p Chd 25p. Garden & Studio open Easter until mid-Oct, Sats &*

Suns (2-6). For NGS Suns May 24, June 21 (2-6)

14 Umbers Hill ✿❀ (Mrs K Bellars) Shaftesbury. Take B3091 (Bimport) descend St John's Hill to small Xrds; right into Breach Lane, bear right into Umbers Hill. Small sloping garden with lovely views of Blackmore Vale; large rockery and many stone sinks with variety of rock plants and alpines; over 50 clematis bloom throughout year; Bonsai, dwarf conifers and shrubs; small greenhouse. Refreshments on request. TEA. *Adm 50p (Share to Cancer Research Campaign, Shaftesbury Branch). By appt only all year (Tel Shaftesbury 3312)*

¶**112 Uplands Road** ✿❀ (Mr & Mrs Alfred Miles) West Moors, 7m N of Bournemouth. Leave A31 at West Moors Garage into Pinehurst Rd, take 1st right into Uplands Rd, then 6th on right. No parking in cul-de-sac. Small garden designed round 42ft long pool with waterfall and rockery. Alpines are a special interest of the owners. TEA. *Adm 40p Chd 10p Suns May 3, June 14; also by appt (Tel Ferndown 893545)*

¶**26 Western Avenue** ✿❀ (Mrs Rita Sheehy) Ensbury Park, Northbourne, parallel with and ½m distant from A347 main Wimborne Rd in north Bournemouth. ¼ acre designed and developed by owner and now a mature setting for conifers, heathers, perennials and summer bedding plants. A special feature is a series of cascading pools in a large rock garden. *Adm 40p Chd 20p (Share to Church Knowle Animal Sanctuary, MGFT). Suns June 28, July 5, 12, 19, 26 (2-6)*

Western Avenue Gardens ✿❀ In Ensbury Park, Northbourne, parallel with and ½m distant from A347 main Wimborne Rd in north Bournemouth. *Combined adm 50p Chd 10p (Share to RSPB). Suns July 5, 12 (2-6)*
> **48** (Mr & Mrs G.R. Frewin) Small plantsman's garden (95ft x 33ft); young dwarf conifers, collection of hostas; summer display of fuschias
> **86** (Mr & Mrs Stanley Hill) Small, well maintained and practical suburban garden (95ft x 33ft); many roses, fruit, vegetables

Wincombe Park ❀ (The Hon & Mrs M.D. Fortescue) 2m N of Shaftesbury. Off A350 signed to Wincombe and Donhead St Mary. Plantsman's garden surrounding house set in parkland; raised beds, shrubs, perennials; view of valley with lake and woods. TEAS. *Adm 75p Chd 25p (Share to Donhead St Mary Churches Appeal). Sun June 7 (2-6)*

¶**Woodlands** ♿ (Mr & Mrs I.Beesley) 36 Glenferness Ave, Talbot Woods, Bournemouth. ¾-acre garden established in 1928 and now in maturity with fine trees. Features inc large lawn, herbaceous borders, rose and fuchsia borders and woodland walks leading to paved heather garden. Dogs on leads. *Adm 50p Chd 25p (Share to Tenovus). Suns Aug 9,16 (2-6)*

CO. DURHAM

Hon County Organiser:
MRS IAN BONAS, Bedburn Hall, Hamsterley, Bishop Auckland DL13 3NN

DATES OF OPENING

REGULAR OPENINGS for dates see text:
RABY CASTLE, Staindrop

MAY Sunday 3
SPRING LODGE, Barnard Castle
MAY Sunday 24
WESTHOLME HALL, Winston
JUNE Sunday 7
EGGLESTON HALL GARDENS, nr Barnard Castle
JUNE Sunday 14
BARNINGHAM PARK, nr Barnard Castle
LOW WALWORTH HALL, nr Darlington
JUNE Sunday 21
BRANCEPETH GARDENS, nr Durham
WILDWOODS, Rowlands Gill
JUNE Sunday 28
ST AIDAN'S COLLEGE, Durham
UNIVERSITY OF DURHAM BOTANIC GARDENS
JULY Sunday 5
WESTHOLME HALL, Winston
JULY Sunday 12
BIDDICK HALL, nr Chester-le-Street
CLEATLAM HALL, Cleatlam
MERRYBENT GARDENS, nr Darlington
JULY Sunday 19
12 & 13 DURHAM ROAD, Middle Herrington
HEADLAM HALL, Gainford
SPRING LODGE, Barnard Castle
JULY Sunday 26
BEDBURN HALL, Hamsterley

DESCRIPTIONS OF GARDENS

Barningham Park ❀ (Sir Anthony Milbank) 10m NW of Richmond. Turn S off A66 at Smallways Garage/A66 Motel. Woodland walks, trees and rock garden. Annual spring sale of wide range of trees and shrubs from the nurseries. House (not shown) built 1710. Home-made TEAS. *Adm 75p Chd free. Sun June 14 (1-5)*

Bedburn Hall ❀ (Ian Bonas Esq) Hamsterley, 9m NW of Bishop Auckland. From A68 at Witton-le-Wear, turn off W to Hamsterley;

turn N out of Hamsterley-Bedburn and down 1m to valley. From Wolsingham on B6293 turn off SE for 3m. Medium-sized garden; terraced garden on S facing hillside with streams; lake; woodland; lawns; rhododendrons; herbaceous borders; roses. TEAS. *Adm 60p Chd 20p. Sun July 26 (2-6)*

◆Biddick Hall (The Viscount Lambton) Lambton Park, 3m NE of Chester-le-Street, W of A182. Large formal gardens; Elizabethan walls; rose and clematis specialities; herbaceous borders; large lawns. TEA Chester-le-Street. *Adm 75p CHd 30p. Sun July 12 (2-6)*

Brancepeth Gardens ᏺ❀ 6m SW of Durham on A690 between villages of Brandon and Willington. An attractive sandstone village consisting of a few Georgian and later houses at the gates of the Castle & Church which originate from late C12. TEAS. *Combined adm 75p OAPs/Chd 30p. Sun June 21 (2-5.30)*
    Quarry Hillᏺ (P. D. Nicholson Esq.) Medium-sized garden of fine proportions; herbaceous borders, shrubs and topiary; vegetable garden
    Duke's Meadow (A. Abel Esq.)
    Also other gardens

Cleatlam Hall ᏺ (Mrs Philip Pease) Cleatlam, W of Darlington. 1½m S of Staindrop on A688. Bus routes to Staindrop only. Small garden with splendid view of Raby Castle and surrounding countryside; roses, shrubs, herbaceous borders and vegetable garden. Attractive Elizabethan house (not shown). TEA. *Adm 60p Chd 30p (Share to British Kidney Patients Assn). Sun July 12 (2-6.30)*

12 & 13 Durham Road ⚘ (Mr & Mrs R.F. Heron; Mr & Mrs A. C. Winfield) Middle Herrington, 3½ SW from centre of Sunderland on N side of A690; 300yds E of Board Inn. 1 acre intensively cultivated, mainly shrubs, roses, fuchsias (greenhouse). TEA. *Adm 50p Chd 25p. Sun July 19 (2-6)*

Eggleston Hall Gardens ⚘❀ (Mrs W.T. Gray) Eggleston, NW of Barnard Castle. Route B6278. Large garden with many unusual plants; large lawns, rhododendrons, greenhouses, mixed borders, fine trees, large extension of kitchen garden (all organically grown). Shop in house open. *Adm 70p Chd 30p. Sun June 7 (2-5.30)*

Headlam Hall (J.H. Robinson Esq) 2m N of Gainford; 5m W of Darlington. 3-acre formal garden with beech and yew hedges; small walled rose garden; troutwater; vegetables; extensive lawns. TEAS. *Adm £1 Chd free. Sun July 19 (2-6)*

Low Walworth Hall ᏺ (Mr & Mrs Peter Edwards) 3½m NW of Darlington. Bus: 12, Darlington-West Auckland; alight at gate (½m drive). Old walled garden; herbaceous borders, shrubs, roses; trout rearing pond. Home-made TEAS. *Adm 75p Chd 25p (Share to Northumbria Historic Churches). Sun June 14 (2-6)*

Merrybent Gardens ᏺ On A67 2½m W of Darlington; within easy reach of Darlington centre, with attractive small gardens overlooking R. Tees. TEAS. *Combined adm 75p Chd 35p. Sun July 12 (2-6)*
    10 Merrybent (Mr & Mrs R. Precious)
    22 Merrybent (Mr & Mrs P. V. Mitford)
    24 Merrybent (Mr & Mrs A. Spence)
    42 Merrybent (Mr & Mrs D. Hunter)
    44 Merrybent (Mr & Mrs B. Bristowe)
    51 Merrybent (Mr & Mrs C. Carvey)
    70 Merrybent (Mr & Mrs A. Hodgson)
    71 Merrybent (Mr & Mrs D.V.Mayne)
    72 Merrybent (Mr & Mrs S.N. Thomas)

◆●Raby Castle ᏺ⚘ (The Rt Hon The Lord Barnard) Staindrop, NW of Darlington. 1m N of Staindrop on A688 Barnard Castle-Bishop Auckland. Buses: 75, 77 Darlington-Barnard Castle; 8 Bishop Auckland-Barnard Castle; alight Staindrop, North Lodge, ¼m. Large walled garden; informal garden with ericas; old yew hedges; shrub and herbaceous borders; roses. Castle also open, principally C14 with alterations made 1765 and mid-C19; fine pictures and furniture. Collection of horse-drawn carriages and fire engines. TEAS at Stables. Special terms for parties on application. *Adm Castle Gardens and carriages £1.80 OAPs Chd £1; Gardens & carriages only 75p OAPs Chd 50p. Sat-Wed, April 18-22, May 6-June 28, July 1- Sept 30 daily (except Sats); also Bank Hol weekends, Sat-Tues (Castle 1-5; garden and park 11-5.30, last adm 4.30); also by appt for parties (Tel Staindrop 60202)*

St Aidan's College ⚘ (By kind permission of the Principal, Miss Irene Hindmarsh) Durham. 1m from City centre. A1050 N towards Durham City; turn W at South End House, where St Aidan's College signposted. St Aidan's College was designed by Sir Basil Spence and the grounds laid out according to a plan by Prof Brian Hackett about 1966. The maturing garden (3-acres) includes shrub planting, rose beds, a laburnum walk and raised beds; several specimen trees of interest inc cedrus libani, have been planted. From the garden there are unequalled views of Durham Cathedral, Durham City and Durham University Observatory, designed by Anthony Salvin. In porter's lodge are available booklet 30p & postcards 10p & 15p. TEAS Hollingside House. *Combined adm with University Botanic Gardens 60p Chd 30p. Sun June 28 (2-5)*

Spring Lodge ᏺ (Col W.I Watson) Barnard Castle. A66 Scotch Corner-Carlisle, turn off 1st right after Greta Bridge coming from E; or left in Bowes from W. Bus:UAS Darlington-

Barnard Castle, alight terminus, ½m, opp the Bowes Museum. Medium-sized garden; young rhododendrons and azaleas (May opening); roses, good variety herbaceous plants. TEA. *Adm 50p Chd 20p. Suns May 3, July 19 (2-6)*

University of Durham Botanic Garden. ₺⚭ 1m from centre of Durham. Turn off A167 (old A1) at Cock O'The North roundabout, direction Durham for 1m; turn right into Hollingside Lane (steep narrow angular junction) which is between Grey and Collingwood Colleges; gardens 600yds on right. The gardens are planted over 18 acres on a beautiful South West facing site, surrounded by mature woodland designated as an area of special scientific interest. Started in 1970 the trees and shrubs are of a pleasing mixture of plants of garden merit in the NE and those of botanical interest. Special features include: representations of major forest types from North America, Himalaya and China. The Cactus house and Tropical house hold many rare and exotic plants as well as some typical food crops. TEAS Hollingside House (by kind permission of Prof & Mrs F. Holliday). *Combined adm St Aidans College 60p OAPs/Chd 30p. Sun June 28 (2-6)*

Westholme Hall (Capt & Mrs J.H. McBain) Winston, W of Darlington. From A67 Darlington-Barnard Castle, nr Winston turn N onto B6274. Medium-sized garden; rhododendrons; flowering shrubs; mixed borders; old fashioned rose garden; lawns. Orchard. Jacobean House (not open). TEA. *Adm 60p Chd 10p (Share to St Andrews Church, Winston). Suns May 24, July 5 (2-6)*

Wildwoods ₺⚭❀ (Mrs Raymond Dobson) Orchard Rd, Rowlands Gill. ¼m W of Rowlands Gill on A694. Medium-sized garden; scree, shrub borders and woodland garden; many foliage plants. TEAS. *Adm 50p Chd 10p. Sun June 21 (2-6)*

DYFED

Hon County Organisers:
North (Ceredigion District)
MRS P.A. LATHAM Garreg Farm, Glandyfi, Machynlleth SY20 8SS
South (Carmarthen, Dinefwr, Pembroke & Preseli Districts)
THE LADY JEAN PHILIPPS, Slebech Hall, Haverfordwest SA 62 4AX
Hon County Treasurer (North):
P.H.B. ROSSER ESQ, Coed-y-Garreg, Glandyfi, Machynlleth

DATES OF OPENING

BY APPOINTMENT ONLY for dates see text:
GARREG FARM, Glandyfi
7 NEW STREET, Talybont
PENRALLT FFYNON, nr Newcastle Emlyn
REGULAR OPENINGS for dates see text:
BLAENGWRFACH ISAF, nr Llandysul
THE DINGLE, nr Haverfordwest
SAUNDERSFOOT BAY LEISURE PARK,

APRIL Sunday 26
THE DINGLE, nr Haverfordwest
MAY Sunday 3
THE HALL, Angle
MAY Sunday 10
SLEBECH HALL, Haverfordwest
MAY Sunday 17
POST HOUSE, nr Whitland
MAY Saturday 23 & Sunday 24
MILLINFORD, nr Haverfordwest
MAY Sunday 31
CWM-PIBAU, Haverfordwest
JUNE Sunday 14
THE DINGLE, nr Haverfordwest
JUNE Saturday 20
CARMAENAU FAWR, Clynderwen
JUNE Sunday 21
CARROG, nr Llanddeiniol
POST HOUSE, nr Whitland
JUNE Sunday 28
THE HALL, Angle
WINLLAN WILDLIFE GARDEN, nr Lampeter
JULY Sunday 12
FOUR ASHES, Cosheston, Pembroke Dock
JULY Sunday 19
THE DINGLE, nr Haverfordwest
POST HOUSE, nr Whitland
AUGUST Sunday 2
BOTANY GARDEN, Aberystwyth
AUGUST Sunday 16
POST HOUSE, nr Whitland
SEPTEMBER Sunday 13
THE DINGLE, nr Haverfordwest

DESCRIPTIONS OF GARDENS

Blaengwrfach Isaf ⚭❀ (Mrs Gail M. Farmer) Bancyffordd, 2m W of Llandysul. Leaving Llandysul on Newcastle Emlyn rd, by Half Moon pub fork left; continue on this road; approx 1½m, after village sign Bancyffordd farm track on right. ¾-acre cottage garden with stream and pond; many climbing and old shrub roses; orchard with bluebells in Spring; large border of plants grown with bees and butterflies in mind; young unusual trees planted for all-year interest; wide variety of herbaceous and foliage plants; alpines in scree and raised beds; lots of herbs and sweet-smelling plants. *Adm 50p Chd free (Share to Greenpeace). Daily May, June, July*

(10.30-5.30); By appt April, Aug, Sept (Tel Llandysul 2604)

Botany Garden ⚡︎❀ (University College of Wales) Penglais Rd, Aberystwyth. From A44 turn on to A487. Car parking on main College campus on opp side of A487. 1m from Aberystwyth. Local buses stop at gate. Medium-large garden; botanical collections of herbaceous plants, shrubs and trees; also nursery and general greenhouse collection. TEA. *Adm 50p Chd 25p. Sun Aug 2 (2-6)*

Carmaenau Fawr ❀ (Mr & Mrs Richard Lewis) Clynderwen between Whitland and Robeston Wathen. Take A478 N off A40 at Penbelwin roundabout; 1st drive on right. Charming small garden around pretty farmhouse; border, shrub roses, lawn shaded by orchard trees. TEAS. *Adm 50p Chd 25p. Sat June 20 (2-7)*

Carrog ⚡︎ (Mr & Mrs Geoffrey Williams) Llanddeiniol, NE of Llanrhystyd. From A487 Aberystwyth-Abaraeron Rd, 6m S of Aberystwyth, 1m beyond Blaenplwyf TV mast. Bus stop (Aberystwyth Aberaeron) 1½m from house. 5 acres in setting of mature trees, reclaimed, replanted and maintained entirely by owners; walled garden; lawns; shrubs; young ornamental trees; pond with bog and water plants; shrub roses. TEAS. *Adm 50p Chd 25p. Sun June 21 (2-6)*

¶Cwm-Pibau (Mrs Duncan Drew) New Moat, Clarbeston Rd. 10m NE of Haverfordwest. 4 acre woodland garden bordered by streams and created since 1978. Mainly young, rare shrubs on a hillside. TEA. *Adm 50p Chd over 6 25p. Sun May 31 (2-6)*

The Dingle ⚡︎❀ (Mrs A.J. Jones) Crundale. Take B4329 from Haverfordwest; turn right opp Boot and Shoe; then 1st right into Dingle Lane. 3 acres plantsman's garden; rose garden; formal beds; scree; herbaceous border; unusual shrubs; water garden; woodland walk. Picturesque and secluded; free roaming peacocks. Nursery adjoining. Tearoom. *Adm 60p Chd 30p (Share to Cancer Research). Daily (except Tues) March-Oct. For NGS Suns April 26, June 14, July 19, Sept 13 (10-6)*

¶Four Ashes (Mr & Mrs R. Hayes) Cosheston, off A477 at Slade Cross opp garden centre to Cosheston village. At top of hill after X-rds turn left down Ridgeway Lane, entrance gates and sign post indicate car parking. 5-7 acre riverside garden planned for year-round beauty. Simple natural layout of trees, rare shrubs, rhododendrons, azaleas, camellias, conifers and heathers; herbaceous plants, ornamental trees and rare flowering shrubs; roses; alpine walks and rockery, ground covering plants, mixed borders. Over 1,000 varieties of trees, shrubs. TEA. *Adm £1 Chd 50p. Sun July 12 (2-6)*

Garreg Farm ❀ (Lt-Col & Mrs P.A. Latham) Glandyfi, 5m W of Machylleth. On A487 to Aberystwyth; white buildings round courtyard, river side of rd on bend immediately after Glandyfi sign. ¾-acre cottage garden; trees and shrubs; tidal stream; courtyard with hanging baskets, troughs, window boxes, wall shrubs. River views. Tea Furnace. *Collecting box. By appt mid-April to Sept 1 (Tel Glandyfi 251)*

The Hall ⚡︎❀ (Maj J.N.S. Allen-Mirehouse) Angle, 9m W of Pembroke on A4320. 10 acres, on banks of Haven Estuary with woodland, shrubs, azaleas and camellias and walled garden. TEAS in garden if fine and beach cafe in village *Adm 50p Chd 25p (Share to Dr Barnados). Suns May 3, June 28 (2.30-5.30)*

Millinford ⚡︎ (Drs B.W. & A.D. Barton) Millin, The Rhos. 3m E of Haverfordwest; on A40 to Carmarthen turn right, signed The Rhos, take turn to Millin, right at Millin Chapel then immediate left over river bridge. 4 acres on bank of Millin Creek, garden begun in 1979 by owner and developing still. Plantsman's garden, varied collection of over 300 trees and shrubs with bulbs and herbaceous plants. TEA. *Adm 50p Chd 25p (Share to NSPCC). Sat, Sun May 23, 24 (11-6.30)*

7 New Street ❀ (Miss M.J. Henry) Talybont, 6m N of Aberystwyth on A487. Garden is at rear of 2nd house past Shell Garage, reached down lane beside garage. Designed in 5 x 25 yds to give wide variety of layout and plants. Conifers, alpines, troughs and pot plants. Teas nearby cafe's. *Collecting box (Share to Cancer Research Campaign). Open all year by appt (Tel Talybont 529)*

Penrallt Ffynnon ⚡︎ (Mr R.D. Lord) Cwm-cou, 3m NW of Newcastle Emlyn. Follow Cwmcou to Cardigan rd (B4570) up long hill for 1¼m; turn right for l50yds; ignore sharp left bend, bear right along narrow lane for 400yds. 4½ acres trees, shrubs with good views, made by owner since 1971 for all year interest; Camellia hedge, daffodils and other bulbs; Japanese and other cherries; eucalypts; sorbus, acer, malus, willow species; shrub roses, rhododendrons; conifers; many other trees, shrubs, herbaceous plants, some uncommon; autumn colour and berries. *Collecting box. Visitors welcome by appt all year (Tel Newcastle Emlyn 710654)*

Post House ⚡︎❀ (Mrs Jo Kenaghan) Cwmbach 6m N of St Clears. From Carmanteu W on A40. Take B4298 through Meidrim; leave by centre lane signed Llanbeidy. Turn right at Xrds signed Blaenwaun; right at Xrds to Cwmbach; garden bottom of hill. From Whitland E on A40, left at Lydean nurseries, right at 3rd Xrds signed Cwmbach. 4 acre valley garden in the making; rhododendrons, azaleas, camellias, unusual trees and shrubs underplanted with hardy orchids, anenomies, trilliums, wild snowdrops, bluebells, etc. Large well stocked pool newly developed bog garden. Old roses, herbaceous plants. Greenhouses and conservatory containing plants from all over the world. TEA. *Adm 50p Chd free (Share to WWF).* △ *Suns May 17, June 21, July 19, Aug 16 (2-6)*

Saundersfoot Bay Leisure Park &❀ (Ian Shuttleworth Esq) Broadfield, Saundersfoot. On B4316, ¾m S from centre of Saundersfoot. Interesting layout of lawns, shrubs and herbaceous borders with many plants of botanical interest in 20-acre modern holiday caravan park. Large rock garden and water feature; laburnum walk. Tea Saundersfoot. *Adm 40p Chd free (Share to Rotary Club of Tenby). April 1 to Oct 30 daily (10-5)*

Slebech Hall &❀ (The Lady Jean Philipps) 6m E of Haverfordwest. From Carmarthen via A40, take 1st turn left after Canaston Bridge, signed The Rhos; drive on left, about ½m with 1 white lodge. Bus: Haverfordwest-Tenby or Haverfordwest-Carmarthen; bus stop 3m. Large garden; fine position on bank of the Cleddau; picturesque ruins of Church of St. John of Jerusalem in garden. TEAS. *Adm 50p Chd 25p. Sun May 10 (2-7)*

¶**Winllan** ⚘❀ (Mr & Mrs Ian Callan) Talsarn. 8m NNW of Lampeter on B4342, Talsarn-Llangeitho Rd. 6 acres wildlife garden with large pond, herb-rich meadow, small woodland and 600 yds of river bank walk. Over 200 species of wildflowers with attendant butterflies, dragonflies and birds. TEAS. *Adm 75p Chd 25p (under 12 free) (Share to The Woodland Trust) Sun June 28 (2-6). Also by appt May to Aug (Tel Aeron 470612)*

ESSEX

Hon County Organiser:
MRS HUGH JOHNSON, Saling Hall, Great Saling, Braintree CM7 5DT
Assistant Hon County Organiser:
MRS CAROLINE DOWLING, 9 London Road, Saffron Walden CB11 4ED
Hon County Treasurer:
ERIC BROWN ESQ, 19 Chichester Road, Saffron Walden

DATES OF OPENING

REGULAR OPENINGS for dates see text:
BETH CHATTO GARDENS, Elmstead Market
HYDE HALL, Rettendon
SALING HALL, Great Saling
VOLPAIA, Hockley

APRIL Sunday 5
THE MAGNOLIAS, Brentwood
APRIL Sunday 12
TERLING PLACE, Terling
THEYDON PRIORY, Theydon Bois
APRIL Easter Sunday 19
BANTAM HOUSE, White Roding
HYDE HALL, Rettendon
THE MAGNOLIAS, Brentwood
APRIL Sunday 26
WETHERBY, South Woodham Ferrers
MAY Sunday 3
THE MAGNOLIAS, Brentwood
MAY Wednesday 6
OLIVERS, nr Colchester
MAY Sunday 10
LE PAVILLON, Newport
OLIVERS, nr Colchester
MAY Wednesday 13
OLIVERS, nr Colchester
MAY Sunday 17
THE MAGNOLIAS, Brentwood
PARK FARM, Great Waltham
WETHERBY, South Woodham Ferrers
MAY Wednesday 20
OLIVERS, nr Colchester
MAY Sunday 24
HYDE HALL, Rettendon
THE MAGNOLIAS, Brentwood
TILTY HILL FARM, nr Dunmow
WARWICK HOUSE, Great Dunmow
MAY Monday 25 (Bank Hol)
PARK FARM, Great Waltham
MAY Wednesday 27
OLIVERS, nr Colchester
MAY Sunday 31
GLAZENWOOD, Bradwell
SALING HALL LODGE, Great Saling
JUNE Sunday 7
THE OLD RECTORY, Sible Hedingham
PARK FARM, Great Waltham
JUNE Sunday 14
FAULKBOURNE HALL, Witham
THE MAGNOLIAS, Brentwood
PARK FARM, Great Waltham
WARWICK HOUSE, Great Dunmow
JUNE Sunday 21
GLAZENWOOD, Bradwell
LE PAVILLON, Newport
PARK FARM, Great Waltham
JUNE Sunday 28
FOLLY FAUNTS HOUSE, Goldhanger
HYDE HALL, Rettendon
THE MAGNOLIAS, Brentwood
WALTONS, Ashdon
JULY Sunday 5
GLAZENWOOD, Bradwell
PARK FARM, Great Waltham
JULY Sunday 12
FEERINGBURY MANOR, Feering
OLIVERS, nr Colchester
PANFIELD HALL, Panfield
TILTY HILL FARM, nr Dunmow
JULY Sunday 19
AMBERDEN HALL, Widdington

JULY Sunday 26
  SALING HALL LODGE, Great Saling
AUGUST Sunday 2
  TERLING PLACE, Terling
AUGUST Sunday 16
  HYDE HALL, Rettendon
SEPTEMBER Sunday 6
  THE MAGNOLIAS, Brentwood
OCTOBER Sunday 18
  THE MAGNOLIAS, Brentwood

DESCRIPTIONS OF GARDENS

¶**Amberden Hall** &% (Mr & Mrs D.Lloyd) Widdington. 6m from Saffron Walden. E off B1383 nr Newport. Follow signs to Mole Hall Wildlife Park. Drive ½m beyond park on right. Medium-sized walled garden with new collection of hardy plants and shrubs. Vegetable garden. TEAS. *Adm 75p OAPs 50p Chd free (Share to St Mary's Church, Widdington). Sun July 19 (2-6)*

Bantam House %❀ (Mrs O.M. Wake) White Roding, 7m NE of Harlow. Take A1060 from Hatfield Heath, turn right in village and right by church. Small garden; spring bulbs in dell. TEAS. *Adm 40p Chd free. Sun April 19 (2-6)*

●**Beth Chatto Gardens** &%❀ (Mrs Beth Chatto) On A133, ¼m E of Elmstead Market. 5 acres of attractively landscaped garden with many unusual plants, shown in wide range of conditions from hot and dry to water garden. Adjacent nursery open. Parties by appt. *Adm 50p Chd free. March 1 to Oct 31, every Mon-Sat but closed Bank Hols (9-5); Nov 1 to March 1 every Mon-Fri but closed Bank Hols (9-4)*

◆**Faulkbourne Hall** %% (Mr & Mrs C.W. Parker) 2m N of Witham, via Chipping Hill towards White Notley. Spacious lawns and parkland surrounding imposing Tudor mansion (not open). Moat; rare lilies. TEA. *Adm £1 OAPs/Chd 50p. Sun June 14 (2-6)*

Feeringbury Manor & (Mr & Mrs G. Coode-Adams) Coggeshall Rd, Feering, 7m SW of Colchester. Take A12 to Kelvedon, in Kelvedon take turn to Feering Village (by Police Stn); after 1½m house on left. New garden on old site with good trees; 2 ponds; ornamental stream. 7 acres with many interesting and unusual plants inc shrub roses and moisture-loving plants. TEAS in aid of Red Cross. *Adm 70p Chd 30p. Sun July 12 (2-6) also open by appt (Tel Coggeshall 61946)*

Folly Faunts House &❀ (Mr & Mrs J.C. Jenkinson) Goldhanger. Between Maldon and Colchester on B1026; signed ½m from both directions. 5-acre garden and grounds, divided into 5 different types of garden, created from scratch since 1962. A large number of unusual and rare trees, shrubs and plants.

Large car park. TEA. *Adm £1 Chd 40p. Sun June 28 (2-6); Coach parties by appt*

Glazenwood &%❀ (Mr & Mrs D. Baer) Bradwell, 4m E of Braintree, ½m S of A120 (follow signs). 7-acre informal garden with roses, shrubs, foliage plants and ground cover, woodland setting; semi-circular avenue of limes; original planting c1805 by Samuel Curtis of the *Botanical Magazine*. Picnic area. TEAS. *Adm £1 OAPs/Chd 50p (Share to Diana Golding Centre, Braintree). Suns May 31; June 21; July 5 (2-6); also by appt to parties*

Hyde Hall &❀ (Hyde Hall Garden Trust) Rettendon, 7m SE of Chelmsford; 6m NE of Wickford. Signed from A130/A132. Flowering trees, shrubs, perennials, roses, bulbs, ornamental greenhouses and ponds; all year round colour. TEAS. *Adm £1 Chd 25p (Share to local charities). Suns April 19, May 24, June 28, Aug 16 (2-7); & Weds April to Oct (11-5); also by appt*

Le Pavillon (H.A.J. Butler Esq) Newport. From A11 turn right at sign N of Newport; from Saffron Walden via B1052 follow signs. Station: Audley End 1½m. Bus: EN 301 Bishop's Stortford-Saffron Walden; alight Coach & Horses, Newport, 1m. Medium-sized garden; herbaceous and shrub borders; roses. *Adm 50p OAPs/Chd 20p. Suns May 10, June 21 (2-7)*

The Magnolias %❀ (Mr & Mrs R.A. Hammond) 18 St John's Ave, Brentwood. From B1023 turn S on A128; after 300 yds right at traffic lights; over railway bridge; St John's Ave 3rd on right. ½-acre well-designed informal garden with particular appeal to plantsmen; good collection spring bulbs; groundcover; trees and shrubs inc maples, rhododendrons, camellias, magnolias and pieris. NCCPG, National collection of Arisaema; koi ponds and other water interests. TEAS. *Adm 50p Chd 25p (Share to Imperial Cancer Research Fund). Suns April 5, 19; May 3, 17, 24; June 14, 28; Sept 6; Oct 18 (10-5); also by appt for parties weekends March-Oct inc (Tel Brentwood 220019)*

The Old Rectory & (Mr & Mrs R.J. Eddis) Sible Hedingham, 3-4m NE of Halstead. From London via A604 through Sible Hedingham; opp Rippers turn left down Rectory Rd; garden 500yds on left. 5 acres; emphasis on flowering/colouring shrubs and trees, mostly young, well labelled; pool and waterside plants; attractive setting for listed Queen Anne/Georgian house (not open). TEA. *Adm £1 Chd 25p (Share to St. Helen's Hospice, Colchester). Sun June 7 (2-6)*

Olivers &%❀ (Mr & Mrs D. Edwards) 3m SW of Colchester. From Colchester via B1022 Maldon rd; at Leather Bottle pub (2m from town centre) turn left into Gosbeck's Rd; right into Oliver's Lane. 20 acres with 3 lakes, fine trees, mature yew hedges and borders; woodland walks with bluebells, azaleas, rhododendrons and old roses; meadow garden; C18 dovecote. Views over Roman River Valley. House (not open) mainly C18. TEA. *Adm £1 Chd 50p. Suns May 10, July 12. All Weds May (2-6);*

¶**Panfield Hall** ♿ (Mr & Mrs R. Newman) 2m Braintree. Turn N off A120 through Great Saling; right (signed Panfield); 1m on right again; 2m through village, right into Hall Rd. 4-acre newly-planted garden surrounding house dated 1520 (not open). Monks stewponds, with collection of wildfowl. Shrub borders, herbaceous borders, many old roses. Parterre. TEAS. *Adm 75p Chd 25p. Sun July 12 (2-6)*

Park Farm ⚘ (Mrs J.E.M. Cowley & Mr D. Bracey) Chatham Hall Lane, Gt Waltham, 5m N of Chelmsford. Take A130 towards Braintree, on Little Waltham bypass left into Chatham Hall Lane, garden on left. New 2-acre garden under construction on farmyard site; old fashioned shrub roses, herbaceous plants, recently planted ponds. TEAS. *Adm 50p Chd 25p. Suns May 17, June 7, 14, 21; July 5. Also Mon May 25 (2-7)*

●**Saling Hall** ♿⚘ (Mr & Mrs H. Johnson) Gt Saling, 6m NW of Braintree. A120; midway between Braintree/Dunmow turn off N at the Saling Oak. 12 acres; walled garden dated 1698; small park with fine trees; extensive new collection of unusual plants with emphasis on trees; water gardens. *Adm £1 Chd free (Share to St James's Church, Gt Saling). Every Wed, Thurs & Fri May 13 - July 31 & Sept 2 - Oct 16 (2-5); also parties by appt*

¶**Saling Hall Lodge**⚘ (Mr & Mrs K. Akers), Great Saling. 6m from Braintree. Turn N off A120 between Braintree and Dunmow at the Saling Oak Pub. Drive at end of village on left, please park in village. Well-designed and maintained ½-acre garden with pond, limestone rock garden, small peat garden, tufa bed and sinks. TEA. *Adm 50p Chd 25p. Suns May 31, July 26 (2-6)*

Terling Place ⚘ (The Lord Rayleigh) Terling, 6m NE of Chelmsford. Spring flowering bulbs and shrubs. Formal garden of clipped yew, roses, many coniferous trees. House built 1772; wings added 1818. Architect: John Johnson. TEAS (in aid of Scouts and Guides). *Adm 50p OAPs/Chd 25p. Suns April 12, Aug 2 (2-5.30)*

Theydon Priory (Sir William Keswick) Theydon Bois, S of Epping. N of A113. Station: Theydon Bois (Tube). Bus: LT 250 Hornchurch-Romford-Epping, alight Coopersale Lane. Bulbs, flowering trees, shrubs, walled garden. *Adm 50p OAPs/Chd 25p. Sun April 12 (2-6)*

Tilty Hill Farm ♿⚘ (Mr & Mrs F.E. Collinson) Duton Hill, 4m N of Dunmow. B184 midway between Dunmow/Thaxted, through Duton Hill village, turn right, follow signs. 2 acres; roses, herbaceous borders, shrubs, conifers, C17 beeboles. Extensive views. Semi-tropical greenhouse. TEA. *Adm 50p Chd free. Suns May 24, July 12 (2-7)*

●**Volpaia** ⚘ (Mr & Mrs D. Fox) 54 Woodlands Rd, Hockley. 2¾m NE of Rayleigh. B1013 Rayleigh-Rochford, turn S from Spa Hotel into Woodlands Rd. On E side of Hockley Woods. 1-acre containing many exotic trees, rhododendrons, camellias besides other shrubs. Carpets of wood anemones and bluebells in spring, underplanting is very diverse esp with woodland, liliaceous plants and ferns. Home of Bullwood Nursery. TEA. *Adm 50p Chd 25p (Share to Essex group of NCCPG). Each Thurs & Sun April May & June (2.30-6)*

Waltons ♿ (E.H. Vestey Esq) Ashdon, 4m NE of Saffron Walden. ½m E of Saffron Walden-Bartlow Rd. Herbaceous borders; roses, flowering shrubs; walled kitchen garden. TEA. *Adm 60p OAPs/Chd 30p. Sun June 28 (2-6)*

Warwick House ♿⚘ (Mr & Mrs B. Creasey) Easton Lodge. 1m N of Gt Dunmow on B184, take rd to Lt Easton, ½m turn left to Easton Lodge, 1¼m to white gates marked Easton Lodge, through these gardens ½m on right. Originally wing of Easton Lodge, home of Countess of Warwick; old house now demolished and gardens of 1½-acres created since 1972 on much of old house site. Features inc C18 dovecote; conservatory; cobbled, herringbone courtyard with fountain; ponds with koi and water fowl. American Air Force Exhibit. TEA. *Adm £1 OAPs/Chd 50p (Share to Local Church Funds, May). Suns May 24, June 14 (2-6)*

¶**Wetherby** (Mr & Mrs C. Hallsworth) 21 Mount Pleasant Rd, South Woodham Ferrers. On B1012 take Hullbridge Rd; pass station and primary school on right; after school take 1st right Pertwee Drive; Mount Pleasant Rd 1st left. Small suburban garden with numerous interesting and uncommon plants. NCCPG National collection of Bergenia Cultivars. TEA. *Adm 40p Chd 20p. Suns April 26, May 17 (10-5)*

THE GLAMORGANS

Hon County Organisers:
(Mid, South and West)
LT-COL & MRS ROY E. HORLEY, St Andrew, High Street, Llandaff, Cardiff CF5 2DX & MRS IVOR PUGH, 1, Court Drive, Llansannor, Cowbridge, CF7 7RX

DATES OF OPENING

BY APPOINTMENT ONLY for dates see text:
COEDARGRAIG, nr Porthcawl

APRIL Sunday 26
DUMGOYNE, Radyr
PENDOYLAN & PETERSON-SUPER-ELY
GARDENS, Cowbridge
MAY Sunday 3
CWMPENNAR GARDENS, nr Mountain
Ash
MAY Sunday 10
EWENNY PRIORY, nr Bridgend
MAY Sunday 17
DUMGOYNE, Radyr
RHOOSE FARM HOUSE, Rhoose, Barry
9 WILLOWBROOK GARDENS, Mayals,
Swansea
MAY Sunday 31
COEDARHYDYGLYN, Cardiff
JUNE Sunday 7
DUMGOYNE, Radyr
4 & 5 THE GROVE, Mumbles
JUNE Sunday 14
HAFOD-Y-COED, St Fagans
JUNE Sunday 21
THE CLOCK HOUSE, Llandaff
JUNE Sunday 28
PENDOYLAN & PETERSTON-SUPER-ELY
GARDENS, Cowbridge
JULY Sunday 5
THE GRANGE, St Brides-super-Ely, nr
Cardiff
JULY Sunday 19
29 MIN-Y-COED, Radyr
RHOOSE FARM HOUSE, Rhoose, Barry
AUGUST Sunday 9
RHOOSE FARM HOUSE, Rhoose, Barry

DESCRIPTIONS OF GARDENS

The Clock House &⋇❀ (Prof & Mrs Bryan Hibbard) Cathedral Close, Llandaff, 2m of Cardiff. Follow signs to Cathedral via A4119. Bus: Cardiff Corp/Western Welsh, alight Maltsters Arms. Small walled garden; fine old trees; wide variety of shrubs and plants; important collection of shrub, species and old roses. TEAS. NT stall. *Adm £1 Chd 50p (Share to Birthright). Sun June 21 (2-6)*

Coedargraig (Sir Leslie Joseph) Newton Porthcawl. Car park. Bus: Bridgend-Porthcawl, alight gates on main rd. Ornamental plants, indigenous shrubs and trees; herbaceous borders; tulips; wall flowers; rock, water and vegetable gardens; aviary; greenhouses. *Adm 50p Chd 30p, Cars 25p. By appt only (Tel Porthcawl 2610)*

Coedarhydyglyn (Sir Cennydd Traherne) 5m W of Cardiff. Bus: Western Welsh, Cardiff-Cowbridge, alight gates. Natural terrain,

pleasant situation; lawns, flowering shrubs, good collection of conifers; Japanese garden, fine trees. TEA. *Adm 40p. Sun May 31 (2.30-6)*

¶**Cwmpennar Gardens** ⋇❀ Mountain Ash 1m. From A4059 turn off at traffic lights; below church; follow sign on church to Cefn-pennar, follow rd uphill through woods for ¾m, bear right sharply uphill before bus shelter, gardens 200 yds. Mixture of formal and informal gardens with some natural woodland in all three of conservation interest. Variety of shrubs, rhododendrons and azaleas, rockeries, shrub roses. Rich in bird life, with nest boxes usually occupied. Walk to adjacent bluebell woods. Gardens high on mountain side in secluded rural surroundings of coal mining valley. TEA. Plant stall and Glamorgan Wildlife Trust Sales stall. *Combined adm £1.50 Chd 50p (Share to St Margarets Church Restoration Fund). Sun May 3 (2-6)*
   Woodview & (Mrs V. Bebb)
   The Cottage (Mr & Mrs H. Jones)
   Ivy Cottage (Mr & Mrs D. Phillips)

Dumgoyne ❀ (Mr & Mrs Hubert Jackson) 90 Heol Isaf, Radyr. A4119 Cardiff-Llantrisant Rd; 2m W of Llandaff turn right on to B4262 for Radyr. Rhondda buses: alight at Radyr turning. Cardiff bus service 71 stops near house. Small, immaculate, Chelsea-inspired garden; large glasshouse with superb collection of Pelagoniums. Adm free (Share to Radyr Chain Voluntary Organisation) *For NGS, special plant sale days Suns April 26, May 17, June 7. (2.30-5)*

Ewenny Priory &⋇❀ (R.C.Q. Picton Turbervill Esq) Ewenny, 2m S of Bridgend. Bus: Bridgend-Ogmore, alight Ewenny Bridge, ½m. Medium-sized garden. Old walled priory dating from 1137 (not open); Priory Church open. NT plant/produce stalls. NO DOGS. TEAS. *Adm 50p. Sun May 10 (2-7)*

The Grange (Mr & Mrs John Cory) St Brides-super-Ely, W of Cardiff. Between A48 and A4119. Medium-sized garden; roses, trees, flowering shrubs. TEA. *Adm 40p Chd free. Sun July 5 (2-7)*

4 & 5 The Grove ⋇❀ (Mrs M.P. Burgess-James) Mumbles, 5m SW of Swansea. In Mumbles, to rear of Queen's Rd at its junc with Langland Rd. Example of how a small hillside garden can be terraced in an ornamental manner, inc a small water garden. Excellent view of Swansea Bay. TEAS. *Adm 50p Chd 20p. Sun June 7 (2-6)*

Hafod-y-Coed &⋇❀ (Mr & Mrs I.P. Griffith) Greenwood Lane, St Fagans, 4m W of Cardiff. Reached via Cathedral Rd or Culverhouse Cross; follow signs to St Fagans. Bus: 32 from Westgate St; alight at Museum Gate. Turn right at triangle between Church and

Craft Shop; 4th house on right. ⅓-acre garden; herbaceous and shrub borders, roses and rockery. In picturesque conservation village; adjacent to Welsh Folk Museum. TEAS. *Adm 75p Chd 25p (Share to St Marys Church). Sun June 14 (2.30-6)*

29 Min-y-Coed ⚘❀ (Mr & Mrs J.H. Taylor) Radyr, 6m from Cardiff. On A4119 2m W of Llandaff turn right on B4262 towards Morganstown. From M4 junc 32 on A470 to Taffs Well turn right, then right to B4262 for Radyr. Small hillside terraced informal garden with year round colour. *Adm 50p Chd free (Share to Radyr Chain Voluntary Organisation). Sun July 19 (2-5.30)*

¶Pendoylan & Peterston-super-Ely Gardens ⚘ Cowbridge 4½m. A48 Cardiff-Cowbridge. From Cardiff turn right at Sycamore Cross (½-way between St Nicholas and Bonvilston) to Peterston-super-Ely; take 2nd left to Pendoylan, gardens ½m on left and ¾m on right. TEA Trehedyn House. *Combined adm 50p Chd 20p. Suns Apr 26, June 28 (2-6)*
> **Ffynnon Deilo** (Mr & Mrs John Lloyd) Pendoylan. Small cottage garden with fish pond and Holy well; interesting plants. *(Share to RNLI)*
> **Trehedyn House** (Mr & Mrs D.I. Williams) Peterston-Super-Ely. ½-acre informal garden, lawn; newly planted mixed border and old shrub roses. Spring interest with walks through 1½ acre paddock with established and newly planted trees. Daffodils

Rhoose Farm House (Prof A.L. Cochrane) Rhoose, Barry. Buses from Cardiff, Barry and Llantwit Major to Rhoose. B4265 Barry-Bridgend rd. Large informal, well labelled garden; shrubs, roses, herbaceous plants and important scree garden; C17 troughs with alpines; aviary with pheasants. Sculpture by Hepworth, and Nicholas (whose gallery may be seen). House, 2 rooms shown. TEA. *Adm 50p Chd 25p (Share to Rhoose & Penmark Civic Trust). Suns May 17, July 19, Aug 9 (2.30-5.30); also by appt April to Oct*

9 Willowbrook Gardens ♿⚘ (Dr & Mrs Gallagher) Mayals, 4m W of Swansea on A4067 (Mumbles) rd to Blackpill; take B4436 (Mayals) rd; 1st right leads to Westport Ave along W boundary of Clyne Park; 1st left into cul-de-sac. ½-acre informal garden designed to give natural effect with balance of form and colour between various areas linked by lawns; unusual trees suited to small suburban garden, esp conifers and maples; rock and water garden. TEAS. *Adm 60p Chd 30p. Sun May 17 (2-6)*

GLOUCESTERSHIRE

Hon County Organiser:
MRS ANTHONY SANFORD, Poulton Manor, Cirencester
Assistant Hon County Organisers:
GUY ACLOQUE ESQ, Alderley Grange, Wotton-under-Edge
MRS JOHN BEATSON-HIRD, Oldwell House, Ashton-under-Hill, nr Evesham
MRS CLIVE DAVIES, 56 All Saint's Rd, Cheltenham
MRS J.F. MOORE, Grange Cottage, Blockley, Moreton-in-Marsh
MRS RICHARD PILE, Ampney Knowle nr Cirencester
MR & MRS WITOLD WONDRAUSCH, The New Inn, Poulton, Cirencester
Hon County Auditor:
H.J.SHAVE Esq, ACCA (Brading & Co) 31 Castle St, Circencester

DATES OF OPENING

BY APPOINTMENT ONLY for dates see text:
  8 HYATTS WAY, Bishops Cleeve
  SALTWOOD, Moreton-in-Marsh
REGULAR OPENINGS for dates see text:
  BARNSLEY HOUSE, nr Cirencester
  HUNTS COURT, nr Dursley
  KIFTSGATE COURT, Chipping Campden
  LYDNEY PARK, Lydney
  MISARDEN PARK, nr Stroud
  THE OLD MANOR, Twyning
  PAINSWICK ROCOCO GARDEN, Painswick
  RODMARTON MANOR, nr Cirencester
  RYELANDS HOUSE, Taynton
  SEZINCOTE, nr Moreton-in-Marsh
  STANWAY HOUSE, Winchcombe
  TREVI, Hartpury, nr Gloucester
  YEW TREE COTTAGE, Ampney St Mary

FEBRUARY Sunday 22
  PAINSWICK ROCOCO GARDEN, Painswick
MARCH Sunday 1
  PAINSWICK ROCOCO GARDEN, Painswick
MARCH Saturday 14
  THE HEATHERS, Newent
MARCH Sunday 15
  ‡DERHAMS HOUSE, Minchinhampton
  THE HEATHERS, Newent
  ‡ST FRANCIS, Minchinhampton
MARCH Sunday 22
  ‡DERHAMS HOUSE, Minchinhampton
  ‡ST FRANCIS, Minchinhampton
MARCH Sunday 29
  SUDELEY CASTLE, Winchcombe
APRIL Thursday 2
  TREVI, Hartpury, nr Gloucester
APRIL Sunday 5
  NEWARK PARK, nr Wotton-u-Edge
  RYELANDS HOUSE, Taynton

APRIL Sunday 12
BEVERSTON CASTLE, nr Tetbury
CLOVER HOUSE, Winson
LOWER CHURN, South Cerney
RODMARTON MANOR, nr Cirencester
RYELANDS HOUSE, Taynton
APRIL Monday 13
BEVERSTON CASTLE, nr Tetbury
APRIL Thursday 16
TREVI, Hartpury, nr Gloucester
APRIL Saturday 18
THE HEATHERS, Newent
APRIL Easter Sunday 19
FOSSEBRIDGE MANOR, nr Northleach
THE HEATHERS, Newent
HODGES BARN, Shipton Moyne
RYELANDS HOUSE, Taynton
STANWAY HOUSE, Winchcombe
WILLERSEY HOUSE, nr Broadway
YEW TREE HOUSE, Ampney St Mary
APRIL Easter Monday 20
RYELANDS HOUSE, Taynton
SUDELEY HILL GARDENS (Boilingwell only)
WILLERSEY HOUSE, nr Broadway
YEW TREE HOUSE, Ampney St Mary
APRIL Saturday 25
EASTINGTON GARDENS
APRIL Sunday 26
ABBOTSWOOD, Stow-on-Wold
AMPNEY PARK, nr Cirencester
‡BROADWELL & KENEOT GARDENS (see Oxon)
‡CHURCH HOUSE, Lechlade
EASTINGTON GARDENS
PINBURY PARK, nr Cirencester
RYELANDS HOUSE, Taynton
‡SOUTHROP GARDENS, nr Lechlade
MAY Saturday 2
THE HEATHERS, Newent
MAY Sunday 3
BARNSLEY HOUSE, nr Cirencester
BLOCKLEY GARDENS
EASTINGTON GARDENS (Bank Cottage & Middle End Only)
THE HEATHERS, Newent
HIDCOTE MANOR GARDEN, nr Chipping Campden
‡KITSBURY ORCHARD, Oddington
LITTLE BARROW, Moreton-in-Marsh
MISARDEN PARK, nr Stroud
‡ODDINGTON GARDENS
RYELANDS HOUSE, Taynton
SNOWSHILL MANOR, Broadway
MAY Monday 4 (Bank Hol)
THE HEATHERS, Newent
LITTLE BARROW, Moreton-in-Marsh
‡ODDINGTON GARDENS
THE OLD RECTORY, Stanton
RYELANDS HOUSE, Taynton
SEZINCOTE, nr Moreton-in-Marsh
MAY Thursday 7
TREVI, Hartpury, nr Gloucester
MAY Sunday 10
ABBOTSWOOD, Stow-on-Wold
‡BEAUCHIEF, Hartpury

LYDNEY PARK, Lydney
PRIORS MESNE, nr Aylburton Lydney
153 THRUPP LANE, Stroud
‡TREVI, Hartpury, nr Gloucester
MAY Saturday 16
KIFTSGATE COURT, Chipping Campden
MAY Sunday 17
GLOUCESTERSHIRE COLLEGE OF AGRICULTURE, nr Gloucestser
RODMARTON MANOR, nr Cirencester
YEW TREE COTTAGE, Ampney St Mary
MAY Thursday 21
TREVI, Hartpury, nr Gloucester
MAY Saturday 23
THE HEATHERS, Newent
MAY Sunday 24
BROMESBERROW PLACE, Ledbury
THE CHESTNUTS, Minchinhampton
EASTINGTON GARDENS
THE HEATHERS, Newent
MISARDEN PARK, nr Stroud
NYMPSFIELD GARDENS
WESTONBIRT SCHOOL, nr Tetbury
MAY Monday 25 (Bank Hol)
COLESBOURNE PARK, nr Cheltenham
EASTINGTON GARDENS
THE HEATHERS, Newent
MAY Sunday 31
BROMESBERROW PLACE, Ledbury
SUDELEY HILL GARDENS (Boilingwell only)
JUNE Thursday 4
TREVI, Hartpury, nr Gloucester
JUNE Saturday 6
CHELTENHAM GARDENS
THE OLD MANOR, Twyning
JUNE Sunday 7
BARNSLEY HOUSE, nr Cirencester
CHELTENHAM GARDENS
EASTINGTON GARDENS (Bank Cottage & Middle End Only)
RODMARTON MANOR, nr Cirencester
RYELANDS HOUSE, Taynton
SOUTHROP GARDENS, nr Lechlade
YEW TREE COTTAGE, Ampney St Mary
JUNE Sunday 14
ALDERLEY GRANGE, nr Wotton-u-Edge
AMPNEY PARK, nr Cirencester
BLISS'S COTTAGE, Lower Chedworth
CLOVER HOUSE, Winson
7 THE CONVENT, Church Westcote
HIDCOTE VALE, nr Chipping Campden
HUNTS COURT, nr Dursley
RYELANDS HOUSE, Taynton
STANWAY HOUSE, Winchcombe
WITCOMBE GARDENS, Great Witcombe
JUNE Thursday 18
TREVI, Hartpury, nr Gloucester
JUNE Saturday 20
AMBERLEY HOUSE, Hasfield
JUNE Sunday 21
ADLESTROP GARDENS, nr Stow-on-Wold
ALDERLEY GRANGE, nr Wotton-u-Edge
CECILY HILL GARDENS, Cirencester (38 only)

COMBEND MANOR, Elkstone
GREAT RISSINGTON MANOR,
 Bourton-on-Water
HUNTS COURT, nr Dursley
POULTON GARDENS, Cirencester
STANCOMBE PARK, Dursley
SUDELEY HILL GARDENS (Boilingwell
 only)
JUNE Saturday 27
BROADWELL GARDENS
BURNT NORTON, Chipping Campden
KIFTSGATE COURT, Chipping Campden
JUNE Sunday 28
ALDERLEY GRANGE, nr Wotton-u-Edge
ASHLEY MANOR, Tetbury
BLOCKLEY GARDENS
BROADWELL GARDENS
BLISS'S COTTAGE, Lower Chedworth
BURNT NORTON, Chipping Campden
EWEN GARDENS, Cirencester
HODGES BARN, Shipton Moyne
HUNTS COURT, nr Dursley
KINGSMEAD, Didmarton
SEZINCOTE, Moreton-in-Marsh
STANTON, nr Broadway
STOWELL PARK, nr Northleach
TODENHAM GARDENS,
 Moreton-in-Marsh
UPTON HOUSE, nr Tetbury
YEW TREE COTTAGE, Ampney
JULY Thursday 2
TREVI, Hartpury, nr Gloucester
JULY Sunday 5
ALDERLEY GRANGE, nr Wotton-u-Edge
BARNSLEY HOUSE, nr Cirencester
BEVERSTON CASTLE, nr Tetbury
BLEDINGTON VILLAGE GARDENS
CECILY HILL GARDENS, Cirencester, (38
 only)·
CHURCH FARM, Cirencester
CHURCH FIELDS, Rodborough
EASTINGTON GARDENS (Bank Cottage &
 Middle End Only)
EYFORD HOUSE, Upper Slaughter
HUNTS COURT, nr Dursley
MALT HOUSE COTTAGE, Icomb
MISARDEN PARK, nr Stroud
NYMPSFIELD GARDENS
20 ST PETER'S ROAD, Cirencester
JULY Monday 6
BEVERSTON CASTLE, nr Tetbury
JULY Sunday 12
ADSETT COURT, Westbury-on-Severn
BISLEY GARDENS, nr Stroud
BRACKENBURY, Coombe
BROAD CAMPDEN GARDENS
HUNTS COURT, nr Dursley
KEMBLE GARDENS, nr Cirencester
LITTLE BARROW, Moreton-in-Marsh
‡OLD POST OFFICE (see Oxon)
OXWOLD HOUSE, nr Cirencester
ROOKWOODS, Oakridge, nr Stroud
SUDELEY HILL GARDENS
SYDENHAMS, nr Bisley
TREVI, Hartpury, nr Gloucester

WILLERSEY HOUSE, nr Broadway
‡WINDY RIDGE, nr Moreton-in-Marsh
JULY Monday 13
WILLERSEY HOUSE, nr Broadway
JULY Thursday 16
TREVI, Hartpury, nr Gloucester
JULY Sunday 19
BOURTON HOUSE, Bourton-on-Hill
RODMARTON MANOR, nr Cirencester
RYELANDS HOUSE, Taynton
SHERBORNE PARK, Sherborne
JULY Sunday 26
CECILY HILL GARDENS, Cirencester
‡DERHAMS HOUSE, Minchinhampton
QUENINGTON GARDENS, nr Cirencester
RYELANDS HOUSE, Taynton
‡ST FRANCIS, Minchinhampton
UPTON HOUSE, nr Tetbury
JULY Monday 27
‡DERHAMS HOUSE, Minchinhampton
‡ST FRANCIS, Minchinhampton
AUGUST Sunday 2
CIRENCESTER PARK
COMBEND MANOR, Elkstone
EASTINGTON GARDENS (Bank Cottage
 and Middle End Only)
‡ODDINGTON GARDENS, Oddington
WESTONBIRT SCHOOL, nr Tetbury
AUGUST Thursday 6
TREVI, Hartpury, nr Gloucester
AUGUST Saturday 15
BURNT NORTON, Chipping Campden
AUGUST Sunday 16
BOURTON HOUSE, Bourton-on-Hill
BURNT NORTON, Chipping Campden
CECILY HILL GARDENS, Cirencester
20 ST PETER'S ROAD, Cirencester (38 &
 42)
AUGUST Thursday 20
TREVI, Hartpury, nr Gloucester
AUGUST Saturday 22
KIFTSGATE COURT, Chipping Campden
AUGUST Sunday 23
SAPPERTON GARDENS, nr Cirencester
SUDELEY HILL GARDENS (Boilingwell
 only)
AUGUST Sunday 30
COTSWOLD FARM, Cirencester
EASTINGTON GARDENS
GREAT RISSINGTON MANOR, nr
 Bourton-on-Water
RYELANDS HOUSE, Taynton
YEW TREE COTTAGE, Ampney St Mary
AUGUST Monday 31 (Bank Hol)
COTSWOLD FARM, nr Cirencester
EASTINGTON GARDENS
GREAT RISSINGTON MANOR, nr
 Bourton-on-Water
RYELANDS HOUSE, Taynton
SEPTEMBER Thursday 3
TREVI, Hartpury, nr Gloucester
SEPTEMBER Friday 4
BERKELEY CASTLE, Berkeley
SEPTEMBER Sunday 6
CECILY HILL GARDENS, Cirencester (38 &
 42)

EASTINGTON GARDENS, (Bank Cottage & Middle End Only)
‡HYAM, Minchinhampton
‡THE LAMMAS, Minchinhampton
20 ST PETER'S ROAD, Cirencester
WESTONBIRT SCHOOL, nr Tetbury
SEPTEMBER Saturday 12
THE HEATHERS, Newent
SEPTEMBER Sunday 13
BOURTON HOUSE, Bourton-on-Hill
THE HEATHERS, Newent
SEPTEMBER Thursday 17
TREVI, Hartpury, nr Gloucester
SEPTEMBER Sunday 20
SUDELEY HILL GARDENS (Boilingwell only)
SEPTEMBER Sunday 27
NEWARK PARK, nr Wotton-u-Edge
OCTOBER Sunday 4
ICOMB PLACE, nr Stow-on-Wold
OCTOBER Saturday 24 & Sunday 25
THE HEATHERS, Newent

DESCRIPTIONS OF GARDENS

◆**Abbotswood** & (Dikler Farming Co) 1m W of Stow-on-the-Wold. Bus: Pulhams from Cheltenham, alight Lower Swell ¼m. Beautiful, extensive heather and stream gardens; massed plantings of spring bulbs and flowers; rhododendrons, flowering shrubs, specimen trees; extensive herbaceous borders, roses, formal gardens; fine example of garden landscape. Buses not allowed in grounds. TEA. Car park free. *Adm £1 Chd 50p. Suns April 26, May 10 (2-6)*

Adlestrop Gardens ✿❀ 3m E of Stow-on-the-Wold, off A436. Garden stalls. TEAS. A group of gardens in the village may be visited. *Combined adm 80p Chd free (Share to St Mary Magdalene Church, Adlestrop). Sun June 21 (2-6)*

Adsett Court &✿❀ (Adsett Court Assn) Westbury on Severn, 8m SW of Gloucester. 1m off A38 Gloucester-Chepstow route turn towards Northwood Green. 3¼-acre garden; formal herbaceous borders enclosed by series of hedges; large lawns and mature trees. TEAS. *Adm 75p Chd 25p. Sun July 12 (2-5.30); also by appt May 1 to Aug 31*

Alderley Grange &✿ (Mr Guy & the Hon Mrs Acloque) Alderley, 2m S of Wotton-under-Edge. Turn NW off A46, Bath-Stroud Rd, at Dunkirk (2m equidistant Hawkesbury Upton/Wotton-under-Edge). Walled garden with fine trees, roses; herb gardens and aromatic plants. *Adm 70p Chd free. Suns June 14, 21, 28; July 5 (2-6)*

Amberley House & (Mrs M. Brooksbank) Hasfield 8m N of Gloucester, S of Tewkesbury. 1 acre; roses, shrubs, lawns. TEAS. *Adm (inc Tea) £1 Chd 50p. Sat June 20 (2-5.30)*

Ampney Park &✿ (Mr & Mrs Timothy Eaton) On A417 3m E of Cirencester. Large terraced gardens with fine trees, mature beech walk, many naturalised bulbs, herbaceous borders, trout lake, informal waterside walks. Variety of ducks. *Adm £1 Chd free. Suns April 26, June 14 (2-6)*

Ashley Manor ✿ (Mr & Mrs M.J. Hoskins) 3m NE of Tetbury on A433; turn right through Culkerton to Ashley. Old garden altered since 1982 with new pond garden; mature yew hedges, collection of clematis, climbing and shrub roses, herbaceous border; terrace of herbs; kitchen garden, typical Cotswold pigeon house and tithe barn. Manor house C15 and early C18 (not open); TEAS. *Adm £1 Chd free (Share to Ashley Church). Sun June 28 (2-6)*

Barnsley House &❀ (Mrs David Verey) 4m. NE of Cirencester on A433. Old garden, altered since 1962; interesting collection of shrubs and trees; ground cover; herbaceous borders; pond garden; laburnum walk; knot and herb gardens; formal kitchen garden; C18 summer houses. C17 house (not open). TEAS in village (parties by appt Tel Bibury 406). *Adm £1.50 OAPs £1 Chd free (no charge Dec-Feb). Daily (10-6) ex Sats & Suns when by appt only (Tel Bibury 281). For NGS (Share to National Star Centre for Disabled Youth) Suns May 3, June 7, July 5 (2-6)*

◆**Berkeley Castle** ✿ (R.J.G. Berkeley Esq) Berkeley 1½m W of A38 midway between Bristol and Gloucester. From M5 Junc 13 or 14. Garden 200 yds from Castle car park. 6 acres; mainly terraced garden with variety of interesting shrubs and climbers; lawns; lily pond. Large free-flight "live" butterfly house. TEAS. *Adm Castle and garden £2.50 Chd £1.20. Fri Sept 4 (2-6)*

Beverston Castle &❀ (Maj & Mrs L. Rook) W of Tetbury on A4135. Herbaceous and shrub borders. C17 house attached to C12-15 castle ruin. TEAS (Suns only). *Adm 60p Chd free (Share to RDA) Suns, Mons April 12, 13, July 5, 6 (2-6)*

Bisley Gardens & 4m NE of Stroud. TEAS ice-cream at Overcourt. *Adm each garden 50p Chd 25p Sun July 12 (2-5)*
  Jaynes Court (Marquis & Marchioness of Reading). Large garden with lawns, herbaceous borders, shrubs and kitchen garden. C18 dovecote and cockpit
  The Old Mansion (Mr & Mrs Anthony Abrahams) 3-acres with lawns, shrubs and herbaceous planting; also kitchen garden
  Overcourt (Mrs J.D. Cowen) Lawns; formal rose garden mediaeval and Elizabethan house (not open) next to Church. C18 gazebo

Bledington Village Gardens &✿ 4½m SE of Stow-on-the-Wold via A436 towards Chipping Norton; after 1m fork right on to B4450. A group of small gardens ranging from 'cottage' to 'fruit and vegetables', 1 with riverside planting. Some gardens suitable for wheelchairs. Fine C13 Church; attractive village green (with swings and seesaws). Lunch Kings Head. TEA. *Adm 80p Chd 20p. Sun July 5 (2-6)*

¶**Bliss's Cottage** &✗ (Mr & Mrs William McWilliam) Lower Chedworth 7m from Cirencester. From A429 turn left for Chedworth, ½m turn right for Lower Chedworth, then ¼m turn right, garden 200 yds on left. ½-acre garden on several levels adjoining small C18 cottage. Upper garden suitable for wheelchairs. Planted for flower and foliage colour. Small spring garden; species, C19 and modern roses for flower continuity; shrubs, herbaceous border; C19 and modern pinks; small pond and waterside planting. *Adm 50p Chd free. Suns June 14, 28 (2-6)*

Blockley Gardens &✗✿ NW of Moreton-in-Marsh. A44 Moreton-Broadway; turning E. TEAS. *Combined Adm £1 or 25p per garden Chd 25p. (Share to GTNC May; Blockley Church, June). Suns May 3, June 28 (2-6)*
    Broughton Cottage (Mr & Mrs R.A. Smeeton) Small garden on steep slope overlooking village
    The Garage (Mr & Mrs Stuart-Turner) Small garden on a steep slope *(Open June 28 only)*
    Grange Cottage (Mrs J. Moore) Small garden with unusual plants
    Malvern Mill (Robert Cook Esq) Converted Mill with pond and stream; 2 acres inc orchard
    The Old Mill (Dr & Mrs Shackleton-Bailey) garden with millpond, stream, bulbs, flowers and shrubs
    The Old Quarry (Mr & Mrs A.T. Hesmondhalgh) 1-acre landscaped garden in old quarry with grass walks and lovely views
    Paxton House (Mr & Mrs Peter Cator) Walled garden on different levels; unusual plants, spring bulbs, shrub roses
    Rock Cottage (Mr P. Litchfield & Mr T. Hudson) Joanna Southcot's house, terraced garden recently restored. *June 28 only*

¶**Bourton House** &✗ (Mr & Mrs Paice) Bourton-on-the-Hill 2m W of Moreton-in-Marsh on A44. 3 acres; herbaceous borders and formal gardens. 1570 tythe barn. TEAS. *Adm 90p Chd free. Suns July 19, Aug 16, Sept 13 (2-6)*

Brackenbury ✿ (Mr & Mrs Peter Heaton) Coombe, 1m N of Wotton-under-Edge. From Wotton Church ½m on on Stroud Rd (B4058) turn right (signed Coombe); from Stroud left off B4058, 300yds past Wotton-under-Edge

sign; house 300yds on right. ⅔-acre terraced plantsman's garden with lawns; mixed borders; 230 different hardy perennials and 120 shrubs; still developing. TEAS. *Adm 50p Chd free (Share to The Wotton-under-Edge & District Community Recreational Trust). Sun July 12 (2-6). Also parties by appt May-Sept (Tel Dursley 842238)*

Broad Campden Gardens Between Chipping Campden and Moreton-in-Marsh. TEAS by WI at Broad Campden Village Hall. *Combined adm £1 or 25p each garden. Sun July 12 (2-6)*
    Briar Hill Cottage & (Mr & Mrs F.A. Smith) ¾ acre; herbaceous, shrubs, roses
    Briar Hill House & (Mr & Mrs Geoffrey Ellerton) 1½ acres, herbaceous, shrubs
    High Barn ✿ (Hon C.T.H. & Mrs Law) Medium-sized garden with shrubs, shrub roses and herbaceous borders
    The Malt House (Mr & Mrs John Robinson) Sheltered garden with small stream, being gradually replanted with shrubs from herbaceous for simplified management
    ¶**Primrose Cottage** (Mr & Mrs K. Harper) Small cottage garden
    ¶**Sharcomb Furlong** (Mr & Mrs Basil Hasberry) ¾ acre; wide range of shrubs, shrub roses and trees
    ¶**Withy Bank** (Mr & Mrs Allen) ½ acre; acers and shrubs
    Wold Cottage & (Dr K.C. Hutchin) Small garden, roses and herbaceous

Broadwell Gardens 1m N of Stow-on-the-Wold off A429. TEAS by WI. *Adm 75p Chd 25p. Sat, Sun June 27, 28 (2-6)*
    Blundells & (Mr & Mrs Joe Elliott) Medium-sized garden with large variety of hardy plants and alpines; trees, shrubs, herbaceous borders, roses, lilies; 15 plus old stone sinks and troughs planted with alpines

Bromesberrow Place ✿ (Miss D.G. Albright) 4m S Ledbury 12m N of Gloucester; adjacent to M50 on A417. 6 acres; flowering trees and shrubs, rhododendrons, azaleas, pieris; nurseries, fuchsias, pelagoniums, house plants, one of the finest collections of orchids in Britain. TEAS. *Adm 50p Chd 10p (Share to Glos Historic Churches Restoration Fund). Suns May 24, 31 (2-6)*

Broughton Poggs & Filkins Gardens see Oxfordshire

Burnt Norton (Viscount Sandon) 1½m N of Chipping Campden on rd to Mickleton; left into farm lane as rd goes downhill; then through wood for ½m. 16 acres; part formal but mostly wooded garden on Cotswold escarpment. Subject of T.S. Elliot's 'Burnt Norton' quartet. House (not open). TEAS. *Adm 60p Chd 25p (Share to GRBS, MSS Trust). Sats, Suns June 27, 28; Aug 15, 16 (2-6)*

Cecily Hill Gardens ✗ Cirencester. On W side of Cirencester nr gates into Park. Tea The Mad Hatter, Castle Street. *Combined adm £1 Chd free. Sun July 26 (2-6)*
> **38 Cecily Hill** ❀ (Revd & Mrs John Beck) Garden on 2 levels 450 different perennials, inc. named delphiniums; *also open Suns June 21, July 5, Aug 16, Sept 6. Adm 40p*
> **42 Cecily Hill** ൠ (Mr & Mrs David Eastall) Medium-sized town garden with good walls; clematis a speciality; roses, herbaceous border; shrubs, pond, rock garden. *Also open Aug 16, Sept 6*
> **Cecily Hill House** (Mr & Mrs Rupert de Zoete) Walled town garden with tranquil atmosphere; herbaceous and shrub borders; small ornamental kitchen garden. *Open July 26 only*, TEAS by WI
> **44 Cecily Hill** Exhibition of Botanical Pictures & China by Annette Firth NDD, SBA. *Adm 75p inc Nos 38 & 42. Suns Aug 16, Sept 6*

Cheltenham Gardens ✗ *Combined Adm 60p. Sat, Sun June 6, 7 (2-6)*
> **56 All Saints Road** (Mr & Mrs C. Davies) nr Pitville Circus off Prestbury Rd. Medium-sized town garden still being developed; mixed borders, etc. TEA
> **Raglan** (Mr & Mrs Roger Turner) 7 All Saints Villas Rd. Walled town garden (75ft x 35ft); crammed with plants; many unusual perennials, inc euphorbias and cranesbill geraniums. RHS Journal Apr '85

The Chestnuts ✗❀ (Mr & Mrs E.H. Gwynn) Minchinhampton. From Nailsworth by Avening rd left Weighbridge Inn ¼m up hill. From Minchinhampton 1m via New Rd or Well Hill. ⅔-acre walled garden; shrubs; bulbs; roses; rock garden; pool garden. ⅔-acre field, planted since 1972 with wide variety of trees and shrubs inc many sorbus, species and shrub roses. *Adm 60p Chd free (Share to GTNC). Sun May 24 (2-6)*

Church Farm ✗ (Mr & Mrs J.A. Paterson-Morgan) Duntisbourne Abbots, through Duntisbourne Valley. 12m S of Gloucester on A417 turn W for 1m; or from Cirencester fork left via Daglingworth through fine scenery. Lovely cluster of Cotswold villages of historic interest. In Duntisbourne Rous, Saxon church with crypt, much loved by John Betjeman. Medium-sized terraced garden with rose beds and flowering shrubs; recently relandscaped to form separate inter-communicating gardens. Listed house (not shown); fine views overlooking Duntisbourne Valley. TEAS (3.30-5.30) by Duntisbourne Abbots in Youth Hostel. *Adm 50p Chd 25p (Share to CPRE). Sun July 5 (2-6)*

¶**Churchfields** ✗❀ (Lt-Col & Mrs R.H.W. Kirkby) Rodborough ½m S of Stroud off Walkly Hill, just below church. 1½ acres hillside garden in the making; interesting trees and shrubs; herbaceous borders. TEA. *Adm 50p Chd 20p. Sun July 5 (2-5)*

Church House (Mr & Mrs M. Boustead) Lechlade. 2 mins walk from Market Place through churchyard. Medium-sized garden; early C18 gazebo and summerhouse of architectural interest. Wharf garden. Tea Lechlade. *Adm 50p. Sun April 26 (2-6)*

♦**Cirencester Park** ൠ (Earl & Countess Bathurst) Cirencester. From town centre ask for the 'Mansion' (not 'Park'), 200 yds. Home of Bathurst family since 1695. Garden and park laid out and planted by 1st Earl starting in 1714. Yew hedge is world's highest hedge; trees, shrubs, flowers, lawns. Early C18 follies in park. TEA. *Adm 50p Chd 25p. Sun Aug 2 (2-6)*

¶**Clover House** (Cdr & Mrs Kenneth Kemble) Winson 6½m from Cirencester. Take A433 Cirencester-Burford rd, then N to Winson just W of Bibury. 4 acres; spring blossom and bulbs; lawns, mixed borders and roses. R. Coln through garden. *Adm 50p Chd 25p. Suns April 12 June 14 (2-6)*

♦**Colesbourne Park** ✗ (Mr & Mrs H.W.G. Elwes) Halfway between Cheltenham and Cirencester on A435. 25 acres of woodland and parkland; arboretum laid out by arboriculturalist, Henry Elwes, FRS 1890-1920 inc several very rare specimens. Conducted tours by H.W.G. Elwes 2pm and 4pm only. TEAS. *Adm £1.50 Chd free. Mon May 25 (2 and 4)*

Combend Manor ✗❀ (Mr & Mrs Noel Gibbs) Elkstone. On A417 7m N of Cirencester turn right to Elkstone immediately right through pillars 1m. 3-acre mature garden, partly laid out by Gertrude Jekyll; arboretum; water garden; currently being restored with parts of Jekyll designs being reintroduced. *Adm £1.50 OAP £1 Chd 50p (Share to Elkstone Parish Church). Suns June 21, Aug 2 (2-6)*

7 The Convent ✗❀ (Mrs V. Murgatroyd) Church Westcote. 3m S of Stow-on-the-Wold. Stow-Burford Rd A424 Westcote. ⅓-acre plantsman's retirement garden started 1974. Gardening writer Felicity North. TEAS Village Hall opposite. *Adm 30p Chd 15p. Sun June 14 (2-6)*

Cotswold Farm ✗ (Maj & Mrs P.D. Birchall) 5m N of Cirencester on A417; signed immediately W of Five Mile House Inn. Cotswold garden in lovely position with terraces; shrubs, mixed borders, alpine border, shrub roses; walled kitchen garden. *Adm £1. Sun, Mon Aug 30, 31 (2-6)*

Derhams House & St Francis ✗❀ 3m SE of Stroud. From Market Sq down High St 100 yds; then right at Xrds; 300 yds turn left at

West End. Car parking. TEA St Francis. *Combined adm £1 Chd 10p. Suns March 15, 22, July 26 & Mon July 27 (2-6)*

Derhams House (Mr & Mrs Mark Byng) 3-acre garden created since 1957; water garden; shrubs, herbaceous borders

St Francis, Lammas Park ᴛ❀ (Mr & Mrs Falconer) Medium-sized garden made in old park round modern Cotswold stone house. Fine beech avenue; terraced garden; trough gardens; bonsai trees; C18 ice-house. Picnickers welcome. Also by appt. (Tel Brimscombe 882188)

Eastington Gardens ❀ 1m SE of Northleach (A40). Charming Cotswold village with lovely views. Bus stop: Northleach. TEAS. *Combined adm 75p Chd 25p (Share to Northleach Church). Sat, Sun April 25, 26; Suns, Mons May 24, 25, Aug 30, 31 (2-7). Middle End & Bank Cottage also open Suns May 3, June 7, July 5, Aug 2, Sept 6. No Teas on these days.*

Bank Cottage ❀ (Mr & Mrs E.S.Holland) Lower End. Cottage garden

Middle End ❀ Eastington (Mr & Mrs Owen Slatter) Medium-sized Cotswold garden of general interest

Yew Tree Cottage (Mr & Mrs M. Bottone) Lower End. Rockery, plants and shrubs

Easton Grey House See Wiltshire section

Ewen Gardens 4m S of Cirencester; via A429 3m from Cirencester turn at signpost, Ewen 1m. TEAS. *Combined adm 80p (Share to Glos Macmillan Nurse Appeal). Sun June 28 (2-6)*

Brooke House ᴛ❀ (Mr & Mrs D.A. George) 1½-acres; formerly kitchen garden of Ewen Manor; walled garden; herbaceous borders, shrubberies, rose beds

Ewen Manor ᴛ (Col & Mrs M. St J.V. Gibbs) Medium-sized garden; herbaceous border, lily pool, sunk garden, cedar trees, yew hedges. Georgian Cotswold manor house (not open). Picnics allowed

Tanners (Mrs Roberts) Small cottage garden, species roses

Walled Garden (Mr & Mrs Reiss) Small, new garden

Eyford House ᴛ (Lady Kleinwort) Upper Slaughter; on B4068 (formerly A436), 2¼m W of Stow-on-the-Wold. 1¼ acres; redesigned and replanted since 1976. Good view. TEAS. *Adm 75p Wheelchair 40p. Sun July 5 (2-6.30)*

Fossebridge Manor ✄ (Maj & the Hon Mrs John Shedden), Coln St Denys. 3m SW of Northleach; ½m E of Fossebridge on A429 (Fosseway). Old Cotswald farmhouse with Norfolk thatch. Bulbs, herbaceous, roses, river and lake. TEAS. *Adm 60p Chd 30p. Sun Apr 19 (2-6)*

♦**Gloucestershire College of Agriculture** ᴛ❀ (Gloucestershire County Council) Hartpury

House, 5m N of Gloucester. Take A4l7 Gloucester-Ledbury; clearly signposted. 4 acres; large lawns; trees, shrubs and terraces; glasshouses; kitchen garden; demonstration gardens, ornamental gardens. TEAS by WI. *Adm 50p Chd 15p. Sun May 17 (2-6)*

Great Rissington Manor ❀ (Mr & Mrs D. Godman) 2½m SE of Bourton-on-the-Water. 4-acre terraced garden around typical Elizabethan farmhouse; many interesting plants and trees; pond with ornamental duck. TEAS. *Adm £1. Sun June 21; Sun, Mon Aug 30, 31 (2-6); by appt April when daffodils good (Tel Cotswold 20312)*

The Heathers ✄❀ (Kenneth Watson Esq) 25 Winfield, Newent. B4215 Gloucester-Newent; through town to Watery Lane (signposted Cliffords Mesne and Falconry Centre); then 2nd on left. Small front garden linked with neighbour having heathers and dwarf conifers; and for all year round interest; Japanese rear garden; with traditional tea, sand and hill gardens. TEA. *Adm 50p Chd 25p. Sats, Suns March 14, 15; April 18, 19; May 2, 3; 23, 24 & Mons 4, 25; Sept 12, 13 (2-6); Oct 24, 25 (11-5); also by appt June, July & Aug (Tel Newent 820048)*

Hidcote Manor Garden ᴛ✄❀ (The National Trust) 3m NE of Chipping Campden. Bus from Evesham or Stratford-on-Avon, alight Xrds ½m S of Mickleton. Series of formal gardens, many enclosed within superb hedges, inc hornbeam on stems. Many rare trees, shrubs, plants. Daily except Tues & Fri, April 1 to Oct 31 (11-8; no entry after 7 or an hour before dusk if earlier) TEAS. *Adm £2.50 Chd £1.25. For NGS Sun May 3 (11-8; no Adm after 7)*

Hidcote Vale ᴛ✄ (Miss B.C. Muir) Hidcote Boyce 3m NE of Chipping Campden, ½m SW of Hidcote NT garden. Small garden with many interesting shrubs, herbaceous and alpine plants. *Adm 60p Chd 30p (Share to Guide Dogs for the Blind). Sun June 14 (2-5.30)*

Hodges Barn ᴛ (Mr & Mrs C.N. Hornby) Shipton Moyne 3m S of Tetbury on Malmesbury side of Shipton Moyne. 8 acres; woodland garden with many spring bulbs; water garden; herbaceous borders, fine roses, shrubs; mature tapestry hedge. TEAS (June 28 only). *Adm 75p Chd 25p. Suns April 19 (2-6) June 28 (2-7); also by appt (Tel Westonbirt 202)*

Hunts Court ᴛ✄❀ (Mr & Mrs T.K. Marshall) North Nibley, Dursley. 2m NW of Wotton-under-Edge. From Wotton B4060 Dursley rd turn right in Nibley at Black Horse; fork left after ¼m. 2½ acres with unusual shrubs, 350 varieties old roses, herbaceous, and heather beds and lawns set against tree clad hills and Tyndale monument. House (not open) probably birth place of William Tyndale. Nursery open daily except Mons & Aug. Home-made TEAS (Suns only). Picnic Area. *Adm 60p Chd 20p (Share to BRCS June 21; CECS June 28; CLIC July 5). Daily except Suns & Mons May 5 to July 31 & Sept 1 to 30 (2-6). For NGS Suns June 14, 21, 28, July 5, 12 (2-6); also by appt (Tel Dursley 47440)*

Hyam & The Lammas, Minchinhampton, 3m SE of Stroud. From Market Square turn right at Cross; bear left at West End to iron gates 50 yds from bus stop. TEAS. *Combined adm £1 OAPs/Chd 50p (Share to Guide Dogs for the Blind). Sun Sept 6 (12-7)*
> **Hyam** ⅁⚘ (Douglas Anderson Esq) Medium sized home-made garden with lawns and glorious views; fine wrought-iron work and some ancient stones; herbaceous borders, lavender hedges, sweet peas, dahlias. Band. Picnic area
> **The Lammas** ⅁ (Mr & Mrs A. Larsson) Entrance through Hyam. 8-acre mature garden with many fine trees and shrubs; herbaceous borders and rose garden; water garden; historic house rebuilt Queen Anne (not open); magnificent tithe barn (open); walled kitchen garden; greenhouses; Band

8 Hyatts Way ⚥⚘ (Mr & Mrs P.M. Herbert) Bishops Cleeve, 4m N of Cheltenham; take A435 towards Evesham, at Bishops Cleeve turn right past Esso Garage, follow road to school, turn left, then 2nd right. Small plantsman's garden, over 500 varieties, inc digitalis and salvia species; many other unusual plants and alpines in sinks. *Adm 50p Chd 25p. By appt only April 25 to Aug 29 (Tel 024267 3503)*

◊¶**Icomb Place** ⚥ (Mr & Mrs T.L.F. Royle) 4m S of Stow-on-the-Wold; after 3m on A424 Burford rd turn left to Icomb village. Large garden being remade; pools, stream; woodland walks; interesting trees; extensive views. TEAS. *Adm 80p Chd 25p. Sun Oct 4 (2-6)*

Kemble Gardens 4m SW of Cirencester on A429 to Malmesbury. TEAS by WI Kemble House. *Combined adm 80p Chd 10p. Sun July 12 (2-6)*
> **Fairacre** ⚥ (Mr & Mrs Peter Woolland) Medium-sized garden; lawns, trees, shrubs, mixed borders, terrace, lily pond
> **Glebe Barn** ⚥ (Mr & Mrs Gordon Gregory) Garden started 1972 round conversion of vicarage barn; mixed shrubs, herbaceous beds with peonies, old roses, clematis; mini orchard and pretty paved court yard
> **Kemble House** ⅁⚘ (Mrs Donald Peachey) Large, mature, old-fashioned garden pertaining to C17 manor house and overlooking its own parkland; adjoining church. Informal planting of shrubs, herbaceous

plants; old-fashioned and floribunda roses
Pigeon House ⚥ (Dr & Mrs Rex Alcock) Medium-sized garden, started 1972 in yard of converted C18 barn with scheduled pigeon loft; roses; lily pond with exotic fish; rockery; tapestry hedge; fruit and flowering trees

Kiftsgate Court ⚥⚘ (Mr & Mrs A. H. Chambers) 3m. NE of Chipping Campden, adjacent to Hidcote Nat Trust Garden. 1m E of A46 and B4081. Bus: Stratford-on-Avon/ Broadway, alight Mickleton, 1m Magnificent situation and views; many unusual plants and shrubs; tree paeonies, hydrangeas, abutilons, species and old-fashioned roses, inc largest rose in England, R.Filipes Kiftsgate. TEAS if fine (starting Whit. Sun to Sept 18). *Adm £1.50 Chd 50p. Suns, Weds, Thurs & Bank Hols April 1 to Sept 30. For NGS (Share to Sue Ryder Home, Leckhampton Court) Sats May 16; June 27; Aug 22 (2-6)*

Kingsmead ⅁⚥ (The Earl & Countess of Westmorland) Didmarton, Badminton. 6m SW of Tetbury on A433 Cirencester-Bath rd. 4 acres; many varieties of roses; old kitchen garden has been completely re-designed and replanted with roses, shrubs and trees by present owners. Topiary yew house. NO DOGS (but can be walked in fields by drive). TEAS. *Adm £1 Chd free. Sun June 28 (2-6)*

Little Barrow ⅁⚘ (Sir Charles & Lady Mander) Moreton-in-Marsh. On E side of A429 ½-way between Stow-on-the-Wold and Moreton-in-Marsh. Infrequent bus passes house. Medium-sized garden with sunken garden, spring flowers, lawns, roses, herbaceous borders with over 300 different plants; yew hedges; vegetable and fruit gardens. *Adm £1 Chd 10p. Sun, Mon May 3, 4; Sun July 12 (2-6)*

Lower Churn ⅁⚥ (Mr & Mrs A.N. Sturt) South Cerney. From A419 (1m S of Cirencester) turn for South Cerney at Xrds. In village turn in bridge down Bow Wow Lane for ½m. 3½-acres. Former cottage gardens, paddocks and orchard re-planted since 1968. *Adm 50p Chd free (Share to GTNC). Sun April 12 (2-6)*

Lydney Park (Viscount Bledisloe) Lydney. On A48 Gloucester-Chepstow rd between Lydney & Aylburton. Drive is directly off A48. 8 acres extensive valley garden with many varieties of rhododendron, azaleas and other flowering shrubs; trees and lakes. Garden round house; magnolias and daffodils (April). Roman Temple Site and Museum. Deer park with fine trees. TEAS; also picnic area (in park). Coach parties of 30 or more by appt (Tel Dean 42844). *Adm £1 (Chd & cars free). Every Sun, Bank Hol & Wed April 19 - June 14; Daily May 25 - May 31 (11-6). For NGS Sun May 10 (11-6)*

¶**Malt House Cottage** & (Mr & Mrs T.W. Jenkins) Icomb 3½m S of Stow-on-the-Wold; after 2½m turn left off A424. ½-acre cottage garden; shrubs, herbaceous borders, water garden and rockery still developing. TEA. *Adm 30p Chd 15p. Sun July 5 (2-6)*

Misarden Park &※֍ (Maj & Mrs M.T.N.H. Wills) 7m NE of Stroud. Spring flowers, shrubs, roses, topiary and herbaceous borders; old Tudor manor house standing high over looking Golden Valley. Garden Nurseries. Shop and tea room in village. Also woodland walk. *Adm £1 Chd free. April 22 to Sept 30 every Wed & Thurs (10-4.30). For NGS Suns May 3, 24, & July 5 (2-6)*

Newark Park (Robert Parsons Esq) Ozleworth, 1½m E of Wotton-under-Edge, 1½m S of junc A4135/B4058. Elizabethan hunting lodge; 10-acre woodland setting; spring bulbs, spring and autumn cyclamen. Spectacular views. TEAS. *Adm 80p Chd 40p. Suns April 5, Sept 27 (2-5)*

Nympsfield Gardens ※ 3m NW of Nailsworth. Signed from B4066 Stroud-Dursley rd. TEAS Coach House (May), Upper Lutheredge (July), Candle Cottage (July). *Combined adm 80p (May 50p) Chd free (Share to Nympsfield Village Hall). Sun July 5 (2-6)*
  Barberi Cottage (Mrs F. Mack) Small garden with alpines. *Also May 24*
  Bell Court ֍ (Mr & Mrs P. Mack) 1-acre plantsman's garden *Also May 24 (not July). Also by appt at short notice (Tel Dursley 860415)*
  Candle Cottage (Mr & Mrs A.N. Pearce) Small landscaped cottage garden
  ¶**The Coach House** (Mr & Mrs R. Overton) Small tree-lined garden constructed in last 3 yrs. *Also May 24 (not July)*
  Four Wells (Miss S. Dennison) Small cottage garden
  Highlands (Mr & Mrs R. Easton)
  Pen-y-Banc (Mr & Mrs C. Ward) Adjoining gardens on sloping windswept site
  Upper Lutheredge (Mr & Mrs S. Bond) 1m outside village on Horsley rd. 2-acres with beautiful views. Cotswold farmhouse (not open)

Oddington Gardens, ※֍ 2½m E of Stow-on-the-Wold. Just off A436 to Chipping Norton; 2nd turn on right (S) into Oddington. TEAS (Aug only) Kitsbury Orchard. *Sun, Mon May 3, 4, Sun Aug 2 (2-6)*
  Fotherop & (Mr & Mrs Victor Barclay). 1½-acre Cotswold, well laid out spring garden; *Adm 60p*
  Kitsbury Orchard (Mr & Mrs Henry Jones) 3-acres; lawns, trees, shrubs, mixed borders; shrub roses; spring flowers. Listed Cotswold house (not open). Picknickers welcome (from 12 pm). *Adm 60p. (Share to Stow & District Day Centre)*

The Old Manor &※֍ (Mrs Joan Wilder) Twyning. 3m N of Tewkesbury via A38; follow sign to Twyning; garden at Xrds at top end of village. 1 acre; variety of shrubs, trees, herbaceous and alpine plants, many unusual; pool garden, rock beds, terrace plants, trough. Field walks for picnics. Small nursery. *Adm £1 (Share to GRBS & RGOF). Every Mon all year; Sats by appt (Tel Tewkesbury 293516/299878, evenings). For NGS Sat June 6 (2-6)*

The Old Rectory, Stanton & (Mrs E. Bonas) 1m off A46 (Broadway-Cheltenham rd), 3m SW of Broadway. 1½ acres. House and garden approached through avenue of lime trees. Garden partly enclosed by stone walls; spacious lawns, mixed borders, trees of exceptional maturity. Tea Broadway. *Adm 50p Chd 25p (Share to Stanton Church). Mon May 4 (2-7)*

Oxwold House (Mr & Mrs James D'Arcy Clark) Barnsley 4m NE of Cirencester. From A433 Burford rd on outskirts of Barnsley, turn left signed Coln Rogers. 3 acres; shrubs, herbaceous borders. Fine view. TEAS. *Adm £1 Chd free. Sun July 12 (2-6)*

Painswick Rococo Garden ※ (Lord & Lady Dickinson) The Stables, Painswick House, Painswick ½m on B4073. Unique Rococo garden in process of restoration to original Thomas Robins portrayal of 1748. C18 buildings; vistas; woodland paths. Weds, Thurs, Suns, Bank Hols (ex Easter) May to Sept (2-5). Parties by appt all year. *Adm £1 OAPs 70p Chd 30p. For NGS Snowdrops last Sun Feb, first Sun March (12-4)*

♦¶**Pinbury Park** (Mr & Mrs John Mullings) Cirencester 6 ½m. Signed off Sapperton-Winston Rd between A419 and A417. 5-acres; topiary, yew avenue, lawns, bulbs, view, gazebo. Tudor Manor house (not open) former Royal residence of King Penda. *Adm 50p. Sun Apr 26 (2-6)*

Poulton Gardens &※֍ 5m E of Cirencester on A417. TEAS by WI Poulton Manor. *Combined adm 90p OAPs 50p Chd free. Sun June 21 (2-6)*
  The New Inn (Mr & Mrs Witold Wondrausch) an idiosyncratic collection of plants in ⅔acre; pond; mini vineyard
  Poulton Manor (Mr & Mrs Anthony Sanford) 2-acres reconstructed for minimal maintenance; old yew hedges, hornbeam avenue, natural garden, trees, shrubs; walled kitchen garden. Charles II house (not open)
  Sarnia (Mr & Mrs W.M. Young) ½-acre; shrubs and perennials to give colour and interest throughout the year

¶**Priors Mesne Cottage** (Mr & Mrs T.F. Cox) Aylburton 4m S of Lydney. Take A48 towards Chepstow. In Aylburton take 1st right at

Hawthorn Inn, Church Rd. 2m up hill to junc, left at sign to Alvington and Woolaston, entrance 1st on right. Woodland walk to remains of 2-acre wild garden with three pools, fine trees, azaleas, bamboos. Subject of book "A Gloucestershire Wild Garden" 1899 and featured in a film "The Assam Garden" 1984. *Adm 80p Chd free. Sun May 10 (2-6)*

The Priory, Kemerton (see Hereford & Worcester section)

Quenington Gardens ⚘ 2m N of Fairford, W of Cirencester. TEAS The Old Rectory. *Combined adm £1 Chd 20p. Sun July 26 (2-6)*
  Coneygar Lodge (Mr & Mrs Frank Gibb) Pretty summer garden and aviary of interesting birds
  Mallards (Mr & Mrs B.R. Roebuck) Summer flowers, aquatics, walled vegetable garden
  The Old Rectory (Mr & Mrs David Abel-Smith) Adjoining church with interesting Norman doorways and tympana
  Pool Hay (Mr & Mrs A.W. Morris) Small is beautiful
  ¶**Quenington House** (Mr & Mrs Geoffrey Murray) Summer garden with plenty of interest
  ¶**River House** (Mrs Evelyn Bailey) 1-acre garden with interesting borders. River walk

Rodmarton Manor &⚘❀ (Mrs Anthony Biddulph) 6m SW of Cirencester; 4m NE of Tetbury, off A433. Cotswold house (not open except Chapel) designed by Ernest Barnsley; featured in *Country Life, RHS Journal (July '82); Stately Gardens of Britain & ITV 1985;* topiary, hornbeam avenue; beech, holly and yew hedges; long vistas, herbaceous borders, terrace and leisure gardens; emphasis on labour-saving. TEAS Suns only. Picnic area. *Adm £1 (Share to Parish Church, Rodmarton & Tarlton Chapel-of-Ease). Suns April 12 (2-6), May 17, June 7, July 19 (2-7). Also March to Aug every Wed (2-5); also by appt (Tel Rodmarton 219)*

Rookwoods &⚘ (Mrs R. Luard) Water Lane, Oakridge, 5m E of Stroud, 7m W of Cirencester; just N of A419; 1¼m from Bisley. 2-acre garden with herbaceous borders, old-fashioned roses, stream, outstanding views. Typical Cotswold house (not open). Coaches by appt (parking difficult). Teas, Over Court, Bisley. *Adm 75p Chd 25p. Sun July 12 (2-6)*

Ryelands House ⚘❀ (Capt & Mrs Eldred Wilson) Taynton, 8m W of Gloucester. ½-way between Huntley (A40) and Newent (B4215) on B4216. Fascinating sunken garden, great variety of plants- many rare, trees, shrubs, bulbs, herbaceous borders, species and old roses; waterside plants, pools and herbs. Also unique, very popular woodland and country walk. Outstanding views and abundance of wild flowers; famed for wild daffo-dils. 2-acre lake in beautiful setting. Good selection plants always for sale. Dogs welcome on walk. TEAS (Suns only). *Adm £1 Chd free (Share to Canine Defence League). Suns April 5, 12, 19, 26; May 3; June 7, 14; July 19, 26; Aug 30 & Mons April 20, May 4, Aug 31 (2-6). Also every Weds June & July (2-6). Private Parties by appt (Tel Tibberton 251)*

20 St Peter's Road ⚘ (Meg & Jeff Blumsom) Cirencester. Small town garden entirely re-made without grass since 1981; herbaceous; clematis; rockery, pond. Sunday Express Garden of Month, Aug '85. *Adm 25p. Suns July 5, Aug 16, Sept 6 (2-6); also by appt (Tel Cirencester 67696)*

Saltwood ⚘❀ (John Taylor Esq) Fosseway Ave, Moreton-in-Marsh. Take Fosseway towards Stow, ¼m turn left, garden immediately on right. ¼ acre; mainly bearded irises, short (flowering May), tall (flowering June). Owner is well-known iris hybridiser. *Adm 30p Chd 15p. By appt only May, June (Tel 0608 50929)*

¶**Sapperton Gardens** Cirencester 6m W A419 to Stroud. *Adm each garden £1 Chd 50p. Sun Aug 23 (2-6)*
  Daneway House (Sir Anthony & Lady Denny) 2-acres; informal layout, fairly wild garden, yew avenue, old roses. C14 and C17 manor completely unspoilt also open. Limited parking
  Upper Dorval House (Mr & Mrs James Marshall) Ernest Barnsley's house with Gimson ceiling in hall (open). Topiary garden, shrubs and trees. Spectacular view. *(Share to British Heart Foundation)*

◆**Sezincote** ⚘ (Mr & Mrs David Peake) 1½m SW of Moreton-in-Marsh. Turn W along A44 towards Evesham; after 1½m (just before Bourton-on-the-Hill) take turn left, by stone lodge with white gate. Repton and Daniell water garden practically unaltered. Trees of unusual size. House in Indian manner, inspiration for The Pavilion, Brighton; architect Samuel Pepy Cockerell. TEAS (June 28 only). *Adm £1.50 Chd 50p. Open every Thurs Fri & Bank Hol (except Dec) (2-6). For NGS Mon May 4 & Sun June 28 (2.30-6)*

◆¶**Sherborne Park** ⚘❀ (Sherborne Park Residents Assoc) 1m N of A40; Northleach 4m, Burford 6m. 12-acre garden largely restored since 1981; herbaceous borders; rose garden; orangery; water garden. House by Webb (1651) Wyatt (1830) (not open). C18 stable block with recently landscaped gardens. TEAS. *Adm 80p Chd free. Sun July 19 (2-6)*

Snowshill Manor ⚘ (The National Trust) 3m S of Broadway, 4m W of A424. Small terraced garden with ponds, old roses and old-fashioned flowers. House with architectural features; large, unique collection of musical instruments, clocks, toys, bicycles. House & garden are open April & Oct Sats, Suns; May to Sept daily except Mons, Tues (but open Bank Hols) (11-1 & 2-6 or sunset if earlier). *Adm house & gdn £2.50 Chd £1.25. For NGS Sun May 3 (11-1, 2-6)*

Southrop Gardens & 1½m. N of Lechlade, turn off A361 at sign to Southrop. Riverside daffodils at neighbouring village of Eastleach may be in flower at time of April opening. TEAS Southrop Manor. *Combined adm £1 OAPs/Chd 50p (Share to Southrop Church). Suns April 26, June 7 (2-6)*

> **Southrop Manor** (Mr & Mrs Kenneth Combe) Large garden beside R. Leach; river and stewpond where monks kept carp and trout; parts newly planted. House originally Norman. C16 tithe barn. Adjacent to Saxon Church
> **Fyfield Manor** (Sir Guy & Lady Millard) Partly walled garden round small manor house c. 1700 (not open); spring shrubs; bulbs; magnolias

Stancombe Park &❀ (Mr & Mrs B.S. Barlow) Dursley ½-way between Dursley and Wotton-under-Edge on B4060. Bus stop: 30yds from gates. Folly garden and Temple; herbaceous borders, new tree and shrub planting. TEAS (inc Austrian cakes & gateaux). *Adm £1 Chd 30p. (Share to Internat Dendrology Soc). Sun June 21 (2-6)*

Stanton &❀ Nr Broadway. A number of village gardens may be seen. Car park free. TEA & scones in Village Hall from 3-5.30. *Adm £1 (advance bookings for 10 or more people 75p each) Chd free (Share to Stanton Church). Sun June 28 (2-6.30)*

◆**Stanway House** &⚘ (Lord & Lady Neidpath) 1m E of A46 Cheltenham-Broadway rd on B4077 Toddington to Stow-on-the-Wold rd. 20 acres of lawns with rare formal terraced mound, flowers inc old roses and daffodils; striking C16 Manor with gatehouse, Tithe Barn, Church and village in planted parkland. Remains ornamental canal and cascade; chestnut and oak avenue; specimen trees inc pinetum; folly. Tea The Bakehouse, Stanway. *Adm 75p, Chd 25p (Share to Wemyss Memorial Hall, Stanway). Suns April 19, June 14 (2-5); also house open Tues & Thurs June - Aug (2-5). Donations to NGS*

Stowell Park ⚘ (The Lord & Lady Vestey) 2m SW of Northleach. Off Fosseway A429. Large garden; terraced lawns with magnificent views; fine collection of climbing roses; recently planted pleached lime avenue; large kitchen garden, vegetables, fruit, cut flowers; range of greenhouses inc peach and vine houses. House (not open) originally C14 with later additions. Nearby church 1172 with original hand paintings of that date on walls.

TEAS. *Adm £1.50 Chd 50p (Share to Royal British Legion). Sun June 28 (2-6)*

◆**Sudeley Castle** ⚘❀ (Lord & Lady Ashcombe) Winchcombe on A46 N of Cheltenham ½m SE of Winchcombe. Entrance via Vineyard St in town. Centrepiece is the formal Queens Garden flanked by its famous yew hedges; extensive mixed borders, 'old fashioned' rose collection in ruined Tithe Barn and formal pools all set in extensive lawns with many fine trees. Magnificent views of surrounding countryside. Restaurant. Open daily March 30-Oct 31. TEAS. *Adm £2 Chd £1.25. For NGS Sun March 29 (11-5)*

Sudeley Hill Gardens ⚘ 1½m SE of Winchcombe; take rd to Bourton-on-the-Water/ Guiting Power. TEA Sudeley Lodge. *Combined adm 50 Chd free (Share to Stanley Pontlarge Church Restoration Fund). Sun July 12 (2-5)*

> **Sudeley Lodge** (Mr & Mrs K.J. Wilson) Medium-sized garden in lovely setting with lawns, borders and stone walls
> **Boilingwell** ❀ (Canon & Mrs R.W. Miles) 1½-acre garden; planted for year round colour and easy maintenance. *Also open Mon April 20; Suns May 31, June 21, Aug 23, Sept 20 Adm 50p*

Sydenhams (Mr & Mrs G.G. Cradock-Watson) 1m N of Bisley on Stroud rd, turn right at Stancombe Corner. Small garden; herbaceous borders, roses, formal beds. Tudor Cotswold house (not open) partly C14 overlooking Slad valley; picturesque farm buildings; medieval stone pillars. Teas Overcourt, Bisley *Adm 75p Chd 25p (Share to GTNC). Sun July 12 (2-7)*

¶**153 Thrupp Lane** ❀ ((Mr & Mrs D. Davies) 1½m from Stroud. Take A419, Thrupp Lane is on left 1m from Stroud, then ½m. ⅓ acre full of plants and interest; rockeries; shrubberies; ponds. TEA. *Adm 50p Chd free. Sun May 10 (2-6); also by appt all year. (Tel Brimscombe 883580)*

¶**Todenham Gardens** 4m NE of Moreton-in-Marsh. Turn right off A429 at N end of Moreton to Todenham. TEAS Todenham Manor. *Adm each garden 50p Chd 25p (Share to Todenham Church). Sun June 28 (2-6)*

> **The Old Rectory** ❀ (Lady Elizabeth Longman) 1 acre new garden replanted and altered since 1980. Shrubs, trees, herbaceous borders, formal kitchen garden, conservatory
> **Todenham Manor** & (Capt & Mrs B.W. Bell) 2 acres walled garden; lawns, herbaceous border; swimming pool

Trevi Garden &❀ (Mr & Mrs G.D. Gough) Hartpury 5m NW of Gloucester via A417. In village sharp back right over Old Road before War Memorial. 1 acre of gardens within a garden; winding water garden; laburnum/ clematis walk, shrubberies, herbaceous border; all year round interest. TEAS. *Adm 50p Chd free. Suns May 10; July 12 & Thurs April 2, 16; May 7, 21; June 4, 18; July 2, 16; Aug 6, 20; Sept 3,17 (2-7); coaches/groups by appt (Tel Hartpury 370). Also open adjoining garden*

  Beauchief ᴅ⚘ (Mr & Mrs J.N. Wilkes) 1 acre with trees, shrubs and water features. *Sun May 10 only*

Upton House ⚘⚙ (R. Seelig Esq) Tetbury Upton, 1m N of Tetbury; take B4014 Avening Rd from Tetbury; after 1m lane to garden on left by'phone box. 4-acres; lawns, herbaceous borders, shrubbery, some fine large trees; kitchen garden, greenhouses. TEAS. *Adm 50p Chd 20p (Share to Tetbury Parish Church Restoration Fund). Suns June 28, July 26 (2-6)*

♦**Westonbirt School** ᴅ 3m S of Tetbury. B432 Tetbury-Bristol. 22 acres. Formal Italian garden, terraced pleasure garden, rustic walks; lake. Rare, exotic trees and shrubs. Tea Hare & Hounds Hotel, Westonbirt, ½m (parties by appt W'birt 233). *Adm 50p Chd 10p. Suns May 24, Aug 2, Sept 6 (2-6)*

Willersey House ᴅ (Col & Mrs P. Arkwright) 1½m N of Broadway (A46), turn right Willersey village to Chipping Campden. Beautiful old Cotswold house. Bulbs; flowering shrubs; daffodils a feature. July openings: Rose gardens; flowering shrubs; herbaceous borders. *Adm 50p Chd 25p (Share to GTNC). Suns, Mons April 19, 20 (11-6) July 12, 13 (11-7)*

Windy Ridge (C.J. Williams Esq) Longborough SW of Moreton-in-Marsh, E of A424. Interesting 3-acre garden planned on different levels since 1951; herbaceous borders, lawns; great variety of plants and shrubs; formal terracing around thatched house, leading through unusual moongate to croquet lawn and old variety shrub roses. Secluded swimming pool and folly. Loose boxes, garages. TEAS. *Adm £1 Chd free. Sun July 12 (2-6)*

Witcombe Gardens At Great Witcombe, 4m E of Gloucester on A436, turn S by 12 Bells; signpost to Gt Witcombe. TEAS Witcombe Park. *Sun June 14 (2-6)*

  Witcombe Park ᴅ⚘ (Mrs W.W. Hicks Beach) Medium-sized garden; roses, flowering shrubs and sunken garden set in beautiful Cotswold scenery. *Adm 50p Chd 25p (Share to GTNC)*

  Church Cottage ᴅ⚘ (Sir Christopher & Lady Lawson) 2 acres; typical cottage flowers; shrubs; stream and ponds. Soft drinks. *Adm 50p Chd 25p*

Yew Tree Cottage ᴅ⚘ (Mrs B. Shuker; Kim & Penny Pollit) Ampney St Mary. At E end of

Ampney St Peter on A417 fork left at Red Lion, 1st left to Ampney St Mary, then 1st right in village. Medium-sized garden; variety of interesting plants throughout year inc alpines, bulbs, perennials, shrubs, clematis. TEAS (by WI Suns & Easter Mon). *Adm 50p Chd free (Share to Sue Ryder Foundation). Sun, Mon April 19, 20; Suns May 17, June 7, 28, Aug 30 (2-6); also every Wed. Collecting box for NGS (10-6)*

GWENT

Hon County Organiser:
MRS GLYNNE CLAY, Lower House Farm, Nantyderry, Abergavenny NP7 9DP

DATES OF OPENING

BY APPOINTMENT ONLY for dates see text:
  THE CHAIN GARDEN, Abergavenny
REGULAR OPENINGS for dates see text:
  PEN-Y-PARC COTTAGE, Llantarnam

APRIL Sunday 26
  YEW TREE NURSERY, Lydart
MAY Sunday 3 & Monday 4 (Bank Hol)
  LOWER HOUSE FARM, Nantyderry
MAY Sunday 10
  BRYNGWYN MANOR, Raglan
MAY Sunday 17
  ROCKSHIEL, Devauden
MAY Sunday 24 & Monday 25 (Bank Hol)
  YEW TREE NURSERY, Lydart
MAY Sunday 31
  PENPERGWM LODGE, nr Abergavenny
JUNE Sunday 7
  THE GRAIG & BOX TREE COTTAGE, nr Monmouth
JUNE Sunday 14
  CLYTHA PARK, nr Abergavenny
JUNE Sunday 21
  OAKGROVE, St Arvans
JUNE Sunday 28
  LANSOR, nr Caerleon
JULY Sunday 5
  LLANFAIR COURT, nr Abergavenny
JULY Sunday 12
  CLYTHA PARK, nr Abergavenny
JULY Sunday 19
  TANGLEWOOD, Nantyderry
JULY Sunday 26
  GREAT KILLOUGH, nr Abergavenny
AUGUST Sunday 30 & Monday 31 (Bank Hol)
  LOWER HOUSE FARM, Nantyderry
SEPTEMBER Sunday 6
  CASTLE HOUSE, Usk
SEPTEMBER Sunday 13
  LLANOVER, nr Abergavenny

DESCRIPTIONS OF GARDENS

Bryngwyn Manor &⊛ (Mr & Mrs S. Inglefield) 2m W of Raglan. Turn S off old A40 (Abergavenny-Raglan rd) at Croes Bychan (Welsh Tree Services); house ¼m up lane. 3 acres; good trees, mixed borders, roses; spring bulbs. TEAS. *Adm 50p Chd 25p. Sun May 10 (2-6)*

Castle House ⊛ (Mrs R.H.J. Humphreys) Usk; 200yds from Usk centre; turn up lane by fire station. Medium-sized garden; a flower garden of orderly disorder around ruins of Usk Castle. TEA. *Adm 50p. Sun Sept 6 (2-7)*

The Chain Garden (Mr & Mrs C.F.R. Price) Chapel Rd, 1m N of Abergavenny. Turn off A40 (on Brecon side of town) into Chapel Rd, garden at top of rd. 2 acres with stream; lawns; rhododendrons; flowering shrubs, rock gardens. *Adm 50p Chd 20p. By appt. April 1 to Sept 30 (Tel Abergavenny 3825)*

Clytha Park & (R.Hanbury-Tenison Esq) ½ way between Abergavenny and Raglan on old rd (not A40). 5 acres; C18 layout; trees, shrubs; lake. Boat hire, donkey cart rides. TEAS (in aid of Gwent National Trust Assn). *Adm 50p Chd 25p. Suns June 14; July 12 (2-7)*

The Graig &⊛ (Mrs Rainforth) Pen-y-Clawdd, SW of Monmouth. Turn S from Raglan-Monmouth Rd (not Motorway) at sign to Pen-y-Clawdd. Bus: Newport-Monmouth, alight Keen's shop, ½m. Mixed cottage garden with heathers. TEAS. Also open **Box Tree Cottage** ⊗⊛ (Miss J.M. Hassall) Dingestow. On old A40 between Mitchel Troy and Raglan; ¾m from The Graig. ¾-acre cottage garden; mixed borders, lawn, shrubs. *Combined adm 60p Chd 30p. Sun June 7 (2-7)*

Great Killough &⊗ (Mr & Mrs John F. Ingledew) Llantilio Crossenny, 6m E of Abergavenny. S of B4233. TEA. *Adm 50p Chd 20p. Sun July 26 (2-7)*

¶Lansor (HH Judge Crowther & Mrs T. Crowther) 4m from Caerleon on B4596; after 3m turn left towards Llandegveth Village; 1m on right. 1-acre; formal lawns with perennial herbaceous borders. Listed Jacobean house (not open). TEA. *Adm 50p Chd 20p. Sun June 28 (2-6)*

Llanfair Court & (Sir William Crawshay) 5m SE of Abergavenny. Route old A40 and B4598. Medium-sized garden; herbaceous border, flowering shrubs, roses, water garden; modern sculpture. TEAS. *Adm 50p Chd 25p. Sun July 5 (2-7)*

Llanover & (R.A.E. Herbert, Esq) S of Abergavenny. Bus: Abergavenny-Pontypool, alight drive gates. Large water garden; some rare plants, autumn colour. TEA. *Adm 50p Chd 20p. Sun Oct 11 (2-6)*

Lower House Farm &⊗⊛ (Mr & Mrs Glynne Clay) Nantyderry, 7m SE of Abergavenny. From Usk-Abergavenny Rd, B4598, turn off at Chain Bridge. Medium-sized garden designed for all year interest; mixed borders, fern island, bog garden, herb bed, paved area, unusual plants. TEA (Suns only). *Adm 50p Chd 20p Suns, Mons, May 3, 4; Aug 30,31 (2-6); also by appt (Tel Nantyderry 880257)*

¶Oakgrove &⊗⊛ (Mr & Mrs P.A. Hughes Davies) St Arvans. 1½m from Chepstow on A466 towards Monmouth, drive on left after Racecourse. 2½-acres; fine beech trees, herbaceous borders, shrub roses; grey and silver border; recently established collection of fagus and nothofagus; wild garden. TEA. *Adm 50p Chd 20p. Sun June 21 (2-6)*

Penpergwm Lodge &⊛ (Mr & Mrs Simon Boyle) 3m SE of Abergavenny on old A40 Raglan-Abergavenny rd, 6m from Raglan, turn R opp. King of Prussia pub; house 1st entrance 500yrds on left. 3-acre mixed garden with lawns, borders and fine mature trees. TEAS. *Adm 50p Chd 25p (Share to St Cadoc's Church). Sun May 31 (2-6)*

Pen-y-Parc Cottage ⊗⊛ (Mr & Mrs M.G. Downes) Llantarnam, Newport 2½m. Take A4042 off M4 at junc 26 for 2m, then right at sign for Ponthir opp Three Blackbirds, ½m, first cottage on right. Cottage flower garden, many old fashioned and less common plants. *Adm 50p Chd 30p. May 14 - Aug 2, Thurs, Fri, Sat, Sun; May & Aug Bank Hols (2-6), and by appt May - end Sept. No coaches. (Tel Cwmbran 4182 allowing time to answer)*

Rockshiel ⊗⊛ (Mrs O. Cowburn) Between Devauden and Llansoy. From B4293 Chepstow-Monmouth rd turn off W at sign to Raglan, Llansoy; down Star Hill for ½m. From Usk or Raglan via Crosshands Xrds; 1m up from Star Inn. ½-acre garden constructed on hillside; terraced and planted for easy maintenance. Panoramic view. *Adm 50p Chd 20p. Sun May 17 (2-6)*

¶Tanglewood ⊗ (Mr & Mrs D. Tracey) Nantyderry 6m N of Abergavenny. 2½ acres mostly planted since 1980; shrubs, hardy plants, old roses; ornamental pool. TEAS. *Adm 50p Chd 20p. Sun July 19 (2-6)*

Yew Tree Nursery ⊗⊛ (Mr & Mrs John Harper) Lydart. 2m S of Monmouth via B4293; fork left for Penallt; Private car park 300 yds on left. Hilly 2-acre garden with stupendous views; many spring bulbs and rhododendrons; large range of unusual plants and rare trees. Tea Wye Valley. *Adm 50p Chd free (Share to Save the Children Fund). Suns April 26; May 24 & Mon May 25 (2-6); also by appt (Tel 0600 2293)*

GWYNEDD
& ANGLESEY

Hon County Organisers:
(Anglesey & North Gwynedd) MRS E.W.
de FIGUEIREDO, Bryn Mor, Penmon,
Beaumaris LL58 8SH
(South Gwynedd) MRS P.A.LATHAM,
Garreg Farm, Glandyfi, Machynlleth,
Powys SY20 8SS
Hon County Treasurer:
(South Gwynedd) P.H.B. ROSSER, ESQ,
Coed-y-Garreg, Glandyfi, Machynlleth,
Powys

DATES OF OPENING

BY APPOINTMENT ONLY for dates see text:
BRYNHYFRYD, Corris
BRYN-Y-BONT, Nantmor
CEFN BERE, Dolgellau
FRONHEULOG, Llanfrothen
HEN YSGOLDY, Llanfrothen
REGULAR OPENINGS for dates see text:
PLAS PENHELIG, Aberdovey

APRIL Wednesday 1
PLAS BRONDANW, Llanfrothen
APRIL Sunday 12
FOXBRUSH, Aber Pwll, Port Dinorwic
APRIL Easter Sunday 19
MAENAN HALL, Llanwrst
PLAS PENHELIG, Aberdovey
MAY Wednesday 6
PLAS BRONDANW, Llanfrothen
MAY Sunday 10
FOXBRUSH, Aber Pwll, Port Dinorwic
HAFOD GARREGOG, Nantmor
PLAS PENHELIG, Aberdovey
MAY Sunday 24
GLANDDERWEN, Bontddu
PEN-Y-PARC, Beaumaris
MAY Monday 25 (Bank Hol)
PLAS BRONDANW, Llanfrothen
MAY Friday 29
GLANDDERWEN, Bontddu
MAY Sunday 31 & JUNE Monday 1
FARCHYNYS COTTAGE, Bontddu
JUNE Wednesday 3
PLAS BRONDANW, Llanfrothen
JUNE Thursday 4
PLAS NEWYDD, Anglesey
JUNE Sunday 7
PLAS PENHELIG, Aberdovey
JUNE Sunday 14
FOXBRUSH, Aber Pwll, Port Dinorwic
JUNE Sunday 21
ARDRAETH, Malltraeth
JULY Wednesday 1
PLAS BRONDANW, Llanfrothen
JULY Saturday 4
MAENAN HALL, Llanwrst

JULY Sunday 12
FOXBRUSH, Aber Pwll, Port Dinorwic
JULY Thursday 16
PENRHYN CASTLE, nr Bangor
JULY Sunday 26
PENCARREG, Glyn Garth, Menai Bridge
AUGUST Wednesday 5
PLAS BRONDANW, Llanfrothen
AUGUST Sunday 9
FOXBRUSH, Aber Pwll, Port Dinorwic
AUGUST Monday 31 (Bank Hol)
PLAS BRONDANW, Llanfrothen
SEPTEMBER Wednesday 2
PLAS BRONDANW, Llanfrothen
SEPTEMBER Sunday 13
FOXBRUSH, Aber Pwll, Port Dinorwic

DESCRIPTIONS OF GARDENS

Ardraeth (Mr & Mrs John Reekie) Malltraeth
4m SW of Llangefni. On approaching Malltraeth, turn right opp red barn. 1½-acre garden recently reconstructed on sand overlooking Nature Reserve Estuary and Snowdon
Range. Fine trees and shrubs; example of
garden exposed to the problems of a coastal
site. TEAS. *Adm £1 Chd 25p. Sun June 21
(2-7)*

Brynhyfryd ✗ (Mrs David Paish) Corris, 6m N
of Machynlleth. 10m S of Dolgellau. At Corris
turn off A487; garden is ¼m up hill on old rd
from Corris. 4 acres on rocky mountainside,
constructed and planted by owners since
1961; species and hybrid rhododendrons
and other peat-loving plants; species roses;
flowering shrubs; alpine, water and cover
plants. Much of interest at medium and low
level, but flat-heeled shoes recommended.
TV 'Gardeners World' 1985. *Collecting box.
By appt only, all year (Tel Corris 278)*

Bryn-y-Bont ❀ (The Misses Davis & Entwisle)
Nantmor. 2½m S of Beddgelert, turn left over
Aberglaslyn Bridge into A4085, 500yds turn
left up hill, 2nd house on right. Small garden
created since 1978 on S facing hillside over
looking Glaslyn Vale; mixed borders, bulbs,
alpines and water garden in woodland setting. *Collecting box. Open by appt only, tel
Beddgelert 448, small parties welcome. April
to October (10.30-5.30)*

Cefn Bere ✗ (Mr & Mrs Maldwyn Thomas)
Cae Deintur, Dolgellau. Turn left at top of
main bridge on Bala-Barmouth rd (not the
by-pass); turn right within 20yds; 2nd right
behind school and up hill. Small garden; extensive collection of alpines, bulbs and rare
plants. Tea Dolgellau. *Collecting box. By appt
only, spring & summer months (Tel Dolgellau 422768)*

Farchynys Cottage ✗❀ (Mrs G. Townshend)
Bontddu, On A496 Dolgellau-Barmouth rd;
well signed West Bontddu village. 4 acres;

partly well-established garden, partly natural woodland with attractive, unusual shrubs and trees; first extensive planting in 1982, new plantings each year. 'Wales in Bloom' Committee Award 1985, 1986. Car park. TEAS. *Adm 50p Chd 25p △ For NGS Sun May 31 (2-6)*

Foxbrush &⊛ (Mr & Mrs B.S. Osborne) Aber Pwll, Port Dinorwic. On Bangor rd, approach to Port Dinorwic opp W lodge to Vaynol Estate; signposted. 1½-acre country garden of family interest on site of old mill; river, ponds, wide variety of plants; semi-tropical conservatory (terrapin pool). Garden featured in *"Popular Gardening"* Feb '87. Coaches. Gift stall. TEA. *Adm 50p Chd 10p. Suns April 12, May 10, June 14, July 12, Aug 9, Sep 13 (2-5)*

Fronheulog ⊀ (Mr & Mrs J. Baily Gibson) Llanfrothen. From Llanfrothen via B4410, after ½m turn left; after 200yds left again; opp Hen Ysgoldy (below). Wild rocky hillside made into garden by owners since 1973; mainly heathers, shrubs and ground cover. *Collecting box. By appt only mid April to mid Sept (Tel 0766 770558)*

Glandderwen (A.M. Reynolds Esq) 5m W of Dolgellau. Take A496 to Bontddu. Garden is on S 100yds past Bontddu Hall Hotel; large white wooden gates. ½ acre on N bank of Mawddach Estuary facing Cader Idris; set amid large oaks; shrubs, trees; steep and rocky nature. *Adm 50p Chd 25p. Sun, Fri May 24, 29 (2-6)*

Hafod Garregog ⊛ (Mr & Mrs Hugh Mason) Nantmor, 5m N of Penrhyndeudraeth towards Aberglaslyn. Small garden made since 1971 in woodland setting with fine mountain views; trees, shrubs, flowers and vegetables; woodland bluebell walk. Home of Rhys Goch Eryri AD 1430. Situated above R. Hafod. Partly suitable for wheelchairs which are welcome. Morning coffee & TEAS. *Adm 50p Chd 20p (Share to St Joseph's Hospice). Sun May 10 (10.30-5.30)*

Hen Ysgoldy ⊀ (Mr & Mrs Peter Corner) Llanfrothen. From Garreg via B4410, after ½m left; garden 200yds on right. Natural garden with streams, shrubs, alpines. *Collecting box. By appt anytime (Tel 0766 770550)*

Maenan Hall &⊀⊛ (The Hon Christopher McLaren) Exactly 2m N of Llanrwst on E side of A470, ¼m S of Maenan Abbey Hotel. Gardens created since 1956 by the late Christabel, Lady Aberconway and then present owner; 10 acres; lawns, shrub, rose and walled gardens; rhododendron dell; many species of beautiful and interesting plants, shrubs and trees set amongst mature oaks and other hardwoods; fine views of mountains across Conway valley. TEAS. *Adm*

£1.40 Chd 50p (share to Friends of Courtald Institute). Sun Apr 19, Sat July 4 (11-5)

Pencarreg &⊀⊛ (Miss G. Jones) Glyn Garth. 1½m NE of Menai Bridge towards Beaumaris, on right down Glan Y Menai Drive. Park in lay-by on rd, in drive for disabled. 1-acre lawns, rose garden, stream and rock garden overlooking Menai Straits. Fine views of Carneddi. Garden featured BBC TV "Gardening Together" and "Palu Mlaen" Aug '86. TEA. *Adm 75p Chd 25p (Share to Friends of Snowdonia). Sun July 26 (2-6)*

Penrhyn Castle ⊀ (The National Trust) 3m E of Bangor on A5122. Coach trips from Llandudno. Buses from Llandudno, Caernarvon, Bettws-y-Coed; alight: Grand Lodge Gate. Large gardens; fine trees, shrubs, wild garden, good views. Castle was rebuilt in 1830 for 1st Lord Penrhyn, incorporating part of C15 building on C8 site of home of Welsh Princes. Museum of dolls; museum of locomotives and quarry rolling stock. NT Shop. TEAS and light lunches. *Adm: castle, grounds, museum & parking £2.10 Chd 80p; parties £1.70 Chd 80p; Garden only £1 Chd 40p. △ Thurs July 16 (11-5)*

Pen-y-Parc &⊀ (Mr & Mrs E.E. Marsh) Beaumaris. A545 Menai Bridge-Beaumaris rd; after Anglesey Boatyard 1st left; after Golf Club 1st drive on left. 6 acres; beautiful grounds, magnificent views over Menai Strait; azaleas, rhododendrons and heathers; interesting terrain with rock outcrops used to advantage for recently planted conifer and rock gardens; small lake in natural setting; 2 further enclosed gardens. We would like to share the pleasure of this garden. TEA. *Adm 75p Chd 25p. Sun May 24 (11-5)*

Plas Brondanw &⊛ (Portmeirion Foundation) Llanfrothen. Station: Penrhyndeudraeth, 2m Bus: Crosville, Garreg village, alight lodge, ¼m. Entrance: arched gatehouse, Llanfrothen. An architectural, topiary, terraced and vista'd garden below C17 house with superb mountain views; only partly suitable for wheelchairs. *Adm 50p Chd 10p. Mons May 26 & Aug 31 (10-5); Collecting box on gate for Weds April 1, May 6, June 3, July 1, Aug 5, Sept 2 (1-4.30)*

Plas Newydd &⊀ (The Marquess of Anglesey; The National Trust) Isle of Anglesey. 1m SW of Llanfairpwll and A5, on A4080. Gardens with massed shrubs, fine trees, and lawns sloping down to Menai Strait. Magnificent views to Snowdonia. C18 house by James Wyatt contains Rex Whistler's largest wall painting; also Military Museum. TEAS and light lunches. *Adm house & garden £1.80 Chd 65p; family adm (2A + 2Chd)-£4.50 parties (over 20) £1.40 Chd 55p; garden only £1 Chd 50p. △ Thurs June 4 (12-5)*

¶**Plas Penhelig** (Mr & Mrs A.C. Richardson) Aberdovey, between 2 railway bridges. Driveway to hotel by island and car park. 14 acres overlooking estuary, exceptional views. Particularly lovely in spring: bulbs, daffodils, rhododendrons, azaleas; rock and water gardens, mature tree heathers, magnolias, euphorbias; herbaceous borders, rose garden; wild and woodland flowers encouraged in large orchard; walled kitchen garden, large range of greenhouses, peaches, herbs. TEAS. *Adm 50p Chd free. Suns April 19 May 10 June 7 (10-5.30); also Tues, Weds, Thurs, Fris, Sats, Suns mid-June to mid-Oct. Collecting box*

HAMPSHIRE

Hon County Organiser:
MRS T.H. FABER, The Drove, West Tytherley, Salisbury SP5 1NX
Assistant Hon County Organisers:
MRS G.E. COKE, Jenkyn Place, Bentley;
MRS DAVID GIBBS, The Clock House, Sparsholt, nr Winchester SO21 2LX;
MRS R.J. GOULD, Ewell House, 44 Belmore Lane, Lymington
J.J. MORRIS ESQ, The Ricks, Rotherwick, Nr Basingstoke
MRS L. MILLER-STIRLING, The Old Stables, Buriton Manor, nr Petersfield;
THE LADY O'NEILL, Lisle Court Cottage, Lymington SO4 8SH;
MRS MILES RIVETT-CARNAC, Martyr Worthy Manor, nr Winchester SO21 1DY
MRS PETER WAKE, Fairfield House, Hambledon PO7 6RY
Hon County Treasurer:
H. SHEARMAN ESQ, Nutshell Cottage, West Tytherley, Salisbury

DATES OF OPENING

BY APPOINTMENT ONLY for dates see text:
FAIRFIELD HOUSE, Hambledon
REGULAR OPENINGS for dates see text:
EXBURY GARDENS, nr Southampton
FURZEY GARDENS, Minstead
THE GILBERT WHITE MUSEUM, Selborne
GREATHAM MILL, nr Liss
HERRIARD PARK OLD GARDENS, Basingstoke
HOUGHTON HOUSE, nr Stockbridge
JENKYN PLACE, Bentley
MACPENNY NURSERIES, Bransgore
PALACE HOUSE, Beaulieu
SPINNERS, nr Lymington
STRATFIELD SAYE HOUSE, Stratfield Saye

FEBRUARY Saturday 14 & Sunday 15
WYCK PLACE, Alton

FEBRUARY Saturday 21
WYCK PLACE, Alton
FEBRUARY Sunday 22
CHERITON COTTAGE, nr Alresford
WYCK PLACE, Alton
FEBRUARY Saturday 28
WYCK PLACE, Alton
MARCH Sunday 1
WYCK PLACE, Alton
MARCH Saturday 7 & Sunday 8
WYCK PLACE, Alton
MARCH Sunday 15
BRAMDEAN HOUSE, nr Alresford
MARCH Sunday 22 & Sunday 23
CHILLAND HOUSE, Martyr Worthy
APRIL Sunday 5
CASTLETOP, Burley, nr Ringwood
HERRIARD PARK OLD GARDENS, nr Basingstoke
MICHELMERSH COURT, nr Romsey
APRIL Sunday 12
ASHFORD GARDENS, nr Petersfield
CHERITON COTTAGE, nr Alresford
CRAWLEY GARDENS, nr Winchester
TICHBORNE PARK, nr Alresford
APRIL Easter Sunday 19
‡BRAMDEAN HOUSE, nr Alresford
HACKWOOD PARK, nr Basingstoke
HOUGHTON LODGE, nr Stockbridge
LONGPARISH HOUSE, nr Andover
‡WOODCOTE MANOR, nr Alresford
APRIL Easter Monday 20
BEECHENWOOD FARM, nr Odiham
BRAMDEAN HOUSE, nr Alresford
HOUGHTON LODGE, nr Stockbridge
APRIL Wednesday 22
EXBURY GARDENS, nr Southampton
APRIL Sunday 26
BYWAYS, Burley, nr Ringwood
KINGSMEAD, Winchester
LITTLE LANGLEYS, Steep
MAY Saturday 2
28 STRAIGHT MILE, Ampfield, Romsey
MAY Sunday 3
CASTLETOP, Burley, nr Ringwood
LITTLE LANGLEYS, Steep
PENNINGTON HOUSE, Lymington
PLOVERS, East Boldre, Lymington
PYLEWELL PARK, Lymington
ROOKLEY MANOR, Upper Somborne
28 STRAIGHT MILE, Ampfield, nr Romsey
VERNON HILL HOUSE, Bishop's Waltham
MAY Monday 4 (Bank Hol)
ROOKLEY MANOR, Upper Somborne
VERNON HILL HOUSE, Bishop's Waltham
MAY Sunday 10
ALVERSTOKE GARDENS, Gosport
THE DOWER HOUSE, Dogmersfield
EVERSLEY GARDENS, nr Fleet
GREATHAM MILL, nr Liss
HOLYWELL, Swanmore
RUMSEY GARDENS, nr Petersfield
TICHBORNE PARK, nr Alresford
THE VYNE, Sherborne St John
MAY Monday 11
RUMSEY GARDENS, nr Petersfield

MAY Friday 15
EXBURY GARDENS, nr Southampton
MAY Sunday 17
ASHFORD GARDENS, nr Petersfield
BRAMDEAN HOUSE, nr Alresford
CHANTRY, nr Wickham
COLD HAYES, Steep Marsh
COMPTON END, nr Winchester
‡THE COTTAGE, Chandler's Ford
‡CRANBURY PARK, Otterbourne
THE DOWER HOUSE, Dogmersfield
HACKWOOD PARK, nr Basingstoke
LITTLE LANGLEYS, Steep
MILL COURT, Alton
THE OLD HOUSE, Silchester
PYLEWELL PARK, Lymington
MAY Monday 18
COMPTON END, nr Winchester
MAY Wednesday 20
WITHY DELL, Bransgore
MAY Saturday 23
VINE COTTAGE, Ewshott, nr Farnham
MAY Sunday 24
BROCKENHURST PARK, Brockenhurst
CHILLAND, Martyr Worthy
EVERSLEY GARDENS, nr Fleet
LITTLE LANGLEYS, Steep
PYLEWELL PARK, Lymington
VINE COTTAGE, Ewshott, nr Farnham
MAY Monday 25 (Bank Hol)
BROCKENHURST PARK, Brockenhurst
CHILLAND, Martyr Worthy
HOUSE-IN-THE-WOOD, Beaulieu
NORTHREPPS, East Boldre, Lymington
MAY Wednesday 27
WITHY DELL, Bransgore
MAY Saturday 30
28 STRAIGHT MILE, Ampfield, nr Romsey
MAY Sunday 31
BEECHENWOOD FARM, nr Odiham
BURKHAM HOUSE, nr Alton
CHILWORTH MANOR, nr Southampton
MERDEN MANOR, nr Winchester
THE OLD HOUSE, Silchester
ROTHERFIELD PARK, nr Alton
28 STRAIGHT MILE, Ampfield, nr Romsey
THE WYLDS, Liss Forest
JUNE Saturday 6
LISLE COURT COTTAGE, nr Lymington
JUNE Sunday 7
CRAWLEY GARDENS (Little Court, Lithend
Only)
HERRIARD PARK OLD GARDENS, nr
Basingstoke
LISLE COURT COTTAGE, nr Lymington
VERONA COTTAGE, Hayling Island
THE VYNE, Sherborne St John
WEST SILCHESTER HALL, Silchester
JUNE Sunday 14
CHERITON COTTAGE, nr Alresford
CROYLANDS, Romsey
FARLEY HOUSE, nr Romsey
JENKYN PLACE, Bentley
THE OLD HOUSE, Silchester
145 PORTSMOUTH ROAD, Horndean
ROTHERFIELD PARK, nr Alton

VERNON HILL HOUSE, Bishop's Waltham
VINE COTTAGE, Ewshott, nr Farnham
WOODGREEN GARDENS, nr
Fordingbridge
JUNE Wednesday 17
CROYLANDS, Romsey
MOTTISFONT ABBEY, nr Romsey
VINE COTTAGE, Ewshott, nr Farnham
JUNE Sunday 21
BRAMDEAN HOUSE, nr Alresford
BROOK HOUSE, Fleet
THE COTTAGE, Chandler's Ford
CROYLANDS, Romsey
DROXFORD GARDENS, nr Wickham
KINGSMEAD, Winchester
LONGSTOCK PARK GARDENS, nr
Stockbridge
SOMERLEY, Ringwood
JUNE Saturday 27
WEST TYTHERLEY GARDENS
JUNE Sunday 28
‡CHURCH FARM, West Dean
EAST WORLDHAM MANOR, Alton
HORDLE HOUSE, nr Milford-on-Sea
LITTLE CHESTERS, Eversley
MARYCOURT, Odiham
MOTTISFONT HOUSE, nr Romsey
ROTHERFIELD PARK, nr Alton
ROTHERWICK GARDENS, nr Hook
UPTON GREY PLACE, nr Basingstoke
‡WEST TYTHERLEY GARDENS
JULY Wednesday 1
MOTTISFONT HOUSE, nr Romsey
JULY Sunday 5
BROADHATCH HOUSE, Bentley
COMPTON END, nr Winchester
CRAWLEY GARDENS, (Little Court,
Lithend Only)
FLOOD'S FARM, Dogsmerfield
THE GILBERT WHITE MUSEUM, Selborne
KINGSMEAD, Winchester
LAVERSTOKE HOUSE, nr Whitchurch
MARYCOURT, Odiham
MONXTON GARDENS, nr Andover
MOUNDSMERE MANOR, Preston
Candover
ROTHERFIELD PARK, nr Alton
VERNON HILL HOUSE, Bishop's Waltham
JULY Monday 6
COMPTON END, nr Winchester
MARYCOURT, Odiham
JULY Wednesday 8
MONXTON GARDENS, nr Andover
JULY Saturday 11
29 ST VINCENTS CRESCENT, Horndean
JULY Sunday 12
ALVERSTOKE GARDENS, Gosport
BROADHATCH HOUSE, Bentley
BURITON GARDENS, nr Petersfield
THE CLOCK HOUSE, Sparsholt
CULVERLEA HOUSE, nr Lymington
EAST WORLDHAM MANOR, Alton
EVERSLEY GARDENS, nr Fleet
THE GILBERT WHITE MUSEUM, Selborne
JENKYN PLACE, Bentley
LOVINGTON HOUSE, nr Alresford

MONXTON GARDENS, nr Andover
29 VINCENTS CRESCENT, Horndean
TUNWORTH OLD RECTORY, nr Basingstoke
WONSTON LODGE, nr Winchester

JULY Monday 13
LOVINGTON HOUSE, nr Alresford
29 ST VINCENTS CRESCENT, Horndean

JULY Saturday 18
HINTON AMPNER, nr Alresford

JULY Sunday 19
BRAMDEAN HOUSE, nr Alresford
CHERITON COTTAGE, nr Alresford
CLOVER FARM, Shalden, nr Alton
COMPTON END, nr Winchester
THE GILBERT WHITE MUSEUM, Selborne
HINTON AMPNER, nr Alresford
ROTHERFIELD PARK, nr Alton
UPHAM GARDENS, nr Bishops Waltham
WHITE WINDOWS, Longparish

JULY Monday 20
COMPTON END, nr Winchester
WHITE WINDOWS, Longparish

JULY Sunday 26
THE GILBERT WHITE MUSEUM, Selborne
‡HILL HOUSE, nr Alresford
‡THE WEIR HOUSE, Alresford

AUGUST Sunday 2
MANOR HOUSE, Newton Stacey
ROTHERFIELD PARK nr Alton

AUGUST Monday 3
MANOR HOUSE, Newton Stacey

AUGUST Sunday 9
‡MARTYR WORTHY MANOR, nr Winchester
OAKLEY MANOR, Church Oakley
‡THE WORTHYS, Martyr Worthy

AUGUST Sunday 16
BRAMDEAN HOUSE, nr Alresford

AUGUST Sunday 23 & Monday 24
COMPTON END, nr Winchester

SEPTEMBER Sunday 6
CHILLAND, Martyr Worthy
NORTHREPPS, East Boldre, Lymington
SOUTHWOOD HOUSE, Itchen Abbas

SEPTEMBER Monday 7
CHILLAND, Martyr Worthy

SEPTEMBER Sunday 13
GREATHAM MILL, nr Liss

SEPTEMBER Sunday 20
MILL COURT, Alton

OCTOBER Sunday 4
COLD HAYES, Steep Marsh

OCTOBER Sunday 11
HACKWOOD PARK, nr Basingstoke

DESCRIPTIONS OF GARDENS

Alverstoke Gardens ✿ Gosport Follow A32 from Fareham S to Fort Brockhurst roundabout; right to Stokes Bay; 2nd left after next roundabout is Westernway/Vectis Rd/Solent Way. Buses from Gosport Ferry 2m. Refreshments at 22 Western Way . *Combined adm £1 Chd 40p. (Share to Wessex Medical School Trust). Suns May 10 & July 12 (2-6)*

22 Western Way ♿ (Mr & Mrs J Maunder) practical garden; flowers, fruit; vegetables

59 Vectis Rd ❀ (Miss M.W. Singleton) Small suburban garden of botanical interest on corner site; bulbs, rare shrubs, small pond; herbaceous borders; bog garden; rock pool

23 Solent Way ❀ (Mr & Mrs H.S. Saverymuttu) Small garden of interesting plants; rare bulbs; shrubs from Southern Hemisphere, herbaceous perennials; rockery

Ashford Gardens ♿ Steep, nr Petersfield. 2m N of Petersfield, off Alresford Rd (no. C18); turn right ½m past Cricketers Inn at Steep. 12 acres set in valley of the Ash under steep wooded hangers of Stoner and Wheatham, described by poet Edward Thomas (who lived for a time at Berryfield before killed in France in 1917). Landscaped pools; waterfalls, beautiful trees; unusual shrubs, banks of azaleas and rhododendrons add colour and variety to this naturally lovely setting. TEAS. *Combined adm £1 Chd 25p. Suns April 12, May 17 (2-6)*

Ashford Chace (Ashford Chace Ltd)
Berryfield (Mr & Mrs Douglas Harris)
Old Ashford Manor (J. Abrahams Esq)

Beechenwood Farm ♿✿❀ (Mr & Mrs M. Heber Percy) Hillside; turn S off A287 2m E of Odiham, follow signs for Roke and Park Corner. Newly created 2-acre garden; woodland garden with spring bulbs; orchard; rock garden; conservatory; vegetable and fruit gardens. TEAS. *Adm 60p Chd 30p. Mon April 20 (2-5) Sun May 31 (2-6)*

Bramdean House ✿❀ (Mr & Mrs H. Wakefield) In Bramdean village on A272. Carpets of spring bulbs. Walled garden with famous herbaceous borders, large collection of unusual plants. *Adm £1 Chd 10p (Share to Bramdean Parish Church). Sun March 15, Sun, Mon April 19, 20, Suns May 17, June 21, July 19, Aug 16 (2-5); also by appt*

Broadhatch House ♿✿❀ (Mr & Mrs P. Powell) Bentley; 4m NE of Alton; on A31 between Farnham/Alton; Bus AV452; go up School Lane. 3½ acres formal garden, double herbaceous borders; rose gardens, old fashioned roses; unusual flowering shrubs. TEAS at Church. *Adm 80p Chd 20p. Suns July 5, 12 (2-6)*

Brockenhurst Park ♿ (The Hon Mrs Denis Berry, Mr & Mrs Richard Berry) Brockenhurst. Entrance by St Nicholas Church off A337 S of railway Xing. Bus: Hants and Dorset 56, Southampton-Lymington; alight Island Shop, Brockenhurst, 1m. 10 acres; woodland garden; rhododendrons, azaleas, interesting young trees and shrubs; old trees, ponds, steps, hedges, topiary. Modern house on site of old house. Beautiful undulating parkland. Tea Brockenhurst. *Adm 80p OAPs/Chd 40p (Share to Wessex Medical School Trust). Sun, Mon May 24, 25 (2-6)*

Brook House ♿ (Mr & Mrs Carron Greig) 1½m N of Fleet. B3013; immediately N of M3 Motorway bridge. Medium-sized garden; walled garden with swimming pool; lawns; herbaceous borders with water; walled kitchen garden; woodland walks. TEA. *Adm 60p Chd 30p (Share to Sue Ryder Foundation). Sun June 21 (2-6)*

Buriton Gardens 3m S of Petersfield off A3. Beside village pond. TEAS. *Combined adm £1 Chd 25p. Sun July 12 (2-6)*

The Manor House ♿ (C.R. Wood Esq) One time home of Edward Gibbon, author of Decline and Fall of Roman Empire, who describes in his autobiography, the prospect from the garden of the 'long hanging woods which could not have been improved by art or expense'! Walled garden, old fashioned rose walk; swimming pool. C18 Dovecote

The Old Rectory ♿ (Mr & Mrs R.A. Wilson) Walled garden; old fashioned roses; very ancient Cedar of Lebanon

Burkham House ♿ (Mr & Mrs D.Norman) 5m NW of Alton. From A339 between Basingstoke and Alton, on Alton side of Herriard, turn off W for Burkham. 10 acres with trees and shrubs. TEA. *Adm 50p Chd 15p. Sun May 31 (2.30-5.30)*

Byways ✗ (Mr & Mrs J.A.F. Binny) Castle Hill Lane, Burley, 6m SE of Ringwood. 1m S from centre of Burley on Bransgore rd. Alpine garden made by the late E.D. Doncaster about 1926; also camellias, magnolias, rhododendrons, roses and other interesting trees and shrubs. NO DOGS. Tea Forest Tea House, Burley. *Adm £1 Chd 50p (Share to Wessex Nuffield Hospital). Sun April 26 (2-6)*

Castletop ♿❀ (Mrs Mackworth-Praed) Castle Hill Lane, Burley, E of Ringwood. A31 to Picket Post, turn S to Burley; ¼m. Bus: HD X17, alight Burley Street. 8 acres; woodland walks; bulbs, rhododendrons (mostly species), camellias, magnolias. TEAS. *Adm 50p OAPs/Chd 25p. Suns April 5, May 3 (2-6)*

Chantry ✗ (Adm Sir Geoffrey & Lady Norman) 100 Acres Rd, 1m E of Wickham. 4m N of Fareham via A32. From Wickham Church turn E along A333 for 1m then left up 100 Acres Rd for 300yds. Garden entirely made by owners with a view to easy maintenance; included in *Gardens of Britain*. Tea Olde Tea Shoppe, Wickham. *Adm 60p Chd 10p. Sun May 17 (2-6)*

Cheriton Cottage ♿✗❀ (Mr & Mrs I. Garnett-Orme) Cheriton, 3m S of Alresford, B3046 in centre of village. 3 acre landscape garden with chalk stream (R. Itchen near source). Trees, shrubs, roses, spring bulbs, lawns. Tea Cheriton. *Adm 50p. Suns Feb 22 (2-4), April 12, June 14, July 19 (2-6)*

Chilland ♿ (L.A. Impey Esq) 4m NE of Winchester, between Martyr Worthy and Itchen Abbas B3047. Bus: 214. Mature garden; fine situation; shrub borders designed for foliage colour many interesting plants. *Adm 60p Chd 25p. Suns, Mons March 22, 23; May 24,25; Sept 6, 7 (2-7)*

Chilworth Manor ♿✗ (University of Southampton) Chilworth, N of Southampton. Signed from Clump Inn on A27, 1m NW of junc with A33. Bus: Hants & Dorset 62 Romsey-Southampton, alight Clump Inn, ¼m. 15 acres, largely informal; well-matured flowering shrubs, mainly rhododendrons; azaleas; conifers; fine specimen trees; walks through woodland beyond garden with indigenous varieties. *Adm 50p Chd 20p. Sun May 31 (2-7)*

¶**Church Farm** ✗❀ (Mr & Mrs W.J.L.Parsons) Westdean 9m E of Salisbury. Take A36, after 4m left to W Dean. Over level Xing, bear left, after 100 yds fork up drive. 1½-acres surrounding early C17 farmhouse with ancient tithe barn;old walled garden; unusual plants, herbaceous borders, shrubs, fruit, kitchen garden. TEAS. *Adm 50p Chd 25p (Share to Salisbury Hospice Trust). Sun June 28 (2-6)*

The Clock House ♿ (Mr & Mrs David Gibbs) Northwood Park, Sparsholt, 3m W of Winchester. Turn off A272 Winchester - Stockbridge rd opp white railings of Agricultural College; signs to garden. 2 acres, mainly walled; recently planted with shrubs; conservatory with tropical plants. TEAS. *Adm 60p Chd 20p. Sun July 12 (2-6)*

Clover Farm (Mrs Lowry-Corry) Shalden, 2m NW of Alton via A339; 2m from Alton turn E for Shalden. 2-acre hillside garden planted in 1971; shrubs; bulbs, pleached lime walk. TEA. *Adm 50p Chd 25p. Sun July 19 (2-6)*

Cold Hayes (Brian Blacker Esq) Steep Marsh. Turn off A325 Petersfield-Farnham Rd to Steep Marsh. Turn off Petersfield-Alresford Rd 3m from Petersfield. From Steep village observe direction signs. Medium-sized garden; flowering shrubs, trees, beautiful views. *Adm 50p Chd 25p. Suns May 17, Oct 4 (2-6)*

Compton End ♿ (Capt & Mrs G.A. Kitchen) Compton St. at end of Compton village, 3m S of Winchester. 1½-acre formal cottage garden beautifully laid out with yew and box hedges and topiary. Pond garden, herbaceous borders, rose beds, rock garden and lawns. Thatched C15 farmhouse (not open) barn and summer house listed Grade 2. Illustrated "Homes & Gardens" March 1986, also TVS May 1986. Most colourful in Spring *Adm*

50p Chd 10p (Share to RNLI). Suns, Mons May 17, 18; (2-6) July 5, 6; 19, 20; Aug 23, 24 (2-7)

The Cottage &%⊛ (Mr & Mrs H. Sykes) 16 Lakewood Rd, Chandlers Ford. W of A33 into Merdon Ave at The Mount Hotel; take third rd on left. ¾ acre; Hostas, paeonies, herbaceous borders, rhododendrons, azaleas, magnolias, conifers, bog garden, and ponds. TEAS. *Adm 60p Chd 10p (Share to BHF) Suns May 17, (2-6) June 21*

Cranbury Park & (Mr & Mrs Chamberlayne-Macdonald) Otterbourne, 5m S of Winchester. 2m N of Eastleigh; main entrance on old A33 between Winchester/Southampton, by bus stop at top of Otterbourne Hill. Extensive pleasure grounds laid out in late C18 and early C19; fountains; rose garden; specimen trees; lakeside walk. Family carriages will be on view. *Adm £1.50 Chd 50p. Sun May 17 (2-5)*

Crawley Gardens %⊛ 5m NW of Winchester, off A272 Winchester-Stockbridge rd. Gardens signed from centre of village. *Combined adm £1 Chd free. Sun April 12 (2-5.30)*
  Glebe House & (Lt-Col & Mrs John Andrews) 1½ acres; mainly lawn, bulbs, shrubs and herbaceous borders
  Rosehill % (Mr & Mrs N.F. Le H. Guiton) A spring garden; flowering shrubs; bulbs, herbaceous and rockery
  Lithend % (Mrs F.L. Gunner) Small cottage garden. *Also open Suns June 7, July 5 (2-5.30). Combined adm Little Court 60p Chd free*
  Little Court &% (Mr & Mrs A.R. Elkington) 2 acres on different levels, entirely maintained by owners; spring bulbs, herbaceous and shrub borders with foliage interest; walled kitchen garden. Free-range bantams. *Also open Suns June 7, July 5. Combined adm Lithend 60p Chd free*

Croylands &% (The Hon Mrs Charles Kitchener) Romsey. From Romsey take A3057, Stockbridge Rd, left after 1m at Duke's Head, fork left after bridge, 1m on right. Wheelwright's cottage on Florence Nightingale's Family Estate, surrounded by 2 acres unusual, interesting trees, shrubs and plants. Peony garden. Home-made TEAS. *Adm 50p Chd 25p. Suns June 14, 21, Wed June 17 (2-6)*

Culverlea House &⊛ (Brig & Mrs R.A. Blakeway) Pennington Common, 1m W of Lymington. A337 Lymington-Bournemouth; turn N at Pennington Cross, through village, 1st house on left past common. 1 acre with wide variety of trees, flowering shrubs, old/new roses, mist propagation, automatic greenhouse. Tea Lymington. *Adm 40p Chd 20p. Sun July 12 (2-6)*

The Dower House &% (Mr & Mrs Michael Hoare) Dogmersfield. Turn N off A287. Medium-sized garden; bluebell wood with collection of over 200 different varieties of rhododendrons and azaleas (largely created since 1950's by Maj & Mrs Rollo Hoare); magnolias and other flowering trees and shrubs; fine views. TEA. *Adm 60p Chd 20p. Suns May 10, 17 (2-6)*

Droxford Gardens⊛ 4½m N of Wickham on A32 approx mid-way between Alton/Portsmouth. *Combined adm £1 OAPs/Chd 25p (Share to Order of St Johns). Sun June 21 (2-6)*
  Fir Hill (Mrs Derek Schreiber) in Droxford village. 5-acres roses, shrubs, herbaceous border. Country TEAS
  Mylor Cottage & (Dr & Mrs ffrench Constant) medium-sized garden; shrubs and herbaceous border.

East Worldham Manor &%⊛ (Dr & Mrs John Greaves) Alton. On B3004 at top of hill in E Worldham turn up lane marked "Private Rd" Manor Farm and take left fork. 1½ acres; herbaceous border; rockery; rose beds; shrubs, view towards S Harting. TEAS. *Adm 50p Chd 20p. Suns June 28, July 12 (2-6)*

Eversley Gardens &⊛ 4m N of Fleet B3016 between A30 and A327 *Combined adm £1 Chd free. Suns May 10, 24; July 12 (2-6)*
  Kiln Copse (Mrs Jervis O'Donohoe) 8 acres; bluebell wood; foxgloves; good collection of rhododendrons; mixed border; roses; natural lake; bog garden. TEAS
  Little Coopers (Mr & Mrs J.K. Oldale) Use car park at Kiln Copse opp. 10 acres; lawns, woodland walk, bluebells, rhododendrons, azaleas, shrubs; water gardens

●**Exbury Gardens** & (Edmund de Rothschild Esq) Exbury, 2½m SE of Beaulieu; 15m SW of Southampton. Via B3054 SE of Beaulieu; after 1m turn sharp right for Exbury. 200 acres of woodland garden incorporating the Rothschild Collection of azaleas, rhododendrons, magnolias, maples and camellias. TEAS. *Adm £2, OAPs/Chd £1.50, under 12 free; Party rate £1.50, (Reduced rates March & July; 50p extra bank holiday week-ends and May Sundays.) Open March 7 to July 26 10-5.30 (prior to Good Friday 1-5.30) and Sept 12-Oct 25 (Adm £1). For NGS Wed April 22, Fri May 15*

Fairfield House &⊛ (Mr & Mrs Peter Wake) Hambledon. 10m SW of Petersfield. In Hambledon village on B2150. Medium-sized garden; large collection of shrub and climbing roses, mixed borders, walled gardens, fine cedar trees. Scheduled Regency house (not open). TEA. *Adm 60p Chd 30p. Open only by appt; suitable for groups (Tel Hambledon 431)*

Farley House ⚘ (Mr & Mrs B.N.A. Hardman) Farley Chamberlayne, nr Romsey, 6m W of Winchester. From A3090 Winchester-Romsey, at Standon turn W 3½m; or from Braishfield turn off A3057 signed Farley, 1m. 3 acres with herbaceous border, roses and trees surrounding Queen Anne house (not open). TEA. *Adm 50p Chd 25p. Sun June 14 (2-6)*

Flood's Farm ⚘❀ (Brig & Mrs C.C. Dunphie) Dogmersfield. Turn N off A 287 for Dogmersfield ¾m. 2 acres; lawns with rose beds, shrub borders and herbaceous border. TEAS. *Adm 50p Chd 10p (Share to Queen Elizabeth's Foundation for the Disabled). Sun July 5 (2-6)*

●**Furzey Gardens** ⅍⚘❀ Minstead, 8m SW of Southampton. 1m S of A31; 2m W of Cadnam and end of M27; 3½m NW of Lyndhurst. 8 acres; informal shrub garden; comprehensive collections of azaleas and heathers; water garden; fernery; summer and winter flowering shrubs. Botanical interest at all seasons. Also open Will Selwood Gallery and ancient cottage (AD 1560); high-class arts and crafts by 150 local craftsmen. Tea Honey Pot ¼m. *Adm £1.50 (winter 90p), Chd 75p (winter 40p). Daily except Dec 25 & 26 (10.30-5; dusk in winter)*

The Gilbert White Museum ⅍⚘❀ (Oates Memorial Trust) Selborne, 4m S of Alton. From A31 S on to B3006; From Petersfield via A325 & B3006. 7 acres; C18 garden of Revd Gilbert White; many interesting features inc wild garden with naturalised bulbs, laburnum arch, old-fashioned roses, Gilbert White's annuals; herb garden, yew topiary, ha-ha, sundial, brick walk and bird hide. Museum and garden separate Adm charge. Tea Selborne. *For NGS garden only. Adm 55p Chd 30p (Share to Wakes Garden fund).* △ *Suns July 5, 12, 19, 26 (10-12 noon)*

Greatham Mill ⅍⚘❀ (Mrs E.N. Pumphrey) Greatham, nr Liss. 5m N of Petersfield (Tel: Blackmoor 219). From A325, at Greatham turn onto B3006 towards Alton; after 600yds left into 'No through rd' lane to garden. Interesting garden with large variety of plants surrounding mill house, with mill stream. *Adm 50p Chd free. April 19 to Sept 27 every Sun & Bank Hol. For NGS Suns May 10, Sept 13 (2-7)*

◆**Hackwood Park (The Spring Wood)** ⅍⚘❀ (The Viscount Camrose) 1m S of Basingstoke. Entrance off Tunworth Rd. Signed from A339 Alton-Basingstoke. 80 acres delightful C17-C18 semi-formal wood with Pavilions, walks, glades; newly replaced magnificent original C18 Hackwood entrance gates; ornamental pools, amphitheatre, interesting trees and bulbs. NO DOGS. Home-made TEAS & produce. *Adm 80p Chd 40p (Share to*

local charities). Suns April 19, May 17, Oct 11 (2-6)

Herriard Park Old Gardens ❀ (Mr & Mrs P.A. Taverner) Basingstoke. On A339 turn by White Lodge (100yds N of Herriard Church). C18 octagonal walled gardens surrounded by walk with specimen trees, rhododendrons, azaleas, bulbs. TEA. *Open all year with garden centre. Collecting box. Tues-Sat (10-6) Sun (12-5) (Oct-Feb close 5). For NGS Suns April 5, June 7 (12-5)*

Hill House ⅍ (Maj & Mrs W.F. Richardson) Old Alresford. From Alresford 1m along B3046 towards Basingstoke, then right by church. 2 acres; large herbaceous border and formal beds set around large lawn; kitchen garden. TEA. *Adm 50p Chd 10p. Sun July 26 (2-6)*

Hinton Ampner ⚘ (The National Trust) S of Alresford. On Petersfield-Winchester Rd A272. 1m W of Bramdean village. Large garden; formal layout; flowering shrubs and trees; roses. Good views. TEAS. *Adm £1 Chd 50p. Sat, Sun July 18, 19 (2-5.30)*

Holywell ⅍❀ (The Lady Rhyl) Swanmore. The Bungalow Lodge is on A32, midway between Wickham and Droxford, well signed. Bus: HD 69 from Fareham, alight Hill Pound (1m) Medium-sized garden; camellias, flowering cherry trees, woodland walks. Dogs welcome. TEA. *Adm 60p Chd 40p. Sun May 10 (2-6)*

Hordle House ⅍ (Hordle House School Trust Ltd) Milford on Sea, Lymington. Off B3058 on seaward side. Small walled garden containing collection of old fashioned and modern roses. Fine view of the Needles. TEA. *Adm 50p Chd 20p. Sun June 28 (2-6)*

Houghton Lodge ⅍⚘❀ (Capt & Mrs Martin Busk) 1½m S of Stockbridge on minor rd signed Houghton. Winchester Bus: 91 stops at gate. 5 acres Grade II landscaped pleasure grounds surround C18 "Cottage Ornee". Beautiful views over R. Test; fine display daffodils, rose garden; rare chalk cob walls enclose traditional kitchen garden; extensive greenhouses and vinery; folly. TEAS Suns, Mons. *Adm £1 Chd 50p. Every Wed, Thurs March 4 to Aug 27. Mons May 4, 25. For NGS Sun, Mon April 19, 20; (2-5)*

House-in-the-Wood (Countess Michalowski) 1½m from Beaulieu; signed from Motor Car Museum, Beaulieu (on B3054 Lymington-Hythe). 13-acre woodland garden; rhododendrons and azaleas. Coach parties by appt. (Tel Beaulieu 612346). *Adm £1.50 Chd 50p (Share to CAFOD). Mon May 25 (2.30-6.30)*

Jenkyn Place ⅍⚘❀ (Mr & Mrs G.E. Coke) Bentley. 400yds N of Xrds in Bentley signed Crondall. Bus: Guildford-Winchester, alight

Bentley village, 400yds. Well designed garden with large collection of rare plants, roses, double herbaceous borders. Car park free (Coaches only by prior appt). *Adm £1 Chd 50p. Thurs, Fris, Sats, Suns & Bank Hol Mons April 16 to Sept 13 (2-6). For NGS Suns June 14, July 12*

Kingsmead ᕱ⚹ (Mr & Mrs Hopkinson) Kingsgate Rd, Winchester. A33 to St Cross Rd, Winchester; turn off at Norman Rd; house on corner of Norman Rd and Kingsgate Rd. ½ acre with collection of roses; rare shrubs and plants; extensive rockery. TEAS June 21 outdoors. *Adm 50p Chd 10p. Suns April 26, June 21, July 5 (2-6)*

Laverstoke House ᕱ (Julian Sheffield Esq) 2m E of Whitchurch; 10m W of Basingstoke. Garden with fine trees, shrubs and bulbs, surrounding C18 house (not open). TEA. *Adm 80p Chd 20p. Sun July 5 (2-5.30)*

Lisle Court Cottage ᕱ⚹ (The Lord & Lady O'Neill of the Maine) Lisle Court Rd, Lymington. From Lymington Pier Station (IOW Car Ferry) follow rd E for 1m at small Xrds right; garden within ½m. 2 acres overlooking Solent; borders of hardy and half-hardy shrubs; small woodland garden. *Adm 50p Chd 10p. Sat, Sun June 6, 7 (2-6)*

Little Chesters ᕱ⚹❀ (Mrs B.H.M. Hatch) Eversley. On A327 9m S Reading, 7m W Camberley. Next to "White Hart" in The Street. Parking "White Hart" by kind permission. ¾-acre flower arrangers garden; shrubs, herbaceous, roses. Black and white beamed Grade II listed cottage (not open). TEAS. *Adm 50p Chd free (Share to Wessex Medical School Trust). Sun June 28 (2-6); also by appt*

Little Langleys (Mr & Mrs Tim Jenkins) Steep. 2m N of Petersfield on Petersfield-Alresford rd, at Cricketers Inn turn E; after 350yds left down Mill Lane; then ½m on left. 5 acres; spring bulbs; flowering cherries, azaleas, camellias, magnolias; rhododendrons; fine flowering trees and shrubs; rock garden; wild garden; kitchen garden. Magnificent views. Featured BBC TV's *Exploring Gardens,* 1985. TEA April 26, May 3. *Adm 50p Chd 15p. Suns April 26, May 3, 17, 24 (2-6)*

Longparish House ᕱ (Mr & Mrs A.T. Etridge) Longparish, 5½m E of Andover. 3½m SW of Whitchurch, on B3048. 3½ acres; mainly wild garden with daffodils and other spring bulbs naturalised in grass. R. Test runs through garden. Elizabethan granary on straddle stones. Col Peter Hawker (1786-1853), famous sportsman, lived here.TEAS. *Adm 50p Chd 10p. Sun April 19 (2.30-5.30)*

Longstock Park Gardens ᕱ⚹❀ (Leckford Estate Ltd; Part of John Lewis Partnership) 3m N of Stockbridge. From A30 turn N on to A3057; follow signs to Longstock. 7 acres woodland and water garden; extensive collection of aquatic and bog plants. Walk through park from water garden leads to arboretum, herbaceous border. *Adm £1 Chd 50p. Sun June 21 (2-5)*

Lovington House (Sir Geoffrey Hawkings) Ovington, nr Alresford. A31 1m W Alresford; right to Ovington; 1st right after Bush Inn; house 400yds on right. 2 acres mixed herbaceous and shrubs with "River Walk" along a carrier of the R. Itchen designated an SSI. TEA. *Adm 70p Chd 10p (Share to The Order of St John, Hampshire). Sun, Mon July 12, 13 (2-6)*

Macpenny Nurseries (Mr & Mrs T.M. Lowndes) Burley Road, Bransgore. Midway between Christchurch and Burley. From Christchurch via A35, at Cat and Fiddle turn left; at Xrds by the Crown, Bransgore turn right and on ¼m. From A31 (travelling towards Bournemouth) left at Picket Post, signed Burley; through Burley to Green Triangle then right for Bransgore and on 1m beyond Thorney Hill Xrds. 12 acres; gravel pit converted into woodland garden; many choice, rare plants inc camellias, rhododendrons, azaleas, heathers. Tea Burley (Forest Tearooms) or Holmsley (Old Station Tea Rooms). *Collecting box. Daily except Dec 25 & 26 (Mons-Sats 9-5 Suns 2-5)*

Manor House ᕱ⚹❀ (Mrs G.S.V. & Mr J.E.R. Govett) Newton Stacey, Stockbridge. 5m SE of Andover off A303. Right by church follow signs. Medium-sized garden; terraced lawns with formal bedding. Ornamental ponds; walled kitchen garden and greenhouse. TEA. *Adm 60p Chd 20p (Share to All Saints Barton Stacey) Sun, Mon Aug 2, 3 (2-6)*

Martyr Worthy Manor ᕱ❀ (Cdr & Mrs M.J. Rivett-Carnac) 3m NE of Winchester; on B3047; white gates in Martyr Worthy, opp War memorial. Bus: AV 214 Winchester-Aldershot. 4 acres; roses, mixed borders, interesting trees and shrubs. Next to fine C11 church on Pilgrims Way; and river walk. TEA. *Adm 50p Chd 20p. Sun Aug 9 (2-6)*

Marycourt ᕱ❀ (Mr & Mrs M. Conville) Odiham 2m S of Hartley Wintney on A30 or Exit 5 on M3; In Odiham High St. 1-acre garden and paddocks. Old garden roses; shrubs; ramblers dripping from trees. New borders ('85 shrubaceous, '86 Pink/Silver and Dry Stone Wall/alpines) thriving. Very colourful herbaceous border. Schedule 'A' house. TEAS Sun 28 only. *Adm 60p Chd 20p (Share to Jonathan Conville Memorial Trust). Suns June 28, July 5 (2-6.30) Mon July 6 (all day)*

Merdon Manor ᕱ⚹❀ (Mr & Mrs J.C. Smith) Hursley, SW of Winchester. From A3090 Winchester-Romsey, at Standon turn on to Slackstead rd; on 2m. Medium-sized garden; fine views; roses, herbaceous border; small formal walled water garden. TEA. *Adm 80p Chd 20p. Sun May 31 (2-6) Also by appt (Tel 0962 75215)*

Michelmersh Court & (Lt-Cmdr & Mrs R. S. de Chair) 4½m N of Romsey. From A3057 Romsey-Stockbridge rd, at Timsbury turn E for Michelmersh. Medium-size garden; peacocks, roses, herbaceous borders, fine trees, woodland walk, C18 Georgian house (not open). Historic church adjoins. Refreshments. *Adm 60p Chd 40p. Sun April 5 (2-6)*

Mill Court & ⊛ (Leila, Viscountess Hampden) 3m NE of Alton, on S side of A31. Turn off at County sign marked Mill Court; immediately after crossing R. Wey, gate and lodge. Medium-sized garden bounded by early stone farm buildings; walls; fine large stone granary with Tudor dwelling attached; herbaceous border; roses, many climbing with clematis; varied collection of shrubs, many with good autumn colours; rare weeping beech at main gate. *Adm 50p Chd 10p. Suns May 17, Sept 20 (2.30-6)*

Monxton Gardens ⊗⊛ 3m W of Andover, between A303 and A343; in Monxton at Xrds take Abbots Ann rd. Parking, picnicking, TEA Field House. *Combined adm 80p Chd 10p. Wed July 8, Suns July 5, 12 (2-5)*
> **Field House** (Dr & Mrs Pratt) 2-acre garden made by owners; herbaceous borders, orchard, chalk-pit garden with pond and kitchen garden
> **Mill Pound Cottage** (Mr & Mrs P. R. Coldicott) Small neat garden by chalk stream. Shrubs, perennials and annuals; greenhouse and vegetables

Mottisfont Abbey &⊗ (The National Trust) Mottisfont, 4½m NW of Romsey. From A3057 Romsey-Stockbridge turn W at sign to Mottisfont. 3 wheelchairs available at garden. 30 acres; originally a C12 Priory; landscaped grounds with spacious lawns bordering R. Test; magnificent trees; remarkable ancient spring pre-dating the Priory; walled garden contains NT's large collection of old-fashioned roses; new extension now open. Tea Mottisfont PO. *Adm £1.50 Chd 75p. △ Wed June 17 (2-6)*

¶**Mottisfont House** ⊗ (Mr & Mrs J. Clutterbuck) nr Romsey. 4½m NW of Romsey. From A3047 turn W at sign to Mottisfont. 4½ acre Old Rectory garden with borders; river and old fashioned roses; lawns and lovely old trees. *Adm 50p Chd 25p (Share to St Andrews Church, Mottisfont). Sun June 28, Wed July 1 (2-6)*

Moundsmere Manor & (Mr & Mrs Andreae) 6m S of Basingstoke on B3046. Drive gates on left just after Preston Candover sign. 20 acres, inc formal rose gardens; herbaceous borders, large greenhouses, unusual trees

and shrubs. Coaches by appt. *Adm 50p Chd 30p. Sun July 5 (2-6)*

Northrepps &⊗ (Mr & Mrs J. McPhie), Main Rd, East Boldre. Leave Lymington on B3054, at Hatchett pond turn right to East Boldre, 1m on left. Small garden, mainly flowering shrubs and trees. *Adm 40p Chd 10p. Mon May 25, Sun Sept 6 (10-6)*

Oakley Manor &⊗⊛ (Mr & Mrs Priestley) Church Oakley. W of Basingstoke. From B3400, Basingstoke-Whitchurch, take turn to Church Oakley. Bus: WD 303 Basingstoke-Church Oakley. Medium-sized garden; lawns; trees; small water garden; borders; rose garden; greenhouses. TEA. *Adm 50p Chd 20p (Share to HAYC). Sun Aug 9 (2-6.30)*

The Old House &⊛ (Mr & Mrs M. Jurgens) Bramley road, Silchester; entrance next to Silchester (Calleva) Roman Museum. Queen Anne rectory with large garden. Camellias; rhododendrons, azaleas, shrub borders, shrub roses, paddocks, ponds, bluebell woodlands. Fine selection of specimen trees and shrubs, spring garden. Roman town walls and Amphitheatre ¼m; medieval Church. TEAS. *Adm 75p OAPs/Chd 30p (Share to St Mary The Virgin Church, Silchester). Suns May 17, 31, June 14 (2-6)*

●**Palace House** &⊛ (Lord Montagu of Beaulieu) Beaulieu. A35 to Lyndhurst, turn off onto B3056. *Adm inc Palace House, Gardens, National Motor Museum and "Wheels", Beaulieu Abbey and exhibition of Monastic Life. TEAS. Open daily (ex Dec 25) all year. Oct - Easter (10-5); Easter - Sept (10-6)*

Pennington Chase see Stop press, pg. 201

Pennington House & (The Lord Lurgan) 2m S of Lymington. From A337 Lymington-Bournemouth turn S of Xrds. Large garden; interesting collection of trees, shrubs and herbaceous plants; water garden. *Adm £1 Chd 50p. Sun May 3 (2-7)*

Plovers &⊗ (Col & Mrs L. Mac L. Young) Main Rd, East Boldre. 5m NE of Lymington, take rd E from Lymington IoW ferry terminal to E Boldre. Garden on E side of rd 1m past E End and ¾m S of E Boldre Church. ½ acre garden designed for year-round interest. *Adm 40p Chd 20p. Sun May 3 (2-6)*

145 Portsmouth Road ⊗ (Mr and Mrs A. H. Wilson) Horndean, on main road between Horndean and Cowplain. A new garden being developed in 1½-acre woodland featuring lawns and classical terrace adjacent to house with borders; stocked with wide selection of shrubs, floribunda roses and perennials giving way to woodland being developed with rhododendrons etc. *Adm 50p Chd 10p. Sun June 14 (2-6)*

◆**Pylewell Park** (W. Whitaker Esq) 2½m E of Lymington beyond IoW car ferry. Large garden of botanical interest; good trees, flowering shrubs, rhododendrons, lake woodland garden. *Adm 75p Chd 10p. Suns May 3, 17, 24 (2-6)*

Rookley Manor ⚘ (The Hon R.C.R. & Mrs Hoyer Millar) Upper Somborne, 6m W of Winchester. Take A272 Winchester-Stockbridge rd; turn left at Rack and Manger for King's Somborne; Upper Somborne 2m on right. 2 acres; spring bulbs, flowers and blossom; herbaceous, shrub roses; kitchen garden. TEAS. *Adm 80p Chd 20p. Sun, Mon May 3, 4 (2-6)*

Rotherfield Park ර (Sir James & Lady Scott) East Tisted, 4m S of Alton on A32. Large garden; walled and rose garden, herbaceous borders; lovely grounds with beautiful trees; very good greenhouses. Picknickers welcome. TEA. *Adm £1 Chd free (Share to other Charities). Suns May 31, June 14, 28, July 5, 19, Aug 2 (12-5); Also by appt (Tel 042058 204)*

Rotherwick Gardens ර⚘❀ 2½m N of Hook via A32. TEAS Village Hall. *Combined adm (tickets from The Ricks) £1.25 Chd 50p. Sun June 28 (2-6)*

  1 Wogsbarne Cottages (Mr & Mrs Whistler)
  2 Wogsbarne Cottages (E. Povey Esq)
  3 Wogsbarne Cottages (Mr & Mrs May)
  The Ricks (Mr & Mrs Morris)
  Froglane Farm (Mr & Mrs Platt)
  The Old Rectory (Mrs Hutchings)

Rumsey Gardens ර❀ (Mr & Mrs N.R. Giles) 117 Drift Rd, Clanfield, 6m S of Petersfield. Turn off A3 N of Horndean, signed Clanfield. 2 acres; alpine, herbaceous; heather, rhododendrons and wild gardens. *Adm 50p Chd 25p. Sun, Mon May 10, 11 (11-5)*

29 St Vincent Crescent ර⚘❀ (Mr & Mrs B. West) 8m S of Petersfield on A3; after leaving Horndean village proceed for ½m to roundabout; right into Catherington Lane; then 2nd turn on right. Small garden designed by owners for easy maintenance and all year round interest. Trees, shrubs, heathers; foliage plants. Roses and begonias grown for exhibition. TEA. *Adm 40p Chd 20p. Sat, Sun, Mon July 11, 12, 13 (10-5). Also by appt (Tel Horndean 591750)*

♦**Somerley** ⚘ (The Earl of Normanton) N of Ringwood. Turn W off A338 at Ellingham. Bus: Bournemouth-Salisbury, alight Ellingham Cross, 1m. Medium-sized garden, wonderful views over Avon valley; formal lay-out; herbaceous borders. *Adm 75p. Sun June 21 (2-6)*

¶**Southwood House** ⚘ (Sir Robert & Lady Atkinson) Itchen Abbas, 3½m E of Winchester. Take the B3047 from Kingsworthy Corner on the A33 or the A31 through Alresford, then B3047 through Itchen Abbas. House clearly signed. 1½-acre garden. Lawns, herbaceous, interesting shrubs and fruit trees; greenhouses. Recently rebuilt and stocked. A detailed and complex garden for its size. Field backs onto River Itchen and Pilgrims Way. TEAS. *Adm 50p Chd 20p. Sun Sept 6 (2-5.30)*

●**Spinners** ⚘❀ (Mr & Mrs P.G.G. Chappell) School Lane, Boldre, 1½m N of Lymington. From A337 Brockenhurst-Lymington, turn E for Boldre (**not** rd to Boldre Church); cross Boldre Bridge; just short of Pilley village, turn right into School Lane. Garden entirely made by owners; azaleas, rhododendrons, camellias, magnolias, etc interplanted with primulas, blue poppies and other choice woodland and ground cover plants, exhibition of flower paintings. *Adm 75p. April 20 to Sept 1 daily (10-6)*

28 Straight Mile ⚘❀ (Mrs D.C. Rowan) Ampfield, 2m E of Romsey. On A31 (S side); parking on service rd. Medium-sized woodland garden made by owners; rhododendrons, azaleas, camellias, spring bulbs, hostas and other foliage and ground cover plants; fine trees. Views. TEAS (Sun May 31) at Wodpeckers, 29, Straight Mile. *Adm 50p Chd 20p (Share to RSPCA). Sats, Suns, May 2, 3 (2-5) 30, 31 (2-6)' also by appt April 28-June 6*

●**Stratfield Saye House** ර❀ (Home of the Dukes of Wellington) Off A33, equidistant between Reading and Basingstoke. House built 1630; presented to the Great Duke in 1817; unique collection of paintings, prints, furniture, china, silver and personal mementoes of the Great Duke. Special Wellington Exhibition; Great Duke's funeral carriage. Wildfowl sanctuary; American, rose and walled gardens and grounds. Refreshments. Also, nearby, Wellington Country Park with woodlands, meadowlands and lake. TEAS. *Adm £2.60 Chd £1.30 special rates for 20 or more. (Tel 0256 882882). Sats, Suns, April; Also Mon April 20; from May 2 to Sept 27 daily except Fri (11.30-5)*

Tichborne Park ර (Mrs John Loudon) 2m S of Alresford. Drive gate between Cheriton and Alresford. Large garden with R. Itchen running through; a waterfall surrounded by fine park. Property famous for annual distribution of Tichborne Dole. Village church with Roman Catholic and Protestant altars. *Adm 60p Chd 20p. Suns April 12 (2-5), May 10 (2-6)*

Tunworth Old Rectory ර⚘ (Col The Hon & Mrs Julian Berry) 5m SE of Basingstoke. 3m from Basingstoke, turn S off A30 at sign to Tunworth. Medium-sized garden; shrubs, lawns, yew hedges, herbaceous borders; fine beech trees and ilex. Interesting beech-lined walk to church. House (not shown) scheduled as Ancient Monument, part dating to 1210; in Domesday Book with adjacent farmhouse and church. TEA. *Adm 50p Chd 25p. Sun July 12 (2-6)*

Upham Gardens ⚘ 3m Bishops Waltham on A333, small right turn to Upham by Woodmans PH. *Combined adm £1.50 or 60p per garden Chd free. Sun July 19 (2-5)*

    The Old Rectory (Mr & Mrs J. R. Vail) beside Church 1½m through village: 1-acre garden; shrubs, herbaceous borders, yew hedges, mainly replanted by present owners over last 4 years. Fine Norman Church through garden.

    Upham Farm (Mr & Mrs J. Walker) Garden made over last 10 years; shrubs, herb borders, trellis old roses, walk to small lake with ornamental ducks, wild fowl.

    West Hall (Capt & Mrs C. Chamberlen) small garden begun only 2 years ago, remade singlehanded; shrub roses, herbaceous

Upton Grey Place ☕ (Michael Wood Esq) 6m SE of Basingstoke. In Upton Grey, 1st House on Greywell Rd; from Basingstoke via Tunworth; or from Odiham via N Warnborough; M3 exit 5 via A352 to Greywell and Upton Grey. 5 acres; small partly walled garden mostly roses and flowering shrubs; arboretum. *Adm 60p Chd 30p. Sun June 28 (2-6)*

Vernon Hill House ✿ (The Lord & Lady Newton) 1m from Bishop's Waltham. Turn off Beeches Hill. Attractive 6-acre spring and summer garden; wild garden with tulips growing informally; fine trees, roses, unusual shrubs. Picnickers welcome. *Adm 50p Chd 25p (Share to Wessex Medical School Trust). Sun, Mon May 3, 4; Suns June 14, July 5 (2-7); groups by appt May, June (Tel 04893 2301)*

Verona Cottage ☕✿ (David J. Dickinson Esq) Webb Lane, Mengham, Hayling Island. 4m S of Havant. From A3023 fork left to Mengham; shops and free public car park 100yds. Regular bus service Havant-Mengham. Entrance to garden opp Rose in June pub. L-shaped medium-sized garden planted since 1976 by owner, designed for ease of maintenance with flowering shrubs and roses (inc latest floribundas) for year-round interest. TEA. *Adm 40p Chd 10p. Sun June 7 (2-6)*

¶**Vine Cottage** ✿ (Mr & Mrs C.F.Hoare) Ewshott, Farnham. NW of Farnham on B3013. Half way down Beacon Hill on left. Approx 11-acres facing north incl small orchard; collection of moisture loving plants on acid soil; small rockery and water garden; double herbaceous beds and shrubbery. *Adm 50p Chd free. Sat, Sun May 23,24, Sun June 14, Wed June 17 (2-7)*

The Vyne ☕✿ (The National Trust) Sherborne St John, 4m N of Basingstoke. Between Sherborne St John and Bramley. From

A340 turn E at NT signs. 17 acres with extensive lawns, lake, fine trees, herbaceous border. TEAS. *Adm house & garden £1.80 Chd 90p; garden only 90p Chd 45p. Sun & Bank Hols house & garden £2.20 Chd £1.10. Garden only £1.10 Chd 55p. △ Suns May 10, June 7 (2-6)*

Walhampton (Walhampton School Trust) Lymington. 1m along B3054 to Beaulieu. 20 acres with azaleas; rhododendrons; lakes; shell grotto. *Adm 75p Chd 25p. Sun May 17 (2-6)*

The Weir House ☕ (Mr & Mrs Joseph Addison) Alresford. Down Broad St, Alresford (B3046); immediately after end of the Great Weir (pond on right) turn left (signed Abbotstone); drive 150yds on left. 3 acres with lawns bordered by R. Arle; walled rose garden. Tea Alresford. *Adm 50p Chd 25p. Sun July 26 (2-6)*

¶**West Silchester Hall** (Mrs Jenny Jowett) Bramley Road, Silchester. Off A340 between Reading and Basingstoke. 1½-acres; rhododendrons, azaleas, many rare spring and summer plants; herbaceous borders; pond and water garden. Kitchen garden. Mrs Jowett is a botanical artist. *Adm 50p Chd 25p. Sun June 7 (2-6)*

West Tytherley Gardens ☕✿ 10m E of Salisbury; 10m NW of Romsey. From A30 4½m W of Stockbridge take turn S signed West Tytherley/Norman Court. TEAS. *Adm 50p each garden Chd 25p Sun June 28 (2-6)*

    Nutshell Cottage (Mr & Mrs H. Shearman) Nr turn to Northaw School on through rd, 1 acre; natural, open, casually planted and relaxing. Cottage of individual charm; also open Sat June 27

    The Old Rectory ✿ (Mr & Mrs C.McVeigh) From village take turning signed Northaw School; house half way up hill on left. Georgian Rectory set in pretty garden with herbaceous borders, shrubs; kitchen garden.

White Windows ☕✿✿ (Mr & Mrs B. Sterndale-Bennett) Longparish. 5m E of Andover off A303 to village centre on B3048. ⅔-acre with unusual range of hardy herbaceous plants and shrubs planted for foliage effect. TEAS. *Adm 50p Chd 10p (Share to NCCPG). Sun, Mon July 19, 20 (2-6)*

Withy Dell ✿ (Mrs Mary Holmes) Valley Lane, Thorney Hill, Bransgore. Between Ringwood and Christchurch (each 5m). Turn E off Burley-Bransgore rd at Thorney Hill on rd to Holmsley; 2nd right down steep gravel lane to double garage; limited parking. Thatched cottage with ⅓-acre garden; semi-wild woodland; stream. TEA. *Adm 50p Chd free. Weds May 20, 27 (2-5)*

Wonston Lodge ⚸ (Admiral of The Fleet Sir Henry & Lady Leach) Wonston. A34 or A30 to Sutton Scotney. At War Memorial turn to Wonston/Stoke Charity; ¾m in Wonston centre. 3 acres; owner maintained. Pond with aquatic plants; shrub roses; clematis; flowering shrubs; topiary. TEA. *Adm 60p Chd free. Sun July 12 (2-6)*

Woodcote Manor & (Mrs J.S. Morton) Bramdean, SE of Alresford. On A272 Winchester-Petersfield, ½m E of Bramdean. Woodland garden; bulbs, shrubs. C17 manor house (not open). TEA. *Adm 50p Chd 10p (Share to Friends to Bramdean Church). Sun April 19 (2-5)*

Woodgreen Gardens 3m NE of Fordingbridge via A338, turn E to Woodgreen; bear left in village; right at Horse & Groom to Common (park on common for Merrie Cottage), for other gardens continue on same rd. TEAS Merrie Cottage. *Combined adm £1.50 Chd £75p (Share to Salisbury Spire Appeal). Sun June 14 (2-6)*

Merrie Cottage ⚸ (Mr & Mrs C.K. Thornton) 1-acre damp garden on sloping site, newly planted with interesting varieties **Fiddlers Cottage** ✿ (Group Capt & Mrs T.C. Musgrave) Enter through garden of Little Barn. 3 acres of woodland with informal plantings of shrubs, bulbs and groundcover plants. Areas of heather mown to replace conventional grass lawns **Little Barn** &✿ (Drs R. & V.A. Crawford) 2½ acres mainly mature garden; newly developed area of peat and scree gardens; rock garden and ponds

The Worthys & (Nicolas McAndrew Esq) Martyr Worthy, 2m NE of Winchester, from Alresford or Winchester By-pass, turn onto B3047 white gates between Abbots Worthy and bridge over M3. 2 acres with R. Itchen flowing through; water garden with shrubs, herbaceous borders; interesting trees. *Adm 50p Chd 20p. Sun Aug 9 (2-5.30)*

Wyck Place (Lady Bonham Carter) 3m E of Alton, between A31 and B3004. Display of snowdrops, aconites; other winter flowers, early flowering shrubs. Picnics welcomed. *Adm 30p Chd free. Sats, Suns Feb 14, 15; 21, 22; 28, March 1; 7, 8 (2-5)*

The Wylds & (Gulf International) Warren Rd, Liss Forest. 6m N of Petersfield; follow signs from Greatham on A325 and Rake on A3. 40 acres; 10-acre lake; 100 acres of woodland; rhododendrons, azaleas, heathers; many other shrubs and trees. TEA. *Adm 75p Chd 25p. Sun May 31 (2-6)*

HEREFORD & WORCESTER

Hon County Organisers:
(Hereford) MRS RICHARD CURTIS, Tarrington Court nr Hereford
(Worcester) MRS GRAEME ANTON, Summerway, Torton, nr Kidderminster

DATES OF OPENING

REGULAR OPENINGS for dates see text:
ABBEY DORE COURT, nr Hereford
BREDON SPRINGS, Ashton-u-Hill
BROOKSIDE, nr Bromyard
EASTGROVE COTTAGE GARDENS NURSERY, nr Little Witley
HERGEST CROFT GARDENS, Kington
HOW CAPLE COURT, Ross-on-Wye
MOCCAS COURT, nr Herford
OLD COURT NURSERIES, Colwall
THE PRIORY, Kemerton
STONE HOUSE COTTAGE GARDENS, nr Kidderminster

APRIL Sunday 12
FROGMORE, nr Ross-on-Wye
GARNONS, nr Hereford
LITTLE MALVERN COURT, Malvern
OVERBURY COURT, nr Tewkesbury
APRIL Good Friday 17
SPETCHLEY PARK, nr Worcester
APRIL Easter Sunday 19
BROOKSIDE, nr Bromyard
APRIL Thursday 23
HOLLAND HOUSE, Cropthorne
APRIL Sunday 26
RIPPLE HALL, nr Tewkesbury
WICHENFORD COURT, nr Worcester
WORMINGTON GRANGE, nr Broadway
MAY Sunday 3
ARLEY HOUSE, nr Kidderminster
BARBERS, nr Worcester
STONE HOUSE COTTAGE GARDENS, nr Kidderminster
MAY Monday 4 (Bank Hol)
CONDERTON MANOR, nr Tewkesbury
MAY Saturday 9
CLACK'S FARM, Ombersley
MAY Sunday 10
BARNARD'S GREEN HOUSE, Malvern
BARBERS, nr Worcester
BODENHAM ARBORETUM, Wolverley
CLACK'S FARM, Ombersley
THE HILL COURT, Ross-on-Wye
SPETCHLEY PARK, nr Worcester
STONE HOUSE COTTAGE GARDENS, nr Kidderminster
MAY Saturday 16
LOEN, nr Bewdley

MAY Sunday 17
ST JAMES & THE ABBEY SCHOOL, West Malvern
STONE HOUSE COTTAGE GARDENS, nr Kidderminster
WIND'S POINT, British Camp, nr Malvern
MAY Monday 18 - Saturday 23
LOEN, nr Bewdley
MAY Friday 22
HERGEST CROFT GARDENS, Kington
MAY Sunday 24
CLENT HALL, Stourbridge
DINMORE MANOR, Leominster
GLEN WYE, Courtfield
HAFFIELD, nr Ledbury
THE PRIORY, Kemerton
STONE HOUSE COTTAGE GARDENS, nr Kidderminster
MAY Monday 25 (Bank Hol)
CLENT HALL, Stourbridge
LOEN, Bewdley
MAY Tuesday 26
CLENT HALL, Stourbridge
MAY Sunday 31
CLENT HALL, Stourbridge
SPETCHLEY PARK, nr Worcester
STONE HOUSE COTTAGE GARDENS, nr Kidderminster
JUNE Sunday 7
BARBERS, nr Worcester
CLENT HALL, Stourbridge
GLEBE HOUSE, Colwall
STONE HOUSE COTTAGE GARDENS, nr Kidderminster
WHITFIELD, nr Hereford
JUNE Saturday 13
CLACK'S FARM, Ombersley
JUNE Sunday 14
CLACK'S FARM, Bmbersley
FROGMORE, nr Ross-on-Wye
LAKESIDE, Whitbourne
STONE HOUSE COTTAGE GARDENS, nr Kidderminster
JUNE Sunday 21
BELL'S CASTLE, Kemerton
BIRTSMORTON COURT, nr Malvern
MOCCAS COURT, nr Hereford
THE PRIORY, Kemerton
STONE HOUSE COTTAGE GARDENS, nr Kidderminster
JUNE Wednesday 24
PERSHORE COLLEGE OF HORTICULTURE, Pershore
JUNE Sunday 28
THE HILL COURT, Ross-on-Wye
HOW CAPLE COURT, Ross-on-Wye
LITTLE MALVERN COURT, Malvern
STONE HOUSE COTTAGE GARDENS, nr Kidderminster
YEW TREE HOUSE, Ombersley
JULY Sunday 5
BERRINGTON HALL, Leominster
CROFT CASTLE, nr Leominster
GRANTSFIELD, nr Leominster
HANBURY HALL, nr Droitwich
HARTLEBURY CASTLE, nr Kidderminster

HOLLAND HOUSE, Cropthorne
LANE HOUSE FARM, Redditch
WICHENFORD COURT, nr Worcester
WITLEY PARK HOUSE, nr Worcester
JULY Saturday 11
CLACK'S FARM, Ombersley
HOLBEACH HOUSE, nr Kidderminster
JULY Sunday 12
BRAMPTON BRYAN HALL, nr Knighton
BREDON POUND, Ashton-u-Hill
CLACK'S FARM, Ombersley
FROGMORE, nr Ross-on-Wye
GATLEY PARK, Leinthall Earles
THE ORCHARD FARM, Broadway
OVERBURY COURT, nr Tewkesbury
STONEHOUSE COTTAGE GARDENS, nr Kidderminster
SUMMERWAY, Torton
JULY Saturday 18
PONTRILAS COURT, Pontrilas
JULY Sunday 19
ARLEY COTTAGE, Upper Arley, nr Bewdley
BREDENBURY COURT, nr Bromyard
MADRESFIELD COURT, nr Malvern
PONTRILAS COURT, Pontrilas
AUGUST Saturday 1
THE ELMS, Colwall
HOLLAND HOUSE, Cropthorne
AUGUST Sunday 2
THE ELMS, Colwall
AUGUST Saturday 8 & Sunday 9
CLACK'S FARM, Ombersley
AUGUST Sunday 23
THE PRIORY, Kemerton
ST CATHERINE'S FARM, Wollashill
AUGUST Sunday 30
GLEN WYE, Courtfield
STONE HOUSE COTTAGE GARDENS, nr Kidderminster
WORMINGTON GRANGE, nr Broadway
AUGUST Monday 31 (Bank Hol)
STONE HOUSE COTTAGE GARDENS, nr Kidderminster
SEPTEMBER Sunday 6
CONDERTON MANOR, nr Tewkesbury
THE PRIORY, Kemerton
SEPTEMBER Saturday 12
CLACK'S FARM, Ombersley
SEPTEMBER Sunday 13
BARNARD'S GREEN HOUSE, Malvern
CLACK'S FARM, Ombersley
SEPTEMBER Sunday 20
BREDON POUND, Ashton-u-Hill
OCTOBER Sunday 11
BODENHAM ARBORETUM, Wolverley

DESCRIPTIONS OF GARDENS

●**Abbey Dore Court** よ⌀❀ (Mrs C.L. Ward)
11m SW of Hereford. From A465 midway between Hereford-Abergavenny turn W, signed Abbey Dore; then 2½m. 4 acres bordered by R. Dore; constantly being extended to

accommodate increasing number unusual plants and shrubs; herbaceous borders, circular herb garden, walled garden, fern border, small orchard; new pond and rock garden made in field. Home of the National Sedum and Euphorbia Collections. Cream TEAS. *Adm £1 Chd 25p (Share to Mother Theresa). Mid-March to Oct 31 daily except Weds (11-6)*

¶**Arley Cottage** ✗ (Lady Woodward) Nr Bewdley. 5m N of Kidderminster off A442. Small country garden with lawns bordered by interesting shrubs and collection of rare trees. *Adm 50p Chd free (Share PRUPA St Thomas Hospital London). Sun July 19 (2-5.30)*

Arley House ✗ (R.D. Turner Esq) Upper Arley, 5m N of Kidderminster. A442. Arboretum containing specimen conifers and hardwoods, rhododendrons, camellias, magnolias, heathers; Italianate garden; greenhouses with orchids, alpines. Aviary with ornamental pheasants, budgerigars. TEAS. *Adm £1 Chd free. (Share to St Peter's Church, Upper Arley). Sun May 3 (2-7)*

Barbers ✗❀ (Mr & the Hon Mrs Richard Webb) Martley 7m NW of Worcester on B4204. Medium-sized garden with lawns, trees, shrubs, pool and wild garden. Homemade TEAS. *Adm 50p OAPs/Chd 25p. Suns May 3 June 7 (2-6)*

Barnard's Green House ꝃ✗❀ (Mr & Mrs Philip Nicholls) 10 Poolbrook Rd, Malvern. On E side of Malvern at junc of B4211 and B4208. 3-acre cultivated garden; herbaceous, rockeries, heather beds, woodland/water garden, vegetable plot; several unusual plants and shrubs; 2 fine cedars, lawns. Mrs Nicholls is a specialist on dried flowers, on which she has written a book. Half-timbered house (not open) dates from 1635; home of Sir Charles Hastings, founder of BMA. Coach parties by appt. TEAS. *Adm 60p Chd free (Share to Save the Children Fund). Suns May 10 & Sept 13 (2-6)*

Bell's Castle ꝃ (Lady Holland-Martin) Kemerton, NE of Tewkesbury. 3 small terraces with battlements; wild garden outside wall. The small Gothic castellated folly was built by Edmund Bell (Smuggler) c. 1820; very fine views. Home-made TEAS (by Overbury WI). *Adm 50p Chd 20p (Share to NSPCC). Sun June 21 (2.30-6)*

Berrington Hall ꝃ✗ (The National Trust) 4m N of Leominster on A49. Signposted. Bus Midland Red (W) x 92, 292 alight Luston, 2m. Extensive views over Capability Brown Park; formal garden with personal favourites; wall plants, unusual trees, camellia collection, herbaceous plants, wisteria. Woodland walk, recent rhododendron planting. TEAS. Sats & Suns & Bank Hol Mon April-Oct (2-5); Wed to Sun & Bank Hol Mon May to Sept (2-6). *Adm £1.60 Chd 80p Parties £1.10 each or combined adm with Croft Castle £2.80 Chd £1.40 Parties £2 each △Sun July 5 (2-6)*

Birtsmorton Court ꝃ✗ (N.G.K. Dawes Esq) nr Malvern. 7m E of Ledbury on A438. Fortified manor house (not shown) dating from C12; moat; Westminster pool, laid down in Henry V11's reign at time of consecration of Westminster Abbey; large tree under which Cardinal Wolsey reputedly slept in shadow of ragged stone. Topiary. Motor Museum extra. *Adm 75p Chd 20p. Sun June 21 (2-6)*

Bodenham Arboretum ✗ (Mr & Mrs J. D. Binnian) 2m N of Wolverley; 5m N of Kidderminster. From Wolverley Church follow signs. 128-acres newly-created arboretum (opened 1973); 10 pools; over 900 varieties, species or cultivars of common and rare interesting trees and shrubs; grove of Taxodium Distitchum planted in shallows of 3-acre lake. TEA. NO COACHES. *Adm 60p Chd 30p (Share to The Kemp House Trust). Suns May 10, Oct 11 (2-6) parties by appt at other times of the year, (Tel Kidderminster 850382)*

Brampton Bryan Hall ꝃ (Mr & Mrs Christopher Harley) Bucknell, 6m E of Knighton, on A4113 Knighton-Ludlow rd. Medium-sized garden; large lawns, old cedars, limes and fine yew hedges and collection of interesting trees. Medieval castle adjoining C18 house. TEA. *Adm 70p Chd 30p. Sun July 12 (2.30-6)*

Bredenbury Court (St Richards) ꝃ (Headmaster: R.E.H. Coghlan Esq) Bredenbury, 3m W of Bromyard. On A44 Bromyard-Leominster rd; entrance on right (N) side of rd. 5-acre garden; 15-acres parkland with fine views. Simple rose garden and herbaceous borders. Picnics allowed. Use of swimming pool 30p extra. TEAS. *Adm £1 Chd 50p (Share to Newman Trust for the Handicapped). Sun July 19 (11-6)*

Bredon Pound ✗❀ (Mr & Mrs David King) Ashton-under-Hill. Recently landscaped (1978) out of old orchard on rising ground at foot of Bredon Hill; fine views and vistas with trees, shrubs and bold sweeps of grass. A feature is a wide steep bank embracing a patio at rear of house providing a delightful alpine effect of heathers, junipers and ground-cover with annuals; fine shrub rose bed. TEAS. *Adm 50p Chd free (Share to St Richard's Hospice at Home). Suns July 12 & Sept 20 (2-5.30)*

Bredon Springs (Ronald Sidwell Esq) Paris, Ashton-under-Hill, 6m SW of Evesham. Take Ashton turning off A435, turn right in village; then 1st left. Limited parking. Coach parties must alight at church (by the old cross) and walk through churchyard (6 mins), following the mown footpath over 2 fields. 1½ acres; large plant collection in natural setting. DOGS welcome. *Adm 50p Chd free (Share to NCCPG). April 4 to Oct 25 every Sat Sun Wed & Thurs; also Bank Hol Mons & Tues following (10-dusk)*

Brookside ⚘ (Mr & Mrs John Dodd) Bringsty; 3m E of Bromyard via A44 10m W of Worcester; turn down track to 'Live & Let Live'; at PH carpark bear left to Bringsty Common. 1½ acres; specimen trees and shrubs in grass sloping to lake; mixed beds with all year interest; expanding alpine collection, unusual plants; daffodils in spring. Parties by arrangement only. TEAS in garden (if fine). *Adm 60p Chd 20p (Share to Save the Children Fund). April to Oct first Thurs & Sun in months (2-6). For NGS Sun Apr 19*

Clack's Farm &⚘ (Mr & Mrs Arthur Billitt) 8m N of Worcester. On 449 1m N of Ombersley turn into Woodfield Lane; follow signs. 2½-acre all seasons garden; ornamental shrubs, trees, flowers; extensive vegetables and fruit; 8 greenhouses. Gardening advice from Billitts with experts from TV 'Gardening Time'. Coaches by appt. TEA & refreshments. *Adm 50p Chd 25p (Share to RNLI, SOS, Horticultural Therapy, Blue Cross). Sats, Suns May 9, 10 June 13, 14 July 11, 12 Aug 8, 9 Sept 12, 13 (10-5); also by appt (Tel Worcester 620250)*

Clent Hall &⚘ (C. Parkes Esq) Clent, 3m S of Stourbridge. Take Clent turning off main Birmingham-Kidderminster rd. (A456). Clent Hall adjoins church. Parking for cars adjoining Lodge entrance, if wet park on rd by church. Gardens planted in latter part of last cent. on 4 terraces with extensive plantings of rhododendrons, hybrid azaleas, primulas, old wistaria, topiary, holly and yew hedges, fine old trees, stream, waterfalls, pools, fountains, 'Sarah's Secret Garden', 'Formal rose garden', 'Pets' Cemetery', C18 landscaped parkland with fine views over 5 counties. House and garden featured in T.V. Production "Give it some 'ommer" 'Exhibition by Clent History Soc of village life through the ages in house (adm 25p). Home-made TEAS (except on May 26). *Adm 60p Chd 20p. Sun, Mon & Tues May 24, 25, 26; Suns May 31, June 7 (2.30-5.30)*

Conderton Manor &⚘⚘ (Mr & Mrs William Carr) 5½m NE of Tewkesbury. Between A435 & B4079. Cotswold stone manor house (not shown), magnificent views of Cotswolds; young trees; shrubs, bulbs; very fine flowering cherries. *Adm 70p Chd 10p. (Share to Overbury Church Roof Fund). Mon May 4, Sept 6 (2-6)*

Croft Castle &⚘ (The National Trust) 5m NW of Leominster. On B43262 (off B4361, Leominster-Ludlow). Large garden; borders;

walled garden; landscape park and walks in Fishpool Valley; fine old avenues. Tea Berrington Hall. Sats, Suns & Bank Hol Mons April - Oct (2-5) Weds - Suns & Bank Hol Mon May - Sept (2-6). *Adm £1.60 Chd 80p, party rate £1.10 each or combined adm with Berrington Hall £2.80 Chd £1.40, party rate £2 each. △Sun July 5 (2-6)*

Dinmore Manor &⚘ (G.H. Murray Esq) Leominster, 6m N of Hereford. Route A49. Bus: Midland Red Hereford-Leominster, alight Manor turning 1m. Unusual garden with many features inc large 1930's rock and water garden and grotto, outstanding views. C12/C14 Church of Knights Hospitaller. *Adm 50p Chd 25p. Sun May 24 (10-6)*

Eastgrove Cottage Garden Nursery ⚘⚘ (Mr & Mrs J. Malcolm Skinner) Sankyns Green, Shrawley, nr Little Witley. 8m NW of Worcester on rd between Shrawley (on B4196) and Great Witley (on A443). Set in 5-acres unspoilt meadow and woodland, 1-acre peaceful garden of interest to both plantsman and novice. Expanding collection of hardy plants in old world country flower garden. C17 half-timbered yeoman farmhouse (not open) Garden and nursery maintained by owners since 1970. Morning/evening (coach) parties by appt. *Adm 60p Chd 20p (Share to RNLI). Open afternoons 2-5 (except Tues and Wed) April 12 to Oct 31; closed throughout August*

¶**The Elms** ⚘ (L.A.C.Ashby, The Headmaster). Colwall. 3m N of Malvern. Medium-sized garden, herbaceous borders, fine views of the Malvern Hills. Open in conjunction with Colwall Horticultural Society Show. TEAS. *Sat, Sun Aug 1, 2 (2.30-5)*

¶**Frogmore** &⚘⚘ (Sir Jonathan & Lady North) Pontshill. 4m SE of Ross-on-Wye. 1m S of A40 through Pontshill. 2 acre garden with fine mature trees and many unusual young trees and shrubs. Mixed borders with nut walk, stream and ha ha. Scillas, daffodils and crocus in spring. TEA. *Adm 60p Chd 20p. Suns Apr 12, June 14, July 12 (2-6)*

◆**Garnons** & (Sir John & Lady Cotterell) 7m W of Hereford on A438; lodge gates on right; then fork left over cattle grid. Large park landscaped by Repton; attractive spring garden. House is remaining wing (1860) of house pulled down in 1957. TEA. *Adm part of house & garden £1.25; garden only 75p Chd 75p (Share to Byford Church). Sun April 12 (2-5)*

Gatley Park (Mr & Mrs Thomas Dunne) Leinthall Earles, 9m NW of Leominster; 9m SW of Ludlow. Turn E off A4110 between Aymestrey and Wigmore follow signs to village, 1½m; drive ½m long. Medium-sized garden; terraced rose gardens; herbaceous borders; old clipped yew walk; Magnificent position and views. TEAS in Jacobean house (Share to Aymestrey & Leinthall Earles Churches). *Adm £1 Chd 10p. Sun July 12 (2-6)*

Glebe House ♿✗❀ (Mr & Mrs J.F. Brown) Colwall 4m S of Malvern; off B4218 ¾m down lane signed Colwall Church. 2¾-acre old rectory garden being revived; woodland; shrubs, rhododendrons, azaleas, fine old trees; rock garden; ponds; rose garden; greenhouse with vines, peaches; fruit and vegetable cage. TEAS. *Adm 75p Chd 35p. Sun June 7 (2-6)*

Glen Wye ♿❀ (Mrs J.H. Vaughan) Courtfield, 5m S of Ross-on-Wye. From A40 turn E to Goodrich; take 'no through rd' signed Courtfield/Welsh Bicknor; ignore all turns to right; over cattle grid at top of hill; on 1m to private drive on left. 2½-acres; Italianate-style garden created since 1955; rockeries, herbaceous borders, interesting water garden, terrace walks with statuary and beautiful views of Wye Valley; woodland garden. Henry V brought up on Courtfield estate of which Glen Wye is the dower house. TEAS. *Adm £1 Chd 25p (Share to St Josephs Foreign Missionary Society). Suns May 24, Aug 30 (2-6)*

Grantsfield ♿✗❀ (Col & Mrs J.G.T. Polley) nr Kimbolton, 3m NE of Leominster. A49 N from Leominster, turn right to Grantsfield. Car parking in field; not coaches which must drop and collect visitors at gate. Contrasting styles in gardens of old stone farmhouse; wide variety of unusual plants and shrubs, old roses, climbers; herbaceous borders; superb views. 4-acre orchard and kitchen garden with flowering and specimen trees. Spring bulbs. TEAS. *Adm 70p Chd 30p (Share to Hamnish Church Fund). Sun July 5 (2-5)*

Haffield ♿❀ (Mr & Mrs Alan Cadbury) 3m S of Ledbury on A417. 4 mins from M50. Exit 2 towards Ledbury. Quarry garden; herbaceous borders; woodland; view; outstanding tulip and ginkgo trees; House (not open) 1815 by Robert Smirke. TEA. *Adm 80p Chd 20p (Share to Save the Children Fund). Sun May 24 (2-6)*

Hanbury Hall ♿✗ (The National Trust) Hanbury, 3m NE of Droitwich. Signed off B4090. Extensive lawns, shrubberies; Victorian forecourt with detailed planting. Wren-style brick house of 1701 with murals by Thornhill; contemporary Orangery. TEAS. *Adm house & garden £1.60, Chd 80p. △Sun July 5 (2-6)*

Hartlebury Castle ♿✗ (The Rt Revd The Lord Bishop of Worcester). Medieval moated castle reconstructed 1675, restored 1964. Many Tudor and Hanoverian Royal connections. Rose garden in forecourt. TEAS. *Adm gardens & state rooms of castle 60p Chd 25p. Sun July 5 (2-5)*

Hergest Croft Gardens ♿❀ (W.L. Banks Esq & R.A. Banks Esq) ½m off A44 on Welsh side of Kington, 20m NW of Hereford: Turn left at Rhayader end of bypass; then 1st right; gardens ¼m on left. 3 gardens owned by Banks' family for 4 generations. Edwardian garden surrounding house (not open); Park wood with rhododendrons up to 30ft tall; old fashioned kitchen garden with spring and herbaceous borders. One of finest private collections trees and shrubs; now selected to hold National Collections Maples and Birches. TEAS (Suns & Bank Hols only) for parties by arrangement (Tel Kington 230160). *Adm £1.20 Chd 60p (Share to NCCPG). April 19 to Sept 20 daily; also Suns in Oct. For NGS Fri May 22 (1.30-6.30)*

The Hill Court ♿❀ (Christopher Rowley Esq) Ross-on-Wye. 2¾m SW of Ross-on Wye; take B4228 towards Walford; after ½m at Prince of Wales, bear right, lodge gates 1½m on right. C18 house Grade I (not open) approached by double avenue. Garden Centre with newly planted walled garden, yew walk and water garden open daily. Private gardens with formal garden, herbaceous borders, flowering shrubs and woodland garden open for NGS. TEAS. *Adm £1 OAP/Chd 50p (Share to Dean Hill Hospital). Suns May 10, June 28 (2-6)*

¶**Holbeach House** ✗ (Mrs James Carpenter) Trimpley. 3m NE of Kidderminster; in Trimpley turn off at signs. 1½-acres terraced garden with views over Wyre Forest towards Clee Hills. Rose and rock gardens and herbaceous borders. *Adm 50p Chd free. Sat July 11 (2-5.30)*

♦**Holland House** ✗ (Warden: Mr Peter Middlemiss) High St, Cropthorne, Pershore. Between Pershore and Evesham, off A44. Car park at rear of house. Gardens laid out by Lutyens in 1904; house dating back to 1636 (not open). TEAS. *Adm 50p (Share to Nkhotakota Laity Centre, Malawi and Modderpoort Retreat and Conference Centre, S Africa). Thurs April 23, Sun July 5, Sat Aug 1 (2-5)*

How Caple Court ✗❀ (Mr & Mrs Peter Lee) How Caple, 5m N of Ross on Wye 10m S of Hereford on B4224; turn right at How Caple Xrds, garden 400 yds on left. 11 acres; mainly Edwardian gardens in process of replanting, set high above R. Wye in park and woodland; formal terraces: yew hedges, statues and pools; sunken florentine water garden under restoration; woodland walks; herbaceous and shrub borders, shrub roses, mature trees: Medieval Church with newly restored C15 tryptych. Nursery specialising in old-fashioned roses, unusual herbaceous plants. Fabrics shop. TEAS. *Adm £1 Chd free. Open daily April-Oct (9-4.30). Suns May - Sept (10-5). For NGS Sun June 28 (10-5)*

¶**Lakeside** ✗❀ (Mr D. Gueroult & Mr C. Philip) Gaines Rd, Whitbourne. 9m W of Worcester off A44 at County boundary sign. 5 acres, of which half was formerly C18 walled kitchen garden and medieval carp lake with fountain. Some fine trees, clearly labelled mixed borders and unusual plants. Recent and continuing extension, inc heather and watergarden hence many plants still young. Steep steps and slopes. TEA. *Adm 75p Chd 25p (Share to Red Cross). Sun June 14 (2-6)*

¶**Lane House Farm** ⚘ (Mrs S.M.Anderson) Callow Hill, Redditch. Callow Hill 4m from Hanbury, turn off B4091 (opp Jinney Ring Craft Centre) signed from Forest Lane 4m to Callow Hill. Wonderful Tudor House (not open) set in rolling countryside with views SW to Malvern Hills. Small garden created for easy maintenance in last 10yrs from Farmyard and overgrown field. Mainly shrubs, lawn and grass tennis court. TEA. *Adm 50p Chd 10p. Sun July 5 (2-6)*

Little Malvern Court ⚘❋ (Mr & Mrs T.M. Berington) 4m S of Malvern on A4104 S of junc with A449. 10 acres attached to former Benedictine Priory, magnificent views over Severn valley. Recently restored chain of lakes; new gardens developed around house; spring bulbs, trees, shrubs, roses. TEAS. *Adm 80p Chd 20p (Share to SSAFA). Suns April 12 & June 28 (2-6)*

Loen ⚘❋ (Mr & Mrs S.K. Quayle) Long Bank, 2m W of Bewdley via A456; after 1¾m left, beside a red brick church, into a small lane. 6 acres; rock and water garden; interesting collection of shrubs in woodland setting. *Adm 60p Chd 10p. Sat May 16 Mon-Sat May 18-23. Mon May 25 (11-6)*

◆**Madresfield Court** ⚘ (The Countess Beauchamp) between A449 & B4211. Formal garden with mature and rare trees set in 60 acres of parkland. TEAS. *Adm £1 Chd 20p (Share to St Mary's Church). Sun July 19 (2.30-5.30)*

◆**Moccas Court** ⚘❋ (Richard Chester-Master Esq) 10m W of Hereford. 1m off B4352. 7-acres; Capability Brown parkland on S bank of R. Wye. House designed by Adam and built by Keck in 1775. TEAS June 21 only. *Adm house & garden £1.50 Chd 50p. April to Sept every Thurs (2-6) For NGS (Share to Moccas Church). Sun June 21 (2-6)*

Old Court Nurseries ⚘❋ (Mr & Mrs Paul Picton) Walwyn Rd, Colwall. 3m W of Malvern on B4218. 1½ acres W of Malvern Hills; herbaceous borders, shrubs, alpines; special display of Ballard's michaelmas daisies Sept/Oct. Coaches by appt. *Collecting box. Daily Aug 8 to Oct 18 except Tues (10-1; 2-5)*

The Orchard Farm ⚘⚘❋ (The Misses S. & M. Barrie) Broadway. On A44. Medium-sized garden with herbaceous and shrub borders; yew hedges; water garden. House (not

shown) c.1602. Home-made TEAS. Free Car Park. *Adm 60p Chd 20p. Sun July 12 (2-6)*

Overbury Court ⚘ (Mrs E. Holland-Martin) 5m NE of Tewkesbury, 2½m N of Teddington Hands Roundabout, where A438 crosses A435. Daffodils. Georgian house 1740 (not shown); landscape gardening of same date with stream and pools. Plane trees, yew hedges. Coloured foliage border, gold and silver border; shrub rose border. Norman church adjoins garden. TEAS. *Adm 70p Chd 30p. Suns April 12 & July 12 (2-6)*

Pershore College of Horticulture ⚘❋ 1m S of Pershore on A44, 7m from M5 junc 7. 180-acre estate; ornamental grounds; arboretum; fruit, vegetables; automated glasshouses; large commercial nursery. *Adm 50p. Wed June 24 (6.30-9)*

Pontrilas Court ⚘ (Mr & Mrs D.A. Keown-Boyd) 11m S of Hereford on B4347 just off A465. Medium-sized garden; riverside walks; trees planted by George Bentham of Bentham and Hooker. Wheelchairs if dry. Home-made TEAS. *Adm 75p Chd 30p (Share to RDA). Sat & Sun July 18 & 19 (2-6)*

The Priory ⚘❋ (Mr & the Hon Mrs Peter Healing) Kemerton, NE of Tewkesbury B4080. Main features of this 4-acre garden are long herbaceous borders planned in colour groups; stream, fern and sunk gardens. Many unusual plants, shrubs and trees. Featured in BBC2 Gardeners' World and 'The Garden magazine'. Small nursery. *Adm £1 Chd free. May 7 to Sept 24 every Thurs; also Suns May 24, June 21, Aug 23, Sept 6 (2-7)*

Ripple Hall ⚘ (Sir Hugo Huntington-Whiteley Bt) 4m N of Tewkesbury. Off A38 Worcester-Tewkesbury (nr junc with motorway); Ripple village well signed. 6 acres; lawns and paddocks with donkeys; walled vegetable garden; cork tree and orangery. TEAS. *Adm 50p Chd 25p. Sun April 26 (2-6)*

St Catherine's Farm (D.S.Jackson Esq) Wolashill, 7m S of Pershore. A4080; ½-way between Tewkesbury and Pershore, turn E for Bredon Norton; then follow signs. Large garden; Victorian rockery, pool with island and rustic bridge; mature trees; superb view. TEAS. *Adm 75p Chd 25p. Sun Aug 23 (2-6)*

St James's & The Abbey School (Miss E.M. Mullenger) 2m from Gt Malvern; off B4232 to W. Malvern, enter from de Walden Rd. 40 acres; parkland; unusual trees. Splendid views of Malvern Hills. Picnics. TEA. *Adm 75p Chd 20p (Share to BRCS). Sun May 17 (2-6)*

◆**Spetchley Park** ⚘⚘❋ (R.J. Berkeley Esq) 3m E of Worcester. A422 ½m. Large garden of general interest; daffodils. Only deer park in Worcestershire; red and fallow deer. TEAS. *Adm £1.20 Chd 60p. △Fri April 17 & Suns May 10, 31 (2-5)*

Stone House Cottage Gardens ๑⊗❋ (Maj & the Hon Mrs Arbuthnott) Stone, 2m SE of Kidderminster via A448 towards Bromsgrove next to church, turn up drive. 1-acre sheltered walled plantsman's garden with towers; rare wall shrubs, climbers and interesting herbaceous plants. In adjacent nursery large selection of unusual shrubs and climbers for sale. Featured in The Garden and Country Life. Coaches by appt only. *Adm £1 Chd free (Share to CAFOD). Suns May 3, 10, 17, 24, 31; June 7, 14, 21, 28; July 11, 18; Aug 30 and Mon Aug 31 (2-6); also open March to Nov every Wed, Thurs, Fri, Sat (10-6)*

Summerway ๑❋ (Mr & Mrs Graeme Anton) Torton, 3m S of Kidderminster; A449, turn off up lane signed Wilden Top. 3-acre garden with interesting collection of young trees, mixed borders, new pool and rock garden. TEAS. *Adm 50p Chd 10p. Sun July 12 (2-5.30)*

Whitfield (G.M. Clive Esq) Wormbridge, 8m SW of Hereford on Abergavenny Rd. Parkland, large garden, ponds, walled kitchen garden, 1½m woodland walk with 1851 Redwood grove and tallest Oak in Britain. Picnic parties welcome. *Adm 50p Chd 25p. Sun June 7 (2-6)*

¶**Wichenford Court** ๑⊗❋ (Lt Col & Mrs P.C.Britten) Wichenford. 7m NW of Worcester; turn right off B4204 at Masons Arms pub; 1m on right. Medium-sized garden dating from 1975; interesting young trees; daffodils and spring bulbs; flowering cherries; clematis; flowering shrubs and shrub roses. House dating back to C11 (not open), parts of original moat still in existence. C17 dovecote (NT). Collection of carriages. Picnic area open at noon. TEA. *Adm 70p Chd 30p (Share to SSAFA). Suns Apr 26, July 5 (2-6)*

Wind's Point (Cadbury Trustees) British Camp. 3m SW of Malvern on Ledbury Rd. Medium-sized garden; unusual setting, lovely views. Last home of great Swedish singer Jenny Lind and where she died 1887. TEA. *Adm 40p Chd 20p. Sun May 17 (11-6)*

Witley Park House ๑ (Mr & Mrs W.A.M. Edwards) Great Witley, 9m NW of Worcester. On A443 1m W of Little Witley Garage on left coming from Worcester and Droitwich. 18 acres inc pool; lakeside walk; many varieties young trees; shrubs, spring flowers, roses. TEA. *Adm 50p Chd 10p. Sun July 5 (2-6)*

Wormington Grange ๑ (The Evetts Family) 4m W of Broadway. A46 from Broadway-Cheltenham, take 2nd turning for Wormington. Large natural garden; herb garden, old fashioned roses. Interesting arts and crafts gates. Croquet lawn, very good views. Exhibition of Lord Ismay's Life 50p. Homemade TEAS. *Adm 60p Chd 30p (Share to St Catherine's Church). Suns April 26, Aug 30 (2-6)*

¶**Yew Tree House** (Mr & Mrs W. Moyle) Ombersley. Turn off A449 up 'Woodfield Lane'; right at T-junc. 2½-acre garden, nearly all replanted since 1979. Perrenial borders with unusual flowering shrubs and old fashioned roses. Pretty alpine/rose garden in walled area, ericas in copse, lawns and beautiful views. Set around C1640 timber framed house. TEA. *Adm 50p Chd 25p. Sun June 28 (2-6)*

HERTFORDSHIRE

Hon County Organiser:
MRS MARTIN ACLAND, Standon Green End, nr Ware SG11 1BN

DATES OF OPENING

BY APPOINTMENT ONLY for dates see text:
1 GERNON WALK, Letchworth
REGULAR OPENINGS for dates see text:
BENINGTON LORDSHIP, nr Stevenage

APRIL Easter Sunday 19
CAPEL MANOR, nr Enfield
COKENACH HOUSE, Barkway
APRIL Sunday 26
ST PAUL'S WALDEN BURY, Hitchin
MAY Sunday 10
GORHAMBURY GARDENS
ST PAUL'S WALDEN BURY, Hitchin
MAY Sunday 24
GREAT SARRATT HALL, nr
Rickmansworth
HIPKINS, Broxbourne
ST PAUL'S WALDEN BURY, Hitchin
JUNE Saturday 6
HOPLEYS, Much Hadham
JUNE Sunday 7
HILL HOUSE, Stanstead Abbotts
HOPLEYS, Much Hadham
WEST LODGE PARK, nr Barnet
JUNE Monday 8
HILL HOUSE, Stanstead Abbotts
JUNE Sunday 21
FURNEAUX PELHAM HALL, nr
Buntingford
JUNE Saturday 27
BENINGTON LORDSHIP, Stevenage
JUNE Sunday 28
BENINGTON LORDSHIP, Stevenage
BURLOES, Royston
GREAT MUNDEN HOUSE, nr Ware
LEVERSTOCK GREEN GARDENS &
GORHAMBURY GARDENS, nr St
Albans
MOOR PLACE, Much Hadham
ST PAUL'S WALDEN BURY, Hitchin
WATERDELL HOUSE, Croxley Green
JULY Sunday 26
THE GARDENS OF THE ROSE, St Albans

SEPTEMBER Saturday 5 & Sunday 6
HOPLEYS, Much Hadham
SEPTEMBER Sunday 27
KNEBWORTH HOUSE, Stevenage
OCTOBER Sunday 25
WEST LODGE PARK, nr Barnet

DESCRIPTIONS OF GARDENS

♦**Benington Lordship** ⚔❀ (Mr & Mrs C.H.A. Bott) 5m E of Stevenage, in Benington village. Terraced plantsman's garden overlooking lakes, formal rose garden; Victorian folly, Norman keep and moat; spring rock and water garden; spectacular double herbaceous borders. Small nursery. Greenhouse display. TEAS Suns (On June 28 & 29 Teas & Floral Festival in Church adjoining garden). *Adm £1 Chd (14-18 yrs) 50p under 14 free. May 1 to Aug 3 every Sun (2-5), May 1 - Oct 31 every Wed (11-5), also Mons April 20; May 4, 25; Aug 31 (2-5). For NGS (Share to St Peters Church). Sat, Sun June 27, 28 (12-6)*

Burloes ⚔⚔ (Sir Gerard Newman) Royston. 1m from Royston Newmarket Rd E of town centre. A garden on chalk with fine view of surrounding countryside; wide variety of plants and shrubs; fine beech trees. *Adm 75p Chd 50p. Sun June 28 (2-6)*

Capel Manor Horticulture & Environmental Centre ⚔❀ (London Borough of Enfield) Bullsmoor Lane, Waltham Cross. M25 junc 25/A10 interchange; Bus or rail, Turkey St/Bullsmore Lane. 25 acres; ornamental and educational gardens; attractive walled garden with old-fashioned roses, mixed herbaceous shrub borders; glasshouses with tropical and carnivorous plants; C17 garden with knot hedges and herbs; Theme gardens of colour and texture; rock and water garden, ornamental fish. 5 acres trials and demonstration gardens in association with Gardening from Which? Fine specimen trees inc 220yr Copper Beech. *Adm £1.25 OAPs/Chd 65p △Sun April 19 (10-5.30)*

Cokenach House ⚔⚔❀ (Mr & Mrs J.E.L. Lebus) Barkway. On B1368 Puckeridge-Cambridge Rd on N side of Barkway; or E off A10, 2m S of Royston, 13 acres; informal garden surrounded by water in parkland setting; spring bulbs; walled garden, vine houses, fine trees. TEA. *Adm 60p OAPs/Chd 25p. Sun April 19 (2.30-6)*

Furneaux Pelham Hall ⚔⚔❀ (Mrs Peter Hughes) nr Buntingford. From A120 N of Little Hadham, NE of Puckeridge; E of A10. Lake, ornamental duck; water garden with fountains playing; walled rose garden; yew hedges; shrubs. Deer Park. Elizabethan house (not open). *Adm 80p Chd 40p. Sun June 21 (2-6)*

The Gardens of the Rose ⚔❀ (The Royal National Rose Society) Chiswell Green Lane, 2m S of St Albans on B4630, follow AA signs. 12-acre display garden; with roses of every description. 30,000 plants of some 1,700 different varieties. LUNCHES & TEAS. *Adm £1.30 Chd free. Registered disabled 60p daily. △For NGS Sun July 26 (10-6)*

¶**1, Gernon Walk** ⚔ (Miss Rachel Crawshay) Letchworth Garden City. Tiny town garden (100ft long but only 8ft wide in middle) planned and planted since 1984 for year-round and horticultural interest. *Collecting box. By appt only. Tel 0462 686399*

Gorhambury Gardens via A4147 midway between Hemel Hempstead/St Albans. Car parking free. Lunch Hill End Farm. *Combined adm £1 Chd free (May); adm with Leverstock Green Gardens, (June) £1.50 Chd free. Suns May 10, June 28*

   Hill End Farm ⚔❀ (Mr & Mrs Alban Warwick) Beech Tree Lane, Gorhambury. Part dates back to 1275. Mature garden; duck pond; grass walk flanked by coniferous and deciduous specimen trees. Spring bulbs. Lunches, teas and picnic facilities. Plant stall (May). Craft stalls (summer). Local craft stalls

   Hill End Farm Cottage ⚔ (Mrs J. Spilman) Beech Tree Lane, Gorhambury. Small Tudor cottage set in small old-world garden made from scratch by owner since 1971. Spring bulbs. Part house also shown (no extra charge) if fine

   Hill End Cottage (Mr & Mrs G.M. Palmer) Beech Tree Lane, Gorhambury. Small Tudor cottage with fine views towards Gorhambury Estate; garden made from scratch by owners since 1977. TEA

Great Munden House ⚔⚔❀ (Mr & Mrs D. Wentworth-Stanley) 7m N of Ware. Off A10 on Puckeridge by-pass turn W; or turning off B1001 via Dane End. 3½-acre informal garden with trees, roses and shrubs. Cream TEAS. *Adm 80p Chd 20p (Share to NSPCC). Sun June 28 (2-5.30)*

Great Sarratt Hall ⚔⚔❀ (H.M. Neal Esq) Sarratt, N of Rickmansworth. From Watford N via A41 (or M1 Exit 5) to Kings Langley; and left (W) to Sarratt; garden is 1st on right after village sign. 4 acres; herbaceous and mixed shrub borders; pond, moisture-loving plants and trees; walled kitchen garden; rhododendrons, magnolias, camellias; new planting of specialist conifers and rare trees. TEAS. *Adm 80p Chd 40p (Share to Courtauld Institute of Art Fund). Sun May 24 (2-6)*

Hill House ⚔ (Mr & Mrs R. Pilkington) Stanstead Abbotts, near Ware. From A10 turn E on to A414; left at end of High St, garden 1st right past Church. Ample car parking. 6-acres inc. wood; species roses, herbaceous border, water garden, conservatory, aviary, woodland walk. Lovely view over Lea Valley. Modern Art Exhibition in loft gallery (20p extra Chd 10p). Home-made TEAS. *Adm 80p Chd 40p (Share to Stanstead Abbotts Church) Sun, Mon June 7, 8 (2-6)*

Hipkins &⊛ (Stuart Douglas Hamilton Esq & Michael Goulding Esq) Broxbourne. From A10 to Broxbourne turn up Bell or Park Lane into Baas Lane. Station: Broxbourne, 1m Bus: LC 310 Enfield-Hertford; GL 715, 715A London-Hertford; alight Station Rd ½m. 3-acre informal garden with ponds; azaleas and rhododendrons; shrub and herbaceous borders specialising in plants for flower arrangements; many unusual specimens; fine trees and well kept kitchen garden. TEAS. *Adm 50p Chd 20p. Sun May 24 (2.30-6)*

¶**Hopleys (Garden and Nursery)** &⊁⊛ (Dr & Mrs David Barker, Mr Aubrey Barker) 5m from Bishop's Stortford on B1004. M11 (exit 8) 7m or A10 (Puckeridge) 5m via A120. 50yds N of Bull public house in centre of Much Hadham. 3½ acres of constantly developing garden; trees, shrubs, herbaceous and alpines; island beds with mixed planting in parkland setting; pond and many unusual and rare (inc variegated) plants. TEAS. *Adm 80p Chd 40p. Sats & Suns June 6,7; Sept 5,6 (11-6)*

Knebworth House &⊛ (The Hon David Lytton Cobbold) Knebworth. 28m N of London; direct access from A1(M) at Stevenage. Station and Bus stop: Stevenage 3m. Historic house, home of Bulwer Lytton; Victorian novelist and statesman. Lutyens garden designed for his brother-in-law, the Earl of Lytton, comprising pleached lime avenues, rose beds, herbaceous borders, yew hedges and various small gardens in process of restoration; Gertrude Jekyll herb garden. Restaurant. *Adm £1.50 OAPs/Chd £1. △ Sun Sept 27 (12-5)*

Leverstock Green Gardens ⊛ via A4147 midway between Hemel Hempstead/St Albans. Car parking free. Lunches at Hill End Farm, Gorhambury. Light refreshments at Westwick Cottage. *Combined adm with Gorhambury Gardens £1.50 Chd free. Sun June 28 (11-6)*

    Westwick Cottage &⊛ (Mrs Sheila Macqueen) Westwick Row. Medium-sized garden specializing in plants for flower arranging: many unusual specimens. Flower arrangements in the house (weather permitting) by Mrs Sheila Macqueen (no extra charge). Plant stall. TEA, coffee & light refreshments

    King Charles II Cottage & (Mr & Mrs F.S. Cadman) Westwick Row. 1-acre; roses a special feature; small, well-stocked ornamental pond. Part house also shown (weather permitting) with flower arrangements by Mrs Sheila Macqueen (no extra charge)

    Swedish Cottage (Doug & Barbara Wiles) Westwick Row. Young ½-acre garden specializing in scented and wild flowers, plants to attract bees, butterflies, birds etc. Aviaries with parakeets, owls and wild fowl

Moor Place & (Mr & Mrs B.M. Norman) Much Hadham. Enter through lodge gates by War Memorial or turning at Hadham Cross on A119. Station Bishop's Stortford 6m. Bus: LC 350 Bishop's Stortford-Ware-Hertford, alight Much Hadham Cross ¼m. Medium-sized garden; C17 kitchen garden, part converted into shrubs; lawns; fine trees and shrubs. TEA. *Adm 90p Chd 35p. Sun June 28 (2-6.30)*

St Paul's Walden Bury &⊁ (Simon Bowes Lyon and family) Whitwell, on B651 5m S of Hitchin; ½m N of Whitwell. Formal woodland garden laid out about 1740, covering more than 40 acres with temples, statues, lake and ponds; also rhododendron and flower gardens. TEAS. *Adm 80p Chd 40p (Shared with other charities). Suns April 26, May 10, 24 June 28 (2-7)*

Tarn, Oxhey Drive, Northwood (see London)

Waterdell House &⊁ (Mr & Mrs Peter Ward) Croxley Green. 1½m from Rickmansworth. From A412 turn left signed Sarratt, along Croxley Green, fork right past Coach & Horses, cross Baldwin Lane into Little Green Lane, then left at top. 1½-acre walled garden developed and maintained over many years to accommodate growing family; mature and young trees, topiary holly hedge, herbaceous borders; modern island beds of shrubs, old fashioned roses; vegetable and fruit garden. *Adm 50p Chd 25p. Sun June 28 (2-6)*

West Lodge Park (T. Edward Beale Esq) Cockfosters Rd, Hadley Wood. On A111 between Potters Bar and Southgate. Exit 24 from M25 signed Cock Fosters. Station: Cockfosters underground (Piccadilly Line); then bus 298 to Beech Hill. Beale Arboretum, set in 10-acre section of West Lodge Park, consists of splendid collection of trees, some 350 varieties, all labelled; many original and interesting specimens, some old-established as well as scores planted since 1965; magnificent leaf colour. TEAS (or lunch) if booked in advance in adjoining hotel. *Adm 50p Chd 10p. Sun June 7 (2-6); Oct 25 (12-4). Organised parties anytime by appt. Collection. (Tel 01 440 8311)*

ISLE OF WIGHT

Hon County Organisers:
Lt Col & Mrs K.J. SHAPLAND, Ningwood
Manor, Ningwood, Nr Newport
Hon County Treasurer:
J. CURETON ESQ, Cornerways, Niton
Undercliff, PO38 2NJ

DATES OF OPENING

APRIL Easter Sunday 19
LISLE COMBE, St Lawrence, Ventnor
APRIL Easter Monday 20
THE CASTLE, St Helens
APRIL Sunday 26
WOOLVERTON HOUSE, St Lawrence,
Ventnor
MAY Sunday 3
3 NORTHCOURT GARDENS, Shorwell
MAY Monday 4 (Bank Hol)
GATCOMBE PARK, nr Newport
MAY Sunday 10
YAFFLES, Bonchurch
MAY Sunday 17
BARTON MANOR, Whippingham
MAY Sunday 24
CEDAR LODGE, Ryde
MAY Monday 25 (Bank Hol)
THE CASTLE, St Helens
MAY Sunday 31
WALDECK, Brightstone
JUNE Sunday 7
KINGS MANOR, Freshwater
JUNE Sunday 14
YAFFLES, Bonchurch
JUNE Sunday 28
NINGWOOD MANOR, nr Newport
JULY Sunday 5
3 NORTHCOURT GARDENS, Shorwell
JULY Sunday 12
OWL COTTAGE, Mottistone
JULY Sunday 19
UPPER CHINE SCHOOL, Shanklin
JULY Sunday 26
NUNWELL HOUSE, Brading
AUGUST Sunday 9
MOTTISTONE MANOR, Mottistone
SEPTEMBER Sunday 6
SHALFLEET MANOR, Shalfleet

DESCRIPTIONS OF GARDENS

¶**Barton Manor** ೬%֎ (Mr & Mrs A.H.Goddard) Whippingham, off A3021 East Cowes to Newport and Ryde Rd, next to Osborne House. 20-acres. Progeny of 225,000 daffodils planted in 1928. Azaleas and rhododendrons; roses and borders later in summer; water/stream garden; scented secret garden.. Home of NCCPG national collection of kniphofias and watsonias. 6-acre vineyard. *Adm £1.75 Chd free. Sun May 17 (10.30-5.30)*

The Castle ֍ (Mr & Mrs D.H. Bacon & Mrs A. Drake) St Helens. 5 acres; about 100ft above sea-level facing S, with spectacular views; white garden; formal and informal lawns, massed spring bulbs, interesting trees and shrubs. Victorian greenhouses. Scheduled house (not open) dates from 1820. *Adm 40p Chd free. Mons April 20, May 25 (2-5)*

Cedar Lodge ֍֎ (Mr & Mrs George Harris) Puckpool Hill, Ryde. Almost opp Puckpool Holiday Camps. 4 acres of garden with large variety of tender flowering trees and shrubs. Water garden area. *Adm 50p Chd 10p. Sun May 24 (2-5.30)*

¶**Gatcombe Park** ೬֍ (Mr & Mrs C.Scott) Newport. 3m SW of Newport. Large park and woodland with ornamental trees, shrubs and lake. Listed C18 house (not open), Norman church. *Adm 50p Chd free. Mon May 4 (2-5)*

King's Manor ೬ (Mr & Mrs A.J. Sheldon) Copse Lane, Freshwater, ½m N of Parish Church. From Yarmouth, take A3054 over bridge W to Norton Green. 5 acres; part formal garden; lawns; wild garden. Bordering R. Yar estuary; lovely views. *Adm 75p Chd free (Share to Wessex Medical School Trust). Sun June 7 (2-5.30)*

Lisle Combe ֍ (Mr & Mrs Hugh Noyes) St Lawrence, 2m W of Ventnor. On sea side of Undercliffe Rd. 4 acres; water gardens; spring flowers and shrubs; rock garden; fine sea views. Large pheasant and waterfowl collection. For many years, home of poet Alfred Noyes. TEAS. *Adm 50p Chd 20p. Sun April 19 (2-6); also by appt (Tel 0983 852582)*

¶**Mottistone Manor** (Sir John & Lady Nicholson, The National Trust) 1m W of Brighstone on B3399. Medium-size formal terraced garden backing on to Tudor House (not open) and set in wooded valley. Fine sea and coastal views. *Adm 70p Chd 35p. Sun Aug 9 (2-5.30)*

Ningwood Manor ೬%֎ (Lt-Col & Mrs K.J. Shapland) 3m E of Yarmouth. A3054 Newport-Yarmouth rd; at Horse & Groom 1m W of Shalfleet, turn left; house ½m from junc, on left. 2-acre formal garden with unusual trees, shrubs and herbaceous plants; Rose and White gardens. Listed C17 house (not open). TEAS. *Adm 50p Chd free. Sun June 28 (2-5)*

3 Northcourt Gardens ೬%֎ (Mrs C.D. Harrison, Mr & Mrs J. Harrison, Mr & Mrs L.1 Harrison) Shorwell 4m S of Newport on B3323, entrance on right after rustic bridge, opp thatched cottage. 12 acres; 3 varied gardens consisting of landscaped terraces, stream and water garden, woodland, walled rose garden, herbaceous borders, shrubs and walled kitchen garden, surrounding Jacobean Manor House (part open). TEAS.

Combined adm 70p Chd 5p (Share to National Trust, I of W Branch) Suns May 3, July 5 (2.30-5.30)

Nunwell House ⚹ (Col & Mrs J.A. Aylmer) Brading. 3m S of Ryde; signed off A3055 in Brading into Coach Lane. 5 acres beautifully set formal and shrub gardens with fountains. Exceptional view of Solent. House developed over 5 centuries, full of architectural interest. Coaches by appt only. TEAS. *Adm 60p Chd 5p; House 60p extra. Sun July 26 (1.30-5)*

Owl Cottage ⚹✿ (Mrs A.L. Hutchinson & Miss S.L. Leaning) Hoxall Lane, Mottistone. 9m SW of Newport, from B3399 at Mottistone turn down Hoxall Lane for 200yds. Interesting cottage garden, view of sea. Part of cottage open. Home-made TEAS. *Adm 50p Chd free. Sun July 12 (2-6)*

¶**Shalfleet Manor**⚹ (Mr & Mrs R. Hedger) Shalfleet 3m E of Yarmouth on B3054 opp church. Medium-size, well designed garden with mature trees, inc liriodendron; divided by hedges into small gardens; double shrub rose and lavender border; C17 house (not open). *Adm 60p Chd 5p. Sun Sept 6 (2-5)*

Upper Chine School ⚹ (Miss Philpott) S of Shanklin. Bus: 16 Shanklin-Ventnor, alight gates. Chine stream through gardens; swimming pool. New School Theatre in grounds. TEAS. *Adm 40p Chd 5p (share to Wessex Medical School Trust). Sun July 19 (2.30-5)*

Waldeck ⚹✿ (Mr & Mrs G.R. Williams) Moor Lane, Brighstone. 8m SW of Newport; ½m W of village centre, limited parking in lane. Informal ¾ acre garden made by owners since 1968. Varied planting to give colour and interest throughout year. Some unusual shrubs, trees, conifers, heathers, rhododendrons and other ericaceous plants. Home-made TEAS. *Adm 40p Chd 10p (Share to IOW Soc for the Blind) Sun May 31 (2.30-5.30)*

Woolverton House (Mr & Mrs S.H.G. Twining) St Lawrence, 3m W of Ventnor; Bus 16 from Ryde, Sandown, Shanklin. Flowering shrubs, bulbs, fine position. TEAS. *Adm 50p Chd 20p. Sun April 26 (2-5)*

Yaffles (Mrs Wolfenden) Bonchurch. Immediately above St Boniface Church; park in rd. ¼-acre sheltered cliff garden sculpted from precipice into ledges and glades; great variety of flowering shrubs and plants of botanical interest; spring bulbs; splendid sea view. 'The Glory of the Garden' by Joan Wolfenden will be sold in aid of funds. TEAS in aid of St Boniface Church. *Adm 50p Chd 10p Suns May 10 & June 14 (2.30-5)*

KENT

Hon County Organiser:
MRS ALAN HARDY, Hillhurst Farm, Hythe, CT21 4HU
Hon County Treasurer:
F.H. MARTIN ESQ, 94 Seabrook Road, Hythe

DATES OF OPENING

BY APPOINTMENT ONLY for dates see text:
  43 LAYHAMS ROAD, West Wickham
  SALTWOOD CASTLE, Hythe (Parties only)
REGULAR OPENINGS for dates see text:
  DODDINGTON PLACE, nr Sittingbourne
  GOODNESTONE PARK, next Wingham, Canterbury
  GREAT COMP CHARITABLE TRUST, Borough Green
  HEVER CASTLE, nr Edenbridge
  MOUNT EPHRAIM, Hernhill, nr Faversham
  NORTHBOURNE COURT, nr Deal
  THE PINES GARDEN, St Margaret's Bay
  RIVERHILL HOUSE, Sevenoaks
  SCOTNEY CASTLE, Lamberhurst

APRIL Sunday 12
  HOLE PARK, Rolvenden
  MERE HOUSE, Mereworth, nr Maidstone
  STREET END PLACE, nr Canterbury
APRIL Easter Sunday 19
  COPTON ASH, Faversham
  CRITTENDEN HOUSE, Matfield
  DENTON COURT, nr Canterbury
  GODINTON PARK, Ashford
  LADHAM HOUSE, Goudhurst
  RINGFIELD, Knockholt
  STREET END PLACE, nr Canterbury
APRIL Easter Monday 20
  CRITTENDEN HOUSE, Matfield
APRIL Wednesday 22
  COPTON ASH, Faversham
APRIL Sunday 26
  CHEVENING, nr Sevenoaks
  COLDHAM, Little Chart Forstal
  GOODNESTON PARK, next Wingham, nr Canterbury
  HOLE PARK, Rolvenden
  MOUNT EPHRAIM, Hernhill
  OLANTIGH, Wye
  OSWALDS, Bishopsbourne
  STREEET END PLACE, nr Canterbury
MAY Saturday 2
  RIVERHILL HOUSE, Sevenoaks
MAY Sunday 3
  BRADBOURNE HOUSE GARDENS, East Malling
  CHURCH HILL COTTAGE, Charing Heath
  CRITTENDEN HOUSE, Matfield
  THE GRANGE, Benenden
  MAURICE HOUSE, Broadstairs
  THE OLD VICARAGE, Ide Hill
  THE PINES GARDEN, St Margaret's Bay

MILTON LODGE, Somerset

D.C. Tudway Quilter Esq

Photograph: Jacqui Hurst

SANDLING PARK, Kent

Mr & Mrs Alan Hardy

Photograph: Country Life

**GRAYTHWAITE
HALL,** Cumbria

Miles Sandys Esq

Photograph:
Alwyne Gardner

BULWICK PARK, Northamptonshire

Mr & Mrs G.T.G. Conant

Photograph: Gerald Hawke

SEZINCOTE, Gloucestershire

Mr & Mrs David Peake

Photograph: Jacqui Hurst

MINTERNE,
Dorset
The Lord Digby

Photograph: Amateur
Gardening

ARLEY HALL, Cheshire

The Hon M.L.W. Flower

Photograph: Jacqui Hurst

SOMERLEYTON HALL, Suffolk

The Lord & Lady Somerleyton

Photograph: Country Life (Charles Hall)

2 THORNDALE CLOSE, Chatham
TURKEY COURT, Maidstone
WITHERSDANE HALL, Wye
MAY Sunday 10
  HOLE PARK, Rolvenden
  ‡LONGACRE, Selling
  ‡LUTON HOUSE, Selling
  SANDLING PARK, nr Hythe
MAY Wednesday 13
  SISSINGHURST CASTLE, nr Cranbrook
MAY Sunday 17
  BRENCHLEY GARDENS, nr Tonbridge
  DODDINGTON PLACE, nr Sittingbourne
  EDENBRIDGE HOUSE, Edenbridge
  THE GRANGE, Benenden
  HALL PLACE GARDENS, Leigh
  HOLWOOD, Keston
  LADHAM HOUSE, Goudhurst
  NIZELS GARDENS, Hildenborough
  THE PHILLIPPINES, Ide Hall
  SANDLING PARK, nr Hythe
  STONEWALL PARK, Chiddingstone Hoath
  2 THORNDALE CLOSE, Chatham
  WOOLTON FARM, Bekesbourne
MAY Wednesday 20
  THE OLD CLOTH HALL, Cranbrook
  ROCK FARM, Nettlestead
MAY Saturday 23
  RIVERHILL HOUSE, Sevenoaks
  ROCK FARM, Nettlestead
MAY Sunday 24
  BEECH COURT, Challock
  CHURCH HILL COTTAGE, Charing Heath
  COPTON ASH, Faversham
  ‡‡CRITTENDEN HOUSE, Matfield
  HALES PLACE, Tenterden
  HALL PLACE GARDENS, Leigh
  HOLE PARK, Rolvenden
  LADHAM HOUSE, Goudhurst
  LARKSFIELD, Crockham Hill
  LARKSFIELD COTTAGE, Crockham Hill
  LONGACRE, Selling
  NORTHBOURNE COURT, nr Deal
  OXON HOATH, Hadlow, nr Tonbridge
  ‡‡THE RED HOUSE, Crockham Hill
  SANDLING PARK, nr Hythe
  SISSINGHURST PLACE GARDENS, nr
    Cranbrook
  STONEWALL PARK, Chiddingstone Hoath
  ‡‡TAWSDEN COTTAGE, Brenchley
  UPDOWN FARM, Betteshanger, nr Deal
  WAYSTRODE MANOR, Cowden
MAY Monday 25 (Bank Hol)
  CRITTENDEN HOUSE, Matfield
  LONGACRE, Selling
  OSWALDS, Bishopsbourne
  SCOTNEY CASTLE, Lamberhurst
MAY Tuesday 26
  GREAT COMP CHARITABLE TRUST,
    Borough Green
MAY Wednesday 27
  COPTON ASH, Faversham
  GREAT COMP CHARITABLE TRUST,
    Borough Green
  HOLE PARK, Rolvenden
  ROCK FARM, Nettlestead

MAY Saturday 30
  EMMETTS HILL, Ide Hill
  ROCK FARM, Nettlestead
MAY Sunday 31
  BEECH COURT, Challock
  BILTING HOUSE, nr Ashford
  LARKSFIELD, Crockham Hill
  ‡LARKSFIELD COTTAGE, Crockham Hill
  MARLE PLACE, Brenchley
  OLANTIGH, Wye
  THE OLD CLOTH HALL, Cranbrook
  THE OLD LAUNDRY, Tudely, nr Tonbridge
  ‡THE RED HOUSE, Crockham Hall
  ‡‡SANDLING PARK, Hythe
  ‡‡SEA CLOSE, Hythe
  SHIRLEY HOUSE, Sutton Valence
  2 THORNDALE CLOSE, Chatham
  TORRY HILL, nr Sittingbourne
JUNE Monday 1 & Tuesday 2
  THE OLD CLOTH HALL, Cranbrook
JUNE Wednesday 3
  KNOLE, Sevenoaks
  THE OLD CLOTH HALL, Cranbrook
  ROCK FARM, Nettlestead
JUNE Saturday 6
  ROCK FARM, Nettlestead
JUNE Sunday 7
  BEECH COURT, Challock
  BELMONT PARK, Faversham
  PUXTED HOUSE, BRENCHLEY GARDENS
  COLDHAM, Little Chart Forstal
  CONGELOW HOUSE, Yalding
  CROWN POINT NURSERY, Ightham
  GOODNESTON PARK, next Wingham, nr
    Canterbury
  HALL PLACE GARDENS, Leigh
  HORTON PRIORY, Sellindge, nr Ashford
  LONGACRE, Selling
  THE OLD CLOTH HALL, Cranbrook
  OLD MILL, Tonge, nr Sittingbourne
  THE PHILLIPPINES, Ide Hall
  RINGFIELD, Knockholt
  SANDLING PARK, Hythe
  SHIRLEY HOUSE, Sutton Valence
  THORNHAM FRIARS, Thurnham, nr
    Maidstone
  TROTTS HALL, Milstead
  ULCOMBE PLACE, nr Maidstone
JUNE Monday 8
  THE OLD CLOTH HALL, Cranbrook
JUNE Wednesday 10
  BOG FARM, Brabourne Lees
  HOLE PARK, Rolvenden
  OLD MILL, Tonge, nr Sittingbourne
  ROCK FARM, Nettlestead
  SISSINGHURST CASTLE, nr Cranbrook
  WAYSTRODE MANOR, Cowden
JUNE Saturday 13
  ROCK FARM, Nettlestead
JUNE Sunday 14
  CHURCH HILL COTTAGE, Charing Heath
  DODDINGTON PLACE, nr Sittingbourne
  FOREST GATE, Pluckley, nr Ashford
  GODINTON PARK, Ashford
  HALL PLACE GARDENS, Leigh
  KYPP COTTAGE, Biddenden

MERE HOUSE, Mereworth, nr Maidstone
THE RECTORY, Fairseat, Sevenoaks
SALISBURY HOUSE, Rainham
2 THORNDALE CLOSE, Chatham
JUNE Monday 15 & Tuesday 16
KYPP COTTAGE, Biddenden
JUNE Wednesday 17
KYPP COTTAGE, Biddenden
ROCK FARM, Nettlestead
JUNE Saturday 20
LULLINGSTONE CASTLE, Eynsford
ROCK FARM, Nettlestead
JUNE Sunday 21
‡‡‡GROOME FARM, Egerton
HAZELPITS, Headcorn
KYPP COTTAGE, Biddenden
‡LILY VALE FARM, Smeeth
‡LODGE HOUSE, Smeeth
LONGACRE, Selling
NORTHBOURNE COURT, nr Deal
PARSONAGE FARM, Boxley
RAMHURST MANOR, Leigh, Tonbridge
SALISBURY HOUSE, Rainham
‡‡TIMBOLD HILL HOUSE, Frinsted, nr
    Sittingbourne
‡‡TORRY HILL, nr Sittingbourne
‡‡‡WEEKS FARM, Egerton Forstal, nr
    Ashford
JUNE Monday 22 & Tuesday 23
KYPP COTTAGE, Biddenden
JUNE Wednesday 24
BREWHOUSE, Boughton Aluph
‡‡DIGGES COURT, Westwell
‡‡THE DOWNINGS, Westwell
HOLE PARK, Rolvenden
KYPP COTTAGE, Biddenden
‡LILY VALE FARM, Smeeth
‡LODGE HOUSE, Smeeth
PEDDARS WOOD, St Michaels, Tenterden
ROCK FARM, Nettlestead
JUNE Saturday 27
ROCK FARM, Nettlestead
‡PRIMROSE HILL, Hawkhurst
‡SLIP MILL, Hawkhurst
JUNE Sunday 28
‡BICKNOR GARDENS, nr Sittingbourne
BREWHOUSE, Boughton Aluph
DUNMORE, Four Elms
GOODNESTON PARK, next Wingham, nr
    Canterbury
‡‡‡‡115 HADLOW ROAD, Tonbridge
‡HARTLIP PLACE, nr Sittingbourne
KYPP COTTAGE, Biddenden
MARLE PLACE, Brenchley
NORTHBOURNE COURT, nr Deal
‡‡‡THE OLD PARSONAGE, Sutton
    Valence
‡‡‡OTHAM GARDENS, nr Maidstone
PARSONAGE FARM, Boxley
PETT PLACE, Charing
‡‡‡‡THE POSTERN, Tonbridge
ST CLERE, Kemsing
SEA CLOSE, Hythe
SMARDEN GARDENS, nr Ashford
2 THORNDALE CLOSE, Chatham
‡‡TURKEY COURT, Maidstone

‡‡ULCOMBE PLACE, nr Maidstone
UPDOWN FARM, Betteshanger, nr Deal
‡‡‡UPPER MILL COTTAGE, Loose
WAYSTRODE MANOR, Cowden
JUNE Monday 29 & Tuesday 30
KYPP COTTAGE, Biddenden
ROSE FARM, Shottenden, nr Chilham
JULY Wednesday 1
BREWHOUSE, Boughton Aluph
DUNMORE, Four Elms
KYPP COTTAGE, Biddenden
ROSE FARM, Shottenden, nr Chilham
UPPER MILL COTTAGE, Loose
JULY Thursday 2 & Friday 3
ROSE FARM, Shottenden, nr Chilham
JULY Saturday 4
ROCK FARM, Nettlestead
JULY Sunday 5
BREWHOUSE, Boughton Aluph
‡‡COPTON ASH, Faversham
FOREST GATE, Pluckley, nr Ashford
GOUDHURST GARDENS, nr Cranbrook
KYPP COTTAGE, Biddenden
‡LITTLE TRAFALGAR, Selling
‡LONGACRE, Selling
MERE HOUSE, Mereworth, nr Maidstone
‡‡MOUNT EPHRAIM, Hernhill, Faversham
THE OLD PARSONAGE, Sutton Valence
JULY Monday 6 & Tuesday 7
KYPP COTTAGE, Biddenden
JULY Wednesday 8
HOLE PARK, Rolvenden
KYPP COTTAGE, Biddenden
SISSINGHURST CASTLE, nr Cranbrook
JULY Sunday 12
CHURCH HILL COTTAGE, Charing Heath
COBHAM COURT, Bekesbourne
THE DOWNINGS, Westwell
EDENBRIDGE HOUSE, Edenbridge
HILLSIDE, Groombridge
KYPP COTTAGE, Biddenden
LADHAM HOUSE, Goudhurst
MONKTON COURT, nr Ramsgate
NORTHBOURNE COURT, nr Deal
OLANTIGH, Wye
PETT PLACE, Charing
SPRIVERS, Horsmonden, nr Tonbridge
2 THORNDALE CLOSE, Chatham
TORRY HILL, nr Sittingbourne
WEEKS FARM, Egerton Forstal, nr Ashford
WITHERSDANE HALL, Wye
JULY Monday 13
KYPP COTTAGE, Biddenden
MONKTON COURT, nr Ramsgate
JULY Tuesday 14
KYPP COTTAGE, Biddenden
JULY Wednesday 15
COBHAM COURT, Bekesbourne
KYPP COTTAGE, Biddenden
ROCK FARM, Nettlestead
JULY Saturday 18
ROCK FARM, Nettlestead
JULY Sunday 19
BENENDEN WALLED GARDEN, Benenden
‡COURT LODGE, Groombridge
6 GRANGE ROAD, Saltwood

‡GROOMBRIDGE PLACE, Tunbridge Wells
HAZELPITS, Headcorn
‡‡LITTLE TRAFALGAR, Selling
‡‡LONGACRE, Selling
NORTHBOURNE COURT, nr Deal
OSWALDS, Bishopsbourne
UPPER MILL COTTAGE, Loose
JULY Monday 20
BENENDEN WALLED GARDEN
JULY Wednesday 22
PEDDARS WOOD, St Michaels, Tenterden
THE RECTORY, Fairseat, Sevenoaks
ROCK FARM, Nettlestead
UPPER MILL COTTAGE, Loose
JULY Saturday 25
ROCK FARM, Nettlestead
JULY Sunday 26
CHERRY ORCHARD COTTAGE,
  Bonnington, Ashford
GRAHAM CHIESMAN HOUSE, Chislehurst
2 THORNDALE CLOSE, Chatham
JULY Wednesday 29
ROCK FARM, Nettlestead
AUGUST Saturday 1
ROCK FARM, Nettlestead
AUGUST Sunday 2
185 BORDEN LANE, Sittingbourne
‡LITTLE TRAFALGAR, Selling
‡LONGACRE, Selling
MAURICE HOUSE, Broadstairs
OSWALDS, Bishopsbourne
SEA CLOSE, Hythe
WEST FARLEIGH HALL, nr Maidstone
AUGUST Wednesday 5
185 BORDEN LANE, Sittingbourne
KNOLE, Sevenoaks
ROCK FARM, Nettlestead
AUGUST Sunday 9
COLDHAM, Little Chart Forstal
MOUNT EPHRAIM, Hernhill, Faversham
WITHERSDANE HALL, Wye
AUGUST Sunday 16
GROOME FARM, Egerton
STANFORD HOUSE, Stanford, nr Hythe
AUGUST Sunday 23
BILTING HOUSE, nr Ashford
WEST STUDDAL FARM, nr Dover
AUGUST Sunday 30
115 HADLOW ROAD, Tonbridge
NORTHBOURNE COURT, nr Deal
THE PINES GARDEN, St Margaret's Bay
WITHERSDANE HALL, Wye
SEPTEMBER Sunday 6
LITTLE TRAFALGAR, Selling
SEPTEMBER Sunday 13
NORTHBOURNE COURT, nr Deal
OSWALDS, Bishopsbourne
TURKEY COURT, Maidstone
SEPTEMBER Sunday 20
COPTON ASH, Faversham
SEPTEMBER Wednesday 23
BOG FARM, Brabourne Lees
OCTOBER Sunday 11
HOLE PARK, Rolvenden
OCTOBER Saturday 17
EMMETTS GARDEN, Ide Hill

OCTOBER Sunday 18
COPTON ASH, Faversham
HOLE PARK, Rolvenden

DESCRIPTIONS OF GARDENS

Beech Court ⋇❀ (Mr & Mrs Vyvyan Harmsworth) Challock, 7m N of Ashford. Entrance on A252, Challock being midway between Charing and Chilham. 6 acres; a young garden created by Maj Botley with Wester Ross in mind. Fine collection rhododendrons, acers, primulas and shrubs. TEAS. *Adm 60p Chd 30p (Share to Birthright). Suns May 24, 31; June 7 (2-6)*

Belmont Park ⅁ (The Lord Harris) Throwley, 5m SW of Faversham. Walled garden, lawns, orangery; small pinetum, kitchen garden. Long walk, folly; Victorian grotto. House by Samuel Wyatt, c.1792. Tea Eastling, 3m. *Adm 50p Chd 20p. Sun June 7 (2.30-6)*

¶**Benenden Walled Garden** ⅁⋇❀ (Mr & Mrs R.W.Cotter) In grounds of Benenden School, 4m SE of Cranbrook. Turn N off B2086 at Benenden X-rds, entrance 1m on left. 1-acre C18 walled garden; herbs, old fashioned and fragrant plants a speciality. Wide variety of plants, well labelled. Picnic area. TEA. *Adm 70p Chd 20p. Sun, Mon July 19, 20 (10-6)*

Bicknor Gardens ⅁ 5m S of Sittingbourne. From E end of A20/M20 junc turn N on to B2163 through Hollingbourne, gardens signed from top of hill; from A249 Sittingbourne-Maidstone, gardens signed from Bredgar turning 200yds S of M2. Also signed from Bredgar, 3m S of Sittingbourne on B2163. Roads not suitable for coaches. To celebrate the NGS Diamond Jubilee, Bicknor Gardens have arranged a special North Downs country walk; for those who wish, we suggest parking at Deans Bottom. After visiting Deans Bank and Deans Bottom, follow signs along valley, 1m to Placketts Hole and TEAS. *Combined adm £1 Chd 25p (Share to St James' Church, Bicknor). Sun June 28 (2-6.30)*

> **Placketts Hole** ⋇❀ (Mr & Mrs D.P. Wainman) Owners have been designing and planting 2-acre informal garden, inc building walls around charming old house (C16 with Georgian additions): interesting mix of shrubs, large borders, formal rose garden, lots of herbs and sweet-smelling plants. TEAS
> **Deans Bank Farm** (Dr & Mrs R. Hickman) 1½-acre informal cottage garden in picturesque rural setting
> **Deans Bottom Farm** (Mr & Mrs Anthony Taylor) Small garden with herbaceous border, roses, shrubs and lilies surrounding C16 farmhouse

Bilting House ⅁⋇ (John Erle-Drax Esq) A28, 5m NE of Ashford, 9m from Canterbury. Wye

1½m. An old-fashioned garden with ha-ha; rhododendrons, azaleas; shrubs, collection of conifers in plantation. In beautiful part of Stour Valley. TEAS 50p. *Adm 75p Chd 25p (Share to BRCS). Suns May 31, Aug 23 (2-6)*

Bog Farm ర&%® (Mr & Mrs K.J. Hewett) Brabourne Lees, 4m E of Ashford. Via A20 Ashford-Folkestone; turn left 3m from Ashford at Smeeth; proceed ½m to Woolpack Inn; bear right, continue 700yds following sign to garden on right down single track lane. 1-acre garden, planned and planted by owners since 1959 around small Kentish farmhouse (not open); good collection of shrubs, trees, species plants, ferns, bulbs arranged to give some interest to each season; mixed borders; moisture plants; old roses, herb garden. *Adm 70p Chd 20p. Weds June 10, Sept 23 (2-7)*

185 Borden Lane %® (Mr & Mrs P.A. Boyce) ½m S of Sittingbourne. 1m from Sittingbourne side of A2/A249 junc. Small informal garden continually improved by present owners since 1976; 75 different varieties of fuchsia; shrubs; pond; fruit and vegetable garden. Home-made TEAS. *Adm 50p Chd 15p. Sun Aug 2, Wed Aug 5 (2-6)*

Bradbourne House Gardens ర& (Institute of Horticultural Research) East Malling, 4m W of Maidstone. Entrance to Bradbourne House is E of New Rd, East Malling. (New Rd runs from Larkfield A20 to East Malling Village). Hatton Fruit Garden, Bradbourne House, consists of demonstration fruit gardens of particular interest to amateur fruit growers occupying walled garden, formerly kitchen garden of Bradbourne House. Gardens include various intensive tree forms of apples and pears. Members of staff available for questions. TEAS. (or West Malling 2m). *Adm 50p Chd 10p. Sun May 3 (2-5.30)*

Brenchley Gardens 6m SE of Tonbridge. From A21 1m S of Pembury turn N on to B2160, turn right at Xrds in Matfield signposted Brenchley. *Combined adm £1.50 Chd free. Sun May 17 (2-6)*
Holmbush ర& (Mr & Mrs B. Hodge) 1½-acre informal garden, mainly lawns, trees and shrub borders, planted since 1960
Portobello (Barry M. Williams Esq) 1½-acres, lawn, trees, shrubs inc azaleas and shrub roses; walled garden. C17 barn containing 50yr old Fire Engine in running order. House (not open) built by Monckton family 1739
Puxted House ర& (P.J. Oliver-Smith Esq) 1½-acre with rare and coloured foliage shrubs, asiatic primulas and woodland plants. Alpine and rose garden all labelled. Present owner cleared 20 yrs of brambles in 1981 before re-planting. Garden **also** open Sun June 7 (2-6). *Adm 50p Chd 20p (Share to Arrow Riding Centre for Disabled, Dartford). Also by appt*

Tanglewood (Mr & Mrs C. Carabott) 3-acre small country garden inc shrubs and bluebell wood. Oak beamed house (not open)

Brewhouse %® (Mr & Mrs J.A.H. Nicholson) Malthouse Lane, Boughton Aluph, 3m N of Ashford. Garden off Pilgrims Way. ¼m N and signed from Boughton Lees village green, on A251 Ashford/Faversham. Small plantsman's garden developed since 1978. C16 farmhouse (not open) with fine views of open chalkland. Collections of old roses, other old fashioned flowers, herbaceous and foliage plants. Orchard available for picnics. TEAS (in aid of St Christopher's Church). *Adm 50p Chd 25p. Wed, Sun June 24, 28; Wed, Sun July 1, 5 (2-6) Also by appt throughout season*

Cherry Orchard Cottage ర& (Prof & Mrs J.A. Dudgeon) Bonnington, 7m SE of Ashford. From A20 at Smeeth turn S onto B2069 to Aldington and Bonnington; garden ½m before junc B2069/B2067. Small garden around C17 cottage with 11 acres of woodland. Shrubs, roses, mixed borders with ornamental stream running through; collection of clematis. TEA. *Adm 50p Chd 20p. Sun July 26 (2-6)*

Chevening ర&% (By permission of The Administrative Trustees of Chevening Estate and the Rt Hon Sir Geoffrey Howe QC, MP) 4m NW of Sevenoaks. Turn N off A25 at Sundridge traffic lights on to B2211; at Chevening Xrds 1½m turn left. 27 acres with lawns and woodland garden, lake, maze, formal rides, parterre. Garden being restored. TEAS and home-made cakes for sale in aid of Kent Church Social Work. *Adm 75p Chd 25p. Sun April 26 (2-6)*

Church Hill Cottage ర&%® (Mr & Mrs Michael Metianu) Charing Heath, 10m NW of Ashford. Leave A20 dual carriageway ½m W of Charing signed Charing Heath and Egerton. After 1m fork right at Red Lion, then right again; cottage 250 yds on right. 1 acre cottage garden redesigned and replanted by present owners since 1981; island beds using wide range unusual perennials, shrubs, alpines, many grey/variegated foliage plants, spring bulbs. TEAS. June/July only. *Adm 50p Chd 25p (Share to WI Denman College Appeal). Suns May 3, 24; June 14, July 12 (2-5); also by appt (Tel Charing 2522)*

Cobham Court ® (Mrs Walter Whigham) Bekesbourne, 3m SE of Canterbury. Turn E off A2 onto Bridge bypass (signposted Bekesbourne); just before railway arch (1m) turn right (signed Adisham); house ¾m. Medium-sized well-stocked garden; herbaceous borders, shrub roses bounded by old walls; good collection of trees (many planted since 1963) inc one of the oldest robinia trees in the country, supposedly planted by John Tradescant; kitchen garden. C14 house (not open) adjoining Norman church (open). Picnics allowed in meadow. Produce stall. TEAS. *Adm 80p Chd free (Share to Kent & Canterbury Cancer Care Centre). Sun July 12, Wed July 15 (2-6)*

Coldham ⅍⚘ (Dr & Mrs J.G. Elliott) Little Chart Forstal, 5m NW of Ashford. Leave A20 at Charing by B2077, to Little Chart, turn E in village, ¼m. Small garden developed since 1970 in setting of old walls; good collection of rare plants, bulbs, alpines, mixed borders, shrub roses. C16 Kent farmhouse (not open). TEA June/August. *Adm £1 Chd 50p. Suns April 26, June 7, Aug 9 (2-6)*

Congelow House ⅍⚘ (Mr & Mrs D.J. Cooper) Yalding, 8m SW of Maidstone. Approx midway between Tonbridge and Maidstone, and S of Yalding. 4-acre garden, created from an orchard since 1973; backbone of interesting ornamental trees planted about 1850; also recent plantings; walled vegetable garden; pleasure gardens inc rhododendrons, azaleas, iris, roses, shrub roses. Vegetables, organically grown, on sale. Dogs on leads. TEAS. *Adm 70p Chd 40p (Share to British Diabetic Assn). Sun June 7 (2-6)*

¶**Copton Ash** ⅍⚘⚘ (Mr & Mrs John Ingram) 105 Ashford Rd, Faversham, 1m. On A251 Faversham-Ashford rd opp E-bound junc with M2. 1½-acre plantsmans garden developed since 1978 on site of old cherry orchard. Wide range of plants in mixed borders and informal island beds; inc spring bulbs, alpine and herbaceous plants, shrubs and young trees. Good autumn colour. Collection of apple and soft fruit varieties. TEA. *Adm 60p Chd 20p (Share to National Schizophrenia Fellowship, Canterbury Group). Sun, Weds April 19, 22; May 24, 27; Suns July 5; Sept 20; Oct 18 (2-6)*

Court Lodge ⅍⚘ (Mr & Mrs T.C.V. Packman) Groombridge, 4½m SW of Tunbridge Wells. C15 house (not open) removed from Udimore in 1912. 7-acre garden with roses, pergola, pond and rockery. Distant views. TEAS at Groombridge Place. *Adm 50p Chd 25p. Sun July 19 (2-6.30)*

Crittenden House ⅍⚘ (B.P. Tompsett Esq) Matfield, 6m SE of Tonbridge. Bus: MD 6 or 297, alight Standings Cross, Matfield, 1m. Garden around early C17 house completely planned and planted since 1956 on laboursaving lines. Featuring spring shrubs (rhododendrons, magnolias), roses, lilies, foliage, waterside planting of ponds in old iron workings, of interest from early spring bulbs to autumn colour. Rare young trees mentioned in Collins Guide to Trees in UK and Europe, by Alan Mitchell. Tea Cherrytrees Matfield Green. Free car park.

Adm 75p Chd 20p (Share to CPRE, Kent Branch). Sun, Mon April 19, 20; Sun May 3; Sun, Mon May 24, 25 (2-6)

Crown Point Nursery ⚘⚘ (Messrs G. Reuthe Ltd) nr Ightham. Car park by tarmac rd in entrance. Access from A25 by drive through woodland. Bus: MD10 Maidstone-Sevenoaks, alight nr Sir Jeffery Amherst Arms. Woodland nursery of 10 acres for culture of rhododendrons, azaleas and other shrubs. Tea Ightham. *Adm 50p Chd 20p. Sun June 7 (11-5)*

Denton Court ⅍ (Mr and Miss Gostling) Denton, 8m SE of Canterbury on A260. Large garden; fine trees and shrubs; spring bulbs; clipped yews. *Adm 50p Chd 20p. Sun April 19 (2-5)*

Digges Court ⅍⚘ (Mr & Mrs Luke Parsons) Westwell, 5m NW of Ashford. From A20, turn N at Tuthill, follow lane between garages, left at Y-fork towards Charing, garden on right. 1 acre old walled garden; roses and paeonies in setting below North Downs, surrounding Grade II listed house (not open). *Adm 50p Chd 25p (Share to Cancer Relief Macmillan Fund). Wed June 24 (2-6)*

Doddington Place ⅍⚘ (Mr Richard & The Hon Mrs Oldfield) 6m SE of Sittingbourne. From A20 turn N opp Lenham or from A2 turn S at Teynham (both 4m). Large garden, landscaped with wide views; trees and yew hedges; woodland garden with azaleas and rhododendrons, rock garden. TEAS, May & June only. *Adm 75p Chd 10p. Suns & Bank Hols May, June, July and Sept. For NGS (Share to Kent Assn for the Blind). Suns May 17, June 14 (2-6)*

The Downings ⅍⚘ (Mr & Mrs Vere Collins) Westwell, 4m NW of Ashford. From A20 turn N at Potters Corner by Hare and Hounds, immediately turn left to village, 1½m. Small garden surrounding Georgian house, planned 1983 for interest of design, colour and variety of plants; small decorative kitchen garden. Lovely country views. *Adm 50p Chd 10p (Share to St Mary's Church, Westwell). Wed June 24 & Sun July 12 (2-6)*

Dunmore ⅍⚘ (Lady Greenaway) Four Elms, 2m NE of Edenbridge. Proceed to Four Elms, take B269 towards Hever, garden 1st on right after church ¼m from Four Elms Xrds, on bus route from Edenbridge/Tunbridge Wells. 3½ acres; rock garden, herbaceous border, roses, shrubs, lawns and orchard. *Adm £1 Chd 20p. Sun June 28, Wed July 1 (2-5)*

Edenbridge House ⚘ (Mrs D.G. Lloyd) Crockham Hill Rd, 1½m N of Edenbridge, nr Marlpit Hill, on B2026. Spring shrubs, herbaceous borders, roses and ornamental pools. House part C16 (not open). TEAS. *Adm 75p Chd 25p. Suns May 17, July 12 (2-6)*

Emmetts Garden (The National Trust) Ide Hill, 5m SW of Sevenoaks. 1½m S of A25 on Sundridge-Ide Hill Rd. 1½m N of Ide Hill off B2042. 5-acre hillside garden. One of the highest gardens in Kent, noted for its fine collection of rare trees and shrubs; lovely spring and autumn colour. (NT members please note, openings in aid of NGS are on days when property would not normally be open therefore adm charges apply). *Adm £1.30 Chd 60p. April to Oct 31 every Sun, Tues, Wed, Thurs & Fri. Open Bank Hol Mons (2-6 last adm 5). For NGS Sats May 30, Oct 17 (2-6)*

¶**Forest Gate** ৬৵❀ (Mr & Mrs Robert Johnson) Pluckley, 8m W of Ashford. From A20 at Charing take B2077 to Pluckley Village; turn left signed Bethersden, follow 1m to garden 100 yds S of Pluckley Station. 2-acre garden on heavy clay; well stocked mixed borders, pond and interesting herb collection. Many plants labelled. C17 house (not open). Picnics allowed in meadow. TEA. *Adm 80p Chd 30p (Share to The Brompton Hospital). Suns June 14, July 5 (2-6)*

Godinton Park ❀ (Alan Wyndham Green Esq) Entrance 1½m W of Ashford at Potter's Corner on A20. Bus: MD/EK 10, 10A, 10B Folkestone-Ashford-Maidstone, alight Hare and Hounds, Potter's Corner. Formal and wild gardens. Topiary. Jacobean mansion with elaborate woodwork. Unique frieze in drawing room depicting arms drill of Kent Halbardiers 1630. Tea Swan Hotel, Charing. *Adm garden only 60p, house & garden £1.20, Chd 60p. △Suns April 19, June 14 (2-5)*

Goodnestone Park ৬৵❀ (The Lady FitzWalter) nr Wingham, Canterbury. Village lies S of B2046 rd from A2 to Wingham. Signpost off B2046 says Goodnestone. Village St is 'No Through Rd', but house and garden at the terminus. Bus: EK13, 14 Canterbury-Deal; bus stop: Wingham, 2m. 5-6 acres; good trees; woodland garden, walled garden with old-fashioned roses. Connections with Jane Austen who stayed here. Picnics allowed. TEAS Suns but not April. *Adm £1 Chd 10p (Adm disabled in wheelchair 80p). April 13 to July 9; Aug 24 to Oct 1 Mon to Thurs (11-5). Suns April 19, May 24, 31, June 14, 21, July 5. For NGS Suns April 26, June 7, 28 (2-6)*

Goudhurst Gardens ৵ 4m W of Cranbrook. Map and tickets available on village green. TEAS available in village. *Combined adm £2, Chd free. Sun July 5 (2-6)*

¶**Riseden Cottage** ৬ (Air Vice Marshal & Mrs John Stacey) Small country garden appropriate to C15 cottage; a random development from recovered field. Raised flower beds and many well planted tubs provide a practical example for other gardeners with limited movement. Pad-

docks with two ponies and two donkeys; pond and waterfowl. Picnickers welcome **Tara** ❀ (Mr & Mrs Peter Coombs) Existing 1-acre garden completely redesigned in 1982. Owners still undertaking structural work and much planting with eventual low maintenance and year round interest in view

Tulip Tree Cottage (Mr & Mrs K.A. Owen) 1 acre with sweeping lawn, established trees in herbaceous and shrub borders; 80ft Liriodendron tulipifera, said to be one of finest in country, also fine Cedrus atlantica glauca

Wall-Pond Field (Mr & Mrs G.V. Kibblewhite) Interesting trees, shrubs and perennials packed into ⅓-acre garden, hedged around. Created by owners since 1967

¶**Graham Chiesman House** ৬ (Diocese of Rochester) Chislehurst. In St Paul's Cray Rd, 1m from station. 4-acre garden with lawns, herbaceous borders, shrubs and kitchen garden. Woodland walk, paddock and orchard. TEAS in aid of the Church Army. *Adm 50p Chd 25p. Sun July 26 (2-6)*

The Grange ৬৵❀ (Mr & Mrs A. Parsons) Benenden, off village green. Fine collection of rhododendrons and other rare plants, many introduced and raised by the late Capt Collingwood Ingram. Many fine trees inc largest eucalyptus in England. Hot and cold snacks: King William IV, Benenden (12-2). *Adm 75p Chd 25p. Suns May 3, 17 (1-6)*

6 Grange Rd ৵ (Mrs C.S. Furneaux) Saltwood, 1m N of Hythe, by village green. Tiny enclosed garden, skilfully planted for year round interest since 1973. Featured in July 1986 edition of RHS 'The Garden'. *Adm 50p Chd 20p (Share to St Peter & St Paul's Church, Saltwood). Sun July 19 (2-5.30)*

Great Comp Charitable Trust ৬৵❀ (Mr & Mrs R. Cameron) 2m E of Borough Green. A20 at Wrotham Heath, take Seven Mile Lane, B2016; at 1st Xrds turn right; garden on left ½m. Bus: MD9; alight Platt Memorial Hall, ¾m. Garden skilfully designed and constructed by present owners with virtually no assistance 1957 to 1981; 7 acres now fully developed, spacious setting of well-maintained lawns and paths with plantsman's collection of trees, shrubs, heathers and herbaceous plants. Good autumn colour. Early C17 house (not shown). Home-made TEAS (3.30-5) on NGS days. *Adm £1.50 Chd 70p (Share to Tradescant Trust). April 1 to Oct 31 (11-6). For NGS Tues, Wed May 26, 27 (11-6)*

Groombridge Place (Mrs R. Newton) Groombridge, SW of Tunbridge Wells. Station: Groombridge. Bus: MD 291 Tunbridge Wells-East Grinstead, alight nr gates. Walled gardens, herbaceous borders, C17 moated house. TEAS. *Adm 50p Chd 25p. Sun July 19 (2-6.30)*

Groome Farm ✿❀ (Mr & Mrs Michael Swatland) Egerton, 10m W of Ashford. From A20 at Charing Xrds take B2077 Biddenden Rd. Past Pluckley turn right at Ghosts Pub; right again, until Newland Green sign on left, house 1st on left. 1½ acres; still being developed around C15 Farm House and Oast (not open). Interesting collection trees, shrubs, roses and herbaceous plants; also water, heather and rock gardens. TEAS. *Adm 50p Chd 25p. Suns June 21, Aug 16 (2-6)*

115 Hadlow Road ✿ (Mr & Mrs Richard Esdale) in Tonbridge. Take A26 from N end of High St signed Maidstone, house 1m on left in service rd. ¼ acre unusual terraced garden with roses, herbaceous borders, clematis, hardy fuchsias, shrubs, alpines, kitchen garden and pond; well labelled. TEA. *Adm 40p Chd free. Suns June 28, Aug 30 (2-7) Also by appt*

Hales Place ✿ (Mr & Mrs Michael Robson) Tenterden. Gates adjoin Police Station in Oaks Rd, off E end of High St. Bus stop: Tenterden, High St, 800yds. Walled garden terraces, gazebos, well house and tythe barn surrounding Tudor mansion, c. 1544. Spring garden and 25 acres of orchard walks. Tea Tenterden. Car park free. *Adm 75p Chd 25p. Sun May 24 (2-6)*

Hall Place Gardens ✿ (The Lord Hollenden) Leigh, 4m W of Tonbridge. From A21 Sevenoaks-Tonbridge; at Hildenborough turn W on to B2027 and on 2½m to Leigh. Large outstanding garden with 11-acre lake, the lakeside walk crossing over picturesque bridges; garden contains many interesting trees and shrubs, well labelled. TEAS. Free car park. *Adm £1 Chd 20p. Suns May 17 to June 21. For NGS Suns May 17, 24, June 7, 14 (2.30-6.30)*

Hartlip Place ✿✿ (Lt Col & Mrs J.R. Yerburgh) Hartlip, 6m W of Sittingbourne; 1m S of A2 on outskirts of Hartlip village (midway between Rainham and Newington). From M20 take exit to Sittingbourne, in 1½m left to Yelsted; continue for 3m passing under motorway bridge; left up small hill; then left again towards Rainham; house 200yds on left. 3¾ acres; a secret garden concealed by rhododendrons and buddleia, planted with shrub roses; young herbaceous and shrub border; lawns sloping S; small wilderness walk; pond made by owner. House (not open) designed 1812-13 by William Bland the younger for his father; Bland later lived here himself and was author of number of works on marine architecture and agriculture. TEAS. *Adm 50p Chd 25p (Share to Church of St Michael & All Angels, Hartlip). Sun June 28 (2-6)*

Hazelpits ✿❀ (T.A. Day Esq) Ulcombe Rd, Headcorn, 9m S of Maidstone. Turn E off A274 in Headcorn at White Horse then 1st left. Informal country garden with two ponds, shrubs, old roses and many unusual plants. Natural grass, small wood around old marl-pits. TEAS. *Adm 75p Chd 35p (Share to Headcorn Parish Church). Suns June 21, July 19 (2-6.30)*

●**Hever Castle** ✿❀ (Broadland Properties Ltd) 3m SE of Edenbridge midway between Sevenoaks and East Grinstead. Train (not Suns) Uckfield service from Victoria hourly (Hever Station 1m). Formal Italian and landscaped garden with statuary, sculpture and topiary; large lake. Moated castle, childhood home of Anne Boleyn, also open. Refreshments. Free car/coach park. NO DOGS in castle, on lead only in gardens. *Adm Castle & Gdns £3.20 Chd £1.60; Gdns only £2 Chd £1.20. April 1 – Nov 1 daily (11-6 last adm 5; Castle opens 12 noon).* **Also see Stop press page 201.**

¶**Hillside** (Mr & Mrs A.Sheikhi) Groombridge Hill, Groombridge, 4m W of Tunbridge Wells. From A264 W of Langton Green take B2110 signed Groombridge, entrance ¼m on right. 3½-acre hillside garden replanted by present owners with wide variety of plants, shrubs, trees and bulbs. Late C19 listed house (not open) with landscape views. Visitors may use the tennis court. TEAS. *Adm to garden and orchid house 75p Chd 25p. (Share to Groombridge Home Physiotherapy for Disabled People). Sun July 12 (2-6.30)*

Hole Park ✿✿ (D.G.W. Barham Esq) Rolvenden-Cranbrook on B2086. Beautiful parkland; formal garden with mixed borders, roses, yew hedges and topiary a feature, many fine trees. Natural garden with rhododendrons, azaleas, daffodils, conifers, dell and water gardens; bluebell wood. Autumn colour. *Adm £1 Chd 25p (Share to Rolvenden Church). Suns April 12, 26, May 10, 24; Weds May 27, June 10, 24; July 8 (2-7); Suns Oct 11, 18 (2-6)*

Holwood ✿❀ (Seismograph Service (England) Ltd) Keston. Bus: Green Line 705 London-Bromley-Biggin Hill-Sevenoaks-Tunbridge Wells. Mansion (not open) in neo-classical style (architect Decimus Burton), picturesquely sited in extensive woodland with fine views across Kent; specimen trees, azaleas and flowering shrubs; greenhouses. One-time home of William Pitt. Historical Wilberforce and Pitt oaks. Iron Age fort and medieval tile kiln. Plant stall. This year is a special occasion and will be shared with the Anti-Slavery Society. **At 3.00pm a special ceremony will take place at the Wilberforce Oak to commemorate the 200th anniversary of William Wilberforce and William Pitt deciding to present the Slavery Abolition Bill to Parliament.** TEA. Free car park. *Adm 50p Chd* under 14, if accompanied free. (Share to Anti-Slavery Society) Sun May 17 (2-6)

Horton Priory & (Mrs A.C. Gore) Sellindge, 6m SE of Ashford. From A20 Ashford-Folkestone, 1m from Sellindge, turn E along Moorstock Lane, signposted Horton Priory. Bus: EK/MD 10, 10A, 10B Maidstone-Ashford-Folkestone; alight Sellindge, 1m. Herbaceous and rose border, lawn, pond and rock garden. Priory dates back to C12; church destroyed in reign of Henry VIII, but remains of W doorway and staircase to S aisle of nave can be seen by front door. Along W front Norman buttresses (all genuine) and C14 windows (some restored); one genuine small Norman window. Outer hall only open to visitors. Parking for cars in front of house, along drive and garage areas. Adm 50p Chd 10p. Sun June 7 (2-6)

◆**Knole** &⚹ (The Lord Sackville; The National Trust) Sevenoaks. Station: Sevenoaks. Bus: 483 West Croydon-Sevenoaks, alight Bus Station; Green Line 706 from Victoria via Bromley, alight Sevenoaks school. Pleasance, deer park, landscape garden, herb garden. Tea Sevenoaks. Adm £4 per car on entering park (inc 1 house admission); garden 50p Chd 25p; house £2 Chd £1. △Weds June 3, Aug 5 (11-5 last adm 4)

Kypp Cottage ⚹ (Mrs Zena Grant) Biddenden. 3½m NW of Tenterden. At Tenterden Rd A262 junc with Benenden Rd. Biddenden is picturesque, historical village with many beautiful old houses (inc a row of Grade I). Cottage garden started about 1964 from rough ground; extensive collection of interesting plants; new and old shrub roses and ground cover plants. Good examples of trees suitable for small gardens. Morning coffee & home-made TEAS. Adm 50p Chd 20p (Share to Biddenden Parish Church Appeal). Suns, Mons, Tues, Weds June 14, 15, 16, 17; 21, 22, 23, 24; 28, 29, 30; July 1; 5, 6, 7, 8; 12, 13, 14, 15 (10-6). Also by appt (Tel Biddenden 291480)

Ladham House ⊛ (Betty, Lady Jessel) Goudhurst. On NE of village, off A262. 10 acres with rolling lawns, fine specimen trees, rhododendrons, camellias, azaleas, shrubs and magnolias. Newly planted arboretum. Spectacular twin mixed borders; fountain and bog gardens. Car park free. Adm £1 Chd 30p. Suns April 19, May 17, 24, July 12 (11-6). Also by appt

Larksfield & (Mr & Mrs P. Dickinson) Crockham Hill, 3m N of Edenbridge. On Limpsfield-Oxted rd B269. Octavia Hill, a founder of the National Trust lived here and helped create the original garden; fine collection of azaleas and shrubs, herbaceous plants, rose beds and woodlands. Views over Weald and Ashdown Forest. **The Red House** and **Larksfield Cottage** gardens also open same days.

TEAS. Combined adm to 3 gardens £1 Chd 50p or 60p OAPs/Chd 30p each garden. Suns May 24, 31 (2-6)

Larksfield Cottage & (Mrs M.J. Johnston) Crockham Hill, 3m N of Edenbridge. On B269. An enchanting garden re-designed in 1981 with attractive lawns and shrubs following the style of and adjacent to Larksfield. Views over the Weald and Ashdown Forest. TEAS. **The Red House** and **Larksfield** gardens open same days. Combined adm £1 Chd 50p or 60p OAPs/Chd 30p each garden. Suns May 24, 31 (2-6)

43 Layhams Road & (Mrs Dolly Robertson) West Wickham. Semi-detached house recognisable by small sunken flower garden in the front. Opp Wickham Court Farm. A raised vegetable garden, purpose-built for the disabled with easy access to wide terraced walkways. The owner, who maintains the entire 24ft x 70ft area herself, would be pleased to pass on her experiences as a disabled gardener so that others may share her joy and interest. Collecting box. By appt only all year (Tel 01-462 4196)

¶**Lily Vale Farm** & (Mr & Mrs R.H.V. Moorhead) Smeeth, 6m E of Ashford. Turn N off A20 at garage opp Converter Station W of Sellindge; follow lane to T-junc turn left, entrance ½m. 1-acre garden on sloping site with pastoral outlook; shrub roses a feature. Ornamental wildfowl. **Lodge House** also open same dates. TEAS. Adm 50p Chd 20p. Sun & Wed June 21 & 24 (2-7)

¶**Little Trafalgar** &⚹ (Mr & Mrs R.J. Dunnett) Selling, 4m SE of Faversham. From A2 (M2) or A251 make for Selling Church, then follow signs to garden. Small informal garden. Extensive mixed borders filled with interesting shrubs, perennials and annuals. Emphasis on attracting wildlife. TEAS. Adm 40p Chd 20p. Suns July 5, 19, Aug 2, Sept 6 (2-5)

¶**Lodge House** &⊛ (Col & Mrs J. Talbot) Smeeth, 4m E of Ashford. From A20, 3m E of Ashford, turn N signed Smeeth. Turn right at The Woolpack, follow rd ½m to entrance. 2-acre garden with sloping lawns, shrubs and herbaceous borders in lovely setting. Children and picnics welcome. **Lily Vale Farm** also open same dates. TEAS. Adm 50p Chd 20p (Share to St Mary's Church, Smeeth). Sun June 21, Wed June 24 (2-7)

Longacre ⚹⊛ (Dr & Mrs G. Thomas) Perry Wood, Selling, 5m SE of Faversham. From A2 (M2) or A251 follow signs for Selling, passing White Lion on left, 1st right and immediately left, continue for ¼m. From A252 at Chilham, take turning signed Selling at Badgers Hill Fruit Farm. Left at 2nd Xrds, next right, left and then right. Small plantsman's garden with wide variety of interesting plants, created and maintained entirely by owners.

Most trees and shrubs planted in 1964; recently added herbaceous plants also alpines in gravel beds. Lovely walks in Perry Woods adjacent to garden. TEAS in aid of local charities. *Adm 50p Chd 25p (Share to Canterbury Pilgrims Hospice). Sun May 10 (no teas); Sun, Mon May 24, 25, Suns June 7, 21, July 5, 19, Aug 2 (2-5); also by appt (Tel Canterbury 752254)*

Lullingstone Castle &✗❀ (Mr & Mrs Guy Hart Dyke) In the Darenth Valley via Eynsford on A225. Eynsford Station ½m. All cars and coaches via Roman Villa. Lawns, woodland and lake, mixed border, small herb garden. Henry VII gateway; Church on the lawn open. Refreshments. *Adm garden £1.50 OAPs/Chd £1; house 50p extra.△ Sat June 20 (2-6)*

Luton House &✗ (Mr & Mrs John Swire) Selling, 4m SE of Faversham. From A2 (M2) or A251 make for White Lion. Entrance 30yds E on same side of rd. 4 acres; C19 landscaped garden; ornamental pond; fine trees underplanted with azaleas, camellias, woodland plants. *Adm 75p Chd 25p. Sun May 10 (2-6)*

Marle Place ❀ (Mr & Mrs Gerald Williams) Brenchley, 8m SE of Tonbridge. On B2162, 1m S of Horsmonden and 1½m NW of Lamberhurst. Turn E on Marle Place Rd. Victorian gazebo; plantmans shrub borders; walled scented garden, large herb rockery and herb nursery. C17 listed House (not open) TEA. *Adm £1 Chd 50p. (Share to NSPCC). Every Wed April 1 - Oct 1 (10-5).For NGS Suns May 31, June 28 (2-7)*

Maurice House &✗ (The Royal British Legion Residential Home) Callis Court Rd, Broadstairs. From Broadstairs Broadway take St Peter's Park Rd; turn right under railway arch into Baird's Hill; join Callis Court Rd entrance on right, 100yds beyond Lanthorne Rd turning. Well-maintained 8-acre garden; lawns, flowering trees, shrubs; formal flower beds; rose and water gardens; orchard. Spring bedding displays of wallflowers, tulips, polyanthus; wide variety of herbaceous plants and shrubs especially suited to coastal conditions. TEAS. *Adm 50p Chd 20p (Share to the Royal British Legion). Suns May 3, Aug 2 (2-5.30)*

Mere House &✗❀ (Sir John & Lady Wells) Mereworth, 7m W of Maidstone. From A26 Maidstone-Tonbridge turn on to B2016 and then into Mereworth village. Bus: MD7 Maidstone-Tonbridge; alight Mereworth village, ¼m. Medium-sized garden; ornamental shrubs, lake, lawns, daffodils. Picnics allowed (but no fires). *Adm 50p Chd 20p. Suns April 12, June 14, July 5 (2-7)*

Monkton Court &✗ (Mr & Mrs Michael Smith) Monkton, midway between Canterbury and Ramsgate on A253. Fork right on to B2047 signed Monkton, garden 150 yds on

behind church. Informal medium-sized garden of unexpected charm, with herbaceous and mixed flower borders planted for visual effect; an oasis in flat cauliflower land. Small collection of waterfowl. Original part of house given by Queen Edgiba in 962 to Monks of Christchurch, Canterbury, as a Rest House. TEA. *Adm 75p Chd 10p (Share to Monkton Church Restoration Fund). Sun, Mon July 12, 13 (2-6)*

Mount Ephraim &❀ (Mrs M.N. Dawes; Mr & Mrs E.S. Dawes) Hernhill, Faversham. From M2 and A299 take Hernhill turning at Duke of Kent. Herbaceous border; topiary; daffodils and rhododendrons; rose terraces leading to a small lake; Japanese rock garden with pools. TEAS. *Adm £1.20 Chd 25p. May 3 - Sept 13 Suns & Bank Hols. For NGS Suns April 26, July 5 & Aug 9 (2-6)*

Nizels Gardens ✗ Nizels Lane, Hildenborough, 3½m S of Sevenoaks. Take A225, at Riverhill roundabout take B245, Nizels Lane 1st right. TEA. *Combined adm £1 Chd 25p. Sun May 17 (2-5.30)*

 Nizels & (Mr & Mrs Richard Furber) 5-acre formal garden. Trees, shrubs, roses and walled kitchen garden. Good views
 Greencroft (Dr & Mrs A. Marr) 2-acre plantsman's garden. Trees, shrubs, mixed borders, interesting planting to screen Tonbridge by-pass, water and woodland garden, being developed by owner-gardeners with view to easy maintenance

Northbourne Court ❀ (The Lord Northbourne) W of Deal. Signs in village. Great brick terraces, belonging to an earlier Elizabethan mansion, provide a picturesque setting for a wide range of shrubs and plants on chalk soil; geraniums, fuchsias and grey-leaved plants. Elizabethan Great Barn. *Adm £1 OAPs/Chd 50p (Share to GRBS & RGOF) Suns May 24, June 21, 28; July 12, 19; Aug 30, Sept 13 (2-6) Weds June, July, Aug (2-5)*

Olantigh &✗ (J.R.H. Loudon Esq) Wye, 6m NE of Ashford. Turn off A28 either to Wye or at Godmersham; ¾ from Wye on rd to Godmersham. Water garden, rockery, shrubbery; beautiful trees. Tea Wye. *Adm 70p Chd 30p (Share to Wye Church). Suns April 26, May 31, July 12 (2-5)*

The Old Cloth Hall ✗ (Mrs John Morgan) 1m E of Cranbrook. Take Tenterden rd, past windmill, fork left at Baker's Cross. 1st private rd on right immediately before cemetery and DCPS. Tudor house visited by Queen Elizabeth I, surrounded by 12 acres of gardens and paddock. Fine rhododendrons and azaleas; spring bulbs; rose garden, pergola. TEAS. *Adm £1 Chd free. May Wed 20, Sun 31; June Mon 1, Tue 2, Wed 3, Sun 7, Mon 8 (10.30-5.30)*

¶**The Old Laundry** ⚘ (Lady d'Avigdor Gold-smid) Tudeley, 3m SE of Tonbridge. From A21 Tonbridge-Hastings rd, turn left at V junc by the Weald of Kent Girls School, proceed past Back Lodge of Somerhill, entrance ½m on right, signed Park Farm and Somerhill Mews. Garden created since 1984 in sec-luded well-wooded valley setting with stream running through. Twin borders, many young shrubs and trees, vegetable garden flanked by wall with newly planted white bor-der. Unique swimming pool, 60' long, 10' wide with water lily beds at each side; sculp-ture of fishes by Julian Hawkes a focal point. *Adm £1 accompanied Chd free. Sun May 31 (2-6)*

Old Mill ⚘⚘ (Jacobs & Thompson Part-nership) Tonge, 1m E of Sittingbourne. Signed from A2, E of Bapchild, 1st left, 500yds. 2-acre informal gardens, begun in 1977, planned around buildings and streams of early Water Mill (listed building and Histor-ic House of Kent); orchard with geese and hens ranging; picturesque rural setting. NO DOGS but dog park in yard. TEAS. *Adm 50p Chd 25p (Share to C of E Children's Society). Sun June 7, Wed June 10 (2-5)*

The Old Parsonage ⚘⚘⚘ (Dr & Mrs Richard Perks) Sutton Valence, 6m SE of Maidstone. A274 from Maidstone or Headcorn, turn E into village at King's Head Inn and proceed on upper rd through village; climb Tumblers Hill and entrance at top on right. 2-acre labour-saving garden planted since 1959 with emphasis on ground-cover; trees, shrubs and mixed borders; cranesbills and shrub roses. Ancient nut plat being de-veloped as a wild garden. Fine views over Low Weald. In grounds is Sutton castle, C12 ruined keep (under restoration). *Adm 70p Chd 30p (Share to CPR, Kent Branch). Suns June 28, July 5 (2-6)*

The Old Vicarage ⚘ (Mrs H.W.Backhouse) Ide Hill, 4½m SW of Sevenoaks. 3-acre wood-land with flowering shrubs and beautiful view; rhododendrons, azaleas, camellias, magnolias, etc. Some of garden suitable for wheelchairs inc the view. *Adm 50p Chd 25p (Share to Hospice at Home, T.Wells Branch). Sun May 3 (2-6.30); also by appt*

Oswalds ⚘⚘⚘ (Mr & Mrs J.C. Davidson) Bishopsbourne, 4m S of Canterbury. Turn off A2 trunk rd at B2065, follow signs to Bishops-bourne, house next to church. 2-acre plants-man's garden created since 1972 by present owners. Year-round interest, with lawns, shrubs, wild garden, pool, rockery and kitch-en garden. House formerly Dower House to Bourne Park and once home of both Joseph Conrad and Waugh family. TEAS at Village Hall nearby. *Adm 70p Chd 25p (Share to RNLI). Sun April 26, Mon May 25, Suns July 19, Aug 2, Sept 13 (2-5.30)*

Otham Gardens ⚘ 4m SE of Maidstone and 15m NW of Ashford. From A2020 or A274 follow signs for Otham 1m. Small village with number of fine old timbered houses. Parking restricted to official car parks except for dis-abled. TEAS and Home-made cakes at Belks and also School House, (garden sadly unable to open as undergoing alterations). Tickets and maps available at all gardens. *Combined adm £2 accompanied Chd free (Share to Friends of Cobtree Hall for Mentally Dis-abled). Sun June 28 (2-6)*

    Belks ⚘ (Mr & Mrs John Chambers) Small garden set among old buildings in res-tricted area for planting, surrounding re-cently renovated Hall House C1380

    Greenhill House (Dr & Mrs Hugh Vaux) Colourful garden at height of summer with many interesting plants

    The Limes ⚘ (Mr & Mrs John Stephens) Well established garden with herbaceous borders and wisteria pergola

    The Oast House (Mr & Mrs James Betts) Fine kitchen garden as seen on TVS; her-baceous borders

    ¶**Rose Cottage** ⚘⚘ (Mr & Mrs Tony Pear-son) ½-acre informal garden on fast draining soil with some unusual shrubs and herbaceous plants; ideas for ground cover under trees; many rare herbs

    Swallows ⚘ (Mr & Mrs Eric Maidment) Cottage garden with colourful terrace

Oxon Hoath ⚘⚘ (Mr & Mrs Henry Bayne-Powell) nr Hadlow, 5m NE of Tonbridge. *Car essential.* Via A20, turn off S at Wrotham Heath on to Seven Mile Lane (B2016); at Mereworth Xrds turn right, through West Peckham. Or via A26, in Hadlow turn off N along Carpenters Lane. 10 acres, landscaped with fine trees, rhododendrons and azaleas; woodland walk; cedar avenue; formal rose garden; peacocks. Large Kentish ragstone house (not shown) principally Georgian but dating back to C14; Victorian additions by Salvin. Once owned by Culpeppers, grand-parents of Catherine Howard. View over C18 lake to Hadlow Folly. TEA in picnic area if fine. *Adm 80p Chd 40p. Sun May 24 (2-7)*

¶**Peddars Wood** (Mr & Mrs B.J.Honeysett) 14 Orchard Rd, St Michaels, Tenterden. From A28, 1m N of Tenterden, turn W into Grange Rd at Crown Hotel, take 2nd right into Orchard Rd. Small plantsmans garden cre-ated by present owner since 1984. Many in-teresting and rare plants, inc about 100 cle-matis, 30 climbing roses and lilies. TEA. *Adm 50p Chd 10p (Share to Baptist Minister's Help Society). Weds June 24, July 22 (2-6); also by appt*

Parsonage Farm ⚘ Boxley, 2m NE of Maid-stone. From M20 junc 7, turn for Maidstone, take 1st right and 1st right again. House on S side of village green. 2 acres on chalk, part walled round old buildings, with duck pond and stream. Old roses, foliage plants and shrubs. TEAS. *Adm 75p Chd 25p (Share to Friends of Boxley Church). Suns June 21, 28 (2.30-6)*

Pett Place ✿❀ Charing, 6m NW of Ashford. From A20 turn N into Charing High St. Turn 1st right to Westwell (Pett Lane). A series of walled gardens surrounding Manor House (not open) built in 1470, encased in brick c1700 with later additions. Ruined C13 Chapel. Set in unspoilt countryside. TEAS. *Adm £1 Chd 50p. Suns June 28, July 12 (2.30-5.30)*

The Phillippines ৬✿❀ (CARE for mentally handicapped people) Ide Hill. 5m SW of Sevenoaks. Between Emmetts (NT) and Toys Hill (NT). 40-acre woodland garden, planted in C19 with rhododendrons, azaleas, fine specimen trees. Being restored with the help of mentally handicapped residents. Imposing Victorian mansion. TEAS. *Adm 50p Chd 20p. Suns May 17, June 7 (2-5)*

The Pines Garden ৬❀ (The St Margaret's Bay Trust) Beach Rd, Bay Hill, St Margaret's Bay, 4½m NE of Dover. Beautiful 6-acre seaside garden. Waterfall, lake, specimen fish, trees, shrubs. Statue of Sir Winston Churchill. TEAS on special days inc NGS dates. *Adm 50p OAPs 25p Chd 10p. Open daily all year. For NGS Suns May 3, Aug 30 (9-7)*

The Postern ✿ (Mr & Mrs David Coaten) Postern Lane, Tonbridge. Postern Lane runs E of Tonbridge between B2017 (1m from its junc with A21) and Vale Rd (the Tonbridge 'inner relief rd'); From London A3/M25/A21 take Tonbridge S exit. 4 acres with lawns, flowering shrubs, old and new shrub roses; apple and pear orchards. Georgian house (not open). TEAS. *Adm £1 Chd 25p (Share to Special Care Baby Unit, Pembury Hospital). Sun June 28 (12-6)*

Primrose Hill (Mr & Mrs Peter Barton) Hawkhurst, 3½m S of Cranbrook. From A21 at Flimwell take A268 signed Hawkhurst; turn 1st left after hospital, ½m. Terraced garden with mixed borders, specialising in old fashioned roses; lawns and lake. Strawberry TEAS at **Slip Mill** also open same date. *Adm 50p Chd 25p. Sat June 27 (10-6)*

Ramhurst Manor ৬ (The Lady Kindersley) Powder Mill Lane, Leigh, Tonbridge. Historic property once belonged to the Black Prince and Culpepper family. Formal gardens; roses. *Adm 50p Chd 10p. Sun June 21 (2.30-6)*

The Rectory ৬❀ (Revd & Mrs David Clark) Fairseat, ½m off A227 (at Vigo Pub) 1½m N of Wrotham. Small, colourful, plantsman's garden; many foliage and ground cover plants; meconopsis; several varieties of cistus, irises and lilies. 14 island and hedge-backed beds,

inc small colourful rockery. TEA. *Adm 60p Chd 20p. Sun June 14 Wed July 22 (2-5.30)*

The Red House ৬ (K.C.L. Webb Esq) Crockham Hill, 3m N of Edenbridge. On Limpsfield-Oxted Rd, B269. Formal features of this large garden are kept to a minimum; rose walk leads on to 3 acres of rolling lawns flanked by fine trees and shrubs inc rhododendrons, azaleas and magnolias. Views over the Weald and Ashdown Forest. TEAS. **Larksfield** and **Larksfield Cottage gardens** also open same days. Combined adm 3 gardens £1 Chd 50p or 60p OAPs/Chd 30p each garden. *Suns May 24, 31 (2-6)*

Ringfield ৬ (Prof Sir David Smithers) Knockholt. Via A21 London-Sevenoaks; from London turn at Pratts Bottom (Stone's Timber); from Sevenoaks at Dunton Green (Rose & Crown). Daffodils, rhododendrons, roses and wide vistas. *Adm 60p Chd 20p. Suns April 19 (2-5), June 7 (2-6)*

⧫**Riverhill House** ✿ (Maj David Rogers) 2m S of Sevenoaks on A225. Mature hillside garden with extensive views. Specimen trees, sheltered terraces with roses and choice shrubs; bluebell wood with rhododendrons and azaleas. Picnics allowed. TEAS. *Adm £1 Chd 30p. Suns, Mons April 5 - Aug 31. For NGS Sats May 2, 23 (12-6)*

Rock Farm ৬✿❀ (Mr & Mrs P.A. Corfe) Nettlestead. 6m W of Maidstone. Turn S off A26 onto B2015 then 1m S of Wateringbury turn right. 1½-acre garden, skilfully set out around old farm buildings; planted since 1968 and maintained by owner; plantsman's collection of shrubs, herbaceous plants, ornamental pond. Tea Nettlestead. *Adm 70p Chd 35p (Share to St Mary's Church, Nettlestead). May Weds 20, 27; Sats 23, 30; June Weds 3, 10, 17, 24, Sats 6, 13, 20, 27; July Weds, 15, 22, 29, Sats 4, 18, 25; Aug Sat 1, Wed 5, (11-5)*

Rosefarm ✿❀ (D.J. Polton Esq) 1m NW of Chilham. 6m equidistant Canterbury and Faversham. ¼m down narrow lane. Signed 'Denne Manor' at Shottenden Xrds. Small garden with interesting plants; many grown from seed; shrub roses; pond. *Adm 50p. (Share to British Tinnibus Assn). June Mon 29, Tues 30, July Wed 1, Thurs 2, Fri 3; also by appt June - Sept (Tel Canterbury 730447)*

St Clere ৬✿ (Mr & Mrs Ronnie Norman) Kemsing, 6m NE of Sevenoaks. Take A25 from Sevenoaks towards Ightham; 1m past Seal turn left signed Heaverham and Kemsing; in Heaverham take rd to right signed Wrotham and West Kingsdown; in 75yds straight ahead marked Private Rd; 1st left and follow rd to house. 4-acre garden with herbaceous borders, shrubs, rare trees. C17 mansion (not open) TEA. *Adm 75p Chd 25p. Sun June 28 (2-6)*

Salisbury House &⚘❀ (Mr & Mrs J.W. Hull) 67 London Rd, Rainham, SE of Gillingham. At junc of London Rd (A2) and Salisbury Ave, ½m W of Rainham centre. ⅓-acre walled garden maintained for easy management, attractive layout and diverse interest. Many exotics, 200 old roses and new rose varieties. Owner pleased to exchange gardening advice with visitors. TEAS. *Adm 40p Chd 20p. Suns June 14, 21 (2-dusk)*

●**Saltwood Castle** & (The Hon Alan Clark MP) 2m W of Hythe, 4m W of Folkestone; from A20 turn S at sign to Saltwood. Medieval castle, subject of quarrel between Thomas a Becket and Henry II. C13 crypt and dungeons; armoury; battlement walks and watch towers. Lovely views; spacious lawns and borders; courtyard walls covered with roses. Picnics allowed. Saltwood Castle closed to the general public in 1987. Private parties of 20 or more by appt weekdays only (Tel 0303 67190)

♦**Sandling Park** ⚘❀ (Mr & Mrs Alan Hardy) NW of Hythe. Entrance off A20 *only*. From M20, exit 11, turn E onto A20. Station: Sandling Junction, ¼m. Bus: EK/MD 10, 10A, 10B Folkestone-Ashford-Maidstone; alight New Inn Green, 1m. Large garden with good views and fine trees. Rhododendrons, azaleas, magnolias and big collection of primulas in a woodland setting. Kitchen garden. *Adm £1 Chd 20p. Suns May 10, 17, 24, 31, & June 7 (10-5)*

Scotney Castle ⚘ (Mrs Christopher Hussey; The National Trust) On A21 London-Hastings, 1¼m S of Lamberhurst. Bus: (Mon to Sat) M & D 246 & 256, Tunbridge Wells-Hawkhurst; alight Spray Hill. Famous picturesque landscape garden, created by the Hussey family in the 1840s surrounding moated C14 Castle. House (not open) by Salvin, 1837. Castle open May 1-end Aug (same times as garden). Gift Shop. Picnic area in car park. Tea Goudhurst. *Adm £1.90 Chd £1; Pre-booked parties of 15 or more (Wed-Fri) £1.50 Chd £1; April - Nov 15, daily except Mons & Tues, but open Bank Hol Mons (closed Good Fri). Wed-Fri 11-6, Sats, Suns & Bank Hol Mons 2-6 or sunset if earlier; last adm ½-hr before closing. For NGS (Share to Trinity Hospice, Clapham Common) Mon May 25 (2-6)*

Sea Close ⚘❀ (Maj & Mrs R.H. Blizard) Cannongate Rd, Hythe. A259 Hythe-Folkestone; ½m from Hythe, signed. 1¼-acres; well-kept garden on steep slope facing S with sea view; developed and landscaped by present owners since 1966; large personal collection of interesting plants and shrubs planted for visual effect and labelled. Light refreshments. *Adm 60p Chd 25p (Share to Royal Signals Assn). Suns May 31, June 28, Aug 2 (2-5.30)*

¶**Shirley House** ⚘❀ (Mr & Mrs R.J.Payne) Sutton Valence, 6m SE of Maidstone. A274 from Maidstone or Headcorn, turn E at Kings Head and proceed through village on upper rd. Small walled garden on sloping site with rockery, pools, alpines and collection of bearded irises. *Adm 40p Chd 20p. Suns May 31, June 7 (2-6)*

Sissinghurst Castle Garden &⚘❀ (Nigel Nicolson Esq; The National Trust) Cranbrook. Station: Staplehurst. Bus: MD5 from Maidstone 14m; 297 Tunbridge Wells (not Suns) 15m. Garden created by the late V. Sackville-West. Spring garden, herb garden. Tudor buildings and tower, partly open to public. Moat. Lunches & TEAS. (In addition to dates below for NGS, garden open April 1 - Oct 15 (Closed Mons inc Bank Hols). Tues to Fri 1-6.30; Sats & Suns 10-6.30 (last adm 6pm). *Adm Suns £3.20 Chd £1.60; Tues - Sats £2.60 Chd £1.30, pre-booked parties (Tues-Fri only) £2.20 Chd £1.30. △ Weds May 13, June 10, July 8 (1-6.30)*

Sissinghurst Place Gardens & Sissinghurst, 2m N of Cranbrook, E of village on A262. *Combined adm £1 Chd 25p. Sun May 24 (2-6)*

Sissinghurst Place (Mr & Mrs Simon MacLachlan) Large garden of mostly lawns, shrubs inc rhododendrons and azaleas. Fine trees inc Durmast oak said to be 700 yrs old and one of the largest in England. TEA

¶**The Coach House** (Mr & Mrs Michael Sykes) House and garden adjacent to, and originally part of Sissinghurst Place. ½-acre with half relating to the old garden, with mature flowering shrubs and trees enclosed within yew hedges; remaining garden planted since 1983, on site of the old kitchen garden.

Slip Mill ⚘ (Mr & Mrs Paul Jeans) Hawkhurst, 3½m S of Cranbrook. From A21 at Flimwell take A268 signed Hawkhurst; turn 1st left after hospital, ½m. !½-acres with lawns, herbaceous, roses and established trees bounded on two sides by streams. House with old mill attached (not working) and other interesting buildings. Strawberry TEAS. **Primrose Hill** also open same date. *Adm 50p Chd 25p. Sat June 27 (10-6)*

Smarden Gardens ⚘ 8m N of Tenterden, 11m W of Ashford. Attractive village in Weald of Kent with many fine houses. TEAS available in two gardens. Tickets, map and information at **Regency Cottage**, at corner where the Biddenden and Bethersden rds meet. *Combined adm £2 Chd free. Sun June 28 (2.30-6)*

Chessenden House (Mr & Mrs John Mather-Black) C15 Wealden Hall House (not open) set in mature garden featuring fine trees, collection of old fashioned roses and clematis. Pond with waterfowl surrounded by flowering trees and shrubs

¶**Haffenden Quarter House** (Mr & Mrs Michael Spratt) Present owners are striving to establish an informal garden on a neglected site; new planting incomplete and immature as yet

¶**Kennels Cottage** (Mr & Mrs N. Cornwell) Small well stocked garden; shrubs and herbaceous plants

Regency Cottage (Mrs P. Askwith) Small garden with old roses and herbaceous borders

¶**The Roundabout** (Commander & Mrs N. Sharrock) Well planted garden with trees, pond and old well surrounding Tudor Thatched Cottage (not open). Vegetable garden

Sprivers ♿⚘ (Mrs M.C.Dibben) Horsmonden, 10m SE of Tonbridge. From A21 turn off N nr AA box onto B2162 for Horsmonden. Bus: 297, alight Shirrenden, ½m. Garden ornaments in a natural setting; yew hedges, flowering and foliage shrubs, herbaceous borders, summer bedding, old walls; woodland walks; ornamental ducks and peafowl. TEAS. *Adm £1 Chd 50p. Sun July 12 (2-5.30)*

Stanford House ♿ (Brigadier Sir Geoffrey Macnab) Stanford North, 2½m NW of Hythe on B2068 Hythe-Canterbury rd; 1m from M20 Stanford interchange (No 11). No direct approach from A20 at Newingreen. A modest garden, full of colour and very well kept. Easy access for wheelchairs. Dogs welcome. *Adm 50p Chd 10p (Share to Stanford Parish Church). Sun Aug 16 (2-6)*

Stonewall Park ⚘ (Mr & Mrs V.P. Fleming) Chiddingstone Hoath, 5m SE of Edenbridge. ½-way between Mark Beech and Penshurst. Large walled garden with herbaceous borders, extensive woodland garden featuring specie and hybrid rhododendrons and azaleas; wandering paths, lake. Also open at no extra charge**North Lodge** (Mrs Dorothy Michie) Traditional Cottage garden full of interest. TEA Penshurst, 2m. *Adm 80p Chd free. Suns May 17, 24 (2-5)*

Street End Place ♿ (Lt-Col John Baker White) Street End. 3m S of Canterbury on Canterbury-Hythe rd (Stone St) B2068. Drive gates at Granville Inn. Long-established garden, inc wall garden, in pleasant setting; large area of naturalised daffodils with lawns and flowering shrubs; fine trees. *Adm 50p Chd 10p. Suns April 12, 19, 26 (2-7)*

Tawsden Cottage ♿ (Mr & Mrs Henry Garton) Brenchley, 8m SE of Tonbridge. From A21 at Kippings Cross take B 2160. At Brenchley take Horsmonden Rd. Right at yellow sign: garden ½m after turning. Bus MD 297. 5-acre woodland garden said to be laid out by Sir Joseph Hooker (Curator of Kew Garden) c.1860; rhododendrons, azaleas, shrubs and

fine trees; 10-acre woodland walk, bluebells. TEAS. *Adm 50p Chd 20p. Sun May 24 (2-6)*

2 Thorndale Close ♿⚘⚘ (Mr & Mrs L.O. Miles) Chatham. From A229 Chatham/Maidstone rd turn E opp Crest Hotel into Watson Ave, next right to Thorndale Close. Minute front and rear gardens of 11 x 18' and 20 x 22'. Alpines a feature with pool, bog garden, rockery, peat and herbaceous beds. *Adm 50p Chd 10p. Suns May 3, 17, 31, June 14, 28, July 12, 26 (2-6); also by appt (Tel Medway 63329)*

Thornham Friars ♿ (Geoffrey Fletcher Esq) Pilgrims Way, Thurnham, 4m NE of Maidstone. From M20 or M2 take A249, at bottom of Detling Hill turn into Detling and 1m along Pilgrims Way to garden. 2-acre garden on chalk. Distant views across parkland. Many unusual shrubs; trees; lawns with special beds for ericaceous shrubs. Tudor house. *Adm 75p Chd 25p. Sun June 7 (2-6)*

Timbold Hill House ♿ (Mr & Mrs N.E. Winch) Frinsted, 4m S of Sittingbourne. For directions see **Torry Hill** (½m) and follow signs from there. Small mixed garden created by owners in 1970 for minimum labour with no paid help; shrubs, roses, etc. TEA Torry Hill. *Adm 45p Chd 20p (Share to St Dunstan's Church, Frinsted). Sun June 21 (2.30-6)*

Torry Hill ⚘⚘ (Mr & Mrs Leigh-Pemberton) 5m S of Sittingbourne. Situated in triangle formed by Frinsted, Milstead and Doddington. From A20 at Lenham turn N for Doddington; at Great Danes N for Hollingbourne and Frinstead (B2163). From M2 Intersection 5 via Bredgar and Milstead. From A2 and E turn S at Ospringe via Newnham and Doddington. 8 acres; large lawns, specimen trees, flowering cherries, rhododendrons, azaleas and naturalised daffodils; walled gardens with lawns, shrubs, roses, herbaceous borders and vegetables. Extensive views to Medway and Thames estuaries. TEA. *Adm 70p Chd 30p (Share to St Dunstan's Church, Frinsted. Suns May 31, June 21, July 12 (2-5.30)*

¶**Trotts Hall** ♿⚘ (Mrs E.Boucher) Milstead, 3½m S of Sittingbourne. From A20 turn N on to B2163 through Hollingbourne and at Bredgar Church turn right for Milstead. From M2, exit 5, turn S for Stockbury on to A249 and immediately left for Bredgar and proceed to Georgian house (not open) opp Milstead Church and Post Office. Colourful 2-acre garden made from old pear orchard in 1978. Shrubs, pool, greenhouse and vegetable garden all within an orchard setting. TEA. *Adm 50p Chd 20p. Sun June 7 (2-5)*

¶**Turkey Court** ♿⚘ (Mr & Mrs Peter Young) Ashford Rd, Maidstone. Leave M20 at Exit 7 to town centre. Take A20 E to entrance ½m. Garden first established in early C17. Large garden with lawns, lake, river and waterfall. Walled rose garden, beautiful trees, herbaceous borders and shrubs; year round interest. TEA. *Adm 75p Chd 20p. Suns May 3, June 28, Sept 13 (2-6)*

Ulcombe Place ❀ (Mr & Mrs H.H. Villiers) Ulcombe, 8m SE of Maidstone. Turn off A20 between Leeds Castle and Harrietsham, signed Ulcombe. 2m to Xrds with garage, straight over, Ulcombe Place on right just after village sign. Wooded garden on different levels with fine view over the Weald. Interesting trees and shrubs. Walled garden with old fashioned roses, maintained by owners. TEAS. *Adm 75p Chd 40p (Share to Ulcombe Church Restoration Fund). Suns June 7, 28 (2.30-5.30)*

Updown Farm ❀❀❀ (Mr & The Hon Mrs Willis-Fleming) Betteshanger, 3m S of Sandwich. From A256 Sandwich-Dover, turn left immediately S of Eastry, signed Northbourne, Deal. Again 1st left; house 1st on right. 3-acre garden begun in 1975 and still in the making, round Tudor and C18 farmhouse. One of the most extensive figgeries in East Kent; cherry and plum orchards with old roses and climbers; terrace garden; herbaceous borders, unusual trees and shrubs. TEAS. *Adm 70p Chd 10p. Suns May 24, June 28 (2-6.30)*

¶**Upper Mill Cottage** ❀❀ (Mr & Mrs D.Seeney) Loose, 3½m S of Maidstone. Turn right off A229 to Loose. Parking in village; proceed 300 yds on foot up Salts Lane. 1½-acre cottage garden created and maintained by owners since 1972, on site of old water mill with natural stream. Plantsmans garden with many unusual varieties inc water plants, herbaceous, alpines, roses, clematis, foliage and ground cover plants. *Adm 50p Chd 25p. Suns June 28, July 19, Weds July 1, 22 (2-6)*

Waystrode Manor ❀❀❀ (Mr & Mrs Peter Wright) Cowden, 4½m S of Edenbridge. From B2026 Edenbridge-Hartfield, turn off at Cowden Pound. Station: Cowden, 1½m. 8 acres; large lawns, small grey garden, borders, ponds, bulbs, shrub roses and clematis. Subject of article in *Mon Jardin et Ma Maison* April '81. All plants and shrubs labelled. House C15 (not open). TEAS. *Adm 90p Chd 40p (Share to GRBS & RGOF on June 28) Suns May 24; June 28 (2-6) & Wed June 10 (1.30-5.30) also by appt for parties*

Weeks Farm ❀❀ (Mrs Pamela Milburne) Egerton Forstal, 3½m E of Headcorn. 1½-acre garden on heavy Weald clay showing varied adaptation of badly drained site. Wide double mixed borders flanking gateway, vista a feature; great horticultural interest. TEAS. *Adm 75p Chd 25p (Share to Regional Opera Trust Ltd, Kent Opera). Suns June 21, July 12 (2-6); also by appt*

West Farleigh Hall ❀ (Mrs C.W.Norman) 4½m W of Maidstone. Turn S off A26 at Tes-

ton Bridge. Roses, herbaceous borders, vegetables; woodland walk. TEA & biscuits. Picnic area. *Adm 50p Chd 10p (Share to All Saints Church, West Farleigh). Sun Aug 2 (2-7)*

West Studdal Farm ❀❀ (Mr & Mrs Peter Lumsden) West Studdal, N of Dover. Farm just off A256 on E side. From Dover area via Whitfield and on 1½m passing High & Dry on right, take 2nd rd on right. From Sandwich area via Eastry and on 2m passing Plough & Harrow on right, then 2nd rd on left; follow rd to 1st Xrds, turn right, then on 500yds, at entrance on left is pair of yellow cottages. Medium-sized garden around old farmhouse set by itself in small valley; herbaceous borders, roses and fine lawns protected by old walls and beech hedges. TEAS in Duodecagonal folly. *Adm 70p Chd 30p. Sun Aug 23 (2-6)*

Withersdane Hall Wye College (University of London) Wye, NE of Ashford. A28 take fork signposted Wye. Bus EK 601 Ashford-Canterbury via Wye. Well-labelled garden of educational and botanical interest, containing several small carefully designed gardens; flower borders and alpines; spring bulbs; early flowering shrubs esp suited to chalk; herb garden. Commemorative Garden created 1980 in honour of a visit by HM Queen Elizabeth The Queen Mother when accepting a Fellowship of the College. Illustrated guide book available. TEA. *Adm 75p Chd 25p. Suns May 3, July 12, Aug 9, 30 (2-5.30)*

Woolton Farm ❀❀ (Sir James & Lady Mount) Bekesbourne. 3m SE Canterbury, ½m off A257 or Bekesbourne Lane. Garden of trees and shrubs (heathers, rhododendrons, azaleas, flowering cherries a feature). TEAS. *Adm 80p Chd 30p. Sun May 17 (2-6)*

LANCASHIRE,

MERSEYSIDE & GREATER MANCHESTER

Hon County Organiser:
THE LADY PILKINGTON, Windle Hall, St Helens, Merseyside WA11 7RG

DATES OF OPENING

APRIL Easter Monday 20
    LINDEN HALL, Borwick
MAY Sunday 17
    191 LIVERPOOL ROAD SOUTH, Maghull
MAY Sunday 24
    191 LIVERPOOL ROAD SOUTH, Maghull
    MAGHULL GARDENS, nr Ormskirk
    STONESTACK, Turton

MAY Monday 25 (Bank Hol)
STONESTACK, Turton
JUNE Sunday 7
MAGHULL GARDENS, nr Ormskirk
JUNE Saturday 13 & Sunday 14
LINDEN HALL, Borwick
JULY Saturday 4
LINDEN HALL, Borwick
JULY Sunday 5
BANK HOUSE, Borwick
LINDEN HALL, Borwick
PARROX HALL, Preesall
WINDLE HALL, St Helens
JULY Sunday 26
GLENTHORN, Thornton
PARBOLD HALL, nr Wigan
AUGUST Sunday 2
BANK HOUSE, Borwick
AUGUST Sunday 16
GREYFRIARS, Fulwood
AUGUST Sunday 30 & Monday 31 (Bank Hol)
STONESTACK, Turton
SEPTEMBER Sunday 6
WINDLE HALL, St Helens

DESCRIPTIONS OF GARDENS

¶**Bank House** ⚘ (Mr & Mrs R. G. McBurnit) Borwick, Junc 35 on M6. Off A6, 1m N of Carnforth signed Borwick. 1½ acres mixed planting for all year interest. Collections of violets, tree peonies, old-fashioned roses, pinks, herbaceous perennials. Features on Gardeners World Sept '86. TEAS. *Adm 50p Chd 25p (Share to WWF). Suns July 5, Aug 2 (2-6)*

¶**Glenthorn** ⚘ (Mr & Mrs Antony Bond) 27 Ince Rd, Thornton, 10m N of Liverpool off A565 to Southport. A typical all-year-round, owner-maintained English garden of ¾ acre. The formal flower garden is supplemented by an orchard, woodland and a small water feature. TEA. *Adm 50p Chd 10p (Share to Hospice International). Sun July 26 (12-6)*

Greyfriars & (Mr & Mrs William Harrison) Walker Lane, Fulwood, 2m N of Preston. Junc 32 off M6 (M55); S to Preston; at Black Bull Xrds right to Boys Lane Xrds ½m entrance on right. 8-acres; lawns, rose beds, fuchsias; 4 greenhouses with hybrid begonias, geraniums and carnations; fountains and water display. TEAS. *Adm 60p Chd 30p. Sun Aug 16 (2-5.30)*

Linden Hall &⚘ (Mr & Mrs E.P. Sharp) Borwick, 3m NE of Carnforth. Leave M6 exit 35; take A6 to Milnthorpe. House in centre of Borwick village. CL9 garden of 5 acres, wide range of trees, shrubs and old-fashioned roses; ornamental lake with Chinese pagoda and herbaceous borders. *Adm 50p OAPs/Chd 20p. Mon April 20, Sats, Suns June 13, 14, July 4, 5 (11-6)*

191 Liverpool Road South &⚘ (Mr & Mrs D. Cheetham) Maghull, A59 Liverpool-Preston Rd; from Ormskirk or Liverpool take rd for Sefton; garden ½m along rd. ⅓-acre suburban garden; rhododendrons, azaleas, camellias, primulas, a variety of shrubs, bulbs, trees, herbaceous plants for all-year colour in the smaller garden. TEA or coffee. *Adm 50p Chd 10p. Suns May 17 & 24 (11-6)*

Maghull Gardens ⚘⚘ A59 Liverpool-Preston Rd; from Ormskirk or Liverpool take B5422, Buckingham Rd is ½m along. From Maghull town centre, Deyes Lane then Foxhouse Lane. TEAS Buckingham Rd. *Combined adm 90p or 50p each Chd 20p. Suns May 24 & June 7 (11-5)*

46 Buckingham Rd (Mr & Mrs Rawlinson) ⅓-acre. Planted with mostly spring flowering trees, shrubs, azaleas, rhododendrons, magnolias and camellias. Many miniature flowering bulbs and heathers; water and rock garden

51 Foxhouse Lane (Mr & Mrs Hancock) ¾ acre; special features - heathers; conifers; rhododendrons, azaleas and other shrubs. Eventually labour-saving with all year round colour. Liverpool Garden Festival Winner

Parbold Hall & (Peter Moores Esq) Parbold, NW of Wigan. On B5239. 3m W of M6 junc 27. 2 acres; symetrical terraced garden with lawns, flowerbeds and canal-shaped pond. TEAS in aid of Friends of Wrightington Hospital. *Adm 50p OAPs 40p Chd 30p. Sun July 26 (2-6)*

Parrox Hall &⚘ (Mrs D.H. Elletson) Preesall, 10m N of Blackpool, 14m S of Lancaster on A588. Rose garden, lawns, orchard, woodland. Late Tudor House. TEAS. *Adm House & garden £1 Chd free (Share to BRCS). Sun July 5 (2-5); also by appt*

Stonestack ⚘ (Mr & Mrs Frank Smith) 283 Chapeltown Rd, Turton; 4½m N of Bolton, via A666 leading to B6391. Bus: 563 or 565 alight Turton Towers. 1½ acres; shrubs, rhododendrons, azaleas; herbaceous border; rockeries, waterfall, ornamental fishpond, fountain, rose borders, bog garden, fuchsias a special feature; greenhouses. As seen on BBC Gardener's World 1985. TEA. *Adm 50p Chd 25p (Share to Bleakholt Animal Sanctuary). Suns, Mons May 24, 25; Aug 30, 31 (2-6)*

Windle Hall & (The Lady Pilkington) N of E Lancs Rd, St Helens. 5m W of M6 via E Lancs Rd, nr Southport junc. Entrance by bridge over E Lancs Rd. 200yr-old walled garden surrounded by 5 acres of lawns and woodland full of spring flowers; rockery with stream and tufa stone grotto; herbaceous borders, pergola and rose gardens containing exhibition blooms, ornamental pheasants; greenhouses. TEAS. *Adm 50p Chd under 5 free. Suns July 5, Sept 6 (2-6)*

LEICESTERSHIRE & RUTLAND

Hon County Organisers:
(Leicestershire) MRS GEORGE JOHNSON,
Long Close, Woodhouse Eaves,
Loughborough LE12 8RZ
(Rutland) MRS STUART TAYLOR, Ashwell
Grange, Ashwell, nr Oakham, LE15 7LT

DATES OF OPENING

APRIL Saturday 25
NOSELEY HALL, Billesdon
APRIL Sunday 26
PRESTWOLD HALL, nr Loughborough
MAY Sunday 3
STONE COTTAGE, Hambleton
MAY Sunday 17
DERWEN, Coalville
FRIARS WELL, Wartnaby
GUNTHORPE
MAY Sunday 24
LONG CLOSE, Woodhouse Eaves
MAY Tuesday 26
WHATTON HOUSE, Loughborough
MAY Sunday 31
ROCKYFIELD GARDEN, Ulverscroft
JUNE Sunday 7
THE CEDARS, Kegworth
ST ANNE'S MANOR, Sutton Bonington
SUTTON BONINGTON HALL, nr
Loughborough
JUNE Sunday 14
THE OLD RECTORY, Teigh
JUNE Sunday 21
BELVOIR LODGE, nr Grantham
THE GARDEN HOUSE, Hambleton
LITLE DALBY HALL, nr Melton Mowbray
1700 MELTON ROAD, Rearsby
RESERVIUR COTTAGE, Knipton
SHORNE HILL, Brooke
STONE COTTAGE, Hambleton
JUNE Sunday 28
ASHWELL HOUSE, nr Oakham
DERWEN, Coalville
FRIARS WELL, Wartnaby
OWSTON GARDENS, nr Oakham
RIDLINGTON GARDENS, nr Oakham
JULY Sunday 5
BARKBY HALL, nr Syston
BROOKSBY AGRICULTURAL COLLEGE,
Brooksby
CLIPSHAM GARDENS
THE LODGE, Bitteswell
STONE HOUSE, Blaston
JULY Sunday 12
ARTHINGWORTH MANOR, nr Market
Harborough
ASHWELL LODGE, nr Oakham
NORTH LUFFENHAM HALL, Oakham
STOKE ALBANY HOUSE, Market
Harborough

JULY Sunday 19
HINCKLEY GARDENS
ROSE COTTAGE, Ratby
JULY Sunday 26
UNIVERSITY OF LEICESTER BOTANIC
GARDEN, Leicester
AUGUST Sunday 2
FRIARS WELL, Wartnaby
SEPTEMBER Sunday 6
DERWEN, Coalville
OCTOBER Sunday 4
1700 MELTON ROAD, Rearsby

DESCRIPTIONS OF GARDENS

Arthingworth Manor ✿ (Mr & Mrs W. Guinness) 5m S of Market Harborough. From Market Harborough via A508 at 3m left to Arthingworth; from Northampton via A508; 1m after Kelmarsh turn right (E) to Arthingworth. 6-7 acre beautiful garden; collection shrub roses; small white border; greenhouses. Ruin of original house in grounds. TEAS. *Adm 80p Chd 10p. Sun July 12 (2-6)*

Ashwell House ර⚇ (Mr & Mrs S.D. Pettifer) 3m N of Oakham, via B668 towards Cottesmore, turn left for Ashwell. 1½-acre vicarage garden, 1812; vegetable garden; almost original format partly given over to specialist flowers for drying. Pleasure garden redesigned 1976; mainly shrubs and lawns planted over old carriage-ways and Victorian flower beds. Ploughman's lunches/TEAS/Home-made produce stall. *Adm 80p Chd 30p (Share to St Mary's Church). Sun June 28 (11-6)*

Ashwell Lodge ර⚇✿ (Mrs Stephen Eve) Ashwell, 3m N of Oakham. From Al, 10m N of Stamford, turn W through Greetham and Cottesmore; then turn right for Ashwell. Park in village st. Medium-sized garden redesigned by Percy Cane c.1973; spring bulbs; herbaceous borders, paved rose garden, shrubs, greenhouse. TEAS. *Adm 60p Chd 10p (Share to Forces Help Soc & Lord Roberts Workshops). Sun July 12 (2.30-6)*

Barkby Hall ර⚇ (Mrs A.F. Pochin) Barkby, nr Syston 5m NE of Leicester. Woodland garden; azaleas, rhododendrons, ericas, conifers, roses, herbaceous, shrubs; mature trees; interesting church nearby. *Adm 50p Chd 20p. (Share to Barkby Church Fabric Fund). Sun July 5 (3-6)*

Belvoir Lodge ර⚇ (The Dowager Duchess of Rutland) 7m W of Grantham. Between A52 and A607, nr Belvoir Castle. Medium-sized garden; roses and delphiniums. TEA *Adm 50p Chd 10p. Sun June 21 (2-6)*

Brooksby Agricultural College ✿ (by permission of Leicestershire County Council) 6m SW of Melton Mowbray. From A607 (9m from Leicester or 6m from Melton Mowbray) turn at Brooksby; entrance 100yds. Bus: MF Leicester-Melton Mowbray-Grantham; alight Brooksby turn, 100yds. Grounds inc extensive lawns, lake, ornamental brook, flowering shrub borders, heather bed, large collection young trees; other ornamental features; glasshouses. Church built 1220 open. TEA. *Adm £1 per car Sun July 5 (2-6)*

The Cedars ❀ (Mrs H.B. Taylor) London Rd, Kegworth. 6m NW of Loughborough on A6 Loughborough end of Kegworth. 1-acre, mixed, old walled garden with interesting selection of trees and shrubs. House dates from 1700 (not open); Thomas Moore once lived here. TEAS. *Adm 50p Chd 10p. Sun June 7 (2.30-5.30)*

Clipsham Gardens ⚘ On B668 2m E of A1 N of Oakham. TEAS Clipsham House. *Combined Adm £1 Chd free (Share to St Mary's Church). Sun July 5 (2-6)*

> **Clipsham Hall** (Sir David & Lady Davenport Handley) 5 acres; shrubs, roses; yew avenue (access from road only). House c.1780
>
> **Clipsham House** ✕ (Mr & Mrs Robert Wheatley) 2 acres around early C19 former vicarage; lawns, good trees, walled garden with summer house; herbaceous borders, roses, variety of shrubs

Derwen ✕❀ (Dr & Mrs M.W. Wenham) 68a Greenhill Rd, Coalville. On E side of town. From A50 turn E at Fox & Goose; fork right at St David's Church. From B587 turn W nr Bull's Head; garden 1m from junc. ¼-acre developed since 1974; wide variety of shrubs, hardy plants and herbs; emphasis on foliage. TEA. *Adm 40p Chd 10p. (Share to Army Benevolent Fund). Suns May 17, June 28, Sept 6 (2-6)*

Friars Well ⚘❀ (Lord & Lady King) Wartnaby, 4m NW of Melton Mowbray. From A606 turn W in Ab Kettleby; from A46 at Durham Ox turn E on A676. Medium-sized garden; shrubs, herbaceous borders and old-fashioned roses. Plant stall. TEAS. *Adm 70p Chd 10p (Share to Gardners Sunday on June 28). Suns May 17 June 28 Aug 2 (2-6); weekdays by appt*

The Garden House ⚘ (Mrs R. Hoare) Hambleton. 2½m from Oakham. Informal garden; lovely views of Rutland Reservoir. TEAS. *Combined adm (with Stone Cottage)50p Chd 25p. Sun June 21 (2.30-6.30)*

Gunthorpe ⚘ (A.T.C. Haywood Esq) 2m S of Oakham. Via Uppingham Rd; entrance by 3 cottages, on right going S. Medium-sized garden; flowering trees in good setting. TEAS. *Adm 70p Chd 30p (Share to Cancer Relief). Sun May 17 (2.30-6)*

¶**Hinckley Gardens** ✕❀ *Combined adm 50p Chd 20p. Sun July 19 (2-6) (Share to Leics. Org. L.O. R.O.S.)*

The Old Post House (Mr & Mrs I.K.Warden) 23A Northfield Rd. Follow A47 signed Nuneaton out of Hinckley centre; left to B5402 (Northfield Rd) signed Sapcote; house on left by post/tel box. Small urban garden; mixed borders; alpines; some unusual plants; small collection euphorbias, hostas, hellebores; plants in containers; foliage plants. TEAS. Also by appt May-Sept (tel: 0455 30586)

7, Hall Road (Mr & Mrs D.R.Baker) From M69 junc 1, take A447 signed Hinckley; 1st roundabout 1st left to Sketchley Lane; 1st right; 1st right again; 1st left to Hall Rd. Medium-sized garden; mixed borders; alpines; sink gardens; scree area; sunken loggia; bog garden; unusual plants; foliage plants; flower arrangements in house

Little Dalby Hall ⚘✕ (Lady Martin) Little Dalby, 3m SE of Melton Mowbray. From A606, Melton Mowbray-Oakham, 3m from Melton, turn W at signpost to Somerby. Large garden beautifully landscaped with lawns and trees; fine cedar trees; Wellingtonia in wood. On hill opp house are trees planted by past owner who fought at Waterloo; the placing of the groups of trees represent how the various companies were placed for that battle. Elizabethan house (not open). TEA. *Adm 50p Chd 15p (Share to Mental Health Foundation). Sun June 21 (2-7)*

The Lodge ⚘✕❀ (Mrs M. A. W. Craig) The Nook, Bitteswell, 1¼m N of Lutterworth; nr Bitteswell Church. House/garden established 1834 former home of Twinning (tea) family; 2 acres; unheated greenhouse, conservatory with tender plants; herbaceous border; ha ha; orchard; 'maidens' garden; parkland with animals, old trees; nursery; hosta and violet collection. TEAS. *Adm 60p Chd 30p (Share to St Mary's Church, Bitteswell). Sun July 5 (2-6), also by appt (Tel Lutterworth 2672)*

Long Close ❀ (Mrs George Johnson) Main St, Woodhouse Eaves, S of Loughborough. From A6, W in Quorn B59l. Bus: Leicester-Loughborough, alight at gates (nr playing fields). 5 acres rhododendrons (many varieties), azaleas, flowering shrubs, old shrub roses, many rare shrubs, trees, heathers, conifers, forest trees; lily pools; fountain; terraced lawns. Featured in *Country Life* Dec 1984. Plant stall. TEAS. *Adm 70p Chd 10p. Sun May 24 (2-6)*

1700 Melton Road ⚘✕❀ (Mr & Mrs J. Kaye) Rearsby, N of Leicester on A607. In Rearsby, on L.H. side from Leicester. 1-acre developing garden recently planted with wide range of interesting herbaceous plants; some shrubs and trees. Nursery. TEAS. *Adm 50p Chd 15p (Share to National Marriage Guidance Council). Suns June 21, Oct 4 (10-6)*

♦**North Luffenham Hall** (Mr & Mrs D.G. & Mrs E. Cotton). 7m Oakham. 6m Stamford. From A1 to A47 (Leicester Rd); on A47 right at sign to Edith Weston and North Luffenham, 1 ½m to village. From Stamford take A6121 through Ketton. 5 ½-acre, formal gardens, orchards, paddock and kitchen garden. Topiary, sunken garden, lovely view over valley. Gardens originally laid out in Georgian era currently being restored. TEAS. *Adm 60p Chd 30p (Share to North Luffenham Community Centre Fund). Sun July 12 (2-6)*

Noseley Hall & (Lord Hazlerigg) S of Billesdon, SE of Leicester. From A47 Leicester-Uppingham Rd, turn S on B6047; then E. Large garden; good show of daffodils; lawns and lakes; C13 chapel. *Adm 60p Chd 30p (Share to Noseley Chapel Trust). Sat April 25 (2-5)*

The Old Rectory &⚘ (Mr & Mrs D.B. Owen) Teigh, 5m N of Oakham. Between Wymondham and Ashwell; or from A1 via Thistleton and Market Overton. Medium-sized walled garden; mixed borders; good variety shrubs, herbaceous and climbing plants. Unusual C18 church next door. TEAS. *Adm 50p Chd free (Share to Forces Help Soc & Lord Roberts Workshops). Sun June 14 (2-6)*

Owston Gardens, &⚘ 6m W of Oakham via Knossington, 3m S of Somerby, 3m NE of Tilton/Oakham rd. TEAS Owston. *Combined adm £1 Chd 25p (Share to St Andrew's Church). Sun June 28 (2.30-6)*
> **Hill Close** (Mr & Mrs S.T. Hammond) ¼-acre enclosed garden; wide variety of border and alpine plants; paved herb garden
> **Manor Farm** (Mr & Mrs R.H. Harvey) 1¼-acre simple country garden; shrub roses, honeysuckle. Georgian house (not open)
> **Rose Cottage** (Mr & Mrs John Buchanan) Recently developed 1½-acres; shrub and flower borders; roses; alpines; pond; fine views ·

Prestwold Hall &⚘ (Simon Packe-Drury-Lowe) 3m E of Loughborough. A6 or M1 to Loughborough; A60 to Hoton. Between Hoton and Burton-on-the-Wolds. Large gardens; terraced lawns; wild garden; cedars; conservatory with temperate trees and plants. House (not open) C19 and earlier, home of the Packe family for over 300yrs. Church with fine monuments. Free car park in attractive surroundings open from 12.30 for picnics. TEA (afternoon only). *Adm 75p Chd free (Share to Prestwold Church Bell Fund). △Sun April 26 (2-6)*

Reservoir Cottage (Lord & Lady John Manners) Knipton, 7m W of Grantham. W of A1; between A52 and A607; nr Belvoir Castle. Medium-sized country garden with lovely views over the lake. TEA. *Adm 75p Chd 25p. Sun June 21 (2-6)*

Ridlington Gardens 2½m N of Uppingham. Turn off A47 to Ayston from Uppingham roundabout. TEAS. *Combined adm £1 Chd 25p. Sun June 28 (2-6)*
> **Ridlington House** & (Mr & Mrs Moubray) 1½ acres; roses; herbaceous border; flowering shrubs; vegetables; orchard
> **Stone Cottage** (Mr & Mrs Gavin Simpson) ¾ acre informal cottage garden; wide views across Chater Valley
> **The Dower House** & (Mr & Mrs Peter Meakin) Holygate Road. ⅓ acre; good mix of plants and small trees
> **The Old Rectory** & (Mr & Mrs G.S. Gee) 2-acre walled rectory garden; shrub and herbaceous borders; orchard and vegetable garden; pond; 2 greenhouses

¶**Rockyfield** ✤ (Mr & Mrs D.W.Smith) Priory Lane, Ulverscroft. 1m N of Markfield, nr to Ex 22 on M1. 6-acre garden; outcrops of natural rock providing backdrop to rhododendron and heather beds; interesting collection of over 250 rhododendrons; trees and shrubs alongside woodland walk. Listed Ernest Gimson Stone Cottage (not open). TEA. Adm 60p Chd 10p. Sun May 31 (2-5.30)

¶**Rose Cottage** ⚘✤ (Mr & Mrs F. Howitt) 182 Station Rd, Ratby. 5m NW of Leicester. Over ⅓-acre cottage garden made by owners; expanding collection of old-fashioned cottage garden plants, foliage, silver plants; hostas; alpines; herbaceous and hardy plant borders and new plantings of old shrub roses. TEA. *Adm 50p Chd 25p (Share to Leicester Hospice). Sun July 19 (2-6)*

St Anne's Manor For details see Nottinghamshire.

Shorne Hill ⚘ (Miss J. Curwen) Brooke, 2½m S of Oakham. 1½ acres; flowering shrubs, bulbs, herbaceous borders; trees. TEAS. *Adm 60p. Sun June 21 (2-6)*

Stoke Albany House &⚘✤ (Mr & Mrs A.M. Vinton) 4m E of Market Harborough via A427 to Corby; turn to Stoke Albany; right at the White Horse (B669); garden ½m on left. Large garden with fine trees; shrubs; herbaceous borders and grey garden. TEAS. *Adm 80p Chd 20p. Sun July 12 (2-6)*

Stone Cottage &✤ (John Codrington Esq) Hambleton, 3m E of Oakham. Turn S off A606 for Hambleton. Small garden with interesting plants, shrubs, herbs, etc. Views of Rutland Water. *Adm 50p Chd 25p (Combined adm with The Garden House). Suns May 3, June 21 (2.30-6.30). By appt April to Oct (Write or Tel Oakham 2156)*

Stone House & (Mrs Pen Lloyd) Blaston, NE of Market Harborough. From A6 Leicester-Market Harborough, at Kibworth Harcourt turn E for Hallaton, Blaston. From B664 turn W for Blaston. Medium-sized gardens; lily ponds, rose gardens, herbaceous borders, small lake. TEA. *Adm 60p Chd 10p. Sun July 5 (2-6)*

Sutton Bonington Hall For details see Nottinghamshire

University of Leicester Botanic Garden &⚘ Stoughton Drive South, Oadby, Leicester. On SE outskirts of Leicester, opp Oadby race course. Bus, Midland Red. Garden incorporates grounds of Beaumont Hall, South Meade House, Hastings House and The Knoll. 16 acres; trees; rose, rock, water and sunken gardens; botanical greenhouses; herbaceous borders; heather garden. TEA. *Adm 50p Chd free (Shared with BRCS & St John's Ambulance). Sun July 26 (2-5)*

Whatton House & (Lord Crawshaw) 4m NE of Loughborough on A6 between Hathern and Kegworth; 2½m SE of junc 24 on M1. 15 acres; shrub and herbaceous borders, lawns, rose and wild gardens, pools; arboretum; Chinese/Japanese garden is unique feature. TEAS. *Adm 70p OAPs 40p Chd 30p Tues May 26 (2-6)*

LINCOLNSHIRE

Hon County Organiser:
MRS J. TOLER, Grove House,
 Fulbeck, Grantham NG32 3JP

DATES OF OPENING

BY APPOINTMENT ONLY for dates see text:
 PARK HOUSE FARM, Walcott
REGULAR OPENINGS for dates see text:
 CAREBY MANOR GARDENS, nr Stamford

MAY Sunday 17
 DODDINGTON HALL, nr Lincoln
MAY Sunday 24
 HARRINGTON HALL, nr Spilsby
JUNE Sunday 7
 THE ORCHARD, Foston, nr Grantham
JUNE Sunday 14
 MARSTON HALL, nr Grantham
JUNE Sunday 21
 CAREBY MANOR GARDENS, nr Stamford
 GUNBY HALL, Burgh-le-Marsh
JUNE Sunday 28
 LITTLE PONTON HALL, Grantham
 STENIGOT HOUSE, nr Louth
JULY Sunday 5
 THE MANOR HOUSE, Bitchfield
 MANOR FARM, Keisby, Bourne
JULY Sunday 12
 CAREBY MANOR GARDENS, nr Stamford
 THE ORCHARD, Foston, nr Grantham
JULY Sunday 19
 SAUSTHORPE OLD HALL, nr Spilsby

DESCRIPTIONS OF GARDENS

Careby Manor Gardens &⚘⚘ (Mr & Mrs Nigel Colborn) Careby, 6m N of Stamford. From A6121 Stamford-Bourne turn at Ryhall W on to B1176, after 3m cross railway bridge into Careby. Walled gardens, terraces, old roses, unusual perennials, bulbs, shrubs; and wild flowers. A picnic area. Coaches by appt only. TEA. *Adm £1 (Share to Nat Deaf, Blind & Rubella Assn). Easter - Sept 27 Suns & Bank Hols only (11-6) For NGS Suns June 21, July 12 (11-6)*

Doddington Hall & (Antony Jarvis Esq) 5m SW of Lincoln. From Lincoln via A46, turn W on to B1190 for Doddington. Superb walled gardens; thousands of spring bulbs; wild gardens; mature trees; Elizabethan mansion. Free Car Park. Lunches and TEAS available from 12pm in fully licensed garden restaurant. *Adm house & garden £2 Chd £1 garden only £1 Chd 50p (Share to Lincolnshire Old Churches Trust). △ Sun May 17 (2-6)*

◆**Gunby Hall** (Mr & Mrs J.D. Wrisdale; The National Trust) 2½m NW of Burgh-le-Marsh; S of A158. 7 acres of formal and walled gardens; old roses, herbaceous borders; herb garden; kitchen garden with fruit trees and vegetables. Tennyson's "Haunt of Ancient Peace". House built by Sir William Massingberd 1700. *Adm garden only 90p Chd 45p (Share to Gunby Church Organ Fund). △ Sun June 21 (2-6)*

Harrington Hall &⚘ (Lady Maitland) 6m NW of Spilsby. Turn off A158, Lincoln-Skegness, at Hagworthingham 2m from Harrington. C18 garden; plantsman's collection of shrub roses, flowering shrubs, herbaceous plants. House rebuilt 1678; porch tower Elizabethan; old walls; high terrace mentioned in Tennyson's *Maud*. Home-made TEAS. *Adm house & garden £1.50 Chd 75p garden only ½ price (Share to St Mary's Church, Harrington) △ Sun May 24 (2-6)*

Little Ponton Hall (Mr & Mrs Alastair McCorquodale) Grantham 3m; 1m E of A1 at S end of Grantham by-pass. Spacious lawns with cedar tree over 200 yrs old. Many varieties of old shrub roses, borders and young trees. Stream and river walk. Kitchen garden and listed dovecot. TEAS. *Adm 80p Chd 40p. Sun June 28 (2-6)*

Manor Farm &⚘ (Mr & Mrs C.A. Richardson) Keisby; 9m NW of Bourne, 10m E of Grantham, signed to Keisby from Lenton and Hawthorpe. ½-acre plantsman's garden. Old fashioned and unusual herbaceous plants a speciality; old shrub and rambler roses; eremurus collection; stream garden. TEAS. *Adm 70p Chd free. Sun July 5 (2-6)*

The Manor House (John Richardson Esq) Bitchfield; 6m SE of Grantham, close to

Irnham and Rippingdale. A52 out of Grantham to Spital Gate Hill roundabout; take B1176 to Bitchfield; House on right after pub. 1½ acres entirely re-created in 1972; essentially a shrub rose garden (80 varieties) with shrubs and other perennials; new 50 by 40ft pond planted spring 1985; small box hedged formal garden; and ha-ha. Coach parties by appt. *Adm 70p Chd free. Sun July 5 (2-6)*

Marston Hall (The Rev Henry Thorold) 6m N of Grantham. Turn off A1, 4½m N of Grantham; on 1½m to Marston. Station: Grantham. Notable trees; wych elm and laburnum of exceptional size. House C16 continuously owned by the Thorold family. Interesting pictures and furniture. *Adm house & garden £1 Chd 50p. △ Sun June 14 (2-6)*

The Orchard ♿✿❀ (Janet and Richard Blenkinship) Foston, 6m NW of Grantham. Turn off A1 for Foston. Garden on narrow one way street nr Coopers Arms. 1-acre recently laid out cottage garden and nursery; over 1500 labelled unusual and traditional plants; bog garden; spring meadow; wild life, kitchen and herb gardens. TEAS. *Adm 50p Chd free. Suns June 7 & July 12 (2-6)*

¶**Park House Farm** ♿✿ (Mr & Mrs Geoffrey Grantham) Walcott 16m S of Lincoln on B1189 between Billinghay and Metheringham. Traditional farm buildings have been adapted to enclose 1 acre of informal gardens with mixed borders, alpines and climbers; wild garden with pond. *Adm 70p Chd 30p. By appt only May to Sept (Tel 0526 860409)*

Sausthorpe Old Hall ♿❀ (Mrs W.F. Kochan) Sausthorpe, NW of Spilsby, A158 Lincoln-Skegness. Old garden, lawns, shrubberies, trees, vistas of Lincolnshire Wolds. Associations with Tennyson, exhibition of modern pottery sculpture by Stanislas Reychan. TEA. *Adm house & garden 80p Chd 40p. △ Sun July 19 (2-6)*

Stenigot House ✿ (Mr & Mrs Peter Dennis) 6m S of Louth. Turn W off A153 at sign to Stenigot, 2m. Spacious lawns with lovely view over Wolds. Water garden with several varieties of astilbes; shrub roses and borders; kitchen garden. Swimming for all (30p extra). Home-made TEAS. *Adm 80p Chd 25p. Sun June 28 (2-6)*

LONDON
(GREATER LONDON Area)

Hon County Organiser:
MRS MAURICE SNELL, Moleshill House,
    Fairmile, Cobham, Surrey
Assistant Hon County Organiser:
MRS STUART POLLARD,
    7 St Alban's Rd,
    Kingston-upon-Thames, Surrey

DATES OF OPENING

BY APPOINTMENT ONLY for dates see text:
42 WOODVILLE GARDENS, W5
REGULAR OPENINGS for dates see text:
CHELSEA PHYSIC GARDEN, SW3

APRIL Wednesday 15
CHELSEA PHYSIC GARDEN, SW3
APRIL Easter Sunday 19
29 DEODAR ROAD, Putney, SW15
APRIL Saturday 25
TRINITY HOSPICE, SW4
APRIL Sunday 26
KENSINGTON, W8 Group 2
TRINITY HOSPICE, SW4
MAY Sunday 3
CANONBURY, N1
CHISWICK MALL, W4
HAMPSTEAD SUBURB GARDENS, NW11
MAY Sunday 10
ASHBERRY COTTAGE, SE23
THE GRANGE, Grange Lane, Dulwich
1 THE LITTLE BOLTONS, SW10
17 PARK PLACE VILLAS, W2
MAY Sunday 17
HIGHGATE VILLAGE, N6 Group 1
HIGHWOOD ASH, NW7
26 PRINCES AVENUE N10
SUDBROOK COTTAGE, Ham, Richmond
MAY Sunday 24
49 ETCHINGHAM PARK ROAD, N3
37 HEATH DRIVE, NW3
MAY Wednesday 20
12 LANSDOWNE ROAD, W11
MAY Sunday 31
CANFORD, NW3
CHISWICK GARDENS, W4
29 DEODAR ROAD, Putney, SW15
HORNBEAMS, Priory Drive, Stanmore
PINNER HILL GARDENS
SOUTH LONDON BOTANICAL INSTITUTE, SE24
TARN, Oxhey Drive South, Northwood
JUNE Saturday 6
TRINITY HOSPICE, SW4
JUNE Sunday 7
15 CHEPSTOW VILLAS, W11
CHISWICK MALL, W4
KENSINGTON, W8 Group 1
47 STREATHBOURNE ROAD, SW17
TRINITY HOSPICE, SW4
JUNE Saturday 13
27 WOOD VALE, N10
JUNE Sunday 14
24 GROVE TERRACE, NW5
LITTLE LODGE, Thames Ditton
26 PRINCES AVENUE, N10
TRADESCANT TRUST, SE1
27 WOOD VALE, N10
JUNE Wednesday 17
4 HOLLAND VILLAS ROAD, W14
JUNE Sunday 21
28 BARNSBURY SQUARE, N1

15A BUCKLAND CRESCENT, NW3
53 CLOUDESLEY ROAD, N1
MALVERN TERRACE, N1
7 UPPER PHILLIMORE GARDENS, W8
JUNE Thursday 25
13 SELWOOD PLACE, SW7
JUNE Sunday 28
29 ADDISON AVENUE, W11
FOX HOUSE, Ham Common, Richmond
HIGHGATE VILLAGE, N6 Group 2
HIGHWOOD ASH, NW7
7 KING WILLIAM IV GARDENS, SE20
338 LIVERPOOL ROAD, N7
53 MANOR ROAD, N16
7 ST GEORGE'S ROAD, Twickenham
48 ST JUDE STREET, N16
47 STREATHBOURNE ROAD, SW17
JULY Sunday 5
ASHBERRY COTTAGE, SE23
THE GRANGE, Grange Lane, Dulwich
JULY Sunday 12
5 GREENWAY GARDENS, NW3
35 PERRYMEAD STREET, SW6
10 WILDWOOD ROAD, NW11
JULY Saturday 18
TRINITY HOSPICE, SW4
JULY Sunday 19
15 CORNWALL MEWS SOUTH, SW7
TRINITY HOSPICE, SW4
JULY Sunday 26
26 GROVE TERRACE, NW5
HAMPSTEAD GARDEN SUBURB
 GARDENS, NW11
57 ST QUINTIN AVENUE W10
AUGUST Sunday 9
96 GREENFIELD GARDENS, NW2
AUGUST Sunday 16
26 PRINCES AVENUE, N10
SEPTEMBER Sunday 6
SOUTH LONDON BOTANICAL INSTITUTE,
 SE24
SEPTEMBER Sunday 13
HIGHGATE VILLAGE, N6 Group 1
SEPTEMBER Saturday 26 & Sunday 27
TRINITY HOSPICE, SW4
OCTOBER Wednesday 14
CHELSEA PHYSIC GARDEN, SW3

DESCRIPTIONS OF GARDENS

29 Addison Avenue, W11 ✕ (Mr & Mrs D.B. Nicholson) No entry for cars from Holland Park Avenue; approach via Norland Square and Queensdale Rd. Station: Holland Park. Bus 12, 88. Walled garden 30ft x 40ft, densely planted; many unusual varieties. First prize for best garden in "Brighter Kensington and Chelsea" competition 1986. *Adm 50p Chd 25p (Share to the Tradescant Trust). Sun June 28 (2-6)*

Ashberry Cottage ✕※ (Hilary Watson Esq) 62 Honor Oak Rd, SE23. From W via S. Circular Rd, pass Horniman Museum, then 1st left. Station: Forest Hill. Mixed garden, pond,

fountain, orangery with sub-tropical shrubs. House (not open) c.1780, occupied by Duke of Clarence, later William IV and Mrs Dorothea Jordan. NO Children. TEA. *Adm 50p (Share to Winged Fellowship Trust). Suns May 10, July 5 (2-6)*

28 Barnsbury Square, N1 (Mr & Mrs F.T. Gardner) Islington N1 ¾m N of King's Cross, off Thornhill Rd. Bus stop: Islington Town Hall, Upper St or Offord Rd, Caledonian Rd, 10 mins. Small Victorian garden; gazebo; pond; grotto; roses, shrubs, plants of interest throughout year. *Adm 60p Chd 20p. Sun June 21 (2-6)*

15a Buckland Crescent, NW3 &✕※ (Lady Barbirolli) Swiss Cottage Tube. Bus: 2, 13 (6 mins). ⅓ acre; interesting collection of shrubs and trees in well-designed garden. *Adm 80p Chd 40p. Sun June 21 (2.30-6)*

Canford ✕※ (Mr & Mrs J. W. Rees) 11 & 13 Daleham Gardens, Hampstead, NW3. Daleham Gardens runs parallel with Fitzjohns Ave at Swiss Cottage end. Station: Swiss Cottage or Finchley Rd. 2 gardens made into one surrounded by trees; lawns, herbaceous borders, rockery, roses, and raised water garden with statuary; speciality is shrubs for all seasons. *Combined adm 90p Chd 30p. Sun May 31 (2-7)*

Canonbury, N1 ✕※ Station: Highbury & Islington. Bus: 19, 30, 43, 104, 279 to Highbury Corner or Islington Town Hall. A1 runs through Canonbury Sq. *Combined adm £1.50 or 60p each garden Chd ½-price. Sun May 3 (2-6)*
 Canonbury House ※ (John Addey Esq) Canonbury Place. Spring bulbs; with much new planting this year; mulberry tree planted in 1509 by Sir Francis Bacon; most historic setting in Islington
 46 Canonbury Square (Miss Peggy Carter) Walled garden lying behind 2 end-of-terrace Georgian houses with statuary; pool
 60 St Paul's Road (Mrs Pat Wardroper) Small walled garden designed on 3 levels with shrub border, spring bulbs

●**Chelsea Physic Garden**, SW3 &✕※ (Trustees of the Garden) 66 Royal Hospital Rd, Chelsea. Bus 39; (Mon-Sat) alight outside garden (Cheyne Court). Station: Sloane Square (10-mins). Cars: restricted parking nr Garden weekdays; free Sundays, or in Battersea Park (across river) weekdays. Entrance in Swan Walk. Second oldest Botanic Garden in UK; 3.8 acres; herb garden, perfumery border; family order beds; collection of over 5,000 trees, shrubs and herbaceous plants, many rare or unusual. TEA (Suns only). *Adm £1.50 Students/Chd £1. April 12 to Oct 18 every Wed & Sun (2-5); also in Chelsea Flower Show week Tues-Fri May 19-22 (12-5). For NGS Weds April 15, Oct 14 (2-5)*

15 Chepstow Villas ✗ (W.J. Hopper Esq) Notting Hill Gate, W11. Nr Notting Hill Gate underground. Garden 60ftx 40ft; example of how small garden planted mostly with perennials and shrubs can be provided with unusually interesting features on several different levels. *Adm 50p Chd 25p Sun June 7 (2.30-5.30)*

Chiswick Gardens ✗ TEAS. *Adm each garden 50p Chd 30p (Share to Chiswick House Friends). Sun May 31 (2-6)*
    36 Staveley Rd (J.G.Luke Esq) Off Gt Chertsey Rd (A316). A shrub garden overlooked by trees of adjacent Chiswick House Grounds
    47 Barrowgate Rd (R.G.Farnham Esq) Off Sutton Court Rd. Garden (originally part of main Chiswick House gardens) 110ft x 75ft on 2 levels; roses, heather bed and lawn overlooked by vast split oak tree; evergreen shrubs in raised borders of York stone

Chiswick Mall, W4 ✗❋ Station: Stamford Brook (District Line). Bus: 290 to Young's Corner 10 mins. By car A4 Westbound turn off at Eyot Gdns S, then right into Chiswick Mall. *Adm 50p Chd 20p each garden. Suns May 3 (2-6), June 7 (2-7)*
    Walpole House (Mr & Mrs Jeremy Benson) Plantsman's garden; peonies; water garden; spring flowers. Features in 'The Englishmans Garden'. Mid C16 to early C18 house, once home of Barbara Villiers, Duchess of Cleveland. Seeds for sale (Share to Bishop Creighton House Settlement)
    Strawberry House (Beryl, Countess of Rothes) Plantsman's small garden with camellias, magnolias; architectural design. (Share to PHAB)
    ¶**Morton House** (Mr & Mrs Michael Manser) Town garden, mixed planting with emphasis on flowering shrubs belonging to a gardener with more enthusiasm than time. (Share to Bishop Creighton House Settlement). Sun June 7 only

53 Cloudesley Rd, N1 ✗ (Dr & Mrs N. Millward) Islington. Cars approach from W via Copenhagen St. Station: Angel. Bus: 30, 73, 19, 38, 104, 171, 214, 279a to Angel. Unusual family garden on 2 levels, designed and made by owners to give year round interest from foliage and flowers. Featured on BBC "Gardeners World" 1983. *Adm 60p Chd 20p (Share to MS Society). Sun June 21 (2-6)*

15 Cornwall Mews South ✗ (Mrs E. Berriedale-Johnson) Kensington, SW7. N up Gloucester Rd from Cromwell Rd; 1st left into Southwell Gardens; 1st right into Cornwall Mews South. Tiny London patio (15ft x 6 ft) brimming with flowers and colour; fascinating example of how much can be achieved in small space; climbers and standards grown in pots and barrels; hanging baskets, fountain and water garden. 1983/4 winner of Kensington and Chelsea Patio Award. Cream TEAS in mews, weather permitting. *Adm 50p Chd 25p. Sun July 19 (2.30-5.30)*

29 Deodar Road, SW15 ✗❋ (Peter & Marigold Assinder) Putney. Off Putney Bridge Rd. Bus: 14, 22, 73, 93, 296, 37. Small garden (130 x 25ft) running down to Thames with lovely view. 1st date camellias, 2nd hardy geraniums. TEA. *Adm 80p Chd 40p (Share to Royal Hospital & Home for Incurables). Suns April 19, May 31 (2-5)*

49 Etchingham Park Rd, N3 ✗❋ (Robert Double Esq & Gilbert Cook Esq) Finchley. Off Ballards Lane overlooking Victoria Park. Station: Finchley Central. 2 rear gardens. ⅝ acre; lawn, small orchard, shrubs, large selection of hostas. Sculpture by Wm Mitchell. Exhibition and sale of water colours/ink drawings by Robert Double. TEAS. *Adm 50p Chd free (Share to Architect's Benevolent Society). Sun May 24 (2-6)*

¶**Fox House** ✗ (Mr & Mrs Paul Evill) Upper Ham Road, Ham Common. 1 ½m Richmond. Follow A307 from Star and Garter; through Petersham village, sharp left hand bend; 1m further on New Inn on right. Houses then cease on both sides of rd; 3rd house on left when houses recommence. Bus route 65 stops nearby. ¼-acre organically grown recreational family garden. Walled with old roses, herbaceous plants in keeping with gracefulness of C17 house (not open) once home of William IV and Mrs Jordan and late Charles James Fox. TEAS. *Adm 60p Chd 30p. Sun June 28 (3-6)*

The Grange ✗❋ (G. Fairlie Esq) Dulwich. Station: Sydenham Hill. Grange Lane runs E along N wall of Toll-Gate Cottage in College Rd Dulwich just S of the S Circular Rd. Setting down only in Grange Lane. Park in College Rd. Old informal 'Country' garden in country setting. Many unusual plants etc and fine old trees. Attractive house dating from 1823 (not open). TEA. *Adm 50p (Share to The British Home & Hospital for Incurables). Suns May 10, July 5 (3.30-6)*

5 Greenaway Gardens, NW3 ✗ (Mrs Marcus) Tube Hampstead, ½m. From Finchley Rd, turn up Frognal Lane, 2nd on left. Large sunny newly laid out garden, Japanese-style water feature, many unusual shrubs; York stone terrace; swimming pool, steps to lawn surrounded by borders, mainly herbaceous perennials; decorative urns and furniture. TEAS. *Adm 65p Chd 25p. Sun July 12 (2-6)*

96 Greenfield Gardens ✗❋ (Terry Makepeace Esq) Cricklewood, NW2. W of Hendon Way between Cricklewood Lane and The Vale. Station: Golders Green or Willesden Green, both ¾m . Bus; 260 from Golders Green or Willesden, alight Hendon Way (nr top of rd). Garden 100ft x 30ft, sweet peas, roses, fuchsias, abutilons, foliage plants large variety of annuals, pond and greenhouses. *Adm 50p OAP/Chd 20p (Share to Cancer Research Fund). Sun Aug 9 (2-7)*

24 Grove Terrace, NW5 ✗ (Mrs Lucy Gent) N Kentish Town; off Highgate Rd, E side. Entry to garden via Grove Terrace Mews. Long narrow plantsman's garden (16' x 120') behind well known Georgian terrace. *Adm 75p Chd 30p. Suns June 14, July 26 (2-6)*

¶**Hampstead Garden Suburb Gardens**, NW11 ✗ Golders Green 1m N. Bus; 102 alight Midholm. *Combined adm 75p Chd 30p. Suns May 3, July 26 (2-6)*

   43 Hill Top ❀ (Mrs G.Webb) ⅓-acre, lawns, fish pond, lily pond, large rockery, herbaceous border, rose bed. Productive vegetable and fruit garden

   45 Midholm (Dr & Mrs M. Altman) Small town garden designed to achieve maximum colour during the year. Bulbs, summer bedding, dahlias, roses, shrubs

Harewood, Chalfont St Giles see Buckinghamshire section

37 Heath Drive, NW3 ⌖✗❀ (Mr & Mrs C. Caplin) Station: Finchley Rd; buses: 2, 13 & 113 Heath Drive. Some uncommon plants; lawn; water garden; rockery; ferns. Unusual treatment of fruit trees, greenhouse and conservatory. 1982 & 1983 winner of Franklyn Moore Trophy. *Adm 60p Chd 30p. Sun May 24 (2-6)*

Highgate Village, N6. ✗ The Grove is between Highgate West Hill & Hampstead Lane Stations: Archway or Highgate (Northern Line, Barnet trains). Bus: 210, 271 to Highgate Village. Tea Lauderdale House & Kenwood. *Combined adm £1.25 or 50p each garden Chd free. Sun June 28 (2-5)*

   4 The Grove (Cob Stenham Esq) 2-tiered with formal upper garden; view across Heath; orchard in lower garden *(Share to Institute of Contemporary Art)*

   5 The Grove (Mr & Mrs A.J. Hines) Newly-designed garden on 2 levels

   82 Highgate West Hill (Mrs T. Kingsley Curtis) Small garden on 2 levels, herbaceous borders above, kitchen garden below. View over London *(Share to Tradescant Trust)*

Highgate Village, N6. ✗❀ The Grove is between Highgate West Hill & Hampstead Lane. Stations: Archway or Highgate (Northern Line, Barnet trains) Bus: 210, 271 to Highgate Village. *Combined adm £1 OAPs/Chd 25p (Share to GRBS & RGOF). Suns May 17, Sept 13 (2-5)*

   7 The Grove ⌖ (The Hon Mrs Judith Lyttelton) ½-acre designed for maximum all-year-round interest with minimum upkeep

The Old Hall, South Grove (Mr & Mrs T. Gilliam) BALI/Fisons Premier Award for the pond as best domestic garden feature 1986 C17 bell tower, folly and other unusual features

Highwood Ash, NW7 ❀ (Mr & Mrs Roy Gluckstein) Highwood Hill, Mill Hill. From London via A41 (Watford Way) to Mill Hill Circus; turn right up Lawrence St; at top bear left up Highwood Hill; house at top on right. Station: Edgware (Northern Line). 3¼-acre inc rose garden, shrub and herbaceous borders, rhododendrons, azaleas; a mixture of formal and informal. Plants for sale May 17 only. TEA. *Adm 60p Chd 30p. Suns May 17, June 28 (2-6)*

4 Holland Villas Rd, W14 ⌖ (The Marquis & Marchioness of Dufferin & Ava) West Kensington. Between Holland Park & Shepherd's Bush, turn S from Addison Rd into Holland Villas Rd; from Holland Rd (north-bound only) turn right into Holland Villas Rd. Station: Shepherd's Bush or Holland Park. Bus: 12, 88; GL 711, 715 along Holland Park Ave, alight Royal Cres, or 49 along Holland Rd, alight Addison Cres. A wide range of shrubs and plants, giving exciting combinations of shapes and colours of particular interest to the artist. TEA. *Adm 50p Chd 10p. Wed June 17 (2-6)*

Hornbeams ⌖✗❀ (Dr & Mrs R.B. Stalbow) Priory Drive, Stanmore. 5m SE of Watford; underground: Stanmore; Priory Drive private rd off Stanmore Hill (A4140 Stanmore-Bushey Heath rd). ½ acre; flowering shrubs, alpines, hardy cyclamen, species tulips; unusual plants; vegetable garden; vine; pool; greenhouse, conservatory. Lemonade & biscuits. *Adm 60p Chd 30p. Sun May 31 (2-6)*

Kensington, W8. Group 1 ❀ From Gloucester Rd turn into Victoria Grove, then into Cottesmore Gardens on right. From Kensington High St turn into Victoria Rd. Stations: Kensington High St or Gloucester Rd. Bus: Milestone for 9, 46, 52, 72; Gloucester Rd for 49, 74. *Adm 80p for 2 Chd 20p. Sun June 7 (2.30-6.30)*

   13 Cottesmore Gardens ✗ (Mrs David McCosh) Informal, densely planted N. facing walled garden. Herbaceous borders with interesting plants and shrubs. Particular emphasis on foliage. *(Share to The Chelsea Physic Garden)*

   Christ Church Garden Eldon Rd, may also be visited free of charge. Herbaceous border 56 yds long

   ¶**11 Cottesmore Gardens** (Hon. Mrs Adrian Berry) typical London garden with potted plants making a feature.

Kensington, W8 Group 2 ❀ From Gloucester Rd turn int Victoria Grove, then into St Albans

Grove. From Kensington High St turn into Victoria Rd. Stations: Kensington High St or Gloucester Rd. Bus: Milestone for 9,46,52,72; Gloucester Rd for 49,74. TEA. *Combined adm 80p Chd 20p or 50p each. Sun Apr 26 (2-6)*

7 St Albans Grove (Mrs Edward Norman-Butler) Off Victoria Rd. A country garden designed for all seasons and one pair of hands. *(Share to Purcell School of Music)*

2 Cottesmore Gdns (J.Garnock) from Kensington Rd turn into Victoria Rd. Cottesmore Gdns on right. A wide range of shrubs and plants, concentrating on foliage shapes, fragrance and unusual plant material. *(Share to Gardening for the Disabled)*

Christ Church Garden Eldon Rd, may also be visited free of charge. Bulbs, shrub border 56 yds long

¶7 King William IV Gardens ⚥❀ (L.Sutton / R.Cooper), off St John's Rd SE20. Look out for Red-Brick Gothic square of 12 houses. Small, cottage-style garden features wild flowers amongst hardy perennials, fruit, shrubs etc. Clover lawn, brick path and small pond designed to compliment 1846 ex-Alms house in Victorian Gothic style by same architect as library at Lincoln's Inn, WC2. Not suitable for disabled, small children, dogs. Winner of Sunday Express/B&Q garden of the year 1986. TEAS. *Adm 50p (Share to RSPCA). Sun June 28 (2-6)*

12 Lansdowne Rd, W11 ⚼ (The Lady Amabel Lindsay) Holland Park. Turn N off Holland Park Ave nr Holland Park Station; or W off Ladbroke Grove ½-way along. Bus: 12, 88, GL 711, 715. Bus stop & station: Holland Park, 4 mins. Medium-sized fairly wild garden; border, climbing roses, shrubs; mulberry tree 200 yrs old. *Adm 30p Chd 15p. Wed May 20 (2-6)*

1 The Little Boltons, SW10 ⚥ (Mr & Mrs Peter Johnson) Between Fulham & Brompton Rd, off Tregunter Rd, next to The Boltons. A London walled garden with stone whippets, a unicorn, a lady reading a book and statue of Pandora amongst the shrubs and flowers. A garden semi-sauvage, designed for practical pleasure with 5 lime trees and a eucalyptus planted for the Silver Jubilee. Certificate of merit Brighter Kensington and Chelsea Scheme. TEAS. *Adm £1 Chd 50p. Sun May 10 (12-5)*

Little Lodge ⚼⚥ ❀ (Mr & Mrs P. Hickman) Watts Rd, Thames Ditton (Station 5 mins). A3 from London; after Hook underpass turn left to Esher; at Scilly Isles turn right towards Kingston; after 2nd railway bridge turn left to Thames Ditton village; house opp library after Giggs Hill Green. ½-acre designed and planted by present owners for subtle colouring, fragrance and easy maintenance; shrubs, old-fashioned roses; productive

vegetable plot. TEAS. *Adm 50p Chd 25p (Share to Cancer Research). Sun June 14 (10-6)*

338 Liverpool Road, N7 (Mr & Mrs Simon Relph) 10 min walk from Highbury & Islington tube; from Angel Islington up Liverpool Rd, 338 on corner of Furlong Rd. towards end of Liverpool Rd. Front garden paved, mainly grey and silver foliage plants; basement area of ivy and ferns; back walled garden, shrubs; small water garden (new). TEAS. *Adm 50p Chd 20p. Sun June 28 (2-6)*

Malvern Terrace Barnsbury, N1. Approach from S via Pentonville Rd into Penton St, Barnsbury Rd; from N via Thornhill Rd opp Albion pub. Tube: Highbury & Islington. Bus: 19, 30 to Upper St Town Hall. Unique London terrace of 1830s houses built on site of Thos Oldfield's dairy and cricket field. Cottage-style gardens in cobbled cul-de-sac; TEAS. *Combined adm 80p Chd free. Sun June 21 (2.30-5.30)*

1 Malvern Terrace (Mr & Mrs D. Parry)
2 Malvern Terrace (V. Cuddon Esq)
3 Malvern Terrace (Mr & Mrs A. Robertson)
4 Malvern Terrace (Mr & Mrs P. Dacre)
5 Malvern Terrace (Mr & Mrs J. Broad)
6 Malvern Terrace (Mrs C. Whitby)
7 Malvern Terrace (Mr & Mrs J. Tooth)
8 Malvern Terrace (Mr & Mrs R. Le Fanu)
10 Malvern Terrace (Dr & Mrs P. Sherwood)

¶53 Manor Rd, N16 ⚥ (Anne Wareham) Nr Hackney. Station; Finsbury Pk. Bus; 106 to St Ann's Home, Manor Rd. Plantsman's garden; 100ft long in 5 sections made from derelict site over last 6yrs. Cottage garden style borders, fruit cage, small vegetable plot. *Adm 75p Chd 50p (Share to Imperial Cancer Research Fund). Sun June 28 (2-6)*

17 Park Place Villas, W2 ⚥ (H.C. Seigal Esq) Little Venice. Park Place Villas is off Maida Ave which runs along Regent's Canal from Maida Vale to Warwick Ave. Station: Warwick Ave. Garden (⅛ acre) is one of an internal square of small gardens each belonging to a single house; rhododendrons, azaleas, alpines in raised beds and sinks; small pond with aquatic and bog plants; grass. *Adm 50p OAPs 25p Chd free. Sun May 10 (2-6)*

35 Perrymead St, SW6 ⚥ (Mr & Mrs Richard Chilton) Fulham. New King's Rd W from Chelsea; 1st on left after Wandsworth Bridge Rd. Bus 22 from Chelsea; 28 from Kensington. Small paved garden with ornamental feature; trees, shrubs, climbers (especially clematis) interspersed with summer planting suitable for shade. *Adm 60p Chd 30p. Sun July 12 (2-6)*

Pinner Hill Gardens ⚥❀ 1200 yds up Pinner HIII Rd from Pinner Green, or 900yds up Potter St from Northwood Hills roundabout. TEAS at Kingscliffe. *Adm 50p each garden. Chd half price (Share to NCCPG). Sun May 31 (2-6)*

Rondor House (Mr & Mrs M.T. Maurice) Hillside Rd, Pinner Hill. ¾-acre garden with central house, terrace and lawn with new pond and waterfall with shrubs, old roses, mixed borders, paved garden, rockery and small woodland

Kingscliffe (Mr & Mrs J. Hanford) Pinner Hill. ⅓-acre sloping garden with fine views over London. Small lily pond, mixed borders with shrubs and rhododendrons

26 Princes Avenue, N10 ⚘⚘ (Mr & Mrs J. Graham) Muswell Hill. A1 to Highgate; signpost to Muswell Hill. Bus: 134, 102. Station: Highgate. Garden of 75'x45'; interesting and unusual layout; shrubs, rhododendrons, conifers, alpines, rockery, tufa and sink gardens for year-round interest. *Adm 50p Chd 25p. Suns May 17, June 14, Aug 16 (2-6)*

7 St George's Rd ⚘⚘ (Mr & Mrs Richard Raworth) St Margaret's, Twickenham. From London A4 left at Hogarth on A316 towards Sunbury and M3; after Twickenham Bridge double back at 1st roundabout; 2nd turning on left. ½-acre town garden backing on to private parkland with mature trees; mixed beds of shrubs and old English roses; hedges; clematis and other climbers cover Victorian brick house; knot garden; large conservatory with rare plants, fuchsias, ferns, ivies; mist propagation. Bee hives. TEA. *Adm 50p Chd 20p. Sun June 28 (2-6)*

¶**48 St Jude Street**, N16 ⚘ (Melita Denaro) Islington. Off King Henry's Walk; off Balls Pond rd between Highbury Corner and Dalston Junc. Small walled terrace garden, unusual plants and shrubs and over 20 old climbing roses. Owner is an Artist and this has had a strong influence on design and colour; studio is in the house and paintings and ceramics inspired by gardens will be on sale. (Share to NGS). TEA. *Adm 50p Chd 25p. Sun June 28 (10-6)*

¶**57 St Quintin Avenue**, W10 ⚘ (H. Groffman Esq) 1m from Ladbroke Grove/White City Underground. Turn into North Park Rd from Wood Lane (White City approach) or left into Cambridge Gdns, right into St Marks Rd from Ladbroke Grove station. Buses; 7,15,72,220. 30ft x 40ft walled garden; year-round selection of shrubs, perennials, summer bedding schemes. Patio; small pond; hanging baskets. TEA. *Adm 50p Chd 30p. Sun July 26 (2-6.30)*

13 Selwood Place, SW7 ♿ (Mrs Anthony Crossley) South Kensington, adjacent to 92 Onslow Gardens (cul-de-sac). Long green and white border; pink border in L-shaped walled garden; collection of roses, peonies, camellias, iris, lilies, poppies, vegetables; terraced herb garden. Suitable for wheelchairs only if dry. *Adm 50p Chd 20p (Share to Church of England Children's Society). Thurs June 25 (2.30-6.30)*

South London Botanical Institute, SE24 ⚘⚘ 323 Norwood Rd. From South Circular Rd (A205) at Tulse Hill, turn N into Norwood Rd; Institute is 100 yds on right. Small botanic garden, formally laid out; many rare and interesting species; over 200 labelled plants. TEA. *Adm 60p (Share to South London Botanical Institute). Suns May 31, Sept 6 (2-5)*

¶**47 Streathbourne Rd**, SW17 ⚘⚘ (Mr & Mrs A. Wells) 7 mins Tooting Bec tube. 80ft town garden on two levels. Flowering shrubs, roses, designed for gardeners and children. Reptorian rustic hut. TEAS. *Adm 50p Chd 25p. Suns June 7, 28 (2-6)*

¶**Sudbrook Cottage** ⚘ (Mrs D. Stephenson) Ham Gate Avenue, Ham Common. 3m Richmond. Off A308 take turn at Ham Common opp The New Inn Pub, garden 200 yds on left. ½ acre designed by the late Beverley Nichols. A spring garden with many interesting and unusual shrubs, bulbs and plants. TEA. *Adm 60p Chd 30p (Share to Autistic Society). Sun May 17 (10-4)*

Tarn ⚘⚘ (Mr & Mrs R. Solley) Oxhey Drive South, Northwood. From Northwood Station turn right into Green Lane then left into Watford Rd at mini roundabout; take 3rd right into Sandy Lane; at top U-turn into Oxhey Drive South, house on left. ⅓-acre garden planted and maintained by owner. Old standard wisteria, rhododendrons, camellias and other shrubs, many unusual roses, climbers, pond and greenhouse. *Adm 60p Chd 30p. Sun May 31 (2-5.30)*

Tradescant Trust, Museum of Garden History ♿⚘⚘ St Mary-at-Lambeth, Lambeth Palace Road, SE1. Bus: Red Arrow from Victoria or Waterloo, alight Lambeth Palace. 7,450 sq ft. Replica of C17 garden planted in churchyard with flowers known and grown by John Tradescant. Opened by HM the Queen Mother in 1983. Museum being established in restored church of St Mary-at-Lambeth saved from demolition by The Trust. TEA. *Collection Box (Share to The Museum of Garden History). Sun June 14 (10.30-5)*

Trinity Hospice ♿⚘⚘ 30 Clapham Common North Side, SW4. Tube: Clapham Common. Bus: 37, 137 stop outside. 2-acre park-like garden restored by Lanning Roper's friends as a memorial to him. TEA. *Adm 50p. Sats, Suns April 25, 26 June 6, 7, July 18, 19 Sep 26, 27 (2-6).*

7 Upper Phillimore Gardens, W8 ⚘ (Mr & Mrs B. Ritchie) From Kensington High St take either Phillimore Gdns or Camden Hill Rd;

entrance Duchess of Bedford Walk. 100ft x 35ft garden; rockery, sunken garden; Italian Wall fountain, shrub roses, ground cover planting, pergola. *Adm 50p Chd 15p. Sun June 21 (2.30-6)*

10 Wildwood Rd, NW11 &⚘ (Dr J.W. McLean) Hampstead. Wildwood rd is between Hampstead Golf Course and N end of Hampstead Heath. From N End Rd turn by Manor House Hospital into Hampstead Way, then fork right. Garden planned and maintained by owner; herbaceous border, pond, HT roses; owner-grown prize winning delphiniums and seedlings. *Adm 50p Chd free. Sun July 12 (2-7)*

¶**27 Wood Vale**, N10 ⚘❀ (Mr & Mrs A.W.Dallman) Muswell Hill 1m. A1 to Woodman Pub; signed Muswell Hill; Muswell Hill Rd sharp right Wood Lane leading to Wood Vale; Highgate tube station. ¾-acre garden with herbaceous borders; ponds; orchard and kitchen garden. Unusual layout full of surprises. Numerous shrubs, roses, trees and conifers. TEA. *Adm 50p Chd free (Share to Hornsey Red Cross). Sat, Sun June 13, 14 (12-5.30)*

42 Woodville Gardens ❀ (J. Welfare) Travelling N on A406 N Circular Rd at Ealing, cross the A4020. After next traffic lights Woodville Gds is 1st on left. Large town garden with alpine and herbaceous borders, paving plants, beds of shade and sun-loving plants, bog garden, shrubs. Plantsman's garden with many unusual plants. Seedlings and cuttings for sale. *Collection box. By appt only April - Sep (Tel 01 998 4134)*

NORFOLK

Hon County Organisers:
MRS CLIVE HARDCASTLE, The Old Rectory, Southacre, King's Lynn
MRS JOHN BLOFELD, Hoveton House Nr Wroxham, Norwich NR12 8JE

DATES OF OPENING

BY APPOINTMENT ONLY for dates see text:
BRAMLEY COTTAGE, Stanhoe
107 UNIVERSITY CRESCENT, Gorleston-on-Sea
REGULAR OPENINGS for dates see text:
NORFOLK LAVENDER LTD, Heacham
RAVENINGHAM HALL, nr Beccles
SANDRINGHAM GROUNDS

APRIL Easter Sunday 19
BRIDGHAM MANOR, East Harling
APRIL Easter Monday 20
THE OLD HOUSE, Ranworth
APRIL Sunday 26
DROVE HOUSE, Thornham
MAY Sunday 17
HOW HILL FARM, Ludham

MANNINGTON HALL, nr Saxthorpe
RYSTON HALL, nr Downham Market
MAY Sunday 24
ELMHAM HOUSE GARDENS, nr East Dereham
RIPPON HALL, Hevingham
MAY Thursday 28
BLICKLING HALL, nr Aylsham
MAY Sunday 31
LEXHAM HALL, nr Swaffham
JUNE Sunday 7
LETHERINGSETT GARDENS
RAINTHORPE HALL, Tasburgh
RAVENINGHAM HALL, nr Beccles
JUNE Sunday 14
HANWORTH HALL, nr Cromer
NORFOLK COLLEGE OF AGRICULTURE & HORTICULTURE, nr Norwich
RAVENINGHAM HALL, nr Beccles
JUNE Sunday 21
BANNINGHAM OLD RECTORY, nr Aylsham
BLAKENEY GARDENS
RAVENINGHAM HALL, nr Beccles
JUNE Sunday 28
EASTON LODGE, Easton
INTWOOD HALL, nr Norwich
LANE HEAD, Garboldhisham
RAVENINGHAM HALL, nr Beccles
JULY Friday 3
FELBRIGG HALL GARDEN, nr Cromer
JULY Sunday 5
ERPINGHAM LODGE, Ingworth, nr Aylsham
THE OLD HOUSE, Ranworth
RAVENINGHAM HALL, nr Beccles
WRETHAM LODGE, East Wretham
JULY Sunday 12
BESTHORPE HALL, Attleborough
GAYTON HALL, nr King's Lynn
HORSTEAD HOUSE, Horstead
MANNINGTON HALL, nr Saxthorpe
JULY Thursday 16
QUARLES HOUSE, nr Wells-on-Sea
JULY Sunday 19
BAYFIELD HALL, Holt
RAVENINGHAM HALL, nr Beccles
SWANINGTON MANOR, nr Norwich
WICKEN HOUSE, Castle Acre
JULY Thursday 23 & Friday 24
OXBURGH HALL & GARDEN, Swaffham
JULY Thursday 30
BLICKLING HALL GARDEN, nr Aylsham
HOLKHAM HALL, nr Wells-on-Sea
AUGUST Sunday 2
RAVENINGHAM HALL, nr Beccles
AUGUST Sunday 30
BARNINGHAM HALL, Matlaske
RAVENINGHAM HALL, nr Beccles
AUGUST Monday 31
RAVENINGHAM HALL, nr Beccles
SEPTEMBER Sunday 6
HOW HILL FARM, Ludham
SEPTEMBER Friday 25
FELBRIGG HALL GARDEN, nr Cromer

DESCRIPTIONS OF GARDENS

Banningham Old Rectory &⚘ (Bryan Hall Esq) 2½m N of Aylsham off A140; two signs to Banningham; house next to church. 4-acre informal garden, woodland; peacocks; late C17 house; interesting pictures and furniture; permanent displays of Victoriana, dolls and bygones. 10 rooms on view; house subject of article in the Connoisseur. Home-made TEAS. *Adm £1 Chd 50p (Share to Brooke Hospital for Animals, Cairo). Sun June 7, 21 (2-5.30)*

Barningham Hall & (Sir Charles & Lady Mott-Radclyffe) Matlaske, NW of Aylsham. Medium-sized garden, vistas, lake. TEAS. *Adm 50p Chd 10p. Sun Aug 30 (2-6.30)*

◆¶**Bayfield Hall** (Mr & Mrs R.H. Combe) 1m N of Holt, off A148. Formal but simple pleasure gardens with medieval church ruin. Nearby lake. TEAS. *Adm £1 Chd 10p. Sun July 19 (2-5)*

Besthorpe Hall &⚘⚘ (John Alston Esq) 1m E of Attleborough. On Attleborough-Bunwell rd; adjacent to Besthorpe Church. Garden with shrubs, trees and herbaceous border within Tudor enclosures; walled kitchen garden; tilting ground. Coach parties by appt. TEAS. *Adm £1 Chd 50p (Share to Besthorpe Church). Sun July 12 (2-6); also by appt*

¶**Blakeney Gardens** ⚘ 4m NW of Holt on coast rd. TEAS *Combined adm £1 Chd 10p. Sun June 21 (2-6)*

The Orchard ⚘ (Mr & Mrs Devas Everington) 140 High St. ½-acre garden; roses shrubs and herbaceous borders
Radnor House (A.B. Henshaw Esq) Back Lane. Small interesting garden; shrubs and herbaceous plants
White Cottage (Mr & Mrs P. Russell) 4 Coronation Lane. Small interesting garden
Friory House (Dr & Mrs Allibone) Small interesting garden with shrubs, plants and pools
4 Wiveton Road (Mr & Mrs E. Edge) Walled garden; mature trees, lawns, roses and herbaceous plants
Scriveners (Mrs B.K. Muir) Cley Rd. 1-acre garden; trees, shrubs, herbaceous plants
Turnstone (Mrs V.M. Scriven) Back Lane. Medium sized garden with roses, shrubs and herbaceous borders
50 High Street (Mr & Mrs R.A. Archer) Small walled flower garden

◆**Blickling Hall** &⚘ (The National Trust) 1½m NW of Aylsham on N side of B1354 (15m N of Norwich on A140). Bus: Cromer/Norwich via Aylsham passes entrance. Large garden; Orangery and walks in Park; crescent lake; azaleas, rhododendrons; herbaceous bor-

ders. Historic Jacobean house (not open this date). Wheelchairs available for the disabled. TEAS. *Adm £1 Chd 50p.* △ *Thurs May 28 July 30 (2-6)*

Bramley Cottage ⚘⚘ (Mr & Mrs Kenneth Beckett) Stanhoe. Fakenham 10m. B1155 between Docking and Burnham Market; W end of Stanhoe, garden backs on to churchyard. 1 acre plantsman's garden; over 2000 different species of plants; spring bulbs, trees and shrubs; rock and alpine plants; peat beds; uncommon greenhouse plants. *Collecting box. Open by appt at any reasonable time (Tel Docking 225)*

¶**Bridgham Manor Farm** ⚘ (C.D.F.Musker Esq) East Harling. 8m E of Thetford. Small garden; spring bulbs; herbaceous border; iris border, greenhouse. *Adm 50p Chd 25p. Sun Apr 19 (2-6)*

◆**Drove House** & (Maj D. Jamieson) Thornham, 4m NE of Hunstanton on A149 to Cromer. Large garden; flowering trees, shrubs, bulbs; walled rose garden; heather garden. TEAS. *Adm 50p Chd 25p. Sun April 26 (2-6)*

Easton Lodge (J.M. Rampton Esq) Easton W of Norwich. A47 from Norwich; white gates in centre of Easton village. Bus: EC Norwich-East Dereham-Swaffham-King's Lynn; alight Easton Dog. Medium-sized garden; azaleas in attractive setting with river at foot. Late Georgian house with Jacobean centre portion. TEAS. *Adm 50p Chd 20p. Sun June 28 (2.30-6)*

Elmham House Gardens & (Mr & Mrs R.S. Don) North Elmham, 5m N of East Dereham, on B1110. Entrance opp Church. Medium-sized garden; wild garden; view of park and lake; vineyard, Tours of Winery. TEAS. *Adm £1 (Share to St Mary's Church N Elmham). Sun May 24 (2-6)*

Erpingham Lodge &⚘ (Mr & Mrs David Clarke) nr Ingworth, 2m N of Aylsham. From A140 Norwich-Cromer rd, turn left signed Ingworth; then first right. Bus: Norwich-Cromer, alight Erpingham Xrds, ½m. Medium-sized garden; rhododendrons, shrubs, lake. Georgian house (not open). TEAS. *Adm £1 OAPs 50p Chd 20p. Sun July 5 (2-6)*

Felbrigg Hall &⚘ (The National Trust) Roughton, 2½m SW of Cromer, S of A148; main entrance from B1436; signed from Felbrigg village. Large pleasure gardens; mainly lawns and shrubs; orangery with camellias; large walled garden recently restored and restocked as fruit, vegetable and flower garden; vine house; dovecote; dahlias; superb colchicum; wooded parks. Wheelchairs available. TEAS. *Adm 50p Chd 25p.* △ *Fris July 3 & Sept 25 (2-6)*

Gayton Hall &֎ (Julian Marsham Esq) 6m E of King's Lynn; signs in Gayton village; 20 acres; wild woodland, water garden. Fete stalls. (in aid of Gayton Church) TEAS. *Adm 25p & Collecting Box. Sun July 12 (2-6)*

Hanworth Hall & (H.M. Barclay Esq) S of Cromer. From A140 5m S of Cromer turn W for Hanworth then 1m. Medium-sized garden with famous old chestnut tree; walled garden; rhododendrons. TEAS. *Adm 75p Chd 25p (Share to Hanworth Church). Sun June 14 (2.30-5.30)*

Holkham Hall ⚘ (The Viscount Coke) 2m W of Wells. S of A149, Wells-Hunstanton. Bus: EC 36 Hunstanton-Wells-Cromer; alight Victoria Hotel or Holkham village, 1m. Arboretum with many rare specimens, trees and shrubs; large formal C19 terraced garden; polyantha roses; fountains. Hall and Exhibition of Bygones & Pottery also open. TEAS. *Adm to house £1.30, OAPs £1 Chd 50p. Arboretum only 20p Chd 10p. △ Thurs July 30 (1.30-5)*

Horstead House ֎ (Dr & Mrs David Nolan) Horstead. 7m from Norwich. Off B1150 N Walsham rd opp "Recruiting Sergeant"; drive gate by Horstead Mill Pool; Bus 736 from Norwich. Landscaped garden on riverbank; walled garden; exceptionally good toolhouse. Home-made TEAS. *Adm 80p Chd free. Sun July 12 (2-5)*

¶**How Hill Farm** ֎ (P.D.S.Boardman) 2m W of Ludham on A1062; then follow signs to How Hill; Farm Garden-S of How Hill. Very pretty garden started in 1968 in water garden setting with three ponds; recent 3-acre broad (dug as conservation project) with variety of water lilies and view over the R. Ant; fine old mill. Winding paths through rare conifers (mainly dwarf); rhododendrons, azaleas; other ornamental trees and shrubs; a few herbaceous plants and lilies; collection of english holly, ilex aquifolion (over 50 varieties). TEA. *Adm £1 Chd 20p. Suns May 17, Sept 6 (2-6)*

Intwood Hall &֎ (Miss M.B. Unthank) 3½m SW of Norwich. Via A11 to Cringleford; fork left (avoid dual carriageway); over Cringleford Bridge, turn left; over Xrds and level Xing for ½m. 2 walled flower gardens (one Tudor); 2 walled vegetable gardens, greenhouses, roses. Saxon Church in grounds. TEAS. *Adm £1 Chd free (Share to CLA). Sun June 28 (2-6)*

Lanehead ⚘֎ (Mrs N.A. Laurie) Garboldisham, 8m W of Diss. Medium-sized garden with natural walks of shrubs, perennials, roses and ground cover; water garden; borders for all-year interest and colour. TEAS. *Adm £1 Chd 50p (Share to Local Church). Sun June 28 (10-dusk). Garden open by appt April to Oct (Tel Garboldisham 380)*

Letheringsett Gardens & 1m W of Holt on A148. Car park King's Head, Letheringsett. Following 4 gardens will be open. TEAS. *Combined adm £1 OAPs 50p Chd 10p. Sun June 7 (2-6)*
　　Letheringsett Hall (Mr & Mrs Mitchell) Home for the elderly. Large garden with river and lake
　　Letheringsett Estate Garden Wooded walks, fountain, lake, water plants, wild flowers. Hydraulic rams 1852 and 1905.
　　Hall Cottage (Mr David Mayes) Small riverside garden; two pools, unusual water plants; shrubs
　　The Glebe (Hon Beryl Cozens-Hardy) Small riverside garden; pool; unusual water plants; clematis; shrubs; trees
　　Old Rectory (Mrs M.E.B. Sparke) Small garden

Lexham Hall &⚘ (W.R.B. Foster Esq) 7m N Swaffham; A1065 N, after 5m go right to W Lexham; then 2m to Lexham Hall, garden on right. 3-acre woodland garden with azaleas and rhododendrons; walled garden, shrubs, roses; lake and parkland. TEA. *Adm £1 Chd 10p (Share to St Andrews Church, E. Lexham). Sun May 31 (2-6)*

Mannington Hall &⚘֎ (The Hon Robin & Mrs Walpole) 2m N of Saxthorpe; 18m NW of Norwich via B1149 towards Holt. At Saxthorpe (B1149 & B1354) turn NE signed Mannington. 20 acres feature roses, shrubs, lake and trees. Heritage rose, scented and walled gardens. Extensive countryside walks and trails. C15 moated manor house (not open). Saxon church with C19 follies. TEAS. *Adm £1 OAPs 75p Chd free (Share to Itteringham Church, May & Village Hall, July). △ Suns May 17 & July 12 (2-5)*

Norfolk College of Agriculture and Horticulture &֎ Burlingham, 9m E of Norwich on A47. Bus: No 701 from Norwich. 25 acres of commercial fruit and glasshouse crops; ornamental gardens. Light refreshments. *Adm 50p OAPs/Chd free. Sun June 14 (1.30-5)*

Norfolk Lavender Ltd & (Caley Mill) Heacham. On A149 13m N of Kings Lynn. National collection of lavenders set in 2 acres (lavender harvest July/Aug); herb garden with many varieties of native herbs; rose garden. TEAS. *Collecting box (Share to Heacham Parish Church). Daily Easter to end Oct (10-5.30)*

¶**The Old House** ⚘ (The Hon Mrs Cator) Ranworth. 9m NE of Norwich. B1140 from Norwich; left in S. Walsham to Ranworth. Shrubs and linked gardens giving views over private Ranworth Broad; spring daffodils; pond with many species of duck and geese; ½m of woodland walk adjacent to Norfolk Naturalist Trust; nature trail; conservation centre; Historic Ranworth Church. TEA. *Adm £1 Chd/*

OAP 25p (Share to Jubilee Sailing Trust).
Mon Apr 20 (2-5.30), Sun July 5 (2-6)

Oxburgh Hall Garden &_⚘ (The National Trust) 7m SW of Swaffham, at Oxburgh on Stoke Ferry rd. Hall and moat surrounded by lawns, fine trees, colourful borders; charming parterre garden of French design. Cream TEAS. *Adm 50p Chd 25p. Thurs, Fri July 23, 24 (2-5)*

Quarles House & (Mr Bryan & Lady Carey Basset) 4m SW of Wells-on-Sea. From Fakenham take King's Lynn Rd, turn right on to B1355 signed Burnham Market; 3½m turn right at Waterden sign, then left by black and white pole for 1¼m. Turn right at Quarles sign. Small garden with good herbaceous border at best in late July. Tea Holkham Hall nearby. *Adm 40p Chd 20p. Thurs July 16 (2-6)*

Rainthorpe Hall &⚘ (G.F. Hastings Esq) 8m S of Norwich, 1m SW of Newton Flotman. From Norwich take A140 for 7m; at Newton Flotman, by garage, fork right; on 1m to red brick gates on left. Large garden; fine trees; botanical interest, inc a collection of bamboos. Elizabethan house (open by appt) connected with Amy Robsart. TEAS. *Adm £1 OAPs/Chd 50p. Sun June 7 (2-5.30)*

Raveningham Hall &⚘ (Sir Nicholas Bacon Bt) 14m SE of Norwich. 3m Beccles off B1136. Large garden specialising in rare shrubs, trees, plants, Euphorbias, Agapanthus, shrub roses, Davidia. Nursery open weekdays and Open Days. TEAS. *Adm £1 Chd free. Suns June 21, 28; July 19; Aug 30; Mon Aug 31; also by appt. For NGS Suns June 7, Aug 2, (Share to Priscilla Bacon Lodge).*

Rippon Hall & (Miss Diana Birkbeck) Hevingham, N of Norwich. From A140 Norwich-Aylsham rd, turn right (E) at Xrds just N of Hevingham Church. Rhododendrons and azalea borders. Large herd of rare breed of British White Cattle. TEAS. *Adm 75p Chd 25p. Sun May 24 (2-5.30)*

Ryston Hall & (Mr & Mrs E.R.M. Pratt) 2m SE of Downham Market. Route A10. Medium-sized garden; rhododendrons, azaleas, rock garden; lawns; ornamental trees. TEA. *Adm 70p Chd 20p. Sun May 17 (2-6)*

♦**Sandringham Grounds:** by gracious permission of HM The Queen, the House and Grounds at Sandringham will be open (except when HM The Queen or any member of the Royal Family is in residence). Donations are given from the Estate to various charities. For further information see p xiii. *Adm house and grounds £1.80 OAPs £1.40 Chd £1; grounds only £1.30 OAPs £1 Chd 70p. Apr 19 to Sept 24 every Sun, Mon, Tues, Wed & Thurs but house closed July 20 to Aug 8 inc & grounds closed July 24 to Aug 5 inc (Hours:*

House 11 (Sun 12 noon)to 4.45; Grounds 10.30 (Sun 11.30) to 5)

Swanington Manor &⚘⚘ (Mr & Mrs Richard Winch) 10m NW Norwich; up A1067 to Attlebridge, follow signs to Swanington. 4-acres romantic, peaceful garden; exquisite small knot and herb garden; large herbaceous borders with many named unusual plants; fine 300 yr old yew and box topiary; well maintained glasshouses; Fascinating Present shop; Home-made TEAS. *Adm £1.20 Chd 50p (Share to NSPCC, Norwich Branch) Sun July 19 (2-6)*

107 University Crescent ⚘⚘ (Mr J Bartram & family) Gorleston, 3m S of Gt Yarmouth. A12 Gorleston turn off at Western Rd; right into Exeter Rd; right into University Cres. A143 Beccles-Yarmouth rd at Bradwell turn into Long Lane across junc, Worcester Way, left into Exeter Rd, right into University Cres. Landscaped town garden, all-year colour; pygmy pinetum, heathers; alpine garden, bulbs, dwarf shrubs; cacti house, herbaceous borders. TEAS. *Adm 40p Chd 15p (Share to International Bible Students Assn). By appt only (Tel Gt Yarmouth 668945)*

Wicken House &⚘⚘ (Lord & Lady Keith) Castle Acre, 5m N of Swaffham. A1065 from Swaffham on Fakenham rd; W at Newton to Castle Acre; then 2m N off Massingham rd. Medium-sized garden; flowering shrubs; roses, new herbaceous borders; rare plants; greenhouses. Part of house dates from 1700. TEAS. *Adm £1 Chd 25p. Sun July 19 (2-6)*

Wretham Lodge &⚘⚘ (Mrs Anne Hoellering) East Wretham. All E from Thetford; left up A1075; left by village sign; right at Xrds then bear left. Hundreds of old, species and climbing roses, walled garden, trained fruit trees, extensive lawns. Fine old trees. TEAS. *Adm 60p Chd 30p (Share to Norfolk Churches Trust). Sun July 5 (2.30-5.30)*

NORTHAMPTONSHIRE

Hon County Organiser:
MRS JOHN BOUGHEY, Butts Close,
  Farthinghoe, Brackley NN13 5NY
Asst Hon County Organiser:
MRS JOHN WALLACE, 63 West St,
  Kingscliffe, Peterborough PE8 6XB
Hon County Treasurer:
MRS R.H.N. DASHWOOD,
  Farthinghoe Lodge, nr Brackley NN13 5NX

DATES OF OPENING

BY APPOINTMENT ONLY for dates see text:
  31 DERWENT CRESCENT, Kettering

APRIL Sunday 12
CHARLTON, nr Banbury.
LILFORD PARK, nr Oundle
APRIL Easter Sunday 19
BOUGHTON HOUSE GARDEN, nr
Kettering
LOIS WEEDON FARM, nr Towcester
APRIL Sunday 26
CASTLE ASHBY HOUSE, nr Northampton
HOLDENBY HOUSE, nr Northampton
SHOLEBROKE LODGE, Towcester
TITCHMARSH GARDENS, Kettering
MAY Sunday 3
BARNWELL MANOR, nr Peterborough
MAY Sunday 24
CHIPPING WARDEN MANOR & THE
SPRING HOUSE, nr Banbury
COTTESBROOKE HALL, nr Creaton
MAY Monday 25 (Bank Hol)
CHIPPING WARDEN MANOR & THE
SPRING HOUSE, nr Banbury
MAY Sunday 31
BARNWELL MANOR, nr Peterborough
‡CHACOMBE GARDENS, nr Banbury
DEENE PARK, nr Corby
‡WARDINGTON MANOR (see Oxon)
JUNE Thursday 4
COTON MANOR, nr Ravensthorpe
JUNE Sunday 7
EDGCOTE, nr Banbury
KELMARSH HALL, nr Market Harborough
SHOLEBROKE LODGE, Towcester
JUNE Sunday 14
OLD RECTORY, Bradden, Towcester
JUNE Saturday 20
BADBY GARDENS, nr Daventry
CANONS ASHBY HOUSE, nr Daventry
JUNE Sunday 21
BADBY GARDENS, nr Daventry
FARTHINGHOE & STEANE GARDENS, nr
Brackley
TITCHMARSH GARDENS, Kettering
JUNE Saturday 27
COTON LODGE, Guilsborough
JUNE Sunday 28
BOWOOD COTTAGE, Geddington
CHERRY ORCHARD YARD, Oundle
COTON LODGE, Guilsborough
COTTESBROOKE HALL, nr Creaton
GUILSBOROUGH COURT, nr
Northampton
GUILSBOROUGH GARDENS, nr
Northampton
HARPOLE GARDENS, Northampton
KILSBY GARDENS, Rugby
THE MANOR HOUSE, Woodend
15, NEW ROAD, Geddington, nr Kettering
THORPE MANDEVILLE GARDENS, nr
Banbury
JUNE Monday 29
THE MANOR HOUSE, Woodend
JULY Wednesday 1
CHERRY ORCHARD YARD, Oundle
JULY Sunday 5
BULWICK RECTORY, Bulwick

JULY Sunday 12
‡AYNHO GARDENS, nr Banbury
‡CHARLTON, nr Banbury
CRANFORD GARDENS, nr Kettering
EASTON NESTON, Towcester
SOULDERN GARDENS (see Oxon)
TURWESTON GARDENS, nr Brackley
JULY Sunday 19
HILL GROUNDS, Evenley Brackley
PYTCHLEY HOUSE, nr Kettering
JULY Monday 20
HILL GROUNDS, Evenley, Brackley
JULY Saturday 25
COTON LODGE, Guilsborough
JULY Sunday 26
BULWICK PARK, nr Corby
COTON LODGE, Guilsborough
GUILSBOROUGH COURT, nr
Northampton
GUILSBOROUGH GARDENS, (Manor
House Farm only)
AUGUST Thursday 13
HOLDENBY HOUSE, nr Northampton
SEPTEMBER Thursday 10
COTON MANOR nr Ravensthorpe
SEPTEMBER Sunday 13
COTTESBROOKE HALL, nr Creaton

DESCRIPTIONS OF GARDENS

Aynho 6m SE of Banbury. TEAS Village Hall. *Combined adm 60p Chd 10p (Share to Katherine House Hospice). Sun July 12 (2.30-6.30)*
2 The Butts (Mrs B. Thoenes) ⅓ acre; designed and planted since 1983; colourful and interesting shrubs and trees; lily pool; newly planted Alpine wall; roses
9 The Butts ❀ (Mr & Mrs R.G. Cheney) Off Charlton rd, from A41 Banbury rd. ⅓ acre; good variety of shrubs; accent on foliage, rockeries; pools; roses
22a Charlton Road (Mr & Mrs R. Thurgood) Mixed with good selection of flowers; vegetables; fruit trees
Hansel House (Mrs P. Belcher) Very attractive medium-sized cottage garden; colourful and interesting collection of plants and shrubs; unusual conifers; rockeries; pool; roses

Badby Gardens ❀ 3m S of Daventry on E side of A361. Close to Badby Woods and Fawsley Park (suitable for walks and picnics). TEAS. *Combined adm 60p Chd 10p. Sat & Sun June 20 & 21 (2-7)*
¶**Berry Green Farm** ⅃ (Dr D.W. & Dr S.M. Roberts) 1-acre inc green garden and new alpine border. 40-acres with field walks and views over the Nene Valley
Church Hill (Dr & Mrs C.M. Cripps) Medium sized informal garden on an irregular sloping site. Old shrub roses and some interesting plants

Barnwell Manor & (H.R.H. Princess Alice Duchess of Gloucester & The Duke & Duchess of Gloucester) nr Peterborough. 2m S of Oundle; 4½m NE of Thrapston on A605. Pleasant grounds, spring flowers. C13 castle ruins. Light Refreshments. Car park free. *Adm 60p Chd 10p. Suns May 3, 31 (2.30-6)*

Boughton House Garden &※ (The Duke & Duchess of Buccleuch & Queensberry) Boughton House is on A43, 3m N of Kettering between Weekley and Geddington; follow special signs. Beautiful grounds with avenues and lakes of historical interest; large walled garden; herbaceous borders. Plants for sale. **The Dower House** NOT OPEN *Adm 75p Chd 40p. Sun April 19 (1-5)*

Bowood Cottage &※※ (Mr & Mrs John Ambery) Queen St, Geddington, 3m NE of Kettering. Take A43, at Geddington fork right; garden is 2nd on right. ⅓-acre planted since 1977; trees, shrubs, climbers clematis collection, double herbaceous borders, small wild garden. *Adm 40p Chd 20p. Sun June 28 (2-6)*

♦Bulwick Park &※ (Mr & Mrs G.T.G. Conant) 8m NE of Corby; 13m NE of Kettering; in Bulwick Village turn into Red Lodge Rd; enter park over cattle grid. Large garden, beautifully set; formal terrace; some fine mature trees, yew avenue; pleasant walks; C19 orangery. TEA. *Adm 50p Chd 20p (Share to Action Research Multiple Sclerosis). Sun July 26 (2-6)*

¶Bulwick Rectory ※ (Rev Mervyn Wilson) Bulwick. 8m NE of Corby; 13m NE of Kettering; next to Bulwick Church. 1½-acre old rectory garden largely re-laid and replanted since 1978 as a number of gardens with vistas and surprises. Dovecote; stonewalls. Shrubs, old roses, mixed borders with wide variety of plants. Fruit trees and vegetables. TEAS. *Adm 50p Chd 25p (Share to St Nicholas Church). Sun July 5 (2-5.30)*

Canons Ashby House &※ (The National Trust) Woodford Halse, nr Daventry. Formal gardens enclosed by walls. Gate piers from 1710; yew court with fine topiary; axial arrangement of patio and terraces; wild flowers, old varieties of pear, apple, plum and soft fruit trees. Home of the Dryden family since C16, Manor House 1550 with Elizabethan and Jacobean plastering. TEAS. *Adm £2 Chd £1. Sat June 20 (1-5.30)*

Castle Ashby House & (The Marquess of Northampton) 6m E of Northampton. 1½m N of A428 Northampton-Bedford; turn off between Denton and Yardley Hastings. Parkland inc avenue planted at suggestion of William III in 1695; lakes etc by Capability Brown; Italian gardens with orangery; extensive lawns and trees. Nature trail. Elizabethan

house (not open). TEAS. *Adm 50p Chd 25p. △ Sun April 26 (2-6)*

Chacombe Gardens 4m NE of Banbury. On A361 2½m from Banbury centre turn right signed to Chacombe. TEAS Poplars Farm. *Combined adm £1 Chd 20p (Share to St Peter & St Paul Church). Sun May 31 (2-6)*

 Poplars Farm &※ (Mr & Mrs G.H. Jones) 2½ acres started 1972, new areas still being planted. Mixed borders; streamside borders with primulas, bog plants; kitchen garden; wild areas. Thatched 1654 farmhouse (not open); stone barns.

 Pear Tree House (Mr & Mrs Peter Northey) 1-acre mature mixed garden surrounding unusual extension of C17 cottage (not open); lawns, flowering trees, bulbs, laid out in 1950s to frame Church

 The Old Vicarage ※ (The Lady Sophia Schilizzi) 2½ acres; flowering shrubs, daffodils, spring bulbs; lawns; orchard; small kitchen garden

Charlton & 7m SE of Banbury, 5m W of Brackley. From A41 turn off N at Aynho; or from A422 turn off S at Farthinghoe. Home-made TEAS The Cottage. *Combined adm 70p Chd 10p (Share to Newbottle Church Fabric Fund). Suns April 12 & July 12 (2-6)*

 The Cottage (The Countess of Birkenhead) Flowering shrubs, spring bulbs, roses, lawns, woodland walk, stream and lakes. House in village street

 Holly House (The Hon Nicholas Berry) Walled garden with beautiful views. C18 house (not open)

Cherry Orchard Yard ※※ (Mr Richard Warwick) 17 Benefield Rd, Oundle. From A1 turn W at signpost Oundle/Corby to A605; drive through Oundle; take A427 W towards Corby; 50 yds free public car park; garden 100 yds on, up gravel drive (behind 9 Benefield Rd). ¾-acre; shrub roses, shrubs, bog garden; bronze sculpture, fine urns; mature trees. TEA (Sun only). *Adm 50p Chd 10p (Share to Oundle Parish Church). Sun June 28 (2-7) & Wed July 1 (2-6)*

Chipping Warden ※ 7m NE of Banbury on A361. TEAS (Mon at the Manor). *Combined adm 75p Chd 10p (Share to Edgcote Church). Sun, Mon May 24, 25 (2.30-6)*

 Chipping Warden Manor (Mr T. & the Hon Mrs Sergison-Brooke) Medium-sized garden; herbaceous borders, formal gardens, unusual plants; pond walk; kitchen garden. Carolean house (not open)

 The Spring House (Mr & Mrs C. Shepley-Cuthbert) 2½ acres originally designed by Miss Kitty Lloyd-Johnes, now fully mature; spring bulbs, blossom; fine trees; tapestry hedge; small water and bog garden; shrub roses; open view of countryside. *Also by appt (Chipping Warden 261)*

¶**Coton Lodge** ⚘❀ (Mr & Mrs A.A. de Nobriga) Guilsborough. 12m E of Rugby, 12m W Northampton off A428. 1½-acre old farmhouse garden redesigned since 1978 to include a water and sunken garden; silver and white garden; raised rock garden and alpine troughs; nut walk planted with collection of hellebores and primulas. TEA. *Adm 60p Chd 10p. Sats, Suns June 27, 28; July 25, 26 (2-5.30)*

Coton Manor ⚘❀ (Cdr & Mrs H. Pasley-Tyler) 10m N of Northampton. 11m SE of Rugby nr Ravensthorpe Reservoir. From A428 & A50 follow Tourist signs. C17 stone manor house with water gardens, herbaceous borders, rose garden, old holly and yew hedges; interesting variety of foliage plants; subtropical house. Large collection of ornamental waterfowl, cranes and flamingoes. Home-made TEAS. Open Easter to Sep 30 Thurs & Suns. *Adm £1.50 Chd 50p △For NGS Thurs June 4, Sep 10 (2-6)*

Cottesbrooke Hall ⚘ (The Hon Lady Macdonald-Buchanan) 10m N of Northampton. Nr Creaton on A50; nr Brixworth on A508. Large formal and wild gardens; herbaceous borders, fine old cedars. Parties shown round greenhouses and kitchen garden. Early C18 house (not shown). (Brixworth Church, 2½m, dates back to C7, is well worth a visit). TEAS. Car park free. *Adm 60p Chd 30p. Suns May 24, June 28, & Sept 13 (2-6)*

Courteenhall House ⚘ (Sir Hereward & Lady Wake) 5m S of Northampton. Entrance at Lodge on A508. 3 acres of arboretum and garden, shrubs, herbaceous. *Adm 80p Chd 20p. Sun July 5 (2-6)*

Cranford Gardens 4½m E of Kettering. A604 Kettering-Thrapston. TEA Manor House, Oakrise. Car parking on the green. *Combined adm £1 Chd 20p (Share to Cranford Churches Restoration Fund). Sun July 12 (2-6)*
   26 Church Lane ❀ (Mr & Mrs Richard Loake) Collection of delphiniums, other herbaceous plants and shrubs; cacti and other succulents
   32 Church Lane (Mr & Mrs Donald Bates) 1-acre landscaped garden developed since 1976
   Oakrise (Mr & Mrs G.T. Oakes) 5 The Green. ½ acre with variety of shrubs, perennials, dwarf conifers; ponds; water plants; lovely view
   Top House (Mr & Mrs I.M. Tait) Large, well-laid out garden, lawns, mature trees, inc conifers, roses
   The Manor House (Mr & Mrs J. Johnson) Lawns; mature trees. Children's amusements, inc swimming pool
   Cranford Hall (Sir John & Lady Robinson) Large garden inc lawns, herbaceous borders, natural woodland

Deene Park ⚘ (Edmund Brudenell Esq) 6m N of Corby. A43 Kettering-Stamford Rd. Medium-sized garden; long borders, old-fashioned roses, rare trees, shrubs; large lake. Interesting church; fine tombs. TEAS. *Adm 50p Chd 25p. △Sun May 31 (2-5)*

31 Derwent Crescent ⚘❀ (Mr & Mrs B.J. Mitchell) Kettering. 10 mins from station (on W of town). Turn off A6 from N or from A43 from S into interconnecting rd (Gypsy Lane); Lakes Housing Estate on E side (map Ref. SP8678). Plantsman's/collector's garden; plants raised from seed from botanical expeditions; many unusual plants; bulbs, hardy plants both alpine and herbaceous; collection of hardy ferns. TEA. *Adm 50p Chd 20p. By appt all year (Tel Kettering 520070)*

Easton Neston ⚘❀ (The Lord Hesketh) Towcester. Entrance on A43. Bus: to Hulcote turning (3rd lodge). Easton Neston, ¼m. Large formal garden; ornamental water, clipped yew hedges, arboretum, C14 church; interesting family tombs. TEA. *Adm £1.10 Chd 35p (Share to BRCS). Sun July 12 (2-6)*

Edgcote ⚘ (Mrs Edward Courage) 6m NE of Banbury. On E of A361; from Banbury turn right in Wardington village. Unspoilt Georgian house (not open) set in grounds of mature trees and lawns with 8 acres of lake; small formal garden. TEA. *Adm 50p Chd 10p. Sun June 7 (2-6)*

Farthinghoe & Steane Gardens 6m E of Banbury on A422,:4m NW of Brackley; or from A41 turn N at Aynho, through Charlton to Farthinghoe. TEAS Farthinghoe Lodge. *Combined adm £1 Chd 10p (Share to Farthinghoe Village Hall Fund). Sun June 21 (2-6)*
   Farthinghoe Lodge ⚘ (Mr & Mrs R. Dashwood) 1 acre with lawns, fine views
   Astwick House ⚘ (Mr & Mrs W.R. Elliott) ¼-acre informal garden; mainly bush, shrub, climbing roses; conifers and other trees; cyclamen, clematis
   Butts Close ⚘ (Mrs John Boughey) Very small walled cottage:garden; mainly shrubs, climbing roses, clematis
   The Old Rectory (Maj & Mrs Simon Cox) Wilderness completely replanned from 1975; new plantings, vistas, views, walled terraced swimming pool garden
   Steane Grounds ⚘❀ (Mr & Mrs R. G. Ellis) Brackley side of Farthinghoe turn to Hinton-in-the-Hedges (gated rd) Steane 1½m; garden on left. 1 acre increasing variety plants. Attractive water layout, spring fed. (Picnic area)

¶**Guilsborough Court** ❀ (Mr & Mrs John Lowther) Guilsborough. 10m N of Northampton off A50. 10m NE of Daventry; 10m E of Rugby; ¼m outside Guilsborough on Cold Ashby rd. 4-acre garden, many fine mature trees, beautiful views, interesting shrubs, large lawn and herbaceous border. *Adm 60p Chd 10p. Suns June 28, July 26 (2-5.30)*

¶**Guilsborough Gardens** 10m NW of Northampton between A50 and A428; 10m E of Rugby. TEAS at The Ward Arms, Guilsborough. *Combined adm (Dripwell House & Spain House) 60p Chd 10p, Manor House Farm 50p Chd free. Sun June 28 (2-7), Manor House Farm also Sun July 26 (2-7)*
Dripwell House (Mr & Mrs J.W.Langfield, Dr C. Moss) 2½-acre mature garden; many fine trees and shrubs on partly terraced slope. Rock garden, herbaceous border, herb garden. Some unusual shrubs and many rhododendrons and azaleas in woodland garden.
Spain House & (Mr & Mrs I.L.May & Miss Heaver) ¾-acre garden with roses and shrubs.
Manor House Farm &⌘ (Mr & Mrs J.M.Clissold) Nortoft. Plantsman's 1-acre garden surrounding old stone farmhouse. Pink border; silver and white garden, heather bank, herbaceous border with unusual plants and shrub roses; use of ground cover plants.

Harpole Gardens 4m N Northampton on A45 towards Weedon; turn right at "The Turnpike" into Harpole. TEAS The Grange. *Combined adm £1 Chd 20p (Share to Harpole Church). Sun June 28 (2-6)*
The Grange & (Mrs L.E. Church) 55 Upper High St; 2-acre plantsman's garden with shrubberies, walks, herbaceous borders, fruit trees, pool, kitchen garden; C18 family home (not shown)
19 Manor Close (Mr & Mrs E. Kemshed) 40 yd x 10 yd flower arranger's garden on new estate; cultivated by present owners since 1975
72 Larkhall Lane (Mr & Mrs R.G. Murton) ⅙-acre well designed garden for all seasons; a flower to bloom everyday of the year; shrubs; variety of conifers
The Close (Mr & Mrs M. Orton-Jones) ¾-acre formal garden; lawns; herbaceous borders; old yew trees

¶**Hill Grounds** (Mr & Mrs C.F. Cropley) Evenley. From Brackley 1m S on A43. 2-acres S-facing sheltered garden developed since 1982; mature trees; 200 yrds of yew hedge; terrace of "old roses", white garden; wide range of unusual plants. Flower festival in Evenley Church. TEAS. *Adm 60p Chd 20p (Share to Nat. Childrens Home, Evenley). Sun & Mon July 19 & 20 (2-6)*

♦**Holdenby House** &⌘ (James Lowther Esq) 7m W of Northampton. Signposted from A50 and A428. Impressive remains of terrace gardens of Holdenby Palace, where Charles I was imprisoned; Elizabethan garden; fragrant and silver borders. Rare breeds farm animals; model trains; museum. Open Suns & Bank Hols April - Sept; also Thurs July & Aug. TEAS. *Adm £1.20 (groups of 20 or more £1) Chd 60p. For NGS Sun April 26 & Thurs Aug 13 (2-6). House open by appt Adm £2*

Kelmarsh Hall ⌘ (Miss C.V. Lancaster) On A508 5m S of Market Harborough, 13m N of Northampton. Gardens, house and church. Open Suns & Bank Hols. April 19 to Sept 27. TEA. *Adm £1 Chd 50p. For NGS Sun June 7 (2-5.30)*

Kilsby Gardens ⌀ 5m SE of Rugby on A478 turn right on B4038 through village. 6m N of Daventry on A361. TEAS Village Hall. *Combined adm £1 Chd 10p (Share to St Faith's Church Restoration Fund). Sun June 28 (2-6)*
¶**Croft Close** & (Mr & Mrs P. Couldrey) Rugby Rd. ¼-acre; herbaceous beds, shrubs, pond and rockery. Productive vegetable garden, soft fruit, greenhouse; row of cordon apple trees and espalier pear tree trained against a wall of special interest
Fairview (Mr & Mrs J. Beeston) North St. Mature small mixed garden of C17 cottage
¶**Hathersage** (Mr & Mrs W. Wood) small garden specialising in climbing roses, clematis, bedding plants and hanging baskets
Pytchley House &⌘ (Mr & Mrs T.F. Clay) Main Rd. 1-acre mature garden; lawns; trees; island beds; vegetable garden; 2 fish ponds; wild garden.
The Old Vicarage & (Mr & Mrs P.G.B. Jackson) On A5 opp George Hotel. 1 acre; lawns; mature trees; shrubs; herbaceous border; small water garden; vegetable garden
The Haven (Mr & Mrs Arthur Old) Essen Lane. ½-acre old established walled garden under restoration

♦**Lilford Park** &⌀⌘ S of Oundle; 17m NE of Kettering. A605 midway between Oundle & Thrapston (AA signed). 240 acres; large area of daffodils, rock gardens, aviaries, animals. Jacobean house (not open). Cafe in park. *Adm £1.40 Chd 70p. Sun April 12 (10-6)*

Lois Weedon Farm &⌀ (Mr & Mrs W.J. Richards) Weedon Lois. 7m W of Towcester, 11m N of Banbury. Off A43 through Wappenham, then signed. 1½ acres; lawns; woodland; conservation area; vegetables; orchard; ha-ha; pool, lilies, goldfish; views S over fields. Church worth a visit. TEA. *Adm inc Tea £1 Chd free. Sun April 19 (2.30-6)*

The Manor House Woodend &⌘ (Maj H.G. Marrack) Woodend; 6m W of Towcester through Greens Norton & Blakesley; 8m NE of Banbury via B4525 towards Northampton, turn off E through Weston. 1-acre walled garden; many varieties of trees and shrubs in layout designed by Col John Codrington;

previously derelict orchard. Strawberry TEAS. *Adm 60p Chd 20p. Sun & Mon June 28 & 29 (2-6); also by appt (Tel Blakesley 860201)*

15 New Road ❀ (Mr & Mrs C.R.Hough) Geddington. 3½m N of Kettering on A43. Parking at White Llon Car Park on A43 opp house. ¼-acre L-shaped garden, borders, rockery; heather beds; pool; 3 greenhouses; fruit trees, soft fruit and vegetable plot. TEA. *Adm 50p Chd 10p. Sun June 28 (2-6)*

Old Rectory ✺❀ (Col & Mrs K.C. Goldie-Morrison) Bradden, Towcester. 5m W of Towcester through Greens Norton. 4 acres; a wild garden entirely maintained by owners; walled garden; croquet lawn; orchard; pond with ducks. Home-made TEAS. *Adm 70p Chd 10p if unaccompanied (Share to St. Michael's Church). Sun June 14 (2-6)*

Pytchley House ৬❀ (Lady Glover) Pytchley, 3m S of Kettering. Between A43 & A509. Rose garden, lawns, fine trees and topiary; Temple of Zeus. House 1633. *Essential* dogs kept on leads. Produce stall. TEAS. *Adm 75p Chd 25p (Share to NSPCC). Sun July 19 (2.30-6)*

Sholebroke Lodge ৬❀ (A.B.X. Fenwick Esq) Whittlebury, 3m S of Towcester. Turn off A413 Towcester end of Whittlebury village. 5 acres informal garden; large new planting of shrubs, bulbs, wild flowers and interesting plants in established setting. Garden shop. Home-made TEAS. *Adm 60p Chd 20p (Share to Whittlebury Reading Room). Suns April 26, June 7 (1-6)*

Thorpe Mandeville Gardens ✺ 4m NE of Banbury on B4525. Home-made TEAS The Manor. *Combined adm £1 Chd 20p (Share to Thorpe Mandeville Church). Sun June 28 (2-6)*

> **Thorpe Mandeville Manor** ৬ (Mr & Mrs D. Ancil) 4 acres extended in 1925 by Mr Oliver Hill; numerous wrought iron gates; intriguing design of shallow circular steps leading to rose garden. House built 1677-1678 by Oliver Cromwell
> **Thorpe Mandeville Court** ৬❀ (Col & Mrs E.T. Smyth-Osbourne) House opp church. 4 acres; lawns, fine trees, shrubs, grey leaved and unusual plants, ponds, greenhouses, kitchen garden. House (not open) 300 yrs old
> **Wheatsheaf House** The Misses Richmond-Watson) Culworth, 1m Thorpe Mandeville. ¾-acre plantsman's garden with herbaceous borders. *Adm 50p Chd 20p*

Titchmarsh Gardens ✺ NE of Wellingborough; on A510 then right onto A604; left into A605 at Thrapston; turn right at signs to Titchmarsh. TEAS Glebe Cottage. *Combined adm 75p Chd 25p (Share to Eastern Northants MacMillan Nurse Appeal, April; St*

Mary's Church, June). *Suns April 26, June 21 (2-6)*

> ¶**Crown Cottage** ৬ (Mrs H.W.Williams) 28, Church Street. Mature but neglected garden being remade by owners. Mixed borders, shrubs, established trees, wide views.
> **Titchmarsh House** ৬ (Mr & Mrs Ewan Harper) 3½ acres extended and laid out since 1972; some borders still to be completed; shrub roses; clematis; range of shrubs, walled borders
> **The Manor House** (Mr Leonard Harper) not opening 21 June
> **Glebe Cottage** (Mr & Mrs J. Bussens) ⅓-acre; NE aspect; informal herbaceous and shrub borders since 1979; developing new beds and clematis around old roses
> **14 Polopit** (Mr & Mrs C. Millard) Developed over since 1984; rockeries, ornamental and herbaceous borders; fruit & decorative shrubs, trees; open views both front and rear; ½-acre

Turweston Gardens A43 from Oxford; in Brackley turn right at traffic lights; A422 towards Buckingham; 1m turn left signposted Turweston. TEAS. *Combined adm £1.50 Chd 50p (Share to Turweston Church Restoration Fund). Sun July 12 (2-6)*

> **Turweston Mill** ৬❀ (Mr & Mrs Harry Leventis) 5 acres; mill stream, water gardens; rose garden; lawns
> **Spring Valley** ৬ (Mr & Mrs A. Wildish) 1 acre terraced garden with ponds
> **Turweston Barn** (Mr & Mrs A.J.M. Kirkland) 1-acre informal walled garden; wall vines, herbaceous borders, roses, lawns
> ¶**Turweston House** ৬ (Mrs Von Hofmanstahl) 5½-acre landscaped garden; walled garden and lake
> **Turweston Lodge** (Mr & Mrs T. R. Sermon) 1¼ acre informal walled garden, roses, herbs, orchard, vines, spinney with pool

NORTHUMBERLAND

CORRESPONDENCE TO: NGS, 57 Lower Belgrave Street, London SW1W 0LR

DATES OF OPENING

REGULAR OPENINGS for dates see text:
CRAGSIDE, Rothbury
LINDISFARNE CASTLE, Holy Island
WALLINGTON, Cambo

JUNE Sunday 21
LOUGHBROW HOUSE, Hexham

DESCRIPTIONS OF GARDENS

NOTTINGHAMSHIRE

Cragside & (The National Trust) Rothbury, 13m SW of Alnwick (B6341); 15m NW of Morpeth (B6344). Extensive grounds of over 900 acres on S edge of Alnwick Moor; famous for magnificent trees; rhododendrons and beautiful lakes. House designed by Richard Norman Shaw, famous Victorian architect; built 1864-1895; contains much original furniture designed by Shaw; also pictures and experimental scientific apparatus (it was 1st house in the world to be lit by electricity generated by water power). Cafe. Shop. *Adm Country Park £1; House & Country Park £2.40. Country Park April 1-Sept 30 daily (10.30-6); Oct daily (10.30-5); Nov-March Sats & Suns only (10.30-4); House: April 1, 16, Wed, Sat, Sun April 17-Sept 30 daily except Mons (but open Bank Hols); Oct Weds, Sats, Suns (1-5)*

Lindisfarne Castle (The National Trust) Holy Island, 5m E of Beal across causeway (which is closed for 5½ hrs at height of tide each day); 6m E of A1. Tiny fort built c.1550 in romantic situation on high rock overlooking sea; converted to private house in 1903 by Sir Edwin Lutyens. Tiny garden (on which Gertrude Jekyll advised) can be entered on application to the Administration. *Adm April 1-16 Wed, Sat, Sun; June to Aug £2.20; other months £1.70 April 17-Sept 30 daily except Fris (but open Good Fri); Oct Sats, Suns (11-5)*

Loughbrow House ❀ (Mrs K.A. Clark) Hexham. Take B6306 from Hexham fork right, lodge gates in intersection of second fork, ½m up drive. 5 acres; woodland garden; herbaceous borders, roses, wide lawns; kitchen garden. Home-made TEAS. *Adm 50p Chd 20p. Sun June 21 (2-6)*

Wallington (The National Trust) Cambo. From N 12m W of Morpeth (B6343); from S via A696 from Newcastle, 6m W of Belsay, B6342 to Cambo. Walled, terraced garden with fine shrubs and species roses; conservatory with magnificent fuchsias; 100 acres woodland and lakes. House dates from 1688 but altered and interior greatly changed c.1740; exceptional rococo plasterwork by Francini brothers; fine porcelain, furniture, pictures, needlework, dolls' houses, museum, display of coaches. Cafe. Shop. *Adm grounds & walled garden: £1; house, grounds & walled garden £2.40. Grounds open all year; walled garden open April 1-Sept daily (10-7); house open April 1-16 Wed, Sat, Sun; April 17-Sept 30 daily except Tues Oct; Weds, Sats, Suns (1-5)*

Hon County Organiser:
THE HON MRS CHAWORTH MUSTERS, Felley Priory, Jacksdale
Asst Hon County Organiser:
MRS PETER GELDART, Langwith Mill House, Nether Langwith, Mansfield
Hon County Treasurer:
GEORGE NOON ESQ, Greasley Castle Farm, Greasley N61 2AB

DATES OF OPENING

BY APPOINTMENT ONLY for dates see text:
MILL HILL HOUSE, East Stoke

APRIL Wednesday 1
THE WILLOWS, Radcliffe-on-Trent
APRIL Easter Sunday 19
FELLEY PRIORY, Underwood
APRIL Saturday 25
ARUM CROFT, Southwell
APRIL Sunday 26
ARUM CROFT, Southwell
THE OLD RECTORY, Staunton
MAY Saturday 2
CROYLANDS, Averham, nr Newark
MAY Sunday 3
CROYLANDS, Averham, nr Newark
GROVE COTTAGE, Coddington
HOLME GARDENS, nr Newark
THE OLD RECTORY, Eakring
PADDOCK HOUSE, Scarrington
MAY Wednesday 6
THE WILLOWS, Radcliffe-on-Trent
MAY Sunday 10
HODSOCK PRIORY, Blyth
ST ANNE'S MANOR, Sutton Bonington
MAY Sunday 17
7 BARRATT LANE, Attenborough
HOLM PIERREPOINT HALL, nr Nottingham
ST HELEN'S CROFT, nr Southwell
MAY Sunday 24
BRAMCOTE GARDENS, nr Nottingham
EPPERSTONE GARDENS
OLD MILL HOUSE, Cuckney
WINTHORPE GARDENS, nr Newark
MAY Sunday 31
CLYDE HOUSE, Southwell
EPPERSTONE GARDENS
MORTON HALL, nr Retford
WELBECK WOODHOUSE, nr Worksop
JUNE Wednesday 3
THE WILLOWS, Radcliffe-on-Trent
JUNE Sunday 7
LANGWITH MILL HOUSE, Nether Langwith
JUNE Sunday 14
7 BARRATT LANE, Attenborough
FELLEY PRIORY, Underwood
GREEN MILE, Babworth
SKRETON COTTAGE, Screveton

JUNE Sunday 21
CUTTLE HILL HOUSE, East Bridgford
EDWINSTOWE GARDENS, nr Mansfield
FLINTHAM HALL, nr Newark
HODSOCK PRIORY, Blyth
THE OLD RECTORY, East Bridgford

JUNE Sunday 28
BRAMCOTE GARDENS, nr Nottingham
GAMSTON GARDENS, nr Retford
GRINGLEY HALL, nr Bawtry
MILL HILL HOUSE, East Stoke

JULY Wednesday 1
THE WILLOWS, Radcliffe-on-Trent

JULY Saturday 4
BISHOP'S MANOR, Southwell

JULY Sunday 5
MAPLEBECK GARDENS
NOTTINGHAMSHIRE COLLEGE OF
AGRICULTURE, Southwell
THRUMPTON HALL, nr Nottingham

JULY Saturday 11
ARUM CROFT, Southwell

JULY Sunday 12
ARUM CROFT, Southwell
MATTERSEY HOUSE, nr Bawtry
ST ANNE'S MANOR, Sutton Bonington
SUTTON BONINGTON HALL

JULY Sunday 19
SILKS COTTAGE, Shelford

AUGUST Saturday 1
CROYLANDS, Averham, nr Newark

AUGUST Sunday 2
CROYLANDS, Averham, nr Newark
OLD MILL HOUSE, Cuckney

AUGUST Wednesday 5
THE WILLOWS, Radcliffe-on-Trent

AUGUST Sunday 23
ST HELENN'S CROFT, Southwell

SEPTEMBER Wednesday 2
THE WILLOWS, Radcliffe-on-Trent

SEPTEMBER Sunday 13
ST HELEN'S CROFT, nr Southwell

SEPTEMBER Sunday 20
MILL HILL HOUSE, East Stoke

DESCRIPTIONS OF GARDENS

Arum Croft ⚲❀ (Mr & Mrs R.C. Cripps) 22 Halloughton Rd. On outskirts of Southwell, between A612/B6386. ¼ acre; many colourful plants; shrubs and trees of interest to flower arrangers; shrub roses, paved garden and pond, rockeries. Featured in 'Garden Answers' May '85. TEA. *Adm 50p Chd 10p. Sats, Suns April 25, 26; July 11, 12 (2-6)*

7 Barratt Lane ⚲❀ (Mr & Mrs D.J. Lucking & Mr & Mrs S.J. Hodkinson) Attenborough, Beeston, 6m SW of Nottingham. Via A6005 left down Attenborough Lane; then 1st right into Barratt Lane. ½-acre mature, well-labelled plantsman's garden; flowering shrubs, clematis, remontant irises, alpines, fruit. *Adm 50p Chd 20p (Share to National Eczema Society) Suns May 17, June 14 (11-1, 2-6)*

¶**Bishops Manor** ⚲❀ (The Bishop of Southwell & Mrs Whinney) end of Bishops Drive on S side of Minster. Turn right for free parking on recreation ground. House lies in part of the ruin of the old Medieval Palace with lawns, orchards and vegetable garden; newly planted garden is approached through a small copse. TEAS locally at Gossips. *Adm 50p Chd 20p. Sat July 4 (2-6)*

Bramcote Gardens ⚲❀ 5m W of Nottingham. At roundabout on A52 to Ilkeston, Stanley Drive is 2nd on left. TEA. *Combined adm 80p Chd 20p. Suns May 24, June 28 (2-6)*
    1 Stanley Drive (Mr & Mrs S.S. Randall) Flower-arrangers garden; mixed shrubs, bulbs, interesting plants. *(Share to St Mary's Church, Ilkeston)*
    17 Stanley Drive (John & Audrey Widdison) Small suburban plot, with uncommon hardy perennials, pond and paved area. *(Share to Leprosy Mission)*

Clyde House ⚲⚲❀ (Mr & Mrs G.H. Edwards) Westgate, Southwell on A612. ⅔-acre walled garden; 'Amateur Gardening 1984'; TEA. *Adm 50p Chd 10p (Share to Lord Mayor Treloar College). Sun May 31*

Croylands ⚲⚲❀ (Mr & Mrs J.T. Du Feu) Church Lane, Averham. 4m W of Newark, on A617. At Averham follow signs to Robin Hood Theatre. Peaceful, varied and colourful ¾ acre garden, much loved by its owners. Nr R Trent. TEAS. *Adm 50p Chd 10p (Share to National Childrens Home). Sats, Suns May 2, 3 Aug 1, 2 (2-6)*

¶**Cuttle Hill House** ⚲❀ (Mr & Mrs P.H. Blandy) East Bridgford, 12m NE of Nottingham, 14m SE of Newark. Medium-sized garden; herbaceous border, roses. Fine view over R. Trent. TEAS. *Adm 60p Chd 20p (Share to YWCA Nottingham Branch). Sun June 21 (2.30-5)*

Edwinstowe Gardens NE of Mansfield. Off A6075 turn S at Warsop/Clipstone Xrds. TEAS Gorse Lodge. *Combined Adm 80p Chd 40p. Sun June 21 (2-6)*
    Gorse Lodge ⚲❀ (Mr & Mrs R. Bealby) Medium-sized garden; interesting mixed shrubs and herbaceous borders
    Broomhill Grange (Mr & Mrs J.R. Bealby) Small pretty garden; shrubs, herbaceous; pond

Epperstone Gardens ⚲❀ 8m N Nottingham off A6097 between Lowdham and Oxton. *Combined Adm £1 Chd 30p (Share to Church of the Holy Cross). Suns May 24, 31 (2-6)*
    Sunny Mead (Mr & Mrs Francis Stokes) ½ acre; rhododendrons, azaleas, heathers; spring garden; S facing view over fields.

Opp Church (private drive), park on main street

White Gates (Mr & Mrs G.T. Pilsworth) rhododendrons, azaleas, heathers; shrubbery; pinetum; apiary. TEAS. Park in field opposite

Felley Priory &⊛ (Maj & the Hon Mrs R.P. Chaworth Musters) Underwood. On A608 ½m W of M1 junc 27. Medium-sized garden with daffodils around old house, herbaceous borders. TEAS. *Adm 50p Chd 10p. Suns April 19 June 14 (2-6)*

Flintham Hall &⊛ (Myles Thoroton Hildyard Esq) 6m SW of Newark on A46. Fine trees, park and lake, borders, walled garden, shrub garden, glasshouses, unique conservatory, woodland walk. Picnics allowed. TEAS. *Adm £1 OAPs 50p Chd 25p (Share to St Augustine's, Flintham) Sun June 21 (2-6)*

Gamston Gardens. ⊛ 3m S of Retford; A638 Retford-Markham Moor Rd. TEAS. Flower festival in church. Combined gardens, near river bridge. *Adm 80p OAPs 50p Chd 10p. Sun June 28 (2-6)*

  Brewery House Cottage & (C.M.D. Polhill Esq) Collection of old and modern shrub roses, interesting shrubs and trees

  Idle House (Mr & Mrs John Roberts) Medium-sized garden; 100 yr old beech hedge; soft fruit; vegetable garden; rockery

Green Mile & (Mr & Mrs A.C.M.B. Scott) Babworth, 2½m W of Retford. Turn off A620 alongside the Prison; or off A638 at Barnby Moor. 8 acres; inc trees, shrubs, rose gardens with hybrid tea, flora and old fashioned roses, woodland garden with rhododendron and azaleas; heather and winter gardens; fine beech hedges. Walled veg/fruit garden; water garden. Picnics. TEAS. *Adm 60p Chd 10p (Share to Notts Trust for Nature Conservation). Sun June 14 (2-6)*

Gringley Hall &⊛ (Mr & Mrs Threlfall) Gringley-on-the-Hill, Bawtry, nr Doncaster. On A631 mid-way between Bawtry and Gainsborough. Medium-sized garden; newly planted; interesting young trees; herbaceous borders. Strawberry TEAS. *Adm 50p Chd 10p (Share to Gringley on the Hill Village Hall) Sun June 28 (2-6)*

Grove Cottage (Miss P.E. Branston) Old Newark Rd, Coddington. 2m E of Newark. Take A17 over A1 then ¼m, turn sharp left at Xrds, 3rd gate on right. ⅓ acre; oaks, yews; surrounding cupressus hedge; shrubs bulbs, annuals for colour; roses. TEA. *Adm 50p Chd 10p (Share to Coddington Village Hall). Sun May 3 (2-6)*

Hodsock Priory &⊛ (Sir Andrew & Lady Buchanan) Blyth, off B6045 Worksop - Blyth Rd. 5 acres; old garden plus varied planting since 1980, trees, mixed borders, roses, water. Tudor gatehouse. Picnics. TEAS. *Adm 60p Chd 10p. Suns May 10, June 21 (2-6)*

Holme Gardens ⊛ 4m N of Newark A46 to Lincoln, left at roundabout onto A1133 Collingham Rd, 1st left after Langford. *Combined adm 80p Chd 20p Sun May 3 (2-6)*

  Holme Hall & (Mr & Mrs W.H. Bradwell) Medium sized garden, herbaceous border; paved courtyard. In village with beautiful C12 Church. TEAS *(Share to St Giles Church, Holme)*

  Main Street (Mr J.G. Calvert) Medium-sized garden, good shrubs and trees, bulbs; close to R Trent. *(Share to Holme Church Restoration Fund)*

Holme Pierrepont Hall &⊠ (Mr & Mrs Robin Brackenbury) 4m E of Nottingham via A52 at edge of West Bridgford, past National Water Sport Centre; see signs. Formal courtyard garden of 1875. Box parterre; tulips, herbaceous border; informal outer garden with old-fashioned roses and yews. Owner maintained. TEAS. *Adm 50p Chd 10p. Sun May 17 (2-6)*

Langwith Mill House ⊠⊛ (Mr & Mrs Peter Geldart) Nether Langwith. On A632 Chesterfield-Cuckney rd. Adjoins historic cotton mill. Small garden being restored around mill-race; herb garden, old-fashioned roses; fine views. TEAS. *Adm 50p Chd 20p. Sun June 7 (2-6)*

Maplebeck Gardens 7m NW of Newark. TEAS The Old Vicarage. *Adm 50p Chd 10p each garden (Share to St Radegunds Church). Sun July 5 (2-6)*

  The Old Vicarage & (Mr & Mrs D. Knight-Jones) Maplebeck, 7m NW of Newark-on-Trent. Garden in centre of Maplebeck village. Large garden with old-fashioned shrub roses and herbaceous borders. TEAS. *Adm 50p Chd 10p (Share to St Radegunds Church). Sun July 6 (2-6)*

  ¶**Long Barn** (Mr & Mrs D.J. Morris) A "postage-stamp" walled garden fronting converted barn; patio; pond; shrubs, alpines, climbing plants

Mattersey House &⊠⊛ (Mr & Mrs T.P. O'Connor-Fenton) Mattersey, 6m N of Retford, 4m SE of Bawtry; from A636 at Ranskill turn E on to B6045 for Mattersey; Buses from Retford and Bawtry. Medium-sized; walled garden; shrub roses, herbaceous borders. TEA. *Adm 50p Chd 10p. Sun July 12 (2-6)*

Mill Hill House &⊛ (Mr & Mrs R.J. Gregory) Elston lane, East Stoke. 5m S of Newark on A46 turn E on Elston Lane garden ½m on right. ½-acre plantsmans garden replanned and planted since 1983; mixed borders, alpines, shade plants, vegetables. *Adm 50p Chd 10p. Open daily April to Sept by appt*

only (Tel E Stoke 460), Suns June 28 Sept 20 (2-6)

Morton Hall &✿ (Lady Mason) Ranby, 4m W of Retford. Entrance on Link Rd from A620 to S bound A1. Medium-sized woodland garden, spring flowers, flowering shrubs, rhododendrons, azaleas, specimen trees; pinetum in park, cedars and cypresses. Picnics. TEAS. *Adm £1.25 per car or 60p per person whichever is the least (Share to Ranby Church). Sun May 31 (2-6)*

◆**Nottinghamshire College of Agriculture** &✿ (Nottinghamshire Education Committee) Brackenhurst, 1m S of Southwell, on A612. Ornamental shrubs, lawns, rose and sunken gardens, walled garden, glasshouses, views. *Adm 60p OAPs 30p Chd 10p (Share to Cancer Research Campaign). Sun July 5 (2-6)*

Old Mill House &✿ (Dr & Mrs E.A. Nicoll) Cuckney. 6m N of Mansfield. On A60 Worksop-Mansfield rd. Bus: 22. In middle of Cuckney. 2 acres. Waterside and bog plants, heather rockeries bordering waterfalls, wild garden and butterfly meadow; over 200 trees, all planted since 1969. TEA. *Adm 60p Chd 20p (Share to Cancer Research Campaign). Suns May 24, Aug 2 (2-6)*

¶**The Old Rectory, Eakring** ✿✿ (Mr & Mrs P. N. Richards) 6m NW of Southwell. 1 acre; attractive rockery, banking, shrubs and herbaceous. TEAS. *Adm 50p Chd 20p. Sun May 3 (2-6)*

The Old Rectory, East Bridgford ✿✿ (Mr & Mrs B.L.C. Dodsworth) 12m NE of Nottingham, 14m SW of Newark. Medium-sized garden. Old trees, herbaceous and shrub borders. Large planting of tall bearded irises, some from USA and many raised by owner (Past President of British Iris Society). Some for sale, if season permits. *Adm 60p Chd 20p (Share to British Iris Society). Sun June 21 (2-4.30)*

The Old Rectory, Staunton ✿ (Mr & Mrs T.W. Readett-Bayley) nr Orston, 7m S of Newark. 1 acre; lawns, trees, shrubs, herbaceous borders. Walks to church and Staunton Hall. TEAS. *Adm 50p Chd/OAPs 25p (Share to Staunton Church). Sun April 26 (2-5.30)*

Paddock House &✿✿ (Mr & Mrs H.J. Davies) Scarrington, nr Bingham, off A46 through Car Colston. N of A52 E of Bingham. Medium-sized garden established since 1978; rare trees, shrubs; conifers and plants of special interest. TEA. *Adm 60p Chd 10p (Share to Imperial Cancer Research Fund). Sun May 3 (2-6)*

St Anne's Manor & (Mr & Mrs C.H.J. Tom) Sutton Bonington, 5m NW of Loughborough; take A6 to Kegworth; turn right (E) onto A6006; 1st left (N) for Sutton Bonington;

right under railway bridge opp The Old Plough. Fair-sized garden with much colour; many interesting plants; shrubs, roses and mixed borders. TEAS Sutton Bonington Hall. *Adm 60p Chd 10p (Share to St Michaels with St Anne Church, Sutton Bonington). Suns May 10, July 12 (2-6)*

St Helen's Croft &✿ (Mrs E. Ninnis) Halam, 2m W of Southwell via The White Post Inn. ½-acre garden; alpine path and trough gardens; mixed borders; silver foliage; flower arranger's plants, shrub roses. Gardeners World 1986, Sunday Express Garden of Month, Sept '85. *Adm 50p Chd 10p Suns May 17, Aug 23, Sep 13 (2-5). Everyday by appt (Tel 0636 813219)*

¶**Silks Cottage** &✿✿ (Mr & Mrs M.J.S. Pearson) Burden Lane, Shelford. 8m from Trent Bridge; A52 to Grantham; 5m left to Radcliffe; in Radcliffe left to Shelford; Burden Lane in middle of Shelford. 1 acre typical cottage garden; good lawns; orchards; pool; climbing plants and summer bedding. TEAS. *Adm 50p Chd 25p (Share to Shelford Church). Sun Jul 19 (10-5)*

Skreton Cottage &✿ (Mr & Mrs J.S. Taylor) Screveton, 8m SW of Newark, 12m E of Nottingham. From A46 Fosse Rd turn E to Car Colston; left at green and on for 1m. Bus: Nottingham-Newark, alight Red Lodge Inn (1m walk). 1¾-acres; established landscaped garden of general interest; set in delightful unspoilt country village; many unusual and interesting plants; large lawns, specimen trees, paved silver garden. TEAS. *Adm 60p Chd 10p (Share to Camphill Village Trust for Mentally Handicapped). Sun June 14 (2-6)*

Sutton Bonington Hall &✿ (Anne, Lady Elton) As for St Anne's Manor. 7 acres with conservatory, formal white garden, variegated leaf borders. Queen Anne house (not open). Picnics. TEAS. *Adm 50p Chd 10p (Share to St Michael's Church, Sutton Bonington) Sun July 12 (2-6)*

Thrumpton Hall & (George Seymour Esq) 8m SW of Nottingham. W of A453; 3m from M1 at Exit 24. Large lawns; massive yew hedges; rare shrubs; C17 larches, cedars, planted to commemorate historic events since George III. Lake. Early Jacobean house shown in 3 parties at 3pm, 4pm & 5pm only. NO DOGS in house. TEAS. *Adm to garden 50p Chd 25p; house £1 extra Chd 50p. △Sun July 5 (2.30-6)*

◆**Welbeck Woodhouse** &✿ (The Lady Anne Bentinck) 4m S of Worksop. Entrance on Worksop-Budby rd, well-marked. Bus: Nottingham-Worksop service; alight Lion gates, 2m. Medium-sized garden; woodland and flowers; lovely views. *Adm 50p Chd 10p. Sun May 31 (2-6)*

The Willows ☪✿❀ (Mr & Mrs R. A. Grout) 5 Rockley Ave, Radcliffe-on-Trent. 6m E of Nottingham; Radcliffe-on-Trent is N of A52; from High st PO turn into Shelford Rd; over railway bridge, 300 yds opp bus shelter turn left into Cliff way, then 2nd right. Designed 1982 62 yds x 12 yds garden; a quart in a pint plot; colour planned island beds; many rare and unusual plants; collections of hostas, hellebores, pulmonarias, snowdrops. TEA. *Adm 50p OAPs/Chd 20p (Share to NCCPG). Weds April 1, May 6, June 3, July 1, Aug 5, Sept 2 (2-6); also by appt (Tel R-on-Trent 3621)*

Winthorpe Gardens nr Newark. Take A46 to Lincoln. Left at roundabout on A1133, in ¼m sign to village. *TEAS* The Grove. *Combined Adm £1.20 Chd 20p. Sun May 24 (2-6)*

  The Grove ☪✿ (Mr & Mrs Peter Thornhill) Main St next to Church gates. Mediumsized old-fashioned garden; spring bulbs, shrubs; conservatory. *(Share to Friends of Newark Hospitals)*

  Fleet Cottage ❀ (Mr & Mrs H.F. Linkie) Holme Lane, 2nd right opp Lord Nelson, then 100 yds on left. Cottage garden with stream. Runner-up Sunday Express Garden of the Year Contest 1986. *(Share to Talking Newspaper for the Blind)*

  Winthorpe House ✿ (Mr & Mrs M. Dolenz) Large garden originally created c.1820. Interesting trees and shrubs. Newly planted with bulbs

OXFORDSHIRE
(including Vale of the White Horse)

Hon County Organisers:
MRS WINSTON FLETCHER, Souldern Mill, Souldern, Bicester OX6 9LB &
(Vale of the White Horse)
MRS R.H. WHITWORTH, Abbey House Farm, Goosey, Faringdon SN7 8PA

Hon County Treasurer:
F.M. BUNBURY ESQ, 4 The Paddocks, Souldern OX6 9LG

DATES OF OPENING

BY APPOINTMENT ONLY for dates see text:
23 BEECH CROFT ROAD, Oxford
REGULAR OPENINGS for dates see text:
KINGSTON BAGPUIZE HOUSE, Kingston Bagpuize
PUSEY HOUSE, nr Faringdon

MARCH Saturday 7
MARTEN'S HALL FARM, Longworth, nr Abingdon
MARCH Saturday & Sunday 28 & 29
MARTEN'S HALL FARM, Longworth, nr Abingdon

APRIL Sunday 5
THE MILL HOUSE, Sutton Courtenay
APRIL Sunday 12
‡THE BAILIFF'S HOUSE, Chippinghurst
BROUGHTON POGGS & FILKINS GARDENS
BUCKLAND, nr Faringdon
KINGSTONE LISLE PARK, nr Wantage
LIME CLOSE, Drayton, nr Abingdon
‡THE MILL HOUSE, Stadhampton
QUARRY BANK HOUSE, nr Tackley
SARSDEN GLEBE, Churchill, nr Chipping Norton
APRIL Easter Saturday 18
FARINGDON HOUSE, Faringdon
APRIL Easter Sunday 19
‡BIGNELL HOUSE, Chesterton
‡CAVERSFIELD HOUSE, nr Bicester
CORNWELL MANOR, Kingham, nr Chipping Norton
FARINGDON HOUSE, Faringdon
WOOTTON PLACE, nr Woodstock
APRIL Easter Monday 20
DRY SANDFORD MANOR, nr Abingdon
APRIL Saturday 25
MARTEN'S HALL FARM, Longworth, nr Abingdon
APRIL Sunday 26
ASHBROOK HOUSE, Blewbury
‡BAMPTON MANOR, WEALD MANOR & BROOK HOUSE
‡‡BROADWELL & KENCOT GARDENS
‡‡CHURCH HOUSE (see Glos)
EPWELL MILL, nr Banbury
LITTLE HASELEY GARDENS, nr Oxford
MARTEN'S HALL FARM, Longworth, nr Abingdon
THE OLD RECTORY, Coleshill
‡‡SOUTHROP GARDENS (see Glos)
‡STANDLAKE GARDENS
WARDINGTON MANOR, nr Banbury
MAY Sunday 3
BARTON ABBEY, Steeple Barton
STANSFIELD, Stanford-in-the-Vale
WESTWELL MANOR, nr Burford
MAY Monday 4 (Bank Hol)
‡DENTON HOUSE, nr Oxford
‡GARSINGTON MANOR, nr Oxford
MAY Sunday 10
‡CHECKENDON COURT, nr Henley-on-Thames
‡‡EAST HANNEY GARDENS, nr Wantage
‡GREYSTONE COTTAGE, Kingwood Common
KINGSTON BAGPUIZE HOUSE, Kingston Bagpuize
‡‡THE MANOR HOUSE, Sutton Courtenay
WHEATLEY GARDENS
MAY Saturday 16
MARTENS HALL FARM, Longworth, nr Abingdon
MAY Sunday 17
MARTENS HALL FARM, Longworth, nr Abingdon
SHOTOVER HOUSE, Wheatley
WESTON-ON-THE-GREEN GARDENS

MAY Sunday 24
SILVER TREES, Kennington & WOOD
CROFT, Boar's Hill, Oxford
WROXTON ABBEY, nr Banbury &
LAURELS FARM, Wroxton, nr Banbury
MAY Monday 25 (Bank Hol)
WROXTON ABBEY, nr Banbury &
LAURELS FARM, Wroxton, nr Banbury
MAY Wednesday 27
BROADWELL HOUSE, nr Lechlade
MAY Saturday 30
MARTENS HALL FARM, Longworth, nr
Abingdon
MAY Sunday 31
ADWELL HOUSE, nr Tetsworth
‡CHACOMBE GARDENS (see Northants)
EPWELL MILL, nr Banbury
THE MALT HOUSE, Henley
MARTEN'S HALL FARM, Longworth, nr
Abingdon
‡WARDINGTON MANOR, nr Banbury
WILCOTE HOUSE, nr Charlbury
JUNE Saturday 6
BROOK COTTAGE & ALKERTON HOUSE,
nr Banbury
JUNE Sunday 7
‡BALSCOTE GARDENS, nr Banbury
‡BROOK COTTAGE & ALKERTON HOUSE,
nr Banbury
STANSFIELD, Stanford-in-the-Vale
WATERPERRY GARDENS
JUNE Thursday 11
PUSEY HOUSE, nr Faringdon
JUNE Saturday 13
HILL COURT, Tackley
JUNE Sunday 14
HILL COURT, Tackley
LITTLE HASELEY GARDENS
JUNE Tuesday 16
CORNWELL MANOR, Kingham, nr
Chipping Norton
JUNE Saturday 20
EPWELL MILL, nr Banbury (Evening)
TADMARTON GARDENS
JUNE Sunday 21
BLADON GARDENS, nr Woodstock
BUSCOT PARK, nr Faringdon
THE GRANGE, Bampton
GREAT HASELEY GARDENS, nr Oxford &
OLD BELCHERS FARM, Great Milton
‡HERON'S REACH, Whitchurch
‡‡HOOK NORTON GARDENS
KINGSTONE LISLE PARK, nr Wantage
MOUNT SKIPPET, Ramsden
OLD INN COTTAGE, Piddington
‡QUERNS & PILGRIM COTTAGE, Goring
Heath
‡‡TADMARTON GARDENS, nr Banbury
JUNE Wednesday 24
BROADWELL HOUSE, nr Lechlade
BROUGHTON CASTLE, nr Banbury
CORNWELL MANOR, Kingham, nr
Chipping Nortn
JUNE Sunday 28
ADDERBURY GARDENS, nr Banbury

BEAUFOREST HOUSE, Newington, nr
Stadhampton
‡BRILL GARDENS (see Bucks)
DRY SANDFORD MANOR, nr Abingdon
EAST HAGBOURNE GARDENS, Didcot
‡‡THE GRANGE & PROSPECT HOUSE,
Bampton
HAUGH HOUSE, Longworth, nr Abingdon
‡‡LANGFORD GARDENS, nr Lechlade
‡‡MANOR FARM, Old Minster Lovell
‡OLD INN COTTAGE, Piddington
JULY Thursday 2
CORNWELL MANOR, Kingham, nr
Chipping Norton
JULY Saturday 4
BROOK COTTAGE & ALKERTON HOUSE,
nr Banbury
JULY Sunday 5
ADWELL HOUSE, nr Tetsworth
‡BROADWELL & KENCOT GARDENS, nr
Lechlade
‡‡BROOK COTTAGE, ALKERTON HOUSE
& LAURELS FARM, nr Banbury
CAVERSFIELD HOUSE, nr Bicester
THE CLOCK HOUSE, Coleshill
‡FULBROOK GARDENS, nr Burford
GREAT ROLLRIGHT GARDENS, nr
Chipping Norton
HANSTEAD, East Hanney
‡‡IVY LODGE (see Warwicks)
WILCOTE HOUSE, nr Charlbury
JULY Saturday 11
DEDDINGTON, MOLLINGTON &
SOULDERN 'BEST KEPT' PRIZEWINNERS
GROUP, nr Banbury
THE OLD POST OFFICE, Chastleton
JULY Sunday 12
‡AYNHO & CHARLTON GARDENS (see
Northants)
‡DEDDINGTON, MOLLINGTON &
SOULDERN 'BEST KEPT' PRIZEWINNERS
GROUP, nr Banbury
GREEN COLLEGE & ST HUGH'S, Oxford
HERON'S REACH, Whitchurch
MARNDHILL, nr Wantage
‡‡THE OLD POST OFFICE, Chastleton
‡SALFORD GARDENS, nr Chipping Norton
SWINBROOK GARDENS, nr Burford
‡‡WINDY RIDGE (see Glos)
JULY Saturday 18
GREYS COURT, Rotherfield Greys
JULY Sunday 19
‡BROUGHTON CASTLE, nr Banbury
‡BUDDLEIA COTTAGE, Wigginton, nr
Banbury
LADY MARGARET HALL, Oxford
‡‡SHIPTON-UNDER-WYCHWOOD
GARDENS
‡SPARROW HALL, Swalcliffe, nr Banbury
‡STONEWALLS, Hempton, nr Deddington
‡‡WESTWELL MANOR, nr Burford
WHITE'S FARM HOUSE, Letcombe
Bassett, nr Wantage
JULY Sunday 26
NEW, THE QUEEN'S & WADHAM
COLLEGES, Oxford

AUGUST Saturday 1
MARTEN'S HALL FARM, Longworth, nr Abingdon
AUGUST Sunday 2
BARTON ABBEY, Steeple Barton
THE COACH HOUSE, Wallingford
MARTEN'S HALL FARM, Longworth, nr Abingdon
STANSFIELD, Stanford-in-the-Vale
AUGUST Sunday 9
SARSDEN HOUSE, Churchill
WATERPERRY GARDENS, nr Wheatley
AUGUST Sunday 16
WARDINGTON MANOR, nr Banbury
AUGUST Sunday 23
CHRIST CHURCH & MERTON COLLEGES, Oxford
COLEGRAVE SEEDS, Adderbury, nr Banbury
AUGUST Wednesday 26
BROADWELL HOUSE, nr Lechlade
AUGUST Saturday 29
BLENHEIM PALACE, Woodstock
AUGUST Sunday 30
BLENHEIM PALACE, Woodstock
AUGUST Monday 31 (Bank Hol)
‡HOME FARM, Balscote
‡WROXTON ABBEY, nr Banbury
SEPTEMBER Saturday 5
HIGHMOOR HALL, Nettlebed
SEPTEMBER Sunday 6
CHASTLETON GLEBE, nr Moreton-in-Marsh
KIDLINGTON GARDENS, Oxford
STANSFIELD, Stanford-in-the-Vale
SEPTEMBER Saturday 12
MARTEN'S HALL FARM, Longworth, nr Abingdon
SEPTEMBER Sunday 13
EVELEGH'S, Long Wittenham & LITTLE PLACE, Clifton Hampden
KIDDINGTON HALL, nr Woodstock
MARTEN'S HALL FARM, Longworth, nr Abingdon
SEPTEMBER Sunday 20
BROADWELL & KENCOT GARDENS, nr Lechlade
THE CLOCK HOUSE & OLD RECTORY, Coleshill
ELSFIELD GARDENS, nr Oxford
‡EPWELL MILL, nr Banbury
‡TADMARTON GARDENS, nr Banbury
SEPTEMBER Saturday 26
HOOK NORTON MANOR,
SEPTEMBER Sunday 27
GARSINGTON MANOR, nr Oxford
HOOK NORTON MANOR
OCTOBER Sunday 4
CAVERSFIELD HOUSE, nr Bicester
THE MILL HOUSE, Sutton Courtenay
ST CATHERINE'S COLLEGE, Oxford
OCTOBER Saturday 10
MARTEN'S HALL FARM, Longworth, nr Abingdon

OCTOBER Sunday 11
MARTEN'S HALL FARM, Longworth, nr Abingdon
NUNEHAM PARK, nr Nuneham Courtney
OCTOBER Saturday 17 & Sunday 18
BROOK COTTAGE & ALKERTON HOUSE, nr Banbury

DESCRIPTIONS OF GARDENS

Adderbury Gardens ⚹ On A423 at A41, 4m S of Banbury. TEAS at Sorbrook Manor. *Combined adm £1 Chd free (Share to DGAA). Sun June 28 (2-6)*
Central Adderbury
    ¶**Ivy House** (Miss E. Suter) 1½-acre old walled garden under restoration; paddock; pond. House (not open) dates from early C17
    The Old Mill House (A. Spencer Esq) Old garden on different levels divided by hedges and specimen trees. Species roses; mill pond
East Adderbury - (E of A423)
    ¶**Fleet Farm House** (Mr & Mrs R.P. Bratt) Cottage garden with herbaceous borders, roses, vegetables, fruit. Farmyard with container plants
    ¶**Longwall House** (Lt-Col & Mrs E.H. Hadfield) 1-acre old-established walled garden with roses, evergreens, yew hedges, large trees. Inner garden set in walled courtyard, the whole formerly stable area for Adderbury House
West Adderbury
    ¶**Crosshill House** (Mr & Mrs Gurth Hoyer Millar) 4 acres classic Victorian walled gardens around stone Georgian house (not open)
    ¶**Sorbrook Manor** (Mr & Mrs R. Thistlethwayte) 3 acres lawns with mature trees and young shrubs, leading down to bridge over Sorbrook

Adwell House ᕕ (Mr & Mrs W.R.A. Birch Reynardson) Tetsworth, 4m SW of Thame. From London leave M40 at exit 6, turn left in Lewknor. From Oxford A40, turn right in Tetsworth. Roses, formal and water garden, ornamental lakes, fine trees, lawns; new tree and shrub planting. TEAS. *Adm 60p Chd free (Share to St Mary's Church PCC). Suns May 31, July 5 (2.30-6.30)*

Ashbrook House ᕕ (Mr & Mrs S.A. Barrett) Blewbury. 4m SE of Didcot on A417; 3½-acre chalk garden with small lake, stream, Spring bulbs. TEAS Lantern Cafe. *Adm 50p Chd free. Sun April 26 (2-6)*

¶**The Bailiff's House** ⚹ (Mr & Mrs J. Noon) Chippinghurst 5m SE of Oxford, off B 480 Cowley-Stadhampton. 1¾-acres; woodland and orchard carpeted with many varieties of spring bulbs surround a formal garden framed by pergolas. TEAS at Mill House,

Stadhampton. *Adm 50p or 80p with The Mill House Chd free. Sun April 12 (2-5.30)*

¶**Balscote Gardens** ✗※ Pretty hill village ½-m off A422 5m W of Banbury. C14 church parking edge of green. Houses not open. TEAS Brook Cottage, Alkerton. *Combined adm 60p or 40p each garden Chd free (Share to St Mary Magdelene Church). Sun June 7 (2-6). (Home Farm also open Mon Aug 31 (2-5.30). TEAS Wroxton Abbey)*

> **Home Farm** (Mr & Mrs Godfrey Royle) C17 house and barn in ½-acre plant-lover's elevated garden re-designed since 1984 for year-round interest with contrasting foliage flowering shrubs, alpines, bulbs, young trees. Attractive views
> **Homeland** (Dr & Mrs J.S. Rivers) ¾-acre developed since 1982 with shrubs, roses, perennials and rock garden, inc field adjacent to church, newly planted with trees

Bampton Gardens Group 1 ⅙ On A4095 Witney/Faringdon rd. TEAS Weald Manor. *Combined adm £1.20 Chd free. Sun April 26 (2.30-5.30)*

> **Bampton Manor** ※ (Earl & Countess of Donoughmore) Medium-sized garden; interesting layout; good trees; Spring garden; *(Share to Dr Clarke Memorial Fund for Kidney Transplant Research)*
> **Brook House** ✗ (Mr & Mrs K.S. Hollebone) Bridge St. Small riverside garden, interesting design, laid out 1982 after conversion of three C18 cottages; Spring bulbs
> **Weald Manor** (Maj & Mrs R.A. Colvile) Medium-sized old garden with many daffodils; fine trees; small lake *(Share to Lord Robert's Workshop)*

Bampton Gardens Group 2 ⅙✗ On A4095. TEAS The Grange. *Combined adm 80p or 50p each Chd free. Suns June 21, 28 (2-6)*

> **The Grange** ※ (Mrs R. Johnston and Mr & Mrs P. Taylor). Large garden, beautiful trees, borders, walled kitchen garden, pond
> **Prospect House** (Mr & Mrs D. Baughan) Small walled garden of Regency House; shrubs, mature trees, herbaceous plants; small pond. *Sun June 28 only*

Barton Abbey ⅙ (Mrs P.Fleming) On B4030; 1m Middle Barton; ½m from junc of A423 and B4030. 4 acres lawns; 3 acres of lake; fine trees; kitchen garden and glasshouses; Shetland pony stud and prize rosette display. Picnics permitted. TEAS in aid of Katharine House Hospice. *Adm 60p Chd free. Suns May 3, Aug 2 (2-6)*

Beauforest House ⅙ (Sir John & Lady Rothenstein) Newington on A329 SW of Oxford. 3½ acres; lawns sloping to R. Thame. Pergola with grapevine, pillars and urns, nut walk; one small formal garden gives struc-ture to free planting elsewhere. Old fashioned roses interplanted with other subjects to enhance colour; some rare trees; orchard. Garden flanked by C11 to C14 Church. Views over farmland to Berkshire downs. Riverine wild flowers. C16-C18 house (not open). TEAS and parking Newington House, C17 house/garden in process of restoration. *Adm 70p Chd free. Sun June 28 (2-6)*

23 Beech Croft Road ✗ (Mrs Anne Dexter) Oxford. A 23 yd by 7 yd, south-facing plant lover's, paved garden of a terraced house has been made secluded by planting evergreen shrubs, roses and clematis all round the brick walls; the 2 herbaceous, 2 alpine, 2 shady beds all contain many unusual plants, shrubs, ferns, troughs filled with small alpines. NO push-chairs. *Adm £1. By appt only April to Sept 30 (Tel Oxford 56020)*

Bignell House ⅙ (Mr & Mrs P.J. Gordon) On A4095 2m SW Bicester. 16-acre traditional English country house garden; lawns leading to lake system with rock pool, stone arches, bridge to daffodil island; fine mature trees inc Wellingtonia and Spruce; aconites, primroses, variety of wild species, woodland plants. House (not open) designed by Wm Wilkinson mid C19 (one wing only remains). Stall in aid of Guide Dogs. TEAS. *Adm 50p Chd free (Share to Guide Dogs for the Blind). Sun April 19 (2-6)*

Bladon Gardens ✗ On A4095, 2m Woodstock, 8m Witney. Within easy walking distance centred on Church. Car parking in school yard and official village CP. TEAS. *Combined adm £1 Chd free (Share to Cancer & Leukaemia in Childhood). Sun June 21 (2-6)*

> **Brackenwood** ※ (Mr & Mrs N. M. Earl) Landscaped 1½ acres including woodland. Large variety of trees, shrubs, roses and perennials
> **4 Grove Road** (Mrs M. E. Gordon) Small enclosed garden started 1981. Planned for easy maintenance in retirement
> **16 Park Street** (Mrs G. L. Chilton) Small cottage garden with shrubs and herbaceous planting
> **Rannoch Lodge** (Miss S. Menzies) ¼-acre with shrubs, roses and perennials
> **Rectory Farm House** (R. L. Murdock Esq) ⅓ acre old farmhouse garden, derelict in 1979. No special features but shows what can be done by an enthusiastic albeit not very knowledgeable amateur
> **Westbury House** (Dr & Mrs Philip Glazer) Medium-sized garden with mixed shrub and herbaceous planting

♦**Blenheim Palace** ⅙※ (His Grace the Duke of Marlborough) Woodstock, 8m N of Oxford. Bus: 44 Oxford/Chipping- Norton/Stratford, alight Woodstock. Original grounds and garden plan by Henry Wise. Park landscaped and lake created by 'Capability' Brown in late C18. Plant Centre open daily all year; Butterfly House (10-6); Cafeteria; Adventure Play Area; Palace open daily mid-March to Oct 31 (11-6 last adm 5) *Adm charge not available on going to press. For NGS Sat, Sun Aug 29, 30*

Broadwell & Kencot Gardens &♨ ❀ 5m NE Lechlade, E of A361 Lechlade-Burford. 2 charming adjoining Cotswold villages both with interesting churches. TEAS. *Combined adm £1.20 Chd free (Share to Broadwell Church Fund, RSPB) Suns April 26, July 5, Sept 20 (2-6)*

   Broadwell House (Brigadier & Mrs Charles Cox) 2-acre garden; wellingtonia, ginkgo, magnolias, cherries, topiary, maples; aralias and other shrubs of interest; many grey-leaved and variegated plants, several rare plants. Listed house and old barn

   Broadwell Manor (F.R. Goodenough Esq) ¾-acre garden with 1-acre water, 3 islands and lake of historic interest, older than house (house listed 1803) *(Only open April 26)*

   Broadwell Old Manor (Mr & Mrs Michael Chinnery) Old fashioned ½-acre walled garden with spring, herbaceous and shrub borders; courtyard and topiary garden. Listed house. *(Only open April 26, July 5)*

   The Gardens Cottage (Lt-Col & Mrs John Barstow) ¼-acre cottage garden featuring spring bulbs, iris, roses, rock plants, old apple trees and a well

   Ivynook (Mr & Mrs Bill Gasson) Cottage garden; rockeries, lawns, mixed borders. *(Only open April 26, July 5)*

   Kencot Cottage (Mrs Molly Foster) Very small garden with spring bulbs and bedding, also Bonsai trees

   Kencot House (Mr & Mrs Andrew Patrick) 2-acre garden with lawns, trees, borders; quantities of daffodils and other spring bulbs; notable ginkgo tree. Also interesting carved C13 archway

   Manor Farm (Lt-Cdr & Mrs R.H. Fyson) 2-acre garden with lawns; spring bulbs in rough grass; fritillaries a speciality; clipped yew bushes a feature, newly constructed rockery and small pond; C17 farmhouse, listed building (only open April 26, July 5)

   The Old Rectory (Mr & Mrs Alan Lamburn) 1-acre family garden with lawns, trees and bulbs

Broadwell House &♨❀ (Brigadier & Mrs Charles Cox) 5m NE of Lechlade, E of A361 Lechlade-Burford. 2-acre garden; wellingtonia, ginkgo, magnolias, cherries, topiary, maples, aralias and other shrubs of interest. Many greyleaved and variegated plants, several rare plants; Listed house and old barn. *Adm 50p Chd free Parties by prior appt.*

Weds May 27, June 24, Aug 26; Suns April 26, June 28, Sept 20 (2-6)

Brook Cottage ❀ (Mr & Mrs David Hodges) Alkerton, 6m W of Banbury. From A422, Banbury-Stratford; turn W at sign to Alkerton, left opp Alkerton War Memorial. 4 acres, mostly formed since 1964, surrounding C17 house (not open); bulbs, shrubs, collection shrub roses, many clematis, alpine garden made 1985, water garden, white, yellow borders. Local crafts stall. TEAS (on dates shown below and for parties by prior arrangement); also Ploughman's lunch in Oct only. Also open ¶**Alkerton House** with 2½ acres of newly planted trees, shrubs and conifers. *Adm £1 or 70p Brook Cottage only, Chd free (Share to Shenington with Alkerton VHF). Sats, Suns June 6, 7; July 4, 5 (2-7); Oct 17, 18 (11-6); also by appt April 1 to Oct 31 (Tel Edge Hill 303 or 590)*

♦**Broughton Castle** &❀ (Lord Saye & Sele) 2½m W of Banbury on Shipston-on-Stour rd (B4035). 1-acre shrub, herbaceous borders, walled garden, roses, climbers seen against background of C13-C16 castle surrounded by moat in open parkland. House also open, extra charge. TEAS. *Adm 70p Chd 30p. Wed June 24, Sun July 19 (2-5)*

Broughton Poggs & Filkins Gardens. Enchanting limestone villages between Burford and Lechlade, just E of A36l. A number of gardens varying in size from traditional cottage garden to over 2 acres, growing wide variety of plants. TEA. *Combined adm £1 Chd free. Tickets from The Court House, Broughton Hall or Little Peacocks (Share to Broughton & Filkins Church Funds). Sun April 12 (2-6)*

Broughton Poggs:
   Broughton Hall (Mr & Mrs C.B.S.Dobson)
   Corner Cottage (Mr & Mrs E. Stephenson)
   The Court House (Richard Burls Esq)
   The Old Rectory (Mrs E.Wansborough)
   Rectory Cottage (Mrs S. Dore)
Filkins:
   Barn Corner (Mrs C. Ede)
   Cotswold (G.Swinford Esq who celebrates his 100th birthday this year)
   Fox House (Sir John & Lady Cripps)
   Little Peacocks (Colvin & Moggridge, Landscape Consultants)
   ¶**St Peter House** (J.Cambridge Esq)

Buckland ❀ (Mrs Richard Wellesley) NE of Faringdon. Turn N off A420 at Buckland Xrds. Bus: 66 Oxford-Swindon, 67 Oxford-Faringdon, alight Buckland Xrds. Beautiful lakeside walk; fine trees; daffodils, shrubs. Norman church adjoins garden. TEA. *Adm 75p Chd 40p. Sun May 5 (2-7)*

Buddleia Cottage ♨ (Miss M.J. Bartlett) Wigginton. 6m SW Banbury, 1m W A361 Banbury-Chipping Norton. Small plantsman's garden with all-year interest, ground cover plants to minimise work; scented shrubs, climbers, bulbs, alpines. Unsuitable for wheel and pushchairs. *Adm 40p Chd free. Sun July 19 (2-6)*

Buscot Park &⚘❀ (Lord Faringdon; The National Trust) Buscot. 2½m W of Faringdon on A417 ½-way between Faringdon and Lechlade. Beautiful grounds, ornamental trees; lake and water gardens; newly planted walled garden with theme of The Four Seasons. House not open this date. Tearooms. *Adm garden only £1 Chd 50p. △Sun June 21 (2-6)*

Caversfield House &❀ (Maj & Mrs H.W.O. Bradley) 2m N of Bicester on A41. Spacious lawns, good trees, orchard, flowering shrubs, seasonal bedding; marvellous daffodils; woodland walk around lake; interesting statuary. Church (part C10) in grounds. TEAS. *Adm 75p Chd free (Share to St Lawrence Church) Suns April 19, July 5, Oct 4 (2-6)*

Chastleton Glebe &⚘❀ (Mr & Mrs C.R. Kruger) 3m SE of Moreton-in-Marsh. From Chipping Norton W on A44, turn L to Chastleton, right at T-junc, 1m. From M-in-Marsh: E on A44 right after 3m. 5 acres; old trees; terraces (one all red); small lake, island; chinese-style bridge, pagoda; formal vegetable garden; Cotswold house (not open); views. TEAS. *Adm 70p Chd free (Share to Chastleton Church Fund). Sun Sept 6 (2-6)*

Checkendon Court &⚘ (Sir Nigel & Lady Broackes) Checkendon, NW of Reading. 2m NE of Woodcote on B479 nr Checkendon church. 4 acres, attractively laid out with yew hedges, large herbaceous borders, roses, kitchen garden; the whole backed by beech woods. *Adm 50p Chd free. Sun May 10 (2-5) TEAS at Greystone Cottage*

Clock House ❀ (Michael & Denny Wickham) Coleshill, 3½m SW of Faringdon on N of B4019. Garden at top of village. Planted around site of Coleshill House, which was burnt down in the 50's; walled herb garden in old laundry drying ground; old fashioned roses, vegetables; good views across Vale of the White Horse and parkland. TEAS. *Adm 50p Chd free. Suns July 5 (2-6), Sept 20 (2-5)*

The Coach House &❀ (Lady Hedges) Wallingford. In Castle St 150 yds from traffic lights on Rd from Shillingford, N of Lamb Xrds. Public car park in Wallingford. ½-acre minimum-maintenance garden adjoining public garden (open free with band concert and refreshments). *Adm 40p Chd 10p. Sun Aug 2 (2.15-5.30)*

Colegrave Seeds Ltd &⚘ Milton Rd, West Adderbury 3m S of Banbury. Turn off A423 Banbury-Oxford at sign Milton/Bloxham. Trial grounds ½m on right. 3-acres; flower seed trial grounds comprising over 1,500 rows of summer-flowering annuals and perennials; many new items under trial prior to introduction, inc Fleuroselect Award winners; a festival of colour unique in Oxfordshire. (Note strictly wholesale; no retail sales or enquiries.) Parking for 200 cars. TEAS in aid of Milton Parish Church. *Adm £1 Chd free. Sun Aug 23 (2-5.30)*

Cornwell Manor ⚘❀ (The Hon Mrs Peter Ward) Kingham 3m. Turn S off A44 2m W of Chipping Norton. A plantsman's garden of 9 acres with formal terrace adjacent to listed C17 manor house (not open); rock and water gardens leading to woodland areas and lakes; spring garden; fine specimen trees, spring bulbs, many unusual plants. 1¼-acre walled kitchen garden mainly under organic cultivation. C12 Church. Large free car-park. Parties by appt June & July. TEA. *Adm £1 (April) 80p (June & July) Chd free (Share to St Peter's Church, July 2). Sun April 19 (2-6), Tues June 16, Wed June 24, Thurs July 2 (11-5)*

Deddington Gardens ⚘ 6m S of Banbury 17m N of Oxford on A423. 3 small gardens in old stone village, winner of 'Best Kept' competition. Fine C13-C19 church. TEAS in aid of church. *Adm £1.40 inc gardens in 'Best Kept' prizewinning villages, Mollington and Souldern, Chd free. Sat, Sun July 11, 12 (2-6)*
  Castle End & (Mr & Mrs F.J. Robins) Roses, many old species, surrounding C15-17 house
  Glencree (Canon J.H. & Mrs Wilson) New stone house in ⅓-acre old walled garden completely renovated since 1980; sunken and rock garden; roses, shrubs, annuals
  The Old Malt House & (Sir Brian & Lady Kellett) ⅓-acre walled garden, replanned and replanted in 1979; wall vine, variety of shrubs, herbaceous plants, roses; small vegetable garden

Denton House ⚘ (Mr & Mrs J. Luke) Denton SE of Oxford, 1m E of Garsington between A40 and B480. 3-acre walled garden; large lawns; many mature trees and shrubs; spring bulbs inc fritillaria; wild garden; walled vegetable garden; interesting stable yard. Gothic windows from Brazenose Chapel in high stone wall surrounding garden. Pony rides. TEAS in aid of Cuddesdon Church and Village Hall. *Adm 50p Chd free. Mon May 4 (2-6)*

Dry Sandford Manor &⚘ (Mr David & Lady Daphne Bailey) Dry Sandford 3m NW of Abingdon, off A420 at Frilford or A34 nr Abingdon airport. 3½-acre walled garden; borders, shrubs, unusual plants; large old fashioned shrub rose garden; herbs, 3-acre woodland garden; lake; bulbs. TEAS. *Adm 70p Chd 10p (Share to DGAA & Dry Sandford Church). Mon April 20, Sun June 28 (2-6)*

¶**East Hagbourne Gardens** &⚘❀ 1½m SE of Didcot. 6 gardens in exceptionally pretty vil-

lage. A brook flows through village street and several gardens. Medieval cross and C11-12 church with C14 stained glass, flower arrangements. Renowned bellringers viewable 5.30 till Evensong at 6. Small display of exotic plants. No houses open. TEAS. *Combined adm £1.20 Chd free. Sun June 28 (2-7)*
> **Buckels** (Rear Adm & Mrs Jamieson) ⅓-acre of colourful, partially walled garden on several levels. House (1605) once village bakery
> **1 Church Close** (Mr & Mrs N.V. Linklater) ¼-acre, very much a cottage garden. Small greenhouse with cactus collection. Elizabethan house once 3 cottages
> **Kingsholm** (Mr & Mrs J. Lawson) ¾-acre with fine English and Irish yews and topiary in box and yew. Herbaceous and shrub borders, short nut walk
> **Lime Tree Farm** (Mr & Mrs J.Dixon) 2 ½-acres; mixed shrub, rose and herbaceous borders in attractive setting of trees, with path leading across stream to orchard. Old barns and partly C17 farmhouse
> **Manor Farm** (Mr & Mrs R.W.Harries) Water surrounds the main house in the form of a moat and full use has been made of this feature. 2-acres includes swimming pool with pergola
> **Parsonage Farm** (Sir John & Lady Lucas Tooth) 2-acres lawns, old shrub roses, mixed borders. Early C18 house

East Hanney Gardens ᯑ᪥❀ 4m N of Wantage, signs on village rds W of A338. TEAS. *Combined adm £1 Chd free. Sun May 10 (2-6)*
> **The Grange & Grange Cottage** ᯑ (Dr & Mrs Scott Russell) 2 acres, old stone walls, hedges, trees, shrubs, herbaceous plants, bulbs
> **Hansteads** ᯑ (Mr & Mrs M. B. Sarson) 1 acre; largely developed since 1982 with ornamental trees, shrubs, old roses, herbaceous plants, bulbs; *also open Sun July 5*
> **Rose Cottage** (Mr & Mrs S. Cox) ⅕-acre cottage garden, recently planted with trees, shrubs, roses, flower borders

Elsfield Gardens ᯑ᪥❀ 5m N of Oxford. A40 flyover signed for Marston and Elsfield then right fork for Elsfield. TEAS. *Combined adm 60p Chd free. Sun Sept 20 (2-6)*
> **Hill Farm** (Mr & Mrs J. Garson) Mixed borders, shrubs, trees; good view of Oxford
> **Sescut Farm** (Mr & Mrs D. Brown) Farmhouse garden with autumn colour in shrub borders

Epwell Mill ❀ (R. A. Withers Esq) Epwell, 7m W of Banbury, between Shutford and Epwell. Medium-sized garden, interestingly landscaped in open country based on disused water-mill; terraced pools; bulbs; azaleas. TEAS & Banbury cakes. *Adm 50p Chd free (Share to Epwell Church Restoration Fund).*

Suns April 26; May 31; Sept 20 (2-6); also Sat June 20, see following entry

Epwell Mill (R. A. Withers Esq) For directions and description see previous entry. MIDSUMMER WINE & CHEESE PARTY IN FLOODLIT GARDEN 9 pm-midnight. *Adm £1.50 (inc glass of wine). Sat June 20*

Evelegh's ᯑ᪥ (Mr & Mrs John H. Rose) High St, Long Wittenham. 4m NE of Didcot. From A415 turn S at Clifton Hampden or N from B4016 to Long Wittenham. Long narrow 1 acre garden leading to backwater of R. Thames. Character changes from borders to informal woodland by river. Interesting plantings; herbaceous, shrubs, roses, alpines in scree, annuals to give long season of colour. TEAS Little Place. *Adm 60p Chd free; or Combined adm Little Place 80p Chd free. Sun Sept 13 (2-6)*

Faringdon House ᯑ᪥ (R. Heber-Percy Esq) Faringdon. Medium-sized garden; bulbs; park; lake, orangery; fine trees. Adjoining church. Tea market place. *Adm 30p (Share to Faringdon Folly Tower Trust). Sat, Sun April 18, 19 (2-6)*

Fulbrook Gardens ᪥ ½m N of Burford on A361. 5 gardens in unspoilt Cotswold village within walking distance of C12 church. TEAS at Pytts House. *Combined adm £1 Chd free (Share to Fulbrook Church Bells and Parish Amenities). Sun July 5 (2-6)*
> **Dolphin Cottage** (Mrs D. Williams) Cottage garden near church with brilliantly colourful planting; roses
> **The Knoll** (Mr & Mrs J. Thomson) 1-acre family garden near church
> ¶**The Manor House** (Mr & Mrs A. McLintock) Westhall Hill. Tudor farmhouse (not open). Walled garden in beautiful setting
> **Pytts House** (Mr & Mrs K.P. Murfitt) ½-acre established walled garden of C16 stone house (not open) near church with shrub roses, alpines in troughs and clematis
> ¶**Swallows' Turn** (Mr & Mrs S. Thomas) Upper End. Mature trees in garden created in past 5 yrs; interplanted stone terrace with herb wheel; herbaceous and shrub borders

Garsington Manor (Mr & Mrs L. Ingrams) SE of Oxford N of B480 House C16 of architectural interest (not open). Monastic fish ponds, water garden, dovecot c.1700; flower parterre and Italian garden laid out by Philip and Lady Ottoline Morell; fine trees and yew hedges. TEAS. *Adm £1 Chd free. Mon May 4, Sun Sept 27 (2-6) free car park*

Great Haseley Gardens Off A329 Thame/Stadhampton. From London M40 exit 7; from Oxford turn off A40 at fork for Milton Common. TEAS Old Belchers Farm. *Combined adm 60p Chd free. Sun June 21 (2-6)*

Crucks &⚘ (Mrs Leonard Barnes) ⅓ acre walled garden designed in 1958 around C15 cottage; roses, clematis, shrubs, altroemeria ligtu hybrids; pretty summer house
¶**The Old School House** (Mr & Mrs J.F.X. Harriott) Unusual, still maturing, 1-acre year round quarry garden; formal and wild areas with interesting variety of trees and shrubs. 'Deep bed' vegetable garden; small orchard. Mrs Harriot (Shirley du Boulay) wrote *'The Gardeners'*, biographies of garden experts

Great Rollright Gardens &⚘ 3m N of Chipping Norton, off A34 or A361. TEAS in aid of St Andrews Church Restoration Fund. *Adm £1 Chd free. Sun July 5 (2-6)*
¶**Brasenose Cottage** (Mr & Mrs T.J. Kirk) Walled garden with herbaceous plants and mature trees with cottage garden leading off; vegetable garden
Great Rollright Manor (Mr & Mrs K. Seel) Lawns surrounded by trees and shrubs leading to small lake; walled kitchen garden
¶**The Old Beer House** (Mr & Mrs P.J. Reed) ½-acre village garden with small knot garden and conservatory
¶**Rectory Cottage** (Mrs J. Lawrence) ¼ acre of C17 cottage. Sheltered, S-facing, divided by trellis. Small woodland garden; pond. Art exhibition in barn
¶**The Old Rectory** (Mr Michael & Lady Joanna Stourton) 3 acres with beautiful views to south. Herbaceous border, lawns, rose garden; tree walk; water garden with brook, small lake; many specimen trees

¶**Green College** ⚘ (University of Oxford) Woodstock Rd, next to Radcliffe Infirmary. 3 acres. Lawns; herbaceous borders; medicinal garden with notes on traditional usage of plants. Radcliffe Observatory (Tower of the Winds) open for views of Oxford and TEAS. *Adm 80p OAPs 50p Chd free (inc observatory). Sun July 12 (2-6)*

Greys Court &⚘ (Lady Brunner; The National Trust) Rotherfield Greys, 3m NW of Henley-on-Thames on rd to Peppard. 8 acres largely enclosed amongst ruined walls and buildings of original fortified manor. Rose, cherry, white wisteria; lawns; maze and kitchen gardens. Jacobean house open with C18 alterations on site of original C13 house fortified by Lord Grey in C14. Donkey wheel and tower. Henley Town Band playing. NO DOGS except guide dogs. TEAS. *Adm garden £1.30 Chd 65p House 50p extra, Chd 25p extra. △Sat July 18 (2-6 last adm 5.30)*

Greystone Cottage &⚘❋ (Mr & Mrs W. Roxburgh) Colmore Lane, Kingwood Common. Between B481 Nettlebed-Reading rd and Sonning Common-Stoke rd; turn N at 'Un-

icorn'. 2 acres backed by beechwoods. Shrubs, old-fashioned roses, pinks, primulas. Woodland with azaleas, camellias, bilberries, blueberries. 60 yr-old arched pear tree walk. Small pools, sink gardens. TEAS. *Adm 50p Chd free. Sun May 10 (2-6.30)*

Hansteads ⚘ (Mr & Mrs M.B. Sarson) East Hanney. 4m N of Wantage on A338; follow signs on 2 village rds W of A338 to garden. 3 acre garden largely developed since 1982; ornamental trees; shrubs; old roses and bulbs. NO DOGS. *Adm 40p Chd free. Sun July 5 (2-6)*

Haugh House (Mrs David Faulkner) Church Road, Longworth. 7m Abingdon. Turn off A420 at Southmoor. 2 acres, old shrub roses, mixed borders. TEAS. (Share to St Marys Church, Longworth). *Adm 50p Chd free. Sun June 28 (2-5)*

Heron's Reach ❋ (Mr & Mrs Bernard Vorhaus) Eastfield Lane, Whitchurch. From Pangbourne take tollbridge rd over Thames to Whitchurch; at 'Greyhound'-turn right into Eastfield Lane. 1 acre in beautiful Thamesside setting with views to the Chiltern hills; woodland garden with pond, shrubs and herbaceous borders. TEA. *Adm 50p or £1 combined with Querns & Pilgrim Cottage Chd free. Suns June 21 July 12 (2-6)*

¶**Highmoor Hall** ⚘❋ (Mr & Mrs P.D. Persson) 6m NW of Henley-on-Thames. At Nettlebed take B481 to Reading; 1m on right. 6 acres. Varied collection of trees and shrubs; herbaceous borders, newly landscaped secluded garden; walled vegetable garden. TEAS. *Adm 60p Chd free (Share to Save the Children Fund). Sat Sept 5 (2-6)*

Hill Court ⚘❋ (Dame Felicity Peake & Andrew C. Peake Esq) 9m N of Oxford. Turn off A423 at Sturdy's Castle. 2-acre C16 walled garden influenced by Russell Page in 1960s, closed for 2 years for extensive restoration inc silver/pink/blue terraces, white garden, herbaceous borders, shrubberies, replanted orangery, many rare and unusual plants. C16 pigeon house. Fine views of Norman church and restored Manor House (not open). Overlooking park laid out in 1787 by Sir John Whalley Smythe. TEAS (June 14 only). *Adm 60p Chd free. Sat, Sun June 13, 14 (2-6)*

Hook Norton Gardens &⚘❋ 4m NE of Chipping Norton off A361. Home-made ices and cream TEAS at Fanville Farm. *Combined adm 70p. Sun June 21 (2-6)*
¶**Fanville Farm** (Mr & Mrs C.W.G.Shard) N facing hill garden recently tiered with Wye Valley rocks. Shallow-rooting plants, ferns, alpines and conifers
Harwood Farmhouse (Mr & Mrs E.J.B.Timlin) 2-acre garden created from derelict farmyard and field since 1979, designed by John Codrington, executed by

owners. Paved, gravel and scree garden gives interesting effect of perspective. Lawns, young trees, roses, shrubs, alpines; walled and kitchen gardens ¶**Springside** (Mr & Mrs B.Rye) Brewery Lane ¼-acre sloping to stream. Trees, shrubs, perennial and rock plants, log garden and troughs, an interesting collection. Unusual ornaments inc small water wheel

Hook Norton Manor (Mr & Mrs Nicholas Holmes) SW of Banbury. From A361 1m from Chipping Norton turn N and follow signs. 2½-acres terraced lawns leading down to stream; trees, shrubs, and bog garden. TEAS (in aid of St Peter's Church). *Adm 50p Chd free. Sat, Sun Sept 26, 27 (2-6)*

Kiddington Hall & (Baroness Robson) 4m NW of Woodstock. From A34, Oxford-Stratford, right at Xrds in Kiddington and down hill; entrance on left. Large grounds with lake, parkland designed by Capability Brown; terraced rose garden beside house designed by Sir Charles Barrie; C12 church and C16 dovecote. TEA. *Adm 50p Chd free (Share to Kiddington Church Restoration Fund). Sun Sept 13 (3-7)*

¶**Kidlington Gardens** &✿✿ 5m N of Oxford, between A423 and A43. TEAS. *Combined adm 80p Chd free. Sept 6 (2-6)*
Manor Farmhouse (Dr M. Kettlewell) Church St. Walled garden of just over 1 acre with 50 yd traditional herbaceous border, yew hedges and island shrubberies. Species roses and wild flowers. Pergola covered with vines, roses, clematis.
The Old Rectory (Mr & Mrs Alex Duncan) Mill St. 1-acre walled garden designed for family with young children. Mixed borders, shrub roses, vegetable garden and old orchard. House is part C15, has large medieval dovecote. Mrs Duncan (Felicity Bryan) author of 'The Town Gardener's Companion and 'A Garden for Children'
Mill End (Mr Richard Branson) Large garden on monastery site. Riverside woodland walks. Many water birds

●**Kingston Bagpuize House** &✿✿ (Lady Tweedsmuir) Kingston Bagpuize, A415/A420, 5½m W of Abingdon. Flowering shrubs, bulbs; woodland garden; herbaceous plants; hydrangeas. Charles II Manor house. TEAS. *Adm house & garden £1.50 OAPs Chd £1 (under 5 not admitted to house). Garden only 50p, under 5's free (Share to National Council for Conservation of Plants and Gardens). May, June, Sept every Wed, Sun, Bank Hol, also Aug 30, 31. For NGS Sun May 10 (2.30-5.30)*

Kingstone Lisle Park &✿ (Mrs T.L. Lonsdale) 5m W of Wantage; 1m from White Horse Hill B4507. April opening: daffodils; June opening: delphiniums, peonies, roses, herbaceous border. June 21 Wantage Silver Band playing. TEAS. *Adm 50p Chd 5p Cars free. (Share to Queen Mary's London Needlework Guild).* △*Suns April 12 (2-5) June 21 (2-6)*

Lady Margaret Hall &✿✿ (Principal & Fellows) Norham Gardens, Oxford. 1m N of Carfax from Banbury Rd into Norham Rd, 2nd right into Fyfield Rd. 8 acres of formal and informal gardens; daffodils and water meadows by R. Cherwell. College 100 yrs old includes listed buildings. Exhibition, books for sale in aid of BBONT. TEAS. *Adm 50p Chd free. Sun July 19 (2-6)*

Langford Gardens &✿ E of A361 Burford-Lechlade; W of A4095 Burford-Farington. Mixture of cottage and formal gardens in old limestone village which makes a feature of roses. Saxon church decorated with flowers. Large free car park. TEAS. *Combined adm £1.20 Chd free (Share to St Matthew's Church). Sun June 28 (2-7)*
Bakery Cottage (Miss R. Amies)
Dunford House (Mr & Mrs G.M. Davies)
¶**Greystones** (Miss V. Hirsch)
Lane Hatch (Mr & Mrs K.L. Beak)
3 Lechlade Road (A.J.A. Kibble Esq)
Lockey House (Mr & Mrs A.S. Kemp)
Middle House (Cdr & Mrs C.A. Jenkins)
The Old School (Hardy Amies Esq)
Pember House (Mr & Mrs K. Hughes)
Stonecroft (Mrs R. Webb)
Wellbank House (Mr & Mrs D. Gibb)
Three Ways (Mrs R.G. Wilson)

Laurels Farm ✿✿ (Mr & Mrs Robert Fox) 3m NW Banbury off A422. Small garden made since 1972. Massed cottage garden flowers in summer give colour and interest. TEAS Wroxton Abbey, May; Brook Cottage, July. *Adm 50p or 70p with Wroxton Abbey, Chd free. Sun, Mon May 24, 25 Sun July 5 (2-6)*

Lime Close & (Miss C. Christie-Miller) Henley's Lane, Drayton 2m S of Abingdon. 3-acre plantsman's garden, alpines, bulbs, shrubs. TEAS. *Adm 60p Chd 10p (Share to Mothers Union). Sun April 12 (2-6.30)*

Little Haseley Gardens &✿ SE of Oxford. From Oxford A40 (not M40) turn right on to A329. From London M40 exit 7, left on to A329; 1st left to Great Haseley then to Little Haseley. TEAS. *Combined adm 70p Chd free. Suns April 26, June 14 (2-6)*
Haseley Court (Mr & Mrs Desmond Heyward) 140-yr old 'Chess Garden' in box and yew; woodland garden with many spring flowers. Moat
The Coach House (Mrs C.G. Lancaster) Spring bulbs, orchard, laburnum tunnel; courtyard borders; walled garden with large collection shrub roses

Little Place (H.H. Judge Medd & Mrs Medd) Clifton Hampden, 5m E of Abingdon. A415. At Clifton Hampden village, turn right by garage; garden 400 yds on left. 1-acre terraced garden originally made at turn of century but redesigned and maintained by present owners; newly planted small woodland walk. TEAS. *Adm 50p Chd free (Share to Barristers' Benevolent Assn); or combined adm with Eveleghs, Long Wittenham 80p Chd free. Sun Sept 13 (2-6)*

The Malt House ꙮ (Mr & Mrs D.F.K. Welsh) 59 Market Place, Henley-on-Thames, nr Town Hall. ½-acre unusual, imaginatively-designed town garden, featuring C16 malthouse, lawn, beds of less common plants and shrubs. *(Unsuitable for pushchairs or young children).* TEAS. *Adm 60p Chd free (Share to the Samaritans). Sun May 31 (2-6)*

Manor Farm ♿ꙮ❀ (Sir Peter & Lady Parker) Old Minster Lovell. 1½m NW of Witney on A40 to Burford; turn right at sign to Old Minster Lovell and Leafield; in ¼m cross Windrush bridge, right at Old Swan. No parking in village; follow signs to large free car park. 5 acres made since 1974 around small Cotswold farm house adjoining churchyard and ruins of Minster (open); medieval barns divide garden into sections; grass, informal herbaceous areas; shrub and specie roses. C14 dovecote. TEAS by WI. *Adm 60p Chd free Sun June 28 (2-6)*

♦**The Manor House, Sutton Courtenay** ♿ꙮ (The Hon F.D.L. Astor) S of Abingdon. Bus: Oxford-Milton, alight Cross Trees, 2 mins. Large garden with R. Thames running through it. *Adm 40p Chd 10p. Sun May 10 (2-7)*

Marndhill ♿ꙮ❀ (Lord Chelsea) Ardington, 1½m E of Wantage; S of A417 Wantage-Reading. 3½ acres; grey and shrub borders; herb garden, spring orchard; fine and flowering trees, extensive recent re-planting, new conservatory with variety of house plants. *Adm 70p Chd free. Sun July 12 (2-6)*

Marten's Hall Farm ♿ꙮ❀ (Mr & Mrs John Parker-Jervis) Longworth, 8m W of Abingdon; 2m NW of Kingston Bagpuize. Plantsman's garden surrounding listed farmhouse (not open). Foliage plants and unusual perennials will interest flower arrangers. Adjoining old-fashioned nursery open. Home-made TEAS (Suns only in April, May, Aug, Sept) in aid of St Mary's Church. *Adm 50p Chd 25p. Sat March 7 (2-5.30); Sats, Suns March 28, 29; April 25, 26, May 16, 17, 30, 31, Aug 1, 2, Sept 12, 13 (2-6); Oct 10, 11 (2-5.30)*

¶**The Mill House, Stadhampton** ♿ (Mr & Mrs F.A. Peet) 8m NW of Oxford. 1-acre family garden with old mill and stream. Mill not working but wheel and machinery largely intact. Parking on green; parking for disabled only at house. TEAS. *Adm 50p Chd free (Share to Stadhampton Church Restoration Fund). Sun April 12 (2-5.30)*

The Mill House, Sutton Courtney ♿ꙮ (Mrs Jane Stevens) S of Abingdon. Approx 6 acres; garden on two islands, dissected by mill stream and mill pond. TEA. *Adm £1 Chd free. Suns April 5, Oct 4 (2-6)*

¶**Mollington Gardens** 5m N of Banbury off A423. In prize-winning 'Best Kept'village. Nearby Farnborough Hall (NT) open Sat, terrace walk open Sat & Sun. Teas Granary Museum, Claydon (garden open). *Adm £1.40 inc gardens in 'Best Kept' villages, Deddington & Souldern (Share to Guide Dogs for the Blind). Sat, Sun July 11, 12 (2-6)*

38 Chestnut Road (Mrs H. Dipple) Established 5 yrs and utilises total space of small plot with small plants, shrubs and trees. A natural stream adds interest

12 The Holt (Mrs B. Knight) S-facing terraced garden; mixed borders; pond

Mount Skippet ♿❀ (Dr & Mrs M.A.T. Rogers) Ramsden, 4m N of Witney. Turn off B4022 towards Ramsden, before entering village turn left up lane; at top turn right. 2 acres; 2 rock gardens; alpine house; stone troughs; shrubs; herbaceous beds; primulas; conservatory; many rare plants. Fine views. Cotswold stone house (not open) largely Cl7. TEAS in aid of Finstock Methodist Church June 21 and for groups by prior arrangement; also picnic area. *Adm 50p Chd free. Sun June 21 (2-6.30); also by appt April 1 to Sept 30 (Tel Ramsden 253)*

♦**Nuneham Park** ♿❀ (Nuneham Park Conference Centre) 7m SE of Oxford on A423. 1m from centre of Nuneham Courtney village, sign to Nuneham Park Conference Centre. Landscaped in 1779-82 by "Capability" Brown on spectacular 50-acre site with superb views of R.Thames with, picturesque garden laid out by poet William Mason in 1771; Victorian additions around C18 house (not open); grounds being extensively restored; fine trees; autumn colour. Nearby arboretum open. TEAS by Baldons WI. *Adm 60p Chd free (Share to Hearing Dogs for the Deaf). Sun Oct 11 (2-6, last adm 5)*

Old Belchers Farm ♿ꙮ (Mrs M. Hue Williams) Little Milton 8m SW of Thame, 13m SE of Oxford. Off A329. From London leave M40 Exit 7. From Oxford via A40, turn right on to A329. 3-4 acre partly walled garden, around farmhouse, developed on lines of cottage garden since 1964; roses, iris, lupins, peonies; large orchard; kitchen garden. TEAS in aid of St James's Church. *Adm 40p Chd free. Sun June 21 (2-6)*

Old Inn Cottage ♿ꙮ❀ (Mr & Mrs Michael Farquhar) Piddington, 5m S of Bicester, 2m from A41, 1m E of B4011. 1½-acre plantsman's garden specializing in unusual and cottage garden plants, esp old-fashioned pinks (garden shown in Geoffrey Smith's Favourite Flowers: Dianthus). NCCPG National Collection of Pinks. TEAS. *Adm 50p Chd free (Share to St Nicholas Church Fabric Fund) Suns June 21, 28 (2-7) Also by appt June 1-July 19 (Tel Brill 238301)*

¶**The Old Post Office** &⊛ (Mrs Penelope Mortimer) Chastleton, W of Chipping Norton off A34 or A436. Originally gardener's cottage for Chastleton House (open not for NGS). ⅔ acre. Trees, shrubs, herbaceous borders, over 100 old roses. Primarily a garden of ideas (some more successful than others). Featured in Vogue (Jan 1984), Observer Magazine (Aug 1985), Country Homes & Interiors (Oct 1986). TEAS Old Rectory, Salford. *Adm 50p Chd free (Share to The Downs Children's Association). Sat, Sun July 11, 12 (2-6)*

The Old Rectory, Coleshill &✗ (Mr & Mrs Martin) 3m W of Faringdon. Coleshill (a Nat Trust village) is on B4019, midway between Faringdon and Highworth. Medium-sized garden; lawns and informal shrub beds; wide variety shrubs, inc old-fashioned roses; 30-yr-old standard wisteria. Distant views of Berkshire and Wiltshire Downs. House (not open) dates from late C14. TEAS. *Adm 50p Chd free. Suns April 26 (2-6), Sept 20 (2-5)*

Oxford College Gardens, Group 1 &✗ Four private gardens not normally open to the public, within easy walking distance. Ticket admits to garden of Friends' Meeting House, 43 St Giles for TEAS. *Combined adm £1 or 50p each College Chd free. Sun July 26 (2-5)*
   New College: Warden's garden Entered from New College Lane, off Catte St. Small old garden enclosed among College buildings
   Queen's College: Fellows' garden Entered from High St, ½-acre with splendid herbaceous borders seen against high old stone walls; large ilex tree
   Wadham College: Fellows' Private garden & Warden's garden Entered from Parks Rd. 5-acre garden best known for trees and herbaceous borders. In the Fellows' main garden, superb purple beech, fine Magnolia acuminata, etc; in the Back Quadrangle very large Tilia tomentosa 'petiolaris'; in the Warden's garden an ancient tulip tree; in the Fellows' private garden, Civil War embankment with period fruit tree cultivars, recently established shrubbery with unusual trees and ground cover amongst older plantings

Oxford College Gardens, Group 2 ✗ Entrance through Memorial Gardens off St Aldate's. *Combined adm 80p Chd free. Sun Aug 23 (2-5)*
   Christ Church (The Dean & Students) The Masters' garden created in 1926; fine

views of Cathedral and college. The Priory House has Pocock's plane, an oriental plane planted in 1636. Cathedral garden. Deanery garden where Lewis Carroll's Alice played, with the Cheshire Cat's chestnut tree
   Merton College (Warden & Fellows) Fellows' garden; Early C18 lime avenue; ancient mulberry said to have associations with James I; specimen trees inc sorbus and malus vars; long mixed herbaceous border

Pilgrim Cottage ✗⊛ (Mr & Mrs Bunting) Path Hill, Goring Heath, 2m NW of Pangbourne. Take Whitchurch rd over toll bridge 2nd right Hardwick rd; after 1m left to Path Hill. 1-acre cottage garden with flowers, shrubs, conifers, greenhouses; geraniums and pelargoniums a speciality. TEA Querns. *Adm 50p Chd free; or combined Adm with Querns & Heron's Reach £1. Sun June 21 (2-6)*

•**Pusey House** &⊛ (Mr & Mrs Michael Hornby) 5m E of Faringdon; 12m W of Oxford; ½m S of A420. Large garden; herbaceous borders; walled gardens, water garden; large collection of shrubs and roses; many fine trees. Free car park. TEA ROOMS (3-5). Coaches by appt (Tel Buckland 222). *Adm £1.30 Chd free; parties by appt £1.10 each. April 18 to Oct 25 daily except Mons & Fris; also open Bank Hol Mons (2-6). For NGS Thurs June 11 (2-6)*

Quarry Bank House &✗ (Mr & Mrs D.J. Smith) nr Tackley, 2m E of Woodstock. From A423 take A4095 to Bicester; entrance at bottom of Gibraltar Hill on sharp bend of river bridge. 4¾ acre with abundance of early spring flowers in sheltered situation on R. Cherwell; lawns, fine cedar, orchard and bank of trees and shrubs; attractive walks in natural quarry setting. TEAS in aid of Katherine House Hospice. *Adm 50p Chd free. Sun April 12 (2-6)*

Querns &✗ (Mr Michael & The Hon Mrs Whitfeld) Goring Heath, 3m NE of Pangbourne. Take B4526 from A4074 (Reading/Oxford rd) after ½m follow signs. 2 acres; large box and yew arbours, shrub and herbaceous borders; rose garden and courtyard garden; part of listed house (not open) early C16; large thatched C17 barn. TEA. *Adm 50p Chd free or combined Adm with Pilgrim Cottage & Heron's Reach £1 (Share to Goring Heath Almshouses). Sun June 21 (2-6)*

St Catherine's College &✗ (The Master & Fellows of St Catherine's College) Manor Rd, Oxford. From Magdalen Bridge entrance into Oxford turn right over bridge into Longwall; then first right by St Cross church. From N branch off Banbury Rd into Parks Rd, left into South Parks Rd, then left into Manor Rd. Garden planted around new college 1963-65 designed by late Prof Arne Jacobsen to link modern architecture with river meadow site; water garden; wide range of trees and shrubs planted for autumn colour. TEA. *Adm 50p Chd free. Sun Oct 4 (2-5)*

St Hugh's College ⑤⚘ (Principal & Fellows) Oxford, at intersection of St Margaret's Rd and Banbury Rd, N of city centre. 10 acres comprising main garden, Principal's and Fellows' gardens largely developed from grounds of 3 early C19 houses with some original features remaining. Fine trees, many shrubs, herbaceous plants; dell garden developed from Victorian fernery; large terrace with rock beds now being replanted. TEAS Green College. *Adm 50p Chd free. Sun July 12 (2-6)*

Salford Gardens ⚘⚘ 2m W of Chipping Norton. A44 Oxford-Worcester. From Chipping Norton 2nd right into Salford. TEAS. *Combined adm 60p Chd free. Sun July 12 (2-6)*
   Old Rectory ⑤ (Mr & Mrs M.M. Chambers) 1-acre garden started 1976 ; shrub roses, herbaceous and foliage plants; shrubs; ground cover; Bantams
   Willow Tree Cottage (Mr & Mrs J. Shapley) Small walled twin gardens; one created by owners since 1979 with shrub and herbaceous borders, many clematis; other created 1985 from old farmyard with heathers and large alpine garden

Sarsden Glebe (Miss Judy Hutchinson) Churchill. 3m SW of Chipping Norton. Via B4450 to Churchill; from Burford via A361 and W for Churchill. Medium-sized garden by Repton; fine trees, anemones, bulbs; herbaceous border, roses. *Adm 50p Chd free (Share to BRCS, Oxon Branch). Sun April 12 (2.30-6)*

¶**Sarsden House** ⑤ (A.R. Fleming Esq) Churchill 5m SW of Chipping Norton. Take rd towards Churchill off A361, then left to Sarsden. 20-acre pleasure grounds with lake by Repton c.1795. Mature trees, particularly cedars. House and immediate garden under restoration. Picnickers welcomed. *Adm 50p Chd free (Share to St. James's Church, Sarsden). Sun Aug 9 (2-6)*

Shipton-under-Wychwood Gardens ⚘⚘ 4m N of Burford, 6m S of Chipping Norton on A361. Flowers in church. TEAS. *Combined adm £1 Chd free (Share to St John's Ambulance & St Mary's Church Appeal). Sun July 19 (2-6.30)*
   Kelbrook ⑤ (Mr & Mrs J.H. Kellett) 2-acre extensive water garden with fine trees, leading to R. Evenlode; herbaceous and rose borders
   ¶**The Old Post** (Mr & Mrs G. Hitchcock) Small courtyard garden designed for all-year colour, begun autumn 1983
   Salisbury Place ⑤ (Mr & Mrs K. Schoenenberger) Small garden largely redesigned and replanted 1982 for year-

round interest with emphasis on form, texture and foliage as much as on flowers
Shipton Standing ⑤ (Mr & Mrs O.P. Stedall) 3-acre mature garden on gentle slope with good trees; flowering shrubs, clematis and many roses, inc climbers; alpines in stone sinks

Shotover House ⑤ (Lt-Col Sir John Miller) Wheatley, 6m E of Oxford on A40. Bus: Oxford-Thame or Oxford-High Wycombe-London; alight Islip turn. Landscape garden with lawns, fine trees and lake. TEAS (in arcade). *Adm 50p Chd free. Sun May 17 (2-6)*

Silver Trees ⑤⚘ (Dr & Mrs P.F. Barwood) Bagley Wood Rd, Kennington. From SW junc of Oxford Ring rd, W up Hinksey Hill, left at top continue S to Abingdon 1m, left to Kennington; 3rd house on right. 3 acres, alpine beds, sinks, shady borders merge into wood; conifers, foliage plants and shrubs; small pond with primulas. TEAS. *Adm 60p Chd free (Share to St Nicholas Church, Abingdon for overseas charities); or combined adm Wood Croft 90p Chd free. Suns May 24 (2-6.30); groups by appt (Tel Oxford 735232)*

Souldern Gardens ⚘ Between Banbury (8m) and Bicester (7m) just off A41. 4 gardens in picturesque 'Best Kept' prizewinning village. TEAS Sun. *Combined adm £1.40 inc gardens in two other 'Best Kept' villages, Deddington and Mollington, Chd free (Share to Souldern Village Amenities Fund). Sat, Sun July 11, 12 (2-6)*
   The Barn ⑤ (Mr & Mrs J. Talbot) Sheltered garden with pond; wide mixed borders, kitchen garden
   Great House Close ⑤ (Mr & Mrs C.E. Thornton) Long, varied garden and orchard framed by old farm buildings
   The Old Forge (Mr & Mrs D. Duthie) Resourceful, densely planted cottage garden with stone walling
   Souldern House ⑤ (Maj & Mrs A.H. Gray) Walled garden round C17 house (not open); gazebo dated 1706, ancient yew hedge; bantams

Sparrow Hall ⑤ (Mr & Mrs J. Panks) Swalcliffe W of Banbury on B4035 halfway between Banbury and Shipston-on-Stour. ¾-acre started in 1976 from derelict farmyard, chicken run and small field. Planted for easy care with wide collection of miniature conifers, heathers and alpines. Japanese granite accessories, lanterns, etc. brought from Japan combine to give English/Japanese garden effect. Converted farmhouse backs large patio with stone troughs, etc. filled with plants for seasonal display. Light lunch. *Adm 50p Chd free (Share to Swalcliffe Church). Sun July 19 (12-5)*

Standlake Gardens ⑤⚘ 6m SE of Witney; 3-400 yds E of village on B4449. TEAS at

Gaunt Mill in aid of Northmoor Church. *Adm 50p each garden Chd free. Sun Apr 26 (2-6)*
¶**Gaunt House** (Mr & Mrs P. Maxwell Jones) Large display of Spring bulbs and wide selection of shrubs in 4 acres. R. Windrush tributary forms moat to C15 manor house (not open) which figured in Civil War
Gaunt Mill (Mr & Mrs M. Belmont) 3 acres on 1000 yr old mill site with 2 arms of R. Windrush. Bridge over weir leads to 2 acre island with unusual trees, shrubs, naturalized bulbs

Stansfield ✿❀ (Mr & Mrs David Keeble) 49 High St, Stanford-in-the-Vale. 3½m SE of Faringdon. Turn off A417 opp Vale Garage into High St, 300yds. Park in street. 1¼-acre plantsman's garden on alkaline soil, started in 1979, ¾ completed; informal borders, island beds; damp garden. Planted for year-round interest, much use of coloured foliage; many unusual plants; trees, shrubs, hardy perennials, alpines (some in sinks and troughs), ground cover, flower arrangers plants, mostly labelled. *Adm 50p Chd free. Suns May 3, June 7, Aug 2, Sep 6 (2-6); also by appt (Tel Stanford-in-the-Vale 340)*

¶**Stonewalls** ✿❀ (Mr & Mrs M. Adams) 1½m W of Deddington on B4031. A plantsman's garden of ½-acre divided into many interesting areas, inc shrubbery, herbaceous border, sunken pool, specimen trees, white border, conifer and heather bed, over 150 clematis and climbers. TEA. *Adm 50p Chd free. Sun July 19 (2-7)*

Swinbrook Gardens ♿✿ 2½m E of Burford, off A40. Unspoilt Cotswold village in Windrush Valley with interesting church. TEAS. *Combined adm 70p Chd free. Sun July 12 (2-6.30)*
    Swinbrook House (J.D. Mackinnon Esq) (2m from village on Shipton-under-Wychwood Rd) Large garden; herbaceous borders; shrubs; shrub roses; large kitchen garden; fine views. Picnics allowed
    Swinbrook Manor (Mrs S. Freund) Medium-sized garden in exceptionally pretty surroundings; mixed shrub and herbaceous planting

Tadmarton Gardens ❀ 5m SW of Banbury on B4035. TEAS. *Combined adm 70p Chd free (Share to Berks, Bucks & Oxon Naturalists' Trust). Sat, Sun June 20, 21; also Sun Sept 20 (2-6)*
    The Manor ♿ (Mr & Mrs R.K. Asser) 2½-acre garden with beautiful views of unspoilt countryside; fine trees; mixed and evergreen borders; great variety plants; Thatched C15 barn and C18 dovecote
    Yeomans (Mrs A.E. Pedder) Small garden on 4 levels, featured in 'Easy Plants for Difficult Places' by Geoffrey Smith; C16

thatched cottage. Colourful borders; wide variety annuals, perennials, shrubs; many climbers inc roses, clematis; shrub roses with autumn hips

Wardington Manor ♿❀ (The Lord Wardington) 5m NE of Banbury, A361. 5 acres with topiary, rock garden, flowering shrub walk to pond. Jacobean manor house (not shown) 1665. TEA. *Adm 70p Chd free. Suns April 26, May 31, Aug 16 (2-6)*

Waterperry Gardens ♿❀ 2½m from A40(M) junc to Wheatley. 50m from London, 9m E of Oxford. Gardens well signed locally with Tourist Board rose symbol. 20 acres; ornamental gardens, nurseries, parkland; many interesting plants; shrub, herbaceous and alpine nurseries; glasshouses and comprehensive fruit section. High quality plant centre, garden shop (Tel Ickford 226). Tea shop. Saxon church with famous glasses and brasses in grounds. Open daily, except Christmas and New Year Hls. Open only to visitors to Art In Action July 16 to 19. April to Sept 10-5.30 weekdays 10-6 weekends; Oct to March 10-4.30. Coach parties by appt only (Tel Ickford 254). TEAS. *Adm Gardens & Nurseries £1 OAPs 75p Chd 50p. For NGS (Share to NCCPG) Suns June 7, Aug 9 (10-6)*

Weston-on-the-Green Gardens ♿❀ 4½m SW of Bicester. Just off A43 take Bletchington turn in village centre TEAS. *Adm 50p Chd free (Share to St Mary's Church, Weston-on-the-Green). Sun May 17 (2-6)*
    The Mill House (Mr & Mrs J.A. Cavan) 1¼ acres started 1977; shrubs, trees; spring flowers; mill and trout pools, stream and waterfalls; further 7 acres of meadow, copses, young trees and wild flowers being developed for wildlife conservation with minimum maintenance
    The Old Vicarage (Mrs T.A. Laurie) 2-acre old garden surrounded by mature trees; flowering shrubs, heathers; fish ponds; stream-side and woodland walk

Westwell Manor ♿✿❀ (Mr & Mrs T.H. Gibson) Westwell. An unspoilt hamlet, 2m SW of Burford just off A40. 6 acres surrounding beautiful old Cotswold Manor House (not open); knot and water gardens, potager, shrub roses, herbaceous borders, topiary. TEAS. *Adm £1 Chd 50p (Share to St Mary's Church, Westwell). Suns May 3, July 19 (2-6.30)*

Wheatley Gardens ✿❀ Wheatley 6m E of Oxford just off A40. TEAS at the Old House. *Combined adm £1.20 Chd free (Share to BRCS Oxford Branch). Sun May 10 (2-6)*
    Chestnuts (Mrs D. E. W. Morgan) Park Hill. Small garden designed to maximise width and minimise length; 2 raised beds of alpines; spring flowers and shrubs
    The Doctor's House (Dr R. Flury) 116 Church Rd. 1-acre cottage garden interes-

tingly landscaped with rockery, bulbs and shrubs

High Croft (Mrs L. Barwise) 15 Windmill Lane, ⅓-acre, rhododendrons, azaleas, some bulbs, winter ericas. Lovely views

High Tilt (Mr & Mrs P. Freeborn) 19 Windmill Lane. ⅓-acre spring bulbs, rhododendrons, azaleas, camellias, small specimen trees; herbaceous borders, designed to achieve interesting views from different angles

The Old House ❀ (Mr & Mrs N. Minty) 17 Kiln Lane. 2-acres; stream, small lake, bulbs, shrubs

Rock House (Mrs C.R.S. Harris) 14 Westfield Rd. Alpines and rock plants in natural quarry setting on 4 levels; interesting old well. House part C17, part early C19 (not open)

The Walled Cottage (Mr & Mrs John Prest) 8 Church Rd. Small, enclosed family garden on south-facing slope

White's Farm House ⬧❀ (Dr & Mrs Michael Shone) Letcombe Bassett 3m SW of Wantage. Take B4507 signed Ashbury, then through Letcombe Regis. 2½ acres; mixed borders; wild garden with 25 yrs growth of chalk-tolerant trees, shrubs, herbaceous plants, summer bulbs. New gravel scree bed, pond, playground and monster walk. Wantage Silver Band. TEAS in C18 barn. *Adm 50p Chd free. Sun July 19 (2-6)*

Wilcote House ⬧❀ (The Hon C.E. Cecil) Finstock, 3m S of Charlbury. NW of Oxford between North Leigh and Finstock; E of B4022. Shrubs, mixed borders, beautiful views; old-fashioned rose garden and laburnum arch planted 1984. Stone Cotswold house early C18/C19 (not open). TEAS. *Adm 60p Chd free (Share to DGAA). Suns May 31 July 5 (2-6)*

Wood Croft (Mrs Geoffrey Blackman) Foxcombe Lane, Boar's Hill, S of Oxford. From ring rd; follow signs to Wootton and Boar's Hill. From junc at top Hinksey Hill, house first on left. 1½ acres designed and planted by the late Prof G.E. Blackman FRS. Rhododendrons, camellias, azaleas, many varieties primula in woodland and surrounding natural pond; fine trees. TEAS Silver Trees. *Adm 60p Chd free; or combined adm with Silver Trees 90p Chd free (Share to Royal Marsden Hospital Development Appeal). Sun May 24 (2-6.30)*

Wootton Place ⬧❀ (Mrs Clutterbuck) 3m N of Woodstock off A34, next to Church. Laid out by Capability Brown; 150 varieties of daffodil, very fine trees inc huge ancient walnut; walled garden. TEAS. *Adm 60p Chd free (Share to St Mary's Church, Wootton). Sun April 19 (2-5.30)*

◆**Wroxton Abbey** ⬧ (Wroxton College of Fairleigh Dickinson University) W of Banbury. A422 Banbury-Stratford. Bus: Banbury-Tysoe; alight Wroxton village, 3 mins. 56-acres C18 parkland originally laid out by Sanderson Miller for 1st Earl of Guilford, completely restored. Prize winner in RICS/ The Times Conservation Awards 1983; features inc Doric temple; rose garden; newly created knot garden, dovecote, icehouse; grand cascade into a serpentine river. Stone obelisk commemorates visit in 1739 of Prince of Wales. Wroxton Abbey (Jacobean Manor House) open. TEAS. Free car parking in village; parking in Abbey grounds 50p extra. *Adm £1.50 (Garden only 50p Chd free) (Share to St John's Ambulance, All Saints Church, Wroxton, & Imperial Cancer Research Fund). Sun, Mon May 24, 25 & Mon Aug 31 (2-5)*

POWYS

Hon County Organisers:
North (Montgomery)
MRS DENISE HATCHARD,
  Maenllwyd Isaf, Abermule
  South (Brecknock & Radnor)
MRS C.R.C. INGLIS,
  Llansantffraed House, Brecon

Hon County Treasurer:
ELWYN PUGH ESQ, Post office,
  Kerry, Newton

DATES OF OPENING

BY APPOINTMENT ONLY for dates see text:
  THE WALLED GARDEN, Knill, nr Kington

APRIL Sunday 12
  GLIFFAES COUNTRY HOUSE HOTEL,
    Crickhowell
APRIL Easter Sunday 19
  GLEBE HOUSE, Guilsford
MAY Saturday 9 & Sunday 10
  CAE HYWEL, Llansantffraid-ym-Mechain
MAY Saturday 16 & Sunday 17
  TRAWSCOED HALL, nr Welshpool
MAY Sunday 17
  MAESLLWCH CASTLE, Glasbury
MAY Sunday 24
  LLYSDINAM, Newbridge-on-Wye
MAY Tuesday 26
  POWIS CASTLE GARDENS, Welshpool
MAY Sunday 31
  GARTH HOUSE, Llangmmarch Wells
  MAENLLWYD ISAF, Abermule
JUNE Sunday 7
  THE DINGLE, Welshpool
  FFRWDGRECH, nr Brecon
  GREGYNOG, Tregynon
JUNE Saturday 13 & Sunday 14
  BODYNFOEL HALL, Llanfechain

JUNE Sunday 14
GLIFFAES COUNTRY HOUSE HOTEL,
Crickhowell
JUNE Sunday 21
THE HILL COTTAGE, Bausley
JUNE Saturday 27 & Sunday 28
GLANUSK PARK, Crickhowell
PENMYARTH, Crickhowell
JULY Saturday 25 & Sunday 26
GLEBE HOUSE, Guilsfield
AUGUST Sunday 2
KERRY GARDENS, nr Newton
SEPTEMBER Sunday 6
GLAN SEVERN, nr Welshpool

DESCRIPTIONS OF GARDENS

Bodynfoel Hall &⊛ (Maj & Mrs Bonnor-Maurice) Llanfechain, 10m N of Welshpool. Via A490 to Llanfyllin. Take B4393 to Llanfechain, follow signs to Bodynfoel. 3½acres; rough wild garden in process of restoration; new lake; young and mature trees; shrub roses and heather bank. TEA. *Adm 50p Chd 10p. Sat, Sun June 13, 14 (2-6)*

Cae Hywel ⊛ (Miss Judith M. Jones) Llansantffraid-ym-Mechain, 10m N of Welshpool. On A495; on E (Oswestry) side of village. Car park in village. 1-acre; S facing slope on different levels; rock garden; herb garden; interesting shrubs, trees and plants. TEAS. *Adm 50p Chd 10p. Sat, Sun May 9, 10 (2-6)*

The Dingle &⊛⊛ (Mr & Mrs D.R. Joseph) 3m N of Welshpool. Via A490 to Llanfyllin for 1m; then left for Groespluan; and on for 1¾m then fork left, garden immediately on left. 2 acres; unusual shrubs and trees in S-facing garden; large banks leading to big pool; autumn colour especially good Sept/Oct. TEAS. *Adm 50p Chd 10p. Sun June 7 (2-6); Also by appt all year (Tel Welshpool 2587)*

Ffrwdgrech (Mr & Mrs W.D.D. Evans) 1m S of Brecon. From A40 turn S opp Drover's Arms along Frwdgrech Rd; entrance ¾m on left. Medium-sized garden, owner-maintained; wide variety shrubs, Dingle Arboretum, fine trees, 2 acres lawns, fine views. TEAS. *Adm 50p Chd 15p (Share to Cancer Research Campaign). Sun June 7 (2-6.30)*

¶**Garth House** & (Mr & Mrs F.A. Wilson) Llangammarch Wells, A483 from Builth Wells. Drive through gates in village of Garth by Garth Inn. Large wood with azaleas and rhododendrons, water and shrub garden; fine views. Home of Gwynne family. TEAS. *Adm 50p Chd 10p. Sun May 31 (2-6.30)*

Glan Severn &⊛⊛ (Mr & Mrs N. Thomas) Berriew, 5m S of Welshpool. Take A483. Entrance on left by bridge over R. Rhiew. Large garden being reclaimed during 2½ years by new owners; 3-acre lake with island; stream; new and mature ornamental trees; lawns;

large rockery inc grotto now being replanted. TEAS. *Adm 50p Chd 10p. Sun Sept 6 (2-6); also by appt all year*

Glanusk Park &⊛ (The Viscountess De L'Isle) Garden 2m W of Crickhowell. A40, 12m from Brecon; 8m from Abergavenny. 4-acre garden; formal garden; fine trees; kitchen garden. Original house destroyed during WWII. *Adm 40p Chd 10p. Sat, Sun June 27, 28 (2-6)*

Glebe House &⊛⊛ (Mrs Jenkins & Mrs Habberley) Guilsfield, 3m N of Welshpool. A490 (Llanfyllin) rd from Welshpool for 2m; fork right for Guilsfield. 1½-acres; magnificent spring bulb display; unusual clematis and climbers; several gardens within a garden. Raffle. TEAS. *Adm 50p Chd 10p (Share to Victoria Memorial Hosp Hydrotherapy Pool). Sun April 19; Sat, Sun July 25, 26 (2-6.30)*

Gliffaes Country House Hotel & (Mr & Mrs Brabner) NW of Crickhowell 8m. Bus: Newport-Abergavenny-Brecon, alight Penmyarth. Large garden; shrubs; ornamental trees; fine maples; rhododendrons; fine position high above R.Usk. TEAS. *April-Dec. For NGS Adm 50p Chd 10p (collecting box) Suns April 12, June 14 (all day)*

Gregynog & (University of Wales) Tregynon, 7m N of Newtown. A483 Welshpool-Newtown Rd, turn W at B4389 for Betws Cedewain, 1m through village gates on left. Large garden; fine banks, rhododendrons and azaleas; dell with specimen shrubs; formal garden; short nature trail starting from car park. Descriptive leaflet available. Early C19 black and white house; site inhabited since C12. TEAS. *Adm 50p Chd 10p. Sun June 7 (2-6)*

The Hill Cottage ⊛⊛ (Mr & Mrs A.T. Bareham) Bausley, Crew Green. 8m NE of Welshpool via A458 towards Shrewsbury; after Middletown, travelling E, turn left (N) signed Wollaston; after 1½m right down 'No through rd' for ½m; from Llandrinio B4393 to Crew Green turn right, after 1m left down 'No Through Rd'. 1-acre garden on hillside made and maintained by owners. Alpines, shrubs and conifers. Extensive views. TEAS. *Adm 50p Chd 10p. Sun June 21 (2-6)*

Kerry Gardens ⊛⊛ 3m S of Newtown. Take A489 to Craven Arms. Some gardens featured on BBC TV Wales. Start from Kerry Lamb car park. TEAS. *Combined adm 60p Chd 10p (Share to RDA). Sun Aug 2 (2-6)*
    Post Office (Mr & Mrs E. Pugh) 300 early flowering chrysanthemums grown for exhibition, also small colourful garden
    Mar-Jon Dolforgan View (Mrs O. Hughes) interesting garden; wide variety of annuals, plants
    Westwinds (Mr & Mrs R. Watson) Colourful garden; rockery, pools, shrubs, flower beds

Black Hall (Mrs H. Brooke) Large garden; stream, lawns and shrubs

¶**Lower Cefn Perfa** (Mr & Mrs J. Dugdale) Large easily maintained garden

Llysdinam &❀ (Lady Delia Venables-Llewelyn & Llysdinam Charitable Trust) Newbridge-on-Wye, SW of Llandrindod Wells. Turn W off A479 at Newbridge-on-Wye; right immediately after crossing R. Wye; entrance up hill. Medium-sized garden; rhododendrons, azaleas, shrubs, woodland garden, kitchen garden; fine view of Wye Valley. TEAS. *Adm 50p Chd 15p (Share to NSPCC). Sun May 24 (2-6.30)*

Maenllwyd Isaf &❀❀ (Mrs Denise Hatchard) Abermule, 5m NE of Newtown & 10m S of Welshpool. On B4368 Abermule-Craven Arms, 1½m from Abermule. 3 acres; unusual shrubs and plants, goldfish pool, aviary, a peacock, 'wild' pool, R. Mule. C16 listed house; converted barn of same period. Raffles for wine & cake. TEAS. *Adm 50p Chd 10p (Share to Winged Fellowship Trust). Sun May 31 (2-6); also by appt all year (Tel Abermule 204)*

♦**Maesllwch Castle** (Major G de Winton) * Glasbury. Turn off A438 immediately N of Glasbury bridge. Through Glasbury ½m turn right at Church. Medium-sized garden owner maintained. Views from terrace across River Wye to Black Mountains. Old walled garden, woodland walk, fine trees. TEAS. *Adm 50p Chd 10p (Share to All Saints Church, Glasbury). Sun May 17 (2-5)*

Penmyarth ❀ (Mr & the Hon Mrs Legge-Bourke) Glanusk Park, 2m W of Crickhowell. A40, 12m from Brecon, 8m from Abergavenny. 11-acre rose, rock and wild garden. TEAS. *Adm 50p Chd 10p. Sat, Sun June 27, 28 (2-6)*

Powis Castle Gardens &❀ (The National Trust) Welshpool. Turn off A483 ¾m out of Welshpool, up Red Lane for ¼m. Gardens laid out in 1720 with most famous hanging terraces in the world; enormous yew hedges; lead statuary, large wild garden. The dates shown below are *Special openings* for NGS; garden only. TEAS. *Adm gardens only (Castle closed) £1.40 Chd 55p. △ Tues May 26 (2-6)*

Trawscoed Hall &❀ (Mr & Mrs J.G.K. Williams) 3m N of Welshpool. On A490 towards Llanfyllin. 4 acres; prize-winning woods, lovely view; interesting plants. House (not open) built c.1560; Georgian part 1777. Granary dating from 1772. TEAS. *Adm 50p Chd 10p. Sat, Sun May 16, 17 (2-6)*

The Walled Garden &❀ (Mrs S. Voelcker) Knill, 3m from Kington and Presteigne. Off B4362 Walton-Presteigne rd to Knill village; right over cattle grid; keep right down drive. 3

acres; walled garden; stream; bog garden, primulas; shrub roses; garden made by owners after retirement and owner-maintained. Nr C13 Church in lovely valley. *Adm 60p Chd 30p. By appt any day (10-7) (Tel 0544 267411)*

SHROPSHIRE

Hon County Organisers:
MRS B. JENKINSON, Chetton Grange, Bridgnorth WV16 6UE
MRS J. H. M. STAFFORD, The Old Rectory, Fitz, Shrewsbury SY4 3AS

Hon County Treasurer:
MRS P. TREVOR-JONES, Preen Manor, Church Preen, nr Church Stretton SY6 7LG

DATES OF OPENING

BY APPOINTMENT ONLY for dates see text:
ASHFORD MANOR, nr Ludlow
FARLEY HOUSE, Much Wenlock
LIMEBURNERS, Ironbridge
RUTHALL MANOR, Ditton Priors
REGULAR OPENINGS for dates see text:
HODNET HALL GARDENS, nr Market Drayton

APRIL Sunday 5
MALLARDS KEEP, Church Stretton
APRIL Easter Sunday 19
BURWARTON HOUSE, nr Bridgnorth
MALLARDS KEEP, Church Stretton
APRIL Easter Monday 20
MALLARDS KEEP, Church Stretton
APRIL Sunday 26
ATTINGHAM PARK, nr Shrewsbury
NEW HALL, Eaton-u-Heywood
APRIL Wednesday 29
RYTON GROVE, nr Shifnal
MAY Sunday 3
MALLARDS KEEP, Church Stretton
MAY Monday 4 (Bank Hol)
GLAZELEY OLD RECTORY, Glazeley, nr Bridgnorth
MALLARDS KEEP, Church Stretton
MAY Sunday 10
GATACRE PARK, Six Ashes, nr Bridgnorth
THE GROVE, nr Nesscliff
MAWLEY HALL, Cleobury Mortimer
MILLICHOPE PARK, Munslow
NEW HALL, Eaton-u-Heywood
MAY Saturday 16
CHYKNELL, nr Bridgnorth
MAY Sunday 17
BRYNHFRYD, nr Oswestry
GATACRE PARK, Six Ashes, nr Bridgnorth
MOORTOWN, nr Wellington
MUNSLOW HOUSE, nr Craven Arms

MAY Sunday 24
THE GROVE, nr Nesscliff
HAYE HOUSE, Eardington
MALLARDS KEEP, Church Stretton
PEPLOW HALL, nr Hodnet
WILLEY PARK, Broseley, nr Bridgnorth
MAY Monday 25 (Bank Hol)
DUDMASTON, nr Bridgnorth
MALLARDS KEEP, Church Stretton
MAY Tuesday 26
GREYSTONES, Little Ness
MAY Wednesday 27
GREYSTONES, Little Ness
RYTON GROVE, nr Shifnal
MAY Thursday 28
PREEN MANOR, nr Church Stretton
MAY Saturday 30
BROWNHILL HOUSE, Ruyton XI Towns
RIDGWAY WOOD, Edgton
MAY Sunday 31
BROWNHILL HOUSE, Ruyton XI Towns
LIMEBURNERS, Ironbridge
THE LYTH, Ellesmere
THE MAGNOLIAS, Bomere Heath
THE OLD VICARAGE, Cardington
RIDGWAY WOOD, Edgton
SWALLOW HAYES, nr Albrighton
THE WOOD, nr Wolverhampton
JUNE Saturday 6
BURFORD HOUSE GARDENS, nr Tenbury Wells
PITCHFORD HALL, nr Shrewsbury
JUNE Sunday 7
ADCOTE SCHOOL, Little Ness
HATTON GRANGE, Shifnal
THE LYTH, Ellesmere
MALLARDS KEEP, Church Stretton
PITCHFORD HALL, nr Shrewsbury
SUTHERLAND HOUSE, Sheriffhales
JUNE Monday 8
HATTON GRANGE, Shifnal
JUNE Saturday 13
THE GROVE, nr Nesscliff
LANDSCAPE, Kinnerley
JUNE Sunday 14
ADCOTE SCHOOL, Little Ness
THE GROVE, nr Nesscliff
LANDSCAPE, Kinnerley
THE OLD RECTORY, Fitz
SWALLOW HAYES, nr Albrighton
WALCOT HALL ARBORETUM, Lydbury North
JUNE Monday 15
WALCOT HALL ARBORETUM, Lydbury North
JUNE Thursday 18
PREEN MANOR, nr Church Stretton
JUNE Sunday 21
ADCOTE SCHOOL, Little Ness
DINGLE BANK, nr Bridgnorth
INGA PENGAR, Oswestry
MILLICHOPE PARK, Munslow
MOORTOWN, nr Wellington
OAK COTTAGE HERB GARDEN, Nesscliff
JUNE Wednesday 24
RYTON GROVE, nr Shifnal

JUNE Saturday 27
GREYSTONES, Little Ness
HAZLER CROFT, Church Stretton
1 WELLINGTON ROAD, Donnington
JUNE Sunday 28
ACTON ROUND, Morville, nr Bridgnorth
ADCOTE SCHOOL, Little Ness
GREYSTONES, Little Ness
LOWER HALL, nr Bridgnorth
MAWLEY HALL, Cleobury Mortimer
1 WELLINGTON ROAD, Donnington
WRENTNALL HOUSE, Pulverbatch
JULY Saturday 4
1 WELLINGTON ROAD, Donnington
WHITTINGTON VILLAGE GARDENS
JULY Sunday 5
ADCOTE SCHOOL, Little Ness
OLDFIELD, Craven Arms
1 WELLINGTON ROAD, Donnington
WHITTINGTON VILLAGE GARDENS
JULY Thursday 9
MILLICHOPE PARK, Munslow
JULY Saturday 11
OTELEY, nr Ellesmere
JULY Sunday 12 to Saturday 18
ASTLEY ABBOTTS HOUSE, nr Bridgnorth
THE DAIRY HOUSE, nr Claverley
JULY Sunday 12
OTELEY, nr Ellesmere
JULY Thursday 16
PREEN MANOR, nr Church Stretton
JULY Sunday 19
HAUGHMOND, Felton Butler
INGA PENGAR, Oswestry
MALLARDS KEEP, Church Stretton
THE OLD VICARAGE, Cardington
JULY Saturday 25
BROWNHILL HOUSE, Ruyton X1 Towns
THE MORLEYS, Wallsbank
JULY Sunday 26
BROWNHILL HOUSE, Ruyton X1 Towns
LINLEY HALL, nr Bishop's Castle
THE MORLEYS, Wallsbank
AUGUST Sunday 2
DINGLE BANK, nr Bridgnorth
AUGUST Saturday 15
HODNET HALL GARDENS, nr Market Drayton
AUGUST Sunday 30
DUNVAL HALL, nr Bridgnorth
GREYSTONES, Little Ness
MALLARDS KEEP, Church Stretton
STOTTESDON & CHORLEY VILLAGE GARDENS
AUGUST Monday 31 (Bank Hol)
DUNVAL HALL, nr Bridgnorth
MALLARDS KEEP, Church Stretton
STOTTESDON & CHORLEY VILLAGE GARDENS
SEPTEMBER Sunday 6
THE OLD RECTORY, Fitz
YEATON HOUSE, Yeaton
SEPTEMBER Saturday 19
BURFORD HOUSE GARDENS, nr Tenbury Wells

SEPTEMBER Sunday 27
MALLARDS KEEP, Church Stretton

DESCRIPTIONS OF GARDENS

Acton Round ⚮❀ (Mr & Mrs Hew Kennedy) 6m W of Bridgnorth; A458 Morville-Shrewsbury, 2m after Morville turn left (W). 1½-acre garden with yew hedges; rose, herbaceous and newly planted borders; various follies, attractive church and beautiful early Georgian house (open). TEAS. *Adm 50p Chd 25p (Share to Acton Round Church). Sun June 28 (2-6.30)*

Adcote School ⚮ (Adcote School Educational Trust Ltd) Little Ness, 8m NW of Shrewsbury via A5 to Montford Bridge, turn off NE follow signs to Little Ness. 20 acres; fine trees inc beeches, tulip trees, oaks (American and Evergreen); atlas cedars, Wellingtonia etc; rhododendrons, azaleas; small lake; landscaped garden. House (part shown) designed by Norman Shaw RA; Grade 1 listed building; William Morris windows; De Morgan tiles. (TEA, June 7, 14). *Adm 60p Chd free. Suns June 7, 14, 21, 28; July 5 (2-5). Also by appt (Tel Baschurch 260202)*

Ashford Manor ⚭❀ (Kit Hall Esq) Ashford Carbonel, 2¾m S of Ludlow. E of A49 Ludlow-Leominster. Medium-sized garden devoted to growing constant supply of plant material for flower arrangement, chiefly foliage; maintained solely by owner and not a 'tidy' garden. Picnic Area. *Adm 40p Chd free. By appt only (Tel Ludlow 2100) (2-6)*

Astley Abbotts House ⚭ (H.E. Hodgson Esq) 3m NW of Bridgnorth. B4373 from Bridgnorth turn right at Cross Lane Head. Bus: Bridgnorth-Broseley or the Smithies; alight Cross Lane Head ½m. 5 acres; very fine trees, mostly coniferous; rhododendrons, herbaceous borders; lawns; 120 varieties of herbs. TEA. *Adm 60p Chd 20p. Daily July 12 to 17 (2-6)*

Attingham Park ⚭⚮ (The National Trust) 4m SE of Shrewsbury. Turn off A5 at Atcham. Bus: MR on A5 routes alight Atcham at gates drive. Large park, landscaped by Repton in 1797; deer park (no dogs), long riverside walk with daffodils. Magnificent house designed in 1785 by George Steuart. No dogs in Deer Park. TEAS. *Adm to house and grounds £2 Chd £1; Family tickets £5; grounds only 50p Chd 25p. △Sun April 26 (2-6; house 2-5)*

Brownhill House ⚮❀ (Roger & Yoland Brown) Ruyton XI Towns, 10m NW of Shrewsbury on B4397, in village. Park at Bridge Inn. 1½ acre unusual and distinctive hillside garden bordering R. Perry. Great variety of features and style; laburnum walk; formal terrace with gazebo; parterre; informal banks and woodland paths; glasshouses;

fruit and vegetables. TEAS. *Adm 60p Chd 20p. Sats, Suns May 30, 31; July 25, 26 (2-6)*

Brynhyfryd ⚮❀ (Mr & Mrs M. Ruane) Rhydycroesau, 4m W of Oswestry. From Oswestry town centre B4580 (Llansilin) for 3½m to Rhydycroesau; right towards Llanarmon; garden ½m on left. 2 acres; heather garden, set on steep hillside (not suitable for elderly or infirm); large rockery, unusual alpines, conifers; 3 ponds. *Adm 50p Chd 25p. Sun May 17 (2-5)*

Burford House Gardens ⚭⚮❀ (John Treasure Esq) 1m W of Tenbury Wells. 400yds S of A456. Bus: CM Ludlow-Tenbury Wells. Medium-sized garden designed in 1954 by owner in beautiful surroundings on R.Teme. Flowering shrubs, herbaceous plants, extensive lawns. Clematis Museum: at Burford House is National Clematis Collection (held on behalf of NCCPG; over 300 species; Cultivars collected from clematis enthusiasts all over world. In old Stable block, Exhibition on History and Development of Clematis. Fine church adjacent containing Cornwall monuments. Nursery specialising in clematis. DOGS on lead Nursery only. TEAS; salad lunches. *Adm £1.75 Chd 75p. Season ticket £7.50, Family season £15; Parties (by appt): 25 or more £1.50 each. △Sats June 6, Sept 19 (11-5)*

◆**Burwarton House** ⚮❀ (The Viscount Boyne) Burwarton; 10m SW of Bridgnorth, 10m from Ludlow on B4364. 35 acres; woodland garden, fine trees, specimen conifers; rhododendrons, daffodils, azaleas in natural surroundings. TEAS. *Adm 70p Chd free. Sun April 19 (2-6)*

Chyknell ⚮ (W.S.R. Kenyon-Slaney Esq) 5m E of Bridgnorth between Claverley and Worfield. Medium-sized garden designed by Russell Page. TEAS. *Adm 60p Chd 30p. Sat May 16 (10-6)*

The Dairy House (Miss N.E.Wood) Ludstone, nr Claverley, 7m W of Wolverhampton. S of A454. Bus:MR 890 Wolverhampton-Bridgnorth; alight Red Hill, ¾m. 3-acre garden developed by owner on waterside setting of much natural beauty; heaths, woodland, flowering shrubs and roses, lilies. TEAS (July 12). *Adm 50p (Share to Claverley Church Restoration Fund). Sun July 12 to Sat July 18 (2-7)*

David Austin Roses ⚭❀ (Mr & Mrs David Austin) Bowling Green Lane, Albrighton, 8m NW of Wolverhampton. 4m from Shifnal (A464) left into Bowling Green Lane; or junc 3, M54 to Albrighton, right at sign 'Roses & Shrubs', Bowling Green Lane 2nd right. Famous nursery and gardens; 700 varieties old roses, shrub, species and climbing roses; rose breeding trials; rose fields; over 1,000 different hardy herbaceous plants inc large collections of peonies and irises. Private garden with many plants, shrubs, sculpture. TEAS. *Adm 60p Chd free. Sun July 5 (2-6)*

¶**Dingle Bank** ✗✿ (Mr & Mrs T. Ford) Chelmarsh Common 3m N of Bridgnorth. Take B4373 to Highley Road 3m. Car parking at The Bulls Head, Chelmarsh, then 300 yrds walk. 1 acre colourful cottage garden; island beds, mixed borders, rock garden with wide range of perennials, shrubs, old roses, conifers, alpines; emphasis on perfume, foliage/year-round colour. Also open **The Paddocks** (Mr & Mrs Peter Hales) 1 acre cottage garden. *Combined adm 60p Chd 20p (Share to Infantile Hypercalceamia). Suns June 21, Aug 2 (2-6)*

Dudmaston ✿✿ (Sir George & Lady Labouchere; The National Trust) 4m SE of Bridgnorth on A442. Bus stop at gates ½m. Large garden with fine trees, shrubs; lovely views over Dudmaston Pool and surrounding country. TEAS. *Adm 70p Chd 35p. Mon May 25 (2-6)*

Dunval Hall ✿✗ (G.P.A.Thompson Esq) 2m NW of Bridgnorth, via B4373, through Northgate Arch signed Broseley and Ironbridge; 2m from Bridgnorth turn left; parking. Bus: 909 Bridgnorth-Wellington. Medium-sized garden; roses, herbaceous borders, formal Italian pool garden. Elizabethan black and white house (not open). TEAS. *Adm 50p Chd/OAPs 30p. Sun, Mon Aug 30, 31 (2-7)*

¶**Farley House** ✗ (Mr & Mrs R.W.Collingwood) From A458 at Much Wenlock (1m) turn N on to B4378 signed Ironbridge; house 1m 1st on left. 1acre garden made since 1980 by owners; alpines, herbaceous island beds, shrubs and trees. *Adm 50p Chd free. By appt only Apr-Oct (tel: Much Wenlock 727017)*

Gatacre Park ✿✿ (Sir Edward & Lady Thompson) Six Ashes, 6m SE of Bridgnorth on A458. Stourbridge-Bridgnorth Rd. 8 acres. Originally a Victorian garden partly redeveloped over the last 56 years by present owner. Flowering shrubs, fine trees, inc 100ft tulip tree and manna ash; topiary walk; large woodland garden with pieris, azaleas, rhododendrons inc many interesting species now fully grown. Lovely views over Park. TEA. *Adm 75p Chd free. Suns May 10, 17 (2-6)*

¶**Glazeley Old Rectory** ✗ (Mr & Mrs J.A. Goodall) 3½m S of Bridgnorth on B4363 Bridgnorth/Cleobury Mortimer rd. Medium-sized garden; soil pH 6.5; largely herbaceous borders with some cottage beds; bulbs, shrubs, shady, paved and moisture garden. Very beautiful, natural setting. TEAS. *Adm 50p Chd 25p. Mon May 4 (2-6)*

Greystones ✿✗✿ (Mr & Mrs A. A. Palmer) Little Ness, Baschurch, 8m NE of Shrewsbury. From A5 turn N at Montford Bridge, Shell Garage; follow signs to Little Ness 3m;

then to Ruyton IX Towns; garden ¾m on right. From Ruyton IX Towns follow lane opp church; garden ¾m on left. 1½-acres mixed herbaceous and shrub borders; small nursery specialising in unusual plants. *Adm 60p Chd 25p. Tues, Wed May 26, 27; Sat, Sun June 27, 28, Sun Aug 30 (2-6). Also by appt (Tel Baschurch 260439)*

The Grove ✿✗✿ (Mr & Mrs Philip Radcliffe Evans) Kinton, nr Nesscliff; 10m NW of Shrewsbury; 10m SE of Oswestry. From A5, N of Nesscliffe, turn off W at signpost to Kinton 1m; parking in road. Medium-sized plantsman's garden; informal mixed borders, largely shrubs, old-fashioned roses; fine views to Breiddens. TEAS (June only). *Adm 50p Chd 20p. Sun May 24; Sat, Sun June 13, 14 (2-5.30)*

Hatton Grange ✿✿ (Mrs Peter Afia) Shifnal. Lodge gate entrance on A464, 2m S of Shifnal. 1m up drive. Large dingle with pools, rhododendrons, azaleas, fine old trees; shrubbery; rose-garden; lily pond garden. TEAS. *Adm 50p Chd 25p (Share to Shropshire & Midwales Hospice). Sun, Mon June 7, 8 (2-7)*

¶**Haughmond** ✿✿ (Mr & Mrs G.E. Pearce) Felton Butler 8m NW of Shrewsbury. From Shrewsbury turn left for Felton Butler, then 1½m on left. From Oswestry turn right at Nesscliffe Hotel, over 1st Xrds, left at 2nd Xrds, 1st house on right. A comparitively new 1-acre garden with wildlife area under construction. Trees, shrubs and herbaceous borders. Children's play area. TEAS. *Adm 50p Chd 20p. Sun July 19 (2-6)*

Haye House ✗ (Mrs Eileen Paradise) Eardington 2m S of Bridgnorth. Take B4373 S, through Eardington, 1m on left. 1 acre re-planted and replanned since 1977 by owner; flower arrangers garden, owner National Flower Demonstrator. House (not open) C11 listed. TEAS. *Adm 50p Chd 10p. Sun May 24 (2-6)*

¶**Hazler Croft** ✿✗ (Mrs B. Vaughan) Sandford Avenue, Church Stretton. 200 yrds from traffic lights on A49 by-pass, turning for Much Wenlock on B4371. Medium-sized garden recently redesigned for year-round colour; trees, shrubs, roses and herbaceous. *Adm 60p Chd 10p. Sat June 27 (2-5.30)*

◆**Hodnet Hall Gardens** ✿✿ (Mr & the Hon Mrs Heber-Percy) 5½m SW of Market Drayton; 12m NE Shrewsbury; at junc of A53 and A442. 60-acre landscaped garden with series of lakes and pools; magnificent forest trees, great variety of flowers, shrubs providing colour throughout season; featured on TV and Radio. Unique collection of big-game trophies in C17 tearooms. Gift shop and kitchen garden. TEAS; parties to pre-book. Free car/coach park. Reduced rates for organised parties of 25 or over (Tel Hodnet 202). *Adm £1.40 Chd 70p. April 1 to Sept 26 daily (weekdays 2-5; Suns & Bank Hols 12-6). For NGS Sats Aug 15, 22 (2-5)*

Inga Pengar ✿❀ (Dr & Mrs O. Marrack) 6 High Fawr Ave, Oswestry. From traffic lights by church take Upper Brook Street, turn 2nd right into Oswald Place, follow signs. 1/3-acre maturing suburban garden; shrubs, herbaceous beds; small rock garden, stream, vegetables, soft fruit. Small collection of vintage machinery. *Adm 50p Chd 10p. Suns June 21 July 19 (2-6)*

Landscape ও (Dr & Mrs Symondson) Kinnerley, 8m SW of Oswestry. From A5 at Wolf's Head, Nesscliff, take B4396; then 1st left towards Kinnerley 1/2m; garden on right. 3-acre, family garden on sharp, light dry soil (ex-heathland); herbaceous, shrubs, trees; in progress is re-establishment of a true meadow. Childrens garden hut constructed from windblown trees. *Adm 50p Chd 20p. Sat, Sun June 13, 14 (2-6)*

Limeburners ও✿ (Mr & Mrs J.E. Derry) Lincoln Hill on outskirts of Ironbridge, Telford. Turn off B4380 at W edge of Ironbridge up Lincoln Hill; garden nr top of hill on left, below The Beeches Hospital. 9½ acres; wild garden and light woodland, formerly site of a rubbish tip developed by owners as a Nature Garden to attract wild life, particularly butterflies and moths. Shrubs, good ground cover giving all year round interest. Pools. Tea shops in town. *Adm 50p Chd 10p. Sun May 31 (2-6). Open by appt April to Sept (Tel Ironbridge 3715)*

Linley Hall ও❀ (Sir Jasper & Lady More) 3m NE of Bishop's Castle. Turn E off A488 nr Lydham. Parkland; lawns, rose garden, herbaceous border; lake; temple. Teas nearby. *Adm 50p Chd 10p. Sun July 26 (2-6)*

Lower Hall (Mr & Mrs C.F. Dumbell) Worfield, E of Bridgnorth, 1/2m N of A454 in village centre. 4 acres on R. Worfe; stream, pool; shrub and woodland garden. Tudor half-timbered house (not open). TEAS. *Adm £1 OAPs 75p Chd free. Sun June 28 (2-6)*

The Lyth ও✿❀ (Mr & Mrs L.R. Jebb) 1m SE of Ellesmere; entrance between Whitmere and junc of A528/A495. Medium-sized garden; rhododendrons, azaleas; good outlook on parkland; heath bed, shrub borders. Regency colonial house (not open), birthplace of Eglantyne Jebb. Meres nearby worth a visit. TEAS by local Save the Children Fund. *Adm 60p Chd 30p. Suns May 31, June 7 (2-6)*

The Magnolias ও❀ (Mr & Mrs Percy Thrower) Bomere Heath 6m N of Shrewsbury. Between A528 and B5067 from Shrewsbury. Follow RAC signs. 1½ acres overlooking rolling Shropshire countryside. Informal garden with island beds of hardy border plants, pools, rock garden, shrubs inc azaleas, rhododendrons, spacious lawns; vegetable garden; greenhouses. TEAS. *Adm 70p Chd 30p. Sun May 31 (11-7)*

Mallards Keep ✿ (Mr & Mrs Franklin Barrett) 13, Alison Rd, Church Stretton; S of Shrewsbury on A49, E on B4371 towards Much Wenlock; take 1st left up Watling St N by church, to Helmeth rd - Alison rd. 1/6-acre; interesting shrubs esp dwarf and other rhododendrons; peat plants; alpines; Orchid House. *Adm 50p Chd free. Suns, Mons April 5, 19, 20; May 3, 4, 24, 25; June 7; July 19; Aug 30, 31; Sept 27 (2-6)*

Mawley Hall (Mr & Mrs Galliers-Pratt) 2m NE of Cleobury Mortimer. On A4117 Bewdley-Ludlow Rd. Bus: X92, alight at gate. A natural garden in beautiful country with magnificent views; designed for wandering amongst roses, herbs, flowering shrubs; fine old trees. Home-made TEAS. *Adm 80p Chd 20p. Suns May 10, June 28 (2-6)*

Meadow House ও❀ (Mr & Mrs R. Sidaway) Oldbury. 1/2m SW of Bridgnorth off Cleobury Mortimer Rd. 3-acre garden with shrubs, trees, vegetables, roses, clematis and general interest. TEAS. *Adm 50p Chd free. Sat July 4 (2-6)*

Millichope Park ❀ (Mr & Mrs L. Bury) Munslow, 8m NE of Craven Arms. From Ludlow (11m) turn left off B4368, 3/4m out of Munslow. Large garden with lakes; woodland walks; fine specimen trees, wild flowers; herbaceous borders. TEAS (May only). *Adm 75p Chd 25p. Suns May 10, June 21 & Thurs July 9 (2-6)*

Moortown ✿❀ (David Bromley Esq) 5m N of Wellington. Take B5062 signed Moortown 1m between High Ercall and Crudgington. Large plantsman's garden; mixed borders, mainly old fashioned plants, crammed with interest; collection of Old English Florist's Tulips in May. *Adm 60p Chd 20p. Suns May 17, June 21 (2-5.30)*

The Morleys (Mr & Mrs J. Knight) Wallsbank, 3½m E of Church Stretton. B4371 Church Stretton-Much Wenlock; 3½m fork left for Stone Acton and Cardington; house 200yds on right. Medium-sized garden, made and maintained by present owners; planted for all-the-year colour, inc trees, shrubs, herbaceous; vegetables. TEAS by WI at Village Hall. *Adm 70p Chd 10p. Sat, Sun July 25, 26 (2-6)*

¶**Munslow House** ✿❀ (Mr & Mrs I.A.Beddows) Nr Craven Arms 7m. 15m from Bridgnorth (B4368) 10m Ludlow. Turn at War Memorial in Munslow; 1/4m to Church and House. 2-acre garden; azaleas, roses, flowering shrubs, herbaceous border, pool. Listed house (not open) built in 1805. Adjacent is St Micheal's Church of historial and architectural interest. TEAS. *Adm 50p Chd 25p. Sun May 17 (2-6)*

New Hall & (Mrs R.H. Treasure) Eaton-under-Heywood, 4m SE of Church Stretton. Between B4368 and B4371. 10 acres of woodland with grass walks, pools, wild flowers, streams. Garden suitable for wheelchairs only in dry weather. *Adm 70p Chd free. Suns April 26; May 10 (2-5)*

Oak Cottage Herb Garden ✿❀ (Mr & Mrs J. Thompson) Nesscliffe, 7m NW of Shrewsbury A5. Entrance 100yds down lane opp Nesscliffe Hotel. Car park through farmyard opp white cottage. Cottage garden (⅓-acre) based on herbs and old cottage garden plants. TEAS. *Adm 60p OAPs/Chd 30p. Sun June 21 (2-5.30)*

Oldfield ✿❀ (Mr & Mrs Paul Housden) nr Long Meadow End. From Craven Arms: take B4368 towards Clun; after 1½m turn right at telephone box; after 200yds turn left over cattle grid, continue for ¾m. A sheltered, sunny, 2.7-acres garden created since 1980; shrubs, roses, trees, vegetables, soft-fruits, fan and espalier fruits, orchard, duck pond, hill stream; further development of ½-acre of neglected land being tackled. TEAS. *Adm 80p Chd 40p in aid of St Marys, Hopesay. Sun July 5 (2-6)*

The Old Rectory &✿ (Mrs J. H. M. Stafford) Fitz; A5 NW of Shrewsbury; turn off at Montford Bridge, follow signs; from B5067 turn off at Leaton, follow signs. 1¼-acre botanists garden; shrub roses, vegetables; water garden. TEAS. *Adm 60p Chd 10p. Suns June 14 Sept 6 (2-5.30)*

The Old Vicarage & (W.B. Hutchinson Esq) Cardington, 3m N of B4371 Church Stretton-Much Wenlock Rd, signed, or turn off A49 Shrewsbury/Ludlow Rd at Leebotwood, 2½ acres re-designed for easy maintenance; trees, shrubs, roses, primulas, alpines, water and wild garden. TEAS. *Adm 60p Chd 10p. Suns May 24, July 19 (2-5.30)*

◆**Oteley** ❀ (Mr & Mrs R.K. Mainwaring) Ellesmere 1m. Entrance out of Ellesmere past Mere, opp Convent nr to A528/495 junc. 10-acres running down to Mere, inc walled kitchen garden; many interesting trees, views across Mere to Ellesmere Church. TEAS. *Adm 75p Chd 25p (Share to NSPCC). Sat, Sun July 11,12 (2-6)*

Peplow Hall &❀ (Hon R.V. Wynn) 3m S of Hodnet via A442; turn off E. Large garden with lawns, azaleas, rhododendrons, etc; roses, bedding out; walled kitchen garden; lake. TEAS. *Adm £1.50 Chd 50p. Sun May 24 (2-5)*

◆**Pitchford Hall** &❀ (Mr & Mrs Oliver Colthurst) 6½m S of Shrewsbury. A5/A458 junc (roundabout) signed to Pitchford and Acton Burnell. 4 acres; ½-timbered treehouse in lime tree built C17. Queen Victoria stayed here in 1832 (aged 13). St Michael's Church. Natural bitumen well. Home-made TEAS. *Adm 75p OAPs/Chd 50p (Share to St Michael's & All Angels, Pitchford). Sat, Suns June 6, 7 (2-6)*

Preen Manor ✿❀ (Mr & Mrs P. Trevor-Jones) Church Preen, nr Church Stretton; 5m SW of Much Wenlock. On B4371 3m turn right for Church Preen and Hughley; after 1½m turn left for Church Preen; over Xrds, ½m drive on right. 6 acres on site of C12 Cluniac monastery, later Norman Shaw mansion (now demolished); garden restored and replanned by present owners; terraced and kitchen gardens, wild garden; fine trees in park; woodland walks. C12 monastic church with oldest yew tree in Europe. Roy Lancaster Award 1984. Coach parties by appt (Tel Longville 207) TEAS. *Adm £1 Chd 15p. Thurs May 28, June 18, July 16 (2-7). Also by appt*

Ridgway Wood ✿ (Mr & Mrs A.S. Rankine) Edgton 4m NW of Craven Arms. Turn W off A49 on to A489, 2½m, then left towards Edgton ¾m, drive on right. Informal garden set in 20 acres woodland created and maintained for all year round colour. Extensive heather beds; azaleas, shrubs, trees; woodland walk. TEAS. *Adm 50p Chd free. Sat, Sun May 30, 31 (11-6). Also by appt (Lydbury North 278) All year*

Ruthall Manor &❀ (Mr & Mrs G.T. Clarke) Ditton Priors, Bridgnorth. Weston rd from village church 2nd left, garden ¾m. Medium-sized garden at 800ft; unusual plants collected since 1973 designed for easy maintenance, ground cover; pool. *Adm 50p Chd 10p. All year by appt only April-Oct (Tel Ditton Priors 608)*

Ryton Grove ❀ (Dr & Mrs W.S.A. Allan) Ryton, 4m S of Shifnal. A464 turn left (S) at Whiston Cross; then 1st right signed Ryton; continue (pass turn for Beckbury) to Ryton. Bus: Wolverhampton-Shifnal-Shrewsbury (Midland Red); alight at Whiston Cross. 6 acres; shrubs, rock garden; new experimental layout of Chinese, Himalayan, Australian, New Zealand, North American and some north European plants. woodland. *Adm 50p Chd 15p. Weds April 29, May 27, June 24 (2-6)*

¶**Stottesdon and Chorley Village Gardens** ❀ (Shottesdon & Chorley Garden Committee) 7m from Bridgnorth on B4363 turn right 3m. From Kidderminster 11m on A4117 turn right 4m. 2 village communities in unspoilt countryside. A variety of gardens, new and old, cottage flowers, unusual plants, vegetables, bedding displays, caravan and woodland gardens. TEAS. Plant and produce stalls. *Combined adm 50p Chd/OAPs 10p. Sun, Mon Aug 30, 31 (2-6)*

Sutherland House ৬ (Mr & Mrs J.G. Beasley) Sheriffhales, 2½m NE of Shifnal. E of Wellington via A5; turn off N on to B4379; house ½m on left. 5 acres, mainly lawns and shrubberies laid out since 1962. TEAS by Sheriffhales WI. *Adm 70p Chd 35p. (Share to St Mary's Church, Sheriffhales). Sun June 7 (2-6)*

¶**Sutton Hall** (Mr & Mrs T. Jones) Sutton Maddock, 6m Bridgnorth on A442 to Telford, turn left in Sutton Maddock for Sutton Maddock Church. 2-acres, rhododendrons, azaleas, shrubs, shrub roses, trees with clematis climbing through. *Adm 60p Chd 10p. Sat May 30 (2-6)*

Swallow Hayes ৬ (Mrs Michael Edwards) Rectory Rd, Albrighton, 7m NW of Wolverhampton. At Albrighton on A4l turn off into Rectory Rd (garden ½m from Albrighton). 2 acres; planted since 1968 with emphasis on all-the-year interest, colour and ease of maintenance; over 1500 different plants labelled. TEAS. *Adm 50p Chd 10p. Suns May 31, June 14 (2-6); also by appt for parties (Tel Albrighton 2624)*

◆¶**Walcot Hall** ❀ (The Hon Mrs E.C. Parish) Bishops Castle 3m. B4385 Craven Arms to Bishops Castle, turn left by Powis Arms, is Lydbury N. Arboretum planted by Lord Clive of India's son, now undergoing restoration. Cascades of rhododendrons, azaleas amongst specimen trees and pools. Fine views of Sir William Chambers Clock Towers, with lake and hills beyond. TEAS. *Adm 50p Chd 20p (Share to Walcot Chapel roof appeal). Sun, Mon June 14, 15 (2-6)*

1 Wellington Road ⚘ (Mr & Mrs G. Mansell) Donnington 4m NE of Telford. Take A518 towards Stafford. At Trench Lock roundabout take rd signed Trench for 1m; Garden opp Audi-VW dealers. Large rear garden created since 1980 maintained by owners and award winner in 1986. Planted primarily for year round flower arranging, owner a National Demonstrator. *Adm 60p Chd 20p. Sats, Suns June 27, 28; July 4, 5 (2-6)*

Whittington Village Gardens ৬❀ Daisy Lane, Whittington 2½m NE of Oswestry. Turn off A5 150 yds NW of church into Top Street; then into Daisy Lane. Group of 16 adjoining gardens from small to ⅓ acre, mostly S-facing showing a wide range of gardening activities. Pools; heathers; conifers; colourful annuals; dried flowers; herbaceous plants and herbs, vegetables and fruit. Children's play area at Greystones Daisy Lane. Park Highfields Farm Yard. Home-made TEAS. Cedarville and 21 Top Street. Combined adm 60p Chd 10p (Share to Shropshire Hospice). *Sat, Sun July 4, 5 (2-6)*

◆**Willey Park** (The Lord & Lady Forester) Broseley 5m NW of Bridgnorth. Turn W off B4373. Formal garden with ½m woodland/rhododendron walk; spectacular azalea bed near house. TEAS. *Adm 75p Chd 25p. Sun May 24 (2-6)*

The Wood ⚘ (Maj & Mrs F.J. Yates) Codsall Wood, 9m NW of Wolverhampton. 2m E of Albrighton on A41. Leave M54 at Tong intersection. From A5 turn S at Bradford Arms Hotel. Medium-sized garden; rose garden; shrubs; yew hedge. TEA. *Adm 50p Chd 20p. Sun May 31 (2-6)*

Wrentnall House ৬⚘ (M.W.Holcroft Esq) Pulverbatch. Shrewsbury Bypass (A5) turn S at roundabout 'Longden Road'; 2m beyond Longden turn right to Wrentnall. Interesting collection of plants and shrubs; herbaceous borders; beautiful view. TEAS. *Adm 70p Chd 30p. Sun June 28 (2-6)*

¶**Yeaton House** ⚘ (Mr & Mrs J. Lingford-Hughes) Yeaton. 7m NW of Shrewsbury. On A5 turn off at Montford Bridge, follow signs; or B5067 turn off at Walford Heath Xrds, follow signs. Parking in field behind house. 1¾ acres in delightful setting for both established and young shrubs and trees; lawns leading down to R. Perry. *Adm 60p Chd 10p. Sun Sept 6 (2-6)*

SOMERSET

Hon County Organiser:
MRS PATRICK TAYLOR, Beaumont House, New Street, Wells
Assistant Hon County Organisers:
MISS P. DAVIES-GILBERT, Coombe Quarry, West Monkton, Taunton
MRS BASIL NICHOLSON, Boxbush Farm, Batcombe, Shepton Mallet
Hon County Treasurer:
C.H.N. Scott Esq, Wistaria House, Dinder, Wells

DATES OF OPENING

BY APPOINTMENT ONLY for dates see text:
CHURCH COTTAGE, nr Somerton
EAST END FARM, nr Langport
REGULAR OPENINGS for dates see text:
CLAPTON COURT GARDENS, nr Crewkerne
GREENCOMBE, nr Porlock
HADSPEN HOUSE, nr Castle Cary
MILTON LODGE, Wells
WATERMEADOWS, nr Crewkerne

APRIL Sunday 5
BROADLEIGH COURT, nr Wellington
APRIL Friday 17
BERYL, Wells
APRIL Easter Sunday 19
FAIRFIELD, nr Bridgwater
WAYFORD MANOR, nr Crewkerne
APRIL Sunday 26
BARRINGTON COURT, nr Ilminster
BROADLEIGH COURT, nr Wellington
GREENCOMBE, nr Porlock
WOOTTON HOUSE, nr Glastonbury
MAY Sunday 3
STOWELL HILL, nr Templecombe
MAY Monday 4 (Bank Hol)
STOWELL HILL, nr Templecombe
WORTHY MANOR, Porlock
MAY Sunday 10
SHOWERINGS GARDENS, Shepton Mallet
STOWELL HILL, nr Templecombe
WAYFORD MANOR, nr Crewkerne
WORTHY MANOR, Porlock
MAY Sunday 17
BARRINGTON COURT, nr Ilminster
CANNINGTON COLLEGE
COURT HOUSE, East Quantoxhead
HINTON ST GEORGE GARDENS
INWOOD, nr Templecombe
STOWELL HILL, nr Templecombe
37 WHITMORE ROAD, Taunton
MAY Sunday 24
BROADLEIGH COURT, nr Wellington
MILTON LODGE, Wells
STOWELL HILL, nr Templecombe
WEACOMBE HOUSE, West Quantoxhead
MAY Monday 25 (Bank Hol)
STOWELL HILL, nr Templecombe
MAY Sat 30
GREENCOMBE, Porlock
MAY Sunday 31
CHARLTON MUSGROVE HOUSE, nr
Wincanton
MIDDLE HALSWAY, nr Williton
MILTON LODGE, Wells
WAYFORD MANOR, nr Crewkerne
JUNE Sunday 7
MILTON LODGE, Wells
JUNE Sunday 14
BARFORD PARK, nr Bridgwater
CHAPEL KNAP, Porlock Weir
HEWLETT'S MILL, Galhampton, nr Castle
Cary
LOWER SEVERALLS, nr Crewkerne
MILTON LODGE, Wells
SHEPTON NURSERY GARDEN, Shepton
Mallet
JUNE Sunday 21
GAULDEN MANOR, Lydeard St Lawrence
GREENCOMBE, Porlock
KITES CROFT, Westbury-sub-Mendip
MILTON LODGE, Wells
THE OLD RECTORY, Compton Pauncefoot
JUNE Sunday 28
BARRINGTON COURT, nr Ilminster
BROADMEADOWS, nr Shepton Mallet
KINGSDON, nr Somerton

LYTES CARY MANOR, nr Somerton
MILTON LODGE, Wells
NORTH CURRY GARDENS
STAPLETON MANOR, nr Martock
WAMBROOK HOUSE, nr Chard
YARLINGTON HOUSE, nr Wincanton
JULY Saturday 4
CRABB HALL, nr Beckington
SHAWFORD HOUSE AND MILL,
Beckington
JULY Sunday 5
CRABB HALL, nr Beckington
MILTON LODGE, Wells
JULY Sunday 12
HESTERCOMBE HOUSE, nr Taunton
MANOR HOUSE FARM, Long Sutton
MILTON LODGE, Wells
WASON HOUSE, Castle Cary
JULY Sunday 19
BARFORD PARK, nr Bridgwater
BITTESCOMBE MANOR, nr Wiveliscombe
EAST LAMBROOK MANOR, nr South
Petherton, Kingsdon, nr Somerton
LOWER SEVERALLS, nr Crewkerne
WIVELISCOMBE GARDENS
JULY Sunday 26
BARRINGTON COURT, nr Ilminster
AUGUST Sunday 2
STAPLETON MANOR, Martock
TINTINHULL HOUSE, nr Yeovil
AUGUST Saturday 15
MIDELNEY MANOR, nr Langport
AUGUST Monday 31 (Bank Hol)
BERYL, Wells
SEPTEMBER Sunday 6
BARRINGTON COURT, nr Ilminster
THE PILTON MANOR VINEYARD, nr
Shepton Mallet
SEPTEMBER Sunday 20
KITES CROFT, Westbury-sub-Mendip
NORTH WOOTTON VINEYARD, nr Wells

DESCRIPTIONS OF GARDENS

The Babycham Gardens see **Showering Gardens**

Barford Park &⚘ (Mr & Mrs Michael Stancomb) 5m W of Bridgwater. Take Enmore rd from Bridgwater; turn right on Spaxton rd. 4 acre formal, water and woodland garden. Georgian house and garden open May-Sept every Fri, Sat, Sun, & Bank Hols. TEA. *Adm 60p Chd 20p. For NGS Suns June 14, July 19 (2-6)*

Barrington Court &⚘❀ (A.I.A. Lyle Esq; The National Trust) NE of Ilminster. This virtually undiscovered garden was constructed in 1920 by Col Arthur Lyle from derelict farmland (the C16 cattle stalls still exist); its design and lay-out were approved of by Gertrude Jekyll; attractive paved paths with walled iris, rose and lily gardens. TEA. *Adm House & Garden £1 Chd 50p, House 50p.*

△Suns April 26, May 17, June 28, July 26, Sept 6 (2-6)

¶Beryl (Mr & Mrs E.Nowell) ½m N of Wells off B3139 to Bath. Left at Hawkers Lane. Victorian park created in 1842. Walled vegetable garden broken into quadrangles with box hedging and double flower picking borders. More recent heavy planting of trees and shrubs and creation of walks and vistas. Adm £1 Chd free. Good Fri April 17, Mon Aug 31 (11-6)

♦¶Bittescombe Manor (Mr & Mrs D. Wood) Upton 6m from Dulverton and Wiveliscombe. On A361 Taunton to Wiveliscombe, follow signs to Huish Champflower, left at Castle Inn, left at B3190 to Upton. The present 5-acre garden, 950 ft up on Brendon Hills, was begun in 1975. Formal walled rose garden, shrubbery, water garden and herbaceous borders. TEA. Adm £1 Chd free. Sun July 19 (2-6)

Broadleigh Court ♿⚥❀ (Mr & Mrs R.D. Kathro) Sampford Arundel, 3m SW of Wellington. M5 junc 26. From A38, 2m W of Wellington, turn off S at Beam Bridge Hotel. 5½ acres; informal dell setting surrounding Georgian house (not open); spring bulbs, rockery, hardy cyclamen, trees, shrubs inc. rhododendron, azalea, pieris, embothrium, eucryphia; lawns, small lake. TEA. Adm 80p Chd free. Suns April 5, 26, May 24 (2-6)

Broadmeadows ⚥ (Mrs M.I. Blatchford) 3 The Acorns, Oakhill. 3m NE of Shepton Mallet; off A367 or A37. ⅓ acre garden landscaped in 1981 by owner-housewife, inc fish pool, waterfall, rockeries, arbours, organic vegetable plot. Great variety of plants, common and unusual, from trees to alpines. TEA. Adm 70p Chd free (Share to Ashwick & Oakhill Village Hall). Sun June 28 (2-6)

Chapel Knap ♿❀ (Dr & Mrs H.K.N. Lister) Porlock Weir. A39 to Porlock village, then rd to Porlock Weir. ¼m before Porlock Weir take rd to Worthy (left); 1st house on right. 1½ acres; subtropical and tender species inc specimen Cornus; Trachycarpus; Australian and New Zealand plants; outstanding views over Porlock Bay. C15 nave of chapel incorporated in house. TEAS. Adm 50p Chd 10p. (Share to St Aubricius School, Porlock). Sun June 14 (11.30-5)

¶Charlton Musgrove House ⚥ (Mr & Mrs Alastair Ralston Saul) 1m N of Wincanton on B3081 to Bruton opposite race course; turning to Charlton Musgrove church. Terraced garden overlooking parkland, planted for all year round foliage effect. Sunken water garden with statuary surrounded by yew hedging. TEAS. Adm 75p Chd free. Sun May 31 (2-6)

¶Church Cottage ⚥❀ (Mrs A. Vaughan-Lee) Charlton Adam 3½m Somerton. Take A37 N from A303 Ilchester roundabout for 1½m; left then 1st right, bear left to church. ⅓-acre plantsman's garden. Raised beds with alpines; shrubs and hardy plants. Adm 60p. By appt May 15 to Sept 30 (Tel Charlton Mackrell 3336)

●Clapton Court ♿⚥❀ (Capt S.J. Loder) 3m S of Crewkerne on B3165. 10 acres; many rare trees and shrubs of botanical interest in immaculate formal gardens; fascinating woodland garden; a garden for all seasons. Plant centre offering high quality, unusual plants; pelargoniums, fuchsias a speciality. (Tel Crewkerne 73220). Lunches and TEAS March to Sept. Adm £1.50 OAPs & parties £1.20 Chd 30p. All year daily, ex Sats (weekdays 10-5; Suns 2-5); also Sats April 18 May 2, 9, 16, 23, 30 (2-5)

Court House ♿❀ (Col & Mrs Walter Luttrell) East Quantoxhead 12m W of Bridgwater off A39; house at end of village past duck pond. Lovely 5-acre garden; shrubs, roses and herbaceous. Views to sea and Quantocks. Tudor house (not open). Adm 75p Chd free. Sun May 17 (2-5.30)

Crabb Hall ⚥❀ (Dr & Mrs J. Beviss) Tellisford, 4m N Frome. Turn off A36 Frome-Bath at Woolverton; right in Tellisford. 2 acre informal garden on steep slope from terrace of C17 house to mill leat and lily pond. Species and shrub roses; silver-leafed plants; herb bed; pack horse bridge, riverside walks (picnics). TEA. Adm £1 Chd 50p (Share to Multiple Sclerosis Soc, Bath Branch). Sat & Sun July 4 & 5 (2-6)

East End Farm ⚥❀ (Mrs A.M. Wray) Pitney. Off B3153 Langport-Somerton. Pretty garden set among C17 stone farm buildings; large collection old fashioned and species roses and philadelphus. Adm 75p. Open by appt June 1 to July 31. Tel: Langport 250598

East Lambrook Manor Garden ⚥❀ (Mr & Mrs A.Norton) 2m NE of South Petherton. Off A303 to S Petherton; Martock rd, then left to E Lambrook at bottom of hill. Traditional 'cottage style' garden created by the late Margery Fish and made famous by her many gardening books. Many unusual and now rare plants, trees and shrubs. The Margery Fish Nursery sells plants from the garden. TEAS (July 19 only). Adm £1 Chd free. Open daily except Suns (other than Bank Hols), Xmas, New Year. For NGS Sun July 19 (9-5); parties by appt only (Tel 0460 40328)

Fairfield ♿ (Lady Gass) Stogursey, 11m NW of Bridgwater. From A39 Bridgwater-Minehead turn N; garden 1½m W of Stogursey. Woodland garden with bulbs and shrubs. Elizabethan house (not open). TEA.

Adm 60p (Share to Stogursey Church). Sun Apr 19 (2-5.30)

Farley Hungerford Gardens *(see Wiltshire)*

Gaulden Manor &✻❀ (J.H.N. Starkie Esq) Tolland, nr Lydeard St Lawrence, 9m NW of Taunton off A358. Medium-sized garden with bog plants, primulas, herb garden. TEAS. *Adm garden 75p (Share to Animal Health Trust).* △*Sun June 21 (2-5.30)*

Greencombe &✻❀ (Miss Joan Loraine; Greencombe Garden Trust) ½m W of Porlock, left off road to Porlock Weir. Garden overlooking Porlock Bay; camellias, rhododendrons, azaleas, peat-loving shrubs, maples, ferns under forest trees; many other unusual plants. Completely organic. *Adm £1 Chd 30p. May & June Suns & Bank Hols (2-6), Sats (11-5); July Sat 4 (11-5), Sun 5 (2-6), also by appt (tel Porlock 862363). For NGS Suns April 26, June 21 (2-6); Sat May 30 (11-5)*

●**Hadspen House** &✻❀ (Trustees of the late Sir Arthur Hobhouse) 2m SE of Castle Cary on A371 to Wincanton. 8 acre Edwardian garden with C18 background and house (not shown). Sheltered, south facing, with mature trees; but mainly new planting for bark and foliage interest; fascinating collecton of unusual, tender and rare plants; hostas; nursery. Tea George Hotel, Castle Cary; Suns TEAS at garden. *Adm £1 Chd free. All year round (except Jan) Tues to Sat (10-5); Suns & Bank Hols April to Oct (2-5); also by appt (Tel Castle Cary 50200)*

◆¶**Hestercombe House** ✻ (Somerset Fire Brigade) Cheddon Fitzpaine. Off A361 due N of Taunton to Cheddon Fitzpaine then follow signs. Jane Brown, author of *Gardens of a Golden Afternoon,* and horticultural and architectural experts responsible for the restoration of this marvellous Gertrude Jekyll/Edwin Lutyens garden will be on hand to talk about the garden. TEA. *Adm £1.25 Chd free.* △*Sun July 12 (2-6.30)*

Hewlett's Mill &✻ (Mr & Mrs D.F. Strachan) 2m S of Castle Cary. From A303 Sparkford to Wincanton turn N for N. Cadbury. In village take Galhampton Lane straight ahead. From A359 Sparkford to Castle Cary turn E for Yarlington, then 1st right. C17 watermill, 10 ft waterfall; rock garden with flowing water; bog gardens; large tree/shrub garden planted 1976 with many unusual items. TEAS. *Adm £1 Chd 50p. Sun June 14 (2-6)*

Hinton St George Gardens 2m NW of Crewkerne. N of A30 Crewkerne-Chard; S of A303 at roundabout signed Lopen & Merriott, then right to one of Somerset's prettiest villages. TEA. *Adm £1.50 for all 4, or 50p each, Chd free. Sun May 17 (2-5)*

    Field House & (Dr & Mrs A.M. McCall) Merriott rd ½m. 1½ acres; trees and shrubs planted since 1960. Paths through

camellias, rhododendrons, magnolias. *(Share to St Margaret's Som Hospice)*

    Harford Lodge &❀ (Mr & Mrs D.A. Simister) South St, ½m. Former lodge to Hinton House. 2½ acres; trees, shrubs, herbaceous plants, fruit, vegetables, in woodland setting with many young trees

    The Old Malt House ✻ (The Rt Hon Lord Peyton of Yeovil) Village st. 1¼ acre immaculately kept landscaped garden; views. *(Share to Village Hall)*

    Phoenix House & (Mrs S.Hardy) Gas Lane. ¾-acre partly walled garden. Spring bulbs, alpines, shrubs. *(Share to Village Hall)*

Inwood & (Count & Countess Guy de Pelet) Henstridge. Iron gates on A30 7m E of Sherborne. 7 acres beautiful trees; extensive lawns; gazebos; bulbs; cherry trees; lilac; woodland; statuary. Peacocks. Tea Stowell Hill. *Adm 60p Chd free. Sun May 17 (2-6)*

Kingsdon &✻❀ (Mr & Mrs Charles Marrow) 2m SE of Somerton off B3151 Ilchester rd. From Ilchester roundabout on A303 follow NT signs to Lytes Cary; left opp gates. 2-acre plantsman's garden and nursery garden. Over 500 varieties of unusual plants for sale. TEAS. *Adm £1 Chd 25p (Share to MS). Suns June 28, July 19 (2-7)*

Kites Croft ✻❀ (Dr & Mrs W. I. Stanton) Westbury-sub-Mendip 5m NW of Wells. At Westbury Cross on A371 turn uphill, right to square and left up Free Hill to Kites Croft rd. 2 acre all-year cottage garden on different levels up side of Mendips. Variety of plants, shrubs, trees; rockery; fine views to Glastonbury Tor. TEAS. *Adm 75p Chd 30p (Share to Village Hall). Suns June 21, Sept 20; also by appt Weds in June, July (Tel Wells 870328)*

¶**Lower Severalls** &✻❀ (Audrey & Mary Pring) 1½m NE of Crewkerne. Turning for Merriott off A30; or Haselbury rd from B3165. ¾-acre plantsman's garden beside early Ham stone farmhouse. Herbaceous borders inc collection of salvias and herbaceous geraniums. Herb garden. Nursery sells herbs, unusual herbaceous plants and wide range of fuchsias. TEAS. *Adm 50p Chd 15p. Suns June 14, July 19 (2-6)*

Lytes Cary Manor &✻ (J.B. Chittenden Esq; The National Trust) 2½m NE of Ilchester. Follow NT signs from roundabout on A303. Formal garden with yew hedges and herbaceous border. Tenant's varied and colourful private garden also open. C14/C15 house. Tea Kingsdon. *Adm house and garden £1 Chd 30p.* △*Sun June 28 (2-6)*

The Manor House Farm &✻ (R. Bramble Esq & Mrs M.L. Bramble) Long Sutton 4m E of Langport. On A372 to A303 at Ilchester roundabout. 2 acres; ornamental kitchen garden; lily pond; new planting of pleached limes; young shrub, rose and juniper walk.

TEA. *Adm 75p Chd free. Sun July 12 (2-6.30)*

¶**Middle Halsway** & (Mr & Mrs A.D.Stoddart) 4m from Williton, E off the Taunton-Minehead rd signed Halsway Manor. Right at the Manor. Roses, rhododendrons, shrubs; stream and small ponds. C15 thatched barn. TEAS. *Adm 50p Chd 10p. Sun May 31 (11-5)*

Midelney Manor &✗ (Maj R. Cely Trevilian) Drayton, 3m SW of Langport. Signed on A376 Langport-Taunton by Bell Hotel, Curry Rivel. 3 acres; walled gardens, wild garden. House, Elizabethan and Queen Anne, part shown. Heronry and falcon mews; bring field glasses. *Adm House & Garden £1.50 Chd 30p. △Sat Aug 15 (2-5.30)*

♦**Milton Lodge** ✗❀ (D.C. Tudway Quilter Esq) ½m N of Wells. From A39 Bristol-Wells, turn N up Old Bristol Rd; car park first gate on left. Mature terraced garden overlooking Cathedral and Vale of Avalon. Mixed borders; roses; fine trees. Separate 7-acre arboretum. TEAS. *Adm 70p Chd 30p (Share to St Margaret's Somerset Hospice). Suns May 24, 31, June 7, 14, 21, 28, July 5, 12 (2-6); also by appt for parties only*

¶**North Curry Gardens** ✗ 7m NE of Taunton. ND Turn off A361 or A378. Seven small to medium sized gardens, new and mature, in a beautiful village with church - "Cathedral of the Moors". TEA at Calmady House. *Combined adm £1.50 Chd free. Sun June 28 (2-6)*
   Calmady House (Cdr & Mrs J H Fiddian-Green)
   12 Church Road (Mr & Mrs M J Treble)
   Daisyhill House (Mrs M B McCormick)
   Fosse Cottage (Mrs M M Stone)
   Greenhaze Cottage (Mrs B D Barkham)
   Monksleigh (Major & Mrs I D M McDowall)
   Thatchers (Major & Mrs G W Lamb)

North Wootton Vineyard (Maj & Mrs Colin Gillespie) 3m S of Wells. Vineyard signed on A39, 1m NE of West Pennard. Peaceful cottage garden, stream; lovely position in Mendip foothills. Plus well-known 6-acre vineyard with winery; vineyard shop. WINE & TEAS. *Adm 75p Chd free (Share to Lord Roberts Workshops). Sun Sept 20 (2-6)*

The Old Rectory, Compton Pauncefoot &❀ (Mr & Mrs A.R. Macneal) 7m N of Sherborne, 5m W of Wincanton. Signed Compton Pauncefoot off A303 Wincanton-Sparkford. 3 acres; lawns; yew hedges, herbaceous, roses and vegetable garden. TEAS. *Adm 75p Chd free (Share to St Mary's Church). Sun June 22 (2-6)*

The Pilton Manor Vineyard &✗❀ (Nigel de Marsac Godden Esq) 2½m SW of Shepton Mallet on A361. From A37 Fosse Way turn W for Pilton. Grounds with stream, weir, waterfall and very large chestnuts; lime avenue. Rare square-built dovecote. Vineyard and winery; Manor house and original vineyard date back to 1235. For wheelchairs, vineyard and part of garden only suitable. Light lunch available in wine bar and garden (12-2.30; speciality stuffed vine leaves, French bread & local Cheddar cheese, salads) Video films on harvesting and bottling. LUNCH & TEAS. *Adm (inc 2 free tastings) £1.50 Chd free. △Sun Sep 6 (12-6)*

¶**Shawford House and Mill** ✗❀ (Mr J. Olive & Mrs R.F. Coleman) Beckington, 4m N of Frome on A36 to Bath. A large unspecialised family garden round a Georgian house and adjacent woollen mill (now a small opera house). Superb cedar and splendid walled vegetable garden. TEAS. *Adm 75p Chd 25p. Sat July 4 (11-6)*

Shepton Nursery Garden &✗❀ (Mr & Mrs P. W. Boughton) Old Wells Road, West Shepton. Turning signed Norah Fry Hospital off B3136 Glastonbury rd. Small colourful garden imaginatively laid out with traditonal and unusual plants. Nursery growing alpines and garden-worthy plants. TEA. *Adm 60p Chd 15p. Sun June 14 (2-6)*

Showerings Gardens ❀ (formerly The Babycham Gardens) Shepton Mallet on A37. Very fine rock garden, waterfalls, lake, shrubs, roses. Lunches & TEAS. *Adm 60p Chd 10p. Sun May 10 (11-5)*

Somerset College of Agriculture & Horticulture &✗ Cannington, 3m NW of Bridgwater. On A39 Bridgwater-Minehead rd. Old College: Benedictine Priory 1138; fine Elizabethan W front; 7 old sandstone walled gardens protect wide range of plants, inc many less hardy subjects, Ceanothus, Fremontias, Wistarias etc; 10 very large greenhouses recently built contain exceptionally wide range of ornamental plants. New College (built 1970); magnificent views to Quantocks; tree and shrub collections; ground cover plantings; rose garden; spring bedding in formal garden; lawn grass collection and trials; horticultural science garden; one of the largest collections of ornamental plants in SW England. Tea Ye Old Willow Tree, nr entrance. *Adm for both College grounds 50p Chd (& organised parties of OAPs) 25p. △Sun May 17 (2-6)*

Stapleton Manor &❀ (Mr & Mrs G.E.L. Sant) Martock 6m NW of Yeovil. B3165 Somerton - A303. 2½ acres; some fine trees surrounding scheduled Georgian Hamstone house (not open). Bog garden; roses; shrubs; herbaceous borders. *Adm 60p Chd free. Suns June 28 & Aug 2 (11-6)*

Stowell Hill ✗ (Mr & Mrs Robert McCreery) NE of Sherborne. Turn at Stowell, ½m N of Templecombe on A357. Spring bulbs; collection of flowering shrubs; inc rhododendrons, azaleas, magnolias, Japanese cherries.

TEAS. *Adm 50p Chd 20p. Suns & Mons May 3, 4, 10, 17, 24, 25 (2-6)*

Tintinhull House &⚘ (The National Trust) NW of Yeovil. NT signs on A303, W of Ilchester. Famous 2-acre garden in compartments, developed 1900-1960, influenced by Gertrude Jekyll and Hidcote; many good and uncommon plants. C17 & C18 house (not open). TEAS in aid of St Andrews Church. No free *Adm for NT members. Adm 75p Chd 25p.* △*Sun Aug 2 (2-6)*

Wambrook House ⚘⚘ (Brig & Mrs Guy Wheeler) Wambrook, 2m SW Chard. Turn off A30 1m W of Chard at top of hill. 2 acre organically run garden surrounding Regency Rectory (not open). Mature trees, mixed borders, roses; rockery; small water garden; walled vegetable garden with small vineyard. TEAS. *Adm 60p Chd 20p (Share to Wambrook Church Fabric Fund). Sun June 28 (2-6)*

Wason House ⚘⚘ (Jock Moreton) Upper High St, Castle Cary. Unexpected ½ acre garden abundantly planted with shrubs, climbers, ground cover plants in framework of mature trees and old brick walls. *Adm 50p Chd free. (Share to Save the Children Fund). Sun July 12 (2-6)*

Watermeadows ⚘⚘ (Mr & Mrs R Gawen) Clapton. 2½m S of Crewkerne on B3165 to Lyme Regis, 300yds beyond Clapton Court. All-year-round weed-free informal garden. Exuberant mixed borders with unusual plants, old roses and ditch garden. TEA. *Adm 50p Chd 10p. Open most days and by appt (Crewkerne 74421)*

♦**Wayford Manor** ⚘ (Robin L. Goffe Esq) SW of Crewkerne. Turning on B3165 at Clapton; or on A30 Chard-Crewkerne. 3 acres, noted for magnolias and acers. Bulbs; flowering trees, shrubs; rhododendrons. Garden redesigned by Harold Peto in 1902. Fine Elizabethan manor house (not shown). TEAS. *Adm 80p Chd 30p. Suns April 19, May 10, 31 (2-6); also by appt for parties only*

Weacombe House & (Mr & Mrs A J Greswell) West Quantoxhead. East of Williton on A39. Informal garden with many interesting shrubs, rhododendrons; lake; lawns; walled gardens; herb garden. TEAS. *Adm 75p Chd free (Share to Som BRCS.). Sun May 24 (2-6)*

37 Whitmore Rd &⚘ (Mr & Mrs E Goldsmith) Taunton. Leave Taunton following signs to Kingston; turn 1st left past Bishop Fox School; turn 2nd right into Whitmore rd. ⅓-acre flower garden with herbaceous and perennial plants laid out to make maximum use of space for pleasure garden, fruit and vegetable garden. Tea Taunton. *Adm 40p Chd 20p. Sun May 17 (2-5)*

¶**Wiveliscombe Gardens** A361 from Taunton. Two charming walled gardens in Church St.,

opp church. TEAS. *Combined adm 75p Chd free. Sun July 19 (11-5)*
Caradoc (Mr & Mrs M.K.Edmed) ⅔-acre landscaped walled garden
East Braynes Interesting historical features; gazebo, gardener's cote; monks' walk.

Wootton House & (The Hon Mrs John Acland-Hood) Butleigh Wootton, 3m S of Glastonbury. Herbaceous borders; rose garden; shrubs, trees, bulbs; rock garden; woodland garden. C17 house (not open). TEA. *Adm 60p (Share to BRCS). Sun Apr 26 (2-5.30)*

Worthy Manor ⚘⚘ (Mr & Mrs E.G.C. Voullaire) Porlock, 8m W of Minehead. At Porlock village take rd to Weir; turn left just beyond Riding School at rd signposted Worthy, then on ¾m. 1½ acres divided by walls or shrubs into number of separate gardens designed round water, roses, shrubs or woodland. To S lie wooded combes of Exmoor, to N the sea. Few waterfowl. TEAS. *Adm 50p Chd 20p (Share to BRCS). Sun, Mon May 4, 10 (2-6)*

Yarlington House &⚘⚘ (Count & Countess Charles de Salis) 3½m from both Wincanton and Castle Cary; signed Yarlington off A303 Wincanton-Sparkford, and off A371 Wincanton-Castle Cary. Pleached limes, statuary, rose garden, walled garden, laburnum walk, new woodland planting. Walled kitchen garden. C18 house (not open). TEAS. *Adm 75p Chd 50p (Share to St Mary's Church). Sun June 29 (2-6)*

STAFFORDSHIRE
& part of WEST MIDLANDS

Hon County Organiser:
MRS C. H. MITCHELL, White Lodge, Dayhills, Stone ST15 8RX

DATES OF OPENING

APRIL Saturday 25
  ECCLESHALL CASTLE & GARDENS
MAY Sunday 24
  WIGHTWICK MANOR, Compton
JUNE Sunday 7
  THE GARTH, Milford
  THE WOMBOURNE WODEHOUSE, Wolverhampton
JUNE Sunday 14
  LITTLE ONN HALL, Church Eaton
JUNE Sunday 28
  ARBOUR COTTAGE, Napley
JULY Sunday 5
  MANOR COTTAGE, Chapel Chorlton
JULY Saturday 11
  DOROTHY CLIVE GARDEN, Willoughbridge

JULY Sunday 12
THE GARTH, Milford
JULY Sunday 19
THE FIRS, nr Stone
AUGUST Saturday 22
MOSELEY HALL, Fordhouses
SEPTEMBER Sunday 27
SHUGBOROUGH, nr Stafford

DESCRIPTIONS OF GARDENS

Arbour Cottage &⊗ (Mr & Mrs D.K. Hewitt) Napley, Norton in Hales, 4m N of Market Drayton. Take A53, then B5415 signed Woore, turn left 1¾m at telephone box. 1¾ acre cottage-garden, part being developed from field; rock and alpine areas. TEAS. *Adm £1 Chd 50p. Sun June 28 (10-6)*

Dorothy Clive Garden (Willoughbridge Garden Trust) Elds Wood, Willoughbridge. 7m N of Market Drayton. Off A51 1m E of Woore. 7 acre garden: woodland with rhododendrons and azaleas, spring bulbs, shrub roses; water garden and large scree in fine landscaped setting. Car park. TEAS. *Adm £1 Chd 25p.* △*Sat July 11 (11-7.30)*

Eccleshall Castle and Gardens (Mr & Mrs Mark Carter) ½m N of Eccleshall on A519; 6m from M6, junc 14 (Stafford); 10m from junc 15 (Stoke-on-Trent). 20 acres inc wooded garden with moat lawns around William and Mary Mansion House; herbaceous, rose garden, wide variety of trees and shrubs; also in ruins of medieval Castle. Featured on TV, Radio and National Press. Gift shop. Homemade cream TEAS.Free car/coach parking. Guided tours of house. *Adm 80p Chd 50p (House extra).* △*For NGS Sat April 25 (2.5-30); also by appt (Tel Eccleshall 850250)*

¶**The Firs** ⊗ (Mr & Mrs H. Dulson) Cross Gate, 3m NE of Stone on A5005 approx 1m turn right at signpost. 2m to Spot Acre; garden ½m on Fulford Rd. Delphinium borders in cottage garden setting. TEA. *Adm 50p Chd 15p. Sun July 19 (2-5)*

The Garth ❀ (Mr & Mrs David Wright) 2 Broc Hill way, Milford, 4½m SE of Stafford. A513 Stafford-Rugeley rd; at Barley Mow turn right (S) to Brocton; left after 1m. ½-acre; shrubs, rhododendrons, azaleas, mixed herbaceous borders, naturalized bulbs; plants of interest to flower arrangers. Rock hewn caves. Fine landscape setting. Coach parties by appt. TEAS. *Adm 60p Chd 30p. Suns June 7, July 12 (2-6)*

Little Onn Hall & (Mr & Mrs I.H. Kidson) Church Eaton, 6m SW of Stafford. A449 Wolverhampton-Stafford; at Gailey roundabout turn W on to A5 for 1¼m; turn right to Stretton; 200 yds turn left for Church Eaton; or Bradford Arms-Wheaton Aston & Marston; 1¼m. 6-acre garden; herbaceous lined drive;

abundance of rhododendrons; formal paved rose garden with pavilions at front; large lawns with lily pond around house; old moat garden with fish tanks and small ruin; fine trees; walkways Paddock open for picnics TEA. *Adm £1 Chd 30p. Sun June 14 (2-6)*

Manor Cottage &⊗ (Mrs Joyce Heywood) Chapel Chorlton. 6m S of Newcastle-U-Lyme. On A51 Nantwich/Stone rd turn behind Cock Inn; white house on village green. ⅔ acre; unusual plants in flower arrangers cottage garden. TEAS. *Adm 60p Chd 40p. Sun July 5 (2-6)*

Moseley Hall &⊗❀ (The National Trust) Fordhouses, 3¼m N of Wolverhampton, Between A460 & A449 follow signs. Small modern reconstruction of C17 garden with formal box parterre; mainly includes plants grown in England before 1700; old roses, herbaceous plants, small herb garden, arbour. Late Elizabethan house. TEAS. *Adm House & Garden £1.80, Chd 90p; Garden 60p Chd 30p. Sat Aug 22 (2-5.30)*

◆**Shugborough** (The National Trust) 5m SE of Stafford. From A513 turn off N at Milford. The county seat of the 5th Earl of Litchfield (Royal photographer, Patrick Litchfield). The mansion house has fine C18 furnishings and former servants quarters houses county museum. The Working Park Farm has historic breeds of livestock; the landscaped park and gardens feature neo-classical monuments. TEAS. *Adm £1 OAPs/Chd 50p.* △*For NGS Sun Sept 27 (10.30-5.30)*

Wightwick Manor & (The National Trust) Compton, 3m W of Wolverhampton A454, Wolverhampton-Bridgnorth, just to N of rd, up Wightwick Bank, beside Mermaid Inn. 17-acre, Victorian-style garden laid out by Alfred Parsons; yew hedges; topiary; terraces; 2 pools; remarkable row of Irish yews and golden hollies; terrace by T.H.Mawson with stone fragments from bombed Houses of Parliament. Rhododendrons; azaleas. William Morris house; many treasures of period. TEA. *Adm £1 Chd 50p.* △*Sun May 24 (2.30-5.30)*

¶**The Wombourne Wodehouse** ⊗ (Mr & Mrs J. Philips) 4m S of Wolverhampton just off 449 on A463 to Sedgley. 18-acre garden laid out in 1750. Mainly rhododendrons, woodland walk, water garden. TEAS. *Adm £1 Chd 20p (Share to Arthritis and Rheumatism Council). Sun June 7 (2-6)*

SUFFOLK

Hon County Organisers:
(East) MRS B.A. JENKINS, SRN, SCM,
Paigles, 6 The Street, Holton-St-Peter,
Halesworth 1P19 8PH
(West) MRS MARTIN FORREST, Smallbridge
House, Cockfield, Bury St Edmunds
IP30 0HH

DATES OF OPENING

REGULAR OPENINGS for dates see text:
BLAKENHAM WOODLAND GARDEN, nr
Ipswich
EUSTON HALL, nr Thetford
SOMERLEYTON HALL, Lowestoft

APRIL Thursday 2
ELM GREEN FARMHOUSE, nr Bury St
Edmunds
APRIL Sunday 26
GIFFORD'S HALL, Wickhambrook
MAY Sunday 3
HOLTON-ST-PETER GARDENS
MAY Sunday 10
HARTSHALL NURSERY,
Walsham-le-Willows
MAY Thursday 14
ELM GREEN FARMHOUSE, nr Bury St
Edmunds
MAY Sunday 17
BEARES, Saxtead
BLAKENHAM WOODLAND GARDEN, nr
Ipswich
ST STEPHENS COTTAGE, Spexhall
MAY Sunday 24
CHEQUERS, Boxford
SEQUOIA'S, Athelington
THE WHITE HOUSE, Clare
JUNE Sunday 7
THE OLD RECTORY, Hawstead
SEQUOIA'S, Athelington
JUNE Sunday 14
HARTSHALL NURSERY,
Walsham-le-Willows
HUNTS PARK FARM, Great Thurlow
JUNE Sunday 21
GABLE HOUSE, Redisham
‡THE LAWN, Walsham-le-Willows
SEQUOIA'S, Athelington
‡WYKEN HALL, Stanton
JUNE Sunday 28
BUCKLESHAM HALL, nr Ipswich
GREAT THURLOW HALL, nr Haverhill
JULY Sunday 5
GIFFORD'S HALL, Wickhambrook
NEDGING GARDENS, nr Hadleigh
JULY Sunday 12
ELM GREEN FARMHOUSE, nr Bury St
Edmunds
GREAT THURLOW HALL, nr Haverhill
THE PRIORY, Stoke-by-Nayland
REDISHAM HALL, nr Beccles

JULY Sunday 19
HOLBECKS, Hadleigh
AUGUST Sunday 16 to Saturday 22
1 PARK LANE, Charsfield
SEPTEMBER Sunday 6
BEARES, Saxtead
SEPTEMBER Thursday 10
ELM GREEN FARM HOUSE, nr Bury St
Edmunds
SEPTEMBER Sunday 13
NEDGING HALL, nr Bildeston
SEPTEMBER Sunday 20
ST STEPHENS COTTAGE, nr Halesworth
OCTOBER Sunday 4
BEARES, Saxtead

DESCRIPTIONS OF GARDENS

Beares &⊛ (Mr & Mrs S.A. Notcutt) Saxtead.
Just off A1120 between Saxtead Green (and
windmill) and Dennington. 3m NW of Framl-
ingham (with castle). Garden has been developed around Suffolk pink farmhouse and
its ancient ponds; over 1,000 different trees,
shrubs and perennials; all clearly labelled.
TEA. *Adm 80p Chd free (Share to Suffolk
Naturalists Trust, Sept; Suffolk Historic Churches Trust, Oct). Suns May 17, Sept 6, Oct 4
(2-5.30)*

Blakenham Woodland Garden ✗ Little
Blakenham. 4m NW of Ipswich. Follow signs
from "The Beeches" at Lt Blakenham, 1m off
the old A1100, now called B1113. 5-acre
bluebell wood densely planted with fine collection of trees and shrubs; camellias, magnolias, cornus, azaleas, rhododendrons,
roses, hydrangeas. *Adm £1. Weds, Thurs,
Suns April to Sept (1-5). For NGS Sun May 17
(1-5)*

Bucklesham Hall ✗⊛ (Mr & Mrs P.A. Raven-
shear) Bucklesham 6m SE of Ipswich, E of
A1093. Drive 100yds N and opp to Bucklesham Village School and turning to Village.
7 acres; created and maintained by owners
since 1973; unusual plants, shrubs, trees;
shrub/rose garden; water and woodland gardens. TEAS. *Adm 75p Chd free (Share to
BRCS). Sun June 28 (2-6) also by appt (Tel
0473 88263)*

Chequers & (Miss J. Robinson) Boxford, 5m
W of Hadleigh via A1071. From Sudbury
A134 then A1071. From Ipswich A1071. From
Colchester A134. 2-3 acre plantsman's walled
and stream gardens full of rare plants. TEA.
Adm 50p Chd 20p. Sun May 24 (2-6)

Elm Green Farmhouse ✗⊛ (Dr J.W. Litchfield) Bradfield St Clare, 7m SSE of Bury St
Edmunds. Via A134 (going towards Sudbury), 1m after Sicklesmere turn left (E) and
follow signs to Cockfield Green for 2m; lane
to Elm Green Farm is 1m before Cockfield
Great Green. 1-acre garden created by owner
and his wife, surrounding thatched C17 farm-

house (not open). Plantman's garden with wide variety of shrubs; herbaceous plants, alpines, bulbs inc many lilies. TEA. *Adm 50p Chd 20p (Share to St Nicholas' Hospice, Bury St Edmunds). Thurs April 2, May 14, Sept 10, Sun July 12 (2-6) visitors welcome by appt March to Oct (Tel Cockfield Green 828399)*

Euston Hall ┷▨ (His Grace The Duke of Grafton) 3m S of Thetford on A1088 to Euston and Ixworth. From Newmarket take A11 to Elveden, then right for Barnham and Euston. Large garden; herbaceous and shrub borders, C17 pleasure grounds, lake. C18 house open; famous collection of paintings. C17 church; temple by William Kent. TEAS in old kitchen. *Adm house & garden £1.40 OAPs £1, Chd 60p.* △ *Thurs June to Sept (2.30-5.30)*

Gable House ┷▨❀ (Mr & Mrs John Foster) Redisham, 3½m S of Beccles. Mid-way between Beccles and Halesworth on Ringsfield-Ilketshall St Lawrence Rd. Garden of 1 acre; mixed borders inc irises and primulas; fruit and vegetables. TEAS. *Adm 50p Chd 25p (Share to St Peter's Church, Redisham). Sun June 21 (2-5.30)*

Gifford's Hall ┷▨❀ (Mrs J.M. Gardner) Wickhambrook; 10m SW of Bury St Edmunds, 10m NE of Haverhill, ¾m from Plumbers' Arms, Wickhambrook in direction of Bury St Edmunds on A143, garden ¾m up lane. Medium-sized garden; roses; herbaceous borders. C15 moated manor house (not open). TEA. *Adm 60p Chd 20p (Share to GRBS & RGOF). Suns April 26, July 5 (2-6)*

Great Thurlow Hall ┷ (R.A. Vestey Esq) N of Haverhill. Great Thurlow village on B106l from Newmarket; 3½m N of junc with A143 Haverhill-Bury St Edmunds rd. 20 acres; walled kitchen garden, greenhouses, herbaceous borders, shrubs, roses, spacious lawns, river walk, trout lake. *Adm 60p Chd 10p (Share to GRBS & RGOF). Suns June 28, July 12 (2-6)*

Hartshall Nursery ┷▨❀ (Mr & Mrs J.D.L. Wight) Walsham-le-Willows, 12m NE of Bury St Edmunds. Take Westthorpe rd from Walsham-le-Willows; Nursery is signed 2m on left. Gardens, arboretum, woodland (shelter, ornamental, commercial forestry), created since 1968, on 16 acres round farmstead. Around 2,000 varieties of rare and beautiful trees, shrubs, conifers, perennials, bulbs, alpines and roses. Coach parties by appt. TEA (NGS days only). *Nursery (with plant-finder service) open daily (no charge 10-4.30) except Suns, Mons; Christmas Day. For NGS (Adm 50p Chd free) Suns May 10, June 14 (2-6.30)*

Holbecks ❀ (Sir Joshua & Lady Rowley) Hadleigh. From Hadleigh High St turn into Duke St signed to Lower Layham; immediately over bridge go right up concrete rd to top of hill. 3 acres; early C19 landscape terraced and walled gardens, flowerbeds, roses and ornamental shrubs. TEA. *Adm 50p Chd 15p (Share to Suffolk Historic Churches Trust). Sun July 19 (2-5.30)*

Holton-St-Peter Gardens ┷❀ 1m NE of Halesworth; at junc of B1123 and B1124, 3m from Blythburgh (on A12). At least 6 gardens will be open in the village inc small modern gardens. Flower Festival in church. TEAS at Homestead. *Combined adm 60p Chd free; or 15p per garden. Sun May 3 (2-6)*
> **The Homestead** (Dr & Mrs Pagan)
> **Holton Lodge** (Mr K Spindler)
> **High Mill View** (Mrs Croft)
> **Paigles** (Mr & Mrs Jenkins)
> **33 Lower Park Walk** (Mr & Mrs Bennett)

Hunts Park Farm ▨ (Sir John & Lady Mowbray) Great Thurlow, 4m N of Haverhill 2M off A604 Cambridge-Haverhill, between Withersfield and Gt Thurlow on B1061. 1-acre garden surrounding attractive house (not open) with conservatory containing tender plants; shrubberies planted to make interesting layout; several well-established trees. TEA. *Adm 60p Chd 30p. Sun June 14 (2.30-5.30)*

¶**The Lawn** (Mr & Mrs R.Martineau) Walsham-le-Willows. 10m NE of Bury St Edmunds on A143. Signed Walsham-le-Willows, house on right, ½m short of village. 3-acres herbaceous borders, lawns, small walled garden. The main garden overlooks parkland; woodland walk, short circuit 5-10 mins, longer circuit 15-20 mins. TEA. *Adm 60p Chd 30p. Sun June 21 (2.30-6)*

Nedging Gardens 4m N of Hadleigh via A1141 signed Bildeston. Gardens on E side. Cream TEAS The Old Rectory. *Combined adm 70p Chd 20p (Share to British Diabetic Association, Ipswich Branch). Sun July 5 (2.30-5.30)*
> **Morpheys Cottage** ❀ (Mr & Mrs J.S. Davey) Small thatched cottage garden created 1981
> **The Old Rectory** (Mr & Mrs R.D. Macleod) 2-acres, flowers, shrubs. Fine views of surrounding countryside

Nedging Hall ┷ (Mr & Mrs R. Macaire) 4m N of Hadleigh via A1141 to Bildeston House on E side. 15 acres of park-like grounds with small lake and many fine trees. TEA. *Sun Sept 13 (2-5.30); Adm 70p Chd free*

¶**The Old Rectory** ▨ (Mr & Mrs M. Pampanini) Hawstead, 3M S of Bury St Edmunds. Victorian Rectory garden with fine established trees and recent interesting additions. Shrubberies and borders have been expertly planned with a variety of plants, all surrounded by well conditioned lawns. *Adm 50p Chd 20p. Sun June 7 (2-5.30)*

1 Park Lane &⚘❀ (Mrs E.E. Cole) Charsfield, 6m N of Woodbridge. On B1078, 3m W of Wickham Market. ¼-acre council house garden; vegetables, flowers for drying, 2 greenhouses; small fishponds with water wheel; many pot plants etc. In village of Charsfield (known to many readers and viewers as Akenfield). *Adm 50p. Sun Aug 16 daily to Sat Aug 22 (10-7.30)*

The Priory ❀ (Mr & Mrs H.F.A. Engleheart) Stoke-by-Nayland (1m); 8m N of Colchester, entrance on rd to Sudbury. Lawns; fine trees; small lakes; walled rose garden; mixed borders; greenhouses; peafowl. TEAS. *Adm 70p Chd 20p. Sun July 12 (2-6)*

Redisham Hall & (Mr Palgrave Brown) SW of Beccles. From A145 1½m S of Beccles, turn W on to Ringsfield-Bungay Rd. Beccles, Halesworth or Bungay, all within 6m. 5 acres; parkland and woods 400 acres. Georgian house c. 1760 (not shown). TEAS (3.30-5 only). *Adm 70p Chd 30p. Sun July 12 (2.30-6)*

¶**St Stephens Cottage** ⚘❀ (Mr & Mrs D.Gibbs) Spexhall, 2M N of Halesworth. Approx 1-acre garden. Features inc natural pond leading to new bog, herb and white garden. Many established deciduous and coniferous trees and shrubs, rockeries, herbaceous borders and island beds containing interesting and unusual plants. TEAS. *Adm 40p Chd free.* △*Suns May 17, Sept 20 (10-5), also by appt all year*

Sequoia's &⚘❀ (Mr & Mrs K. Hawes) Athelington, 6m SE of Eye, 1m SW of B1117 at Horham. ¾-acre mixed garden; trees, shrubs, conifers, perennials, rockery, fruit, vegetables; older spinney; fish pond. Most plants labelled. *Adm 50p Chd free. Suns May 24, June 7, 21 (2-6)*

♦●**Somerleyton Hall** &⚘ (The Lord & Lady Somerleyton) 5m NW of Lowestoft. Off B1074. Large garden; famous maze, beautiful trees and avenue. House C16 added to 1844. Grinling Gibbons' carving, library, tapestries. Mentioned in Domesday Book. Miniature railway. *Adm £1.90 OAPs £1.40 Chd £1 (House & Garden); £1.20 Chd 70p (Garden only). House & garden: Easter Sun to Sept 27, Thurs, Suns, Bank Hols; Tues, Weds in July and Aug (2-5.30); Garden only all other days except Sats (2-5.30)*

The White House &⚘ (Sir John & Lady Verney) Nethergate Street, Clare. On A1092, 5m W of Long Melford, 16m SE of Bury St. Edmunds. 1½-acre 'village' garden, bounded by flint wall on street side and R. Stour on S. Home-made TEAS. *Adm 70p Chd 30p (Share to Suffolk Historic Churches Trust). Sun May 24 (2-6)*

¶**Wyken Hall** (Mr & Mrs K.Carlisle) Stanton, 9m NE from Bury St Edmunds along A143; leave A143 between Ixworth and Stanton.

4-acre garden much developed recently; with knot and herb gardens; old fashioned rose garden; wild garden; lawns and gazebo; shrubs and trees. *Adm £1 OAPs 70p Chd free. Sun June 21 (2-6)*

SURREY

Hon County Organiser:
LADY HEALD, Chilworth Manor, Guildford GU4 8NL
Assistant Hon County Organisers:
MRS D.M. LIDDELL, Odd Cottage, West Clandon, Guildford GU4 7TG
MRS P. KARSLAKE, Oakfield Cottage Guildford Road, Cranleigh GU6 8TF
MRS J. FOULSHAM, Vale End, Albury, Guildford GU5 9BE
Hon County Treasurer:
LT. CDR. D. J. DAMPIER

DATES OF OPENING

BY APPOINTMENT ONLY
GORSE HILL MANOR, Virginia Water
SANTERREE, Weybridge
REGULAR OPENINGS for dates see text:
RAMSTER, Chiddingfold

APRIL Saturday 11 to Wednesday 15
CHILWORTH MANOR, Guildford
APRIL Easter Sunday 19
LODKIN, Hascombe
PINEWOOD HOUSE, Woking
APRIL Easter Monday 20
HASCOMBE COURT, Godalming
VANN, nr Hambledon
APRIL Tuesday 21 to Saturday 25
VANN, nr Hambledon
APRIL Sunday 26
BRADSTONE BROOK, Shalford
BROOK LODGE FARM COTTAGE, nr Dorking
CALLUNA, Hindhead
CUTT MILL HOUSE, Puttenham, nr Guildford
LIME TREE COTTAGE, Weybridge
22 WEST HILL AVENUE, Epsom
WOODSIDE, nr Ripley
MAY Sunday 3
FEATHERCOMBE, Hambledon
MALTHOUSE FARM, Hambledon
RAMSTER, Chiddingfold
MAY Monday 4 (Bank Hol)B
FEATHERCOMBE, Hambledon
MALTHOUSE FARM, Hambledon
VANN, nr Hambledon
MAY Tuesday 5 to Friday 8
MALTHOUSE FARM, Hambledon
VANN, nr Hambledon
MAY Saturday 9
VANN, nr Hambledon

MAY Sunday 10
    CALLUNA, Hindhead
    CHOBHAM PLACE, nr Woking
    RAMSTER, Chiddingfold
    WINTERSHALL, Bramley
MAY Saturday 16
    CLAREMONT LANDSCAPE GARDEN,
    Esher
MAY Sunday 17
    CHOBHAM PLACE, nr Woking
    DUNSBOROUGH PARK, Ripley
    RAMSTER, Chiddingfold
    VANN, nr Hambledon
    WINTERSHALL, Bramley
MAY Monday 18 to Friday 22
    VANN, nr Hambledon
MAY Saturday 23
    CHILWORTH MANOR, Guildford
    VANN, nr Hambledon
MAY Sunday 24
    CALLUNA, Hindhead
    CHILWORTH MANOR, Guildford
    COVERWOOD LAKES, Ewhurst
    FAIRWAY LODGE, Wentworth
    FEATHERCOMBE, Hambledon
    POSTFORD HOUSE, Chilworth
    RAMSTER, Chiddingfold
    WINDLESHAM PARK, nr Bagshot
MAY Monday 25 (Bank Hol)
    FEATHERCOMBE, Hambledon
    CHILWORTH MANOR, Guildford
    HASCOMBE COURT, Godalming
MAY Tuesday 26
    CHILWORTH MANOR, Guildford
MAY Wednesday 27
    CHILWORTH MANOR, Guildford
    LIME TREE COTTAGE, Weybridge
MAY Sunday 31
    ANNESLEY, Haslemere
    COVERWOOD LAKES, Ewhurst
    FAIRWAY LODGE, Wentworth
    PYRFORD COURT, nr Woking
    PINEWOOD HOUSE, Woking
    RAMSTER, Chiddingfold
    22 WEST HILL AVENUE, Epsom
    1 YEW TREE COTTAGES, nr Esher
JUNE Saturday 6
    LOXHILL (Park Hatch, Coach House, Round
    House)
    1 YEW TREE COTTAGES, nr Esher
JUNE Sunday 7
    BROOK LODGE FARM COTTAGE, nr
    Dorking
    CALLUNA, Hindhead
    COVERWOOD LAKES, Ewhurst
    LOXHILL (Park Hatch, Coach House, Round
    House)
    PYRFORD COURT, nr Woking
JUNE Sunday 14
    COVERWOOD LAKES, Ewhurst
    HASLEHURST, Haslemere
    LIME TREE COTTAGE, Weybridge
    PINEWOOD HOUSE, Woking
JUNE Wednesday 17 & Thursday 18
    COVERWOOD LAKES, Ewhurst

JUNE Saturday 20
    CHILWORTH MANOR, Guildford
JUNE Sunday 21
    CHILWORTH MANOR, Guildford
    COVERWOOD LAKES, Ewhurst
    25 LITTLE WOODCOTE ESTATE,
    Wallington
    LODKIN, Hascombe
    VALE END, Albury
    VANN, nr Hambledon
    1 YEW TREE COTTAGES, nr Esher
JUNE Monday 22 to Wednesday 24
    CHILWORTH MANOR, Guildford
    LOXHILL GARDENS, Godalming
    VANN, nr Hambledon
JUNE Thursday 25 & Friday 26
    VANN, nr Hambledon
JUNE Saturday 27
    THE MOORINGS, Horley
    VANN, nr Hambledon
JUNE Sunday 28
    APPLE TREE COTTAGE, Cranleigh
    CALLUNA, Hindhead
    THE MOORINGS, Horley
JUNE Monday 29
    THE MOORINGS, Horley
JULY Saturday 4
    SOUTH PARK FARM, South Godstone
JULY Sunday 5
    SOUTH PARK FARM, South Godstone
    22 WEST HILL AVENUE, Epsom
JULY Monday 6
    SOUTH PARK FARM, South Godstone
JULY Saturday 11
    LITTLE MYNTHURST FARM, Norwood Hill
JULY Sunday 12
    CALLUNA, Hindhead
    LITTLE MYNTHURST FARM, Norwood Hill
    MERRIST WOOD AGRICULTURAL
    COLLEGE, Worplesdon
    THE WHITE HOUSE, Cobham
    WINKWORTH ARBORETUM, nr
    Godalming
JULY Saturday 18
    CHILWORTH MANOR, Guildford
    POLESDEN LACEY, Bookham
    POLESDEN LODGE, Bookham
JULY Sunday 19
    CHILWORTH MANOR, Guildford
    DUNSBOROUGH PARK, Ripley
    ST MARY'S HOMES, Godstone
JULY Monday 20 to Wednesday 22
    CHILWORTH MANOR, Guildford
JULY Sunday 26
    CALLUNA, Hindhead
    HASCOMBE COURT, Godalming
AUGUST Saturday 1 to Wednesday 5
    CHILWORTH MANOR, Guildford
AUGUST Saturday 8
    BAKERSGATE, Pirbright
AUGUST Sunday 9
    CALLUNA, Hindhead
AUGUST Sunday 30
    ANNESLEY, Haslemere
    CALLUNA, Hindhead

AUGUST Monday 31 (Bank Hol)
HASCOMBE COURT, Godalming
SEPTEMBER Sunday 6
BROOK LODGE FARM COTTAGE, nr Dorking
25, LITTLE WOODCOTE ESTATE, Wallington
SEPTEMBER Sunday 13
SURREY END COTTAGE, Haslemere
SEPTEMBER Sunday 20
HASLEHURST, Haslemere
SEPTEMBER Sunday 27
CLAREMONT LANDSCAPE GARDEN, Esher
OCTOBER Sunday 25
PYRFORD COURT, nr Woking

DESCRIPTIONS OF GARDENS

Annesley &⊛ (Capt & Mrs Trechman) Three Gates Lane, Haslemere. First right from Haslemere High St (A286), ¼m down lane on right. 3 acres; shrubs, roses, annuals and items of interest to flower arrangers. Also open, entrance from Annesley, **Springfold** & (Mrs G. St G. Kelton) 18 acres overlooking Sussex Weald with magnificent views; mainly shrubs & woodland. Home-made TEAS. *Combined adm 60p Chd 20p. Suns May 31, Aug 30 (2-6)*

Apple Tree Cottage ⊛ (Mrs A.M. Sitwell) The Common, Cranleigh. A28l from Guildford; 1m after Bramley turn left (E) for Cranleigh; turn left at Xrds at the Common; Garden first on left. ⅓-acre; small shrub border, herbaceous border, small pond. Parking on Common. TEAS and ices 30p. *Adm 40p Chd 10p. Sun June 28 (2-6)*

¶Bakersgate ⚘ (Lt Col & Mrs Roland Pennefather) Ash Rd, Pirbright. 5m N of Guildford, 5m W of Woking. M3 exit 3 take A322; under railway bridge right to Pirbright. Left at T-junc, fork right into A324; at 1st turn, sharp left along Ash Rd. Red sign Concealed Entrances on left. 2½-acre first designed by Percy Cane in about 1927 with later alterations by Stuart Lee-Smith. Island herbaceous borders; all types and colours of conifers; rose beds; unexpected vistas. Camelias and mimosa shelter in greenhouse where all-year round propagation takes place. Orchard and extensive kitchen garden. TEAS. *Adm 50p Chd 20p (Share to BRC) Sat Aug 8 (2-6)*

Bradstone Brook &⚘ (Scott Brownrigg & Turner) Shalford. 3m S of Guildford on A281 towards Horsham; in Shalford take A248 to Dorking and Wonersh; past Shalford Common look for sign on left for Bradstone Brook. 20 acres. The layout for the present garden was advised by Gertrude Jekyll; still under reconstruction after 25 yrs of neglect; known for its water gardens, rockeries, herbaceous borders; naturalized bulbs of which there are over 150,000; trees some of which are under a preservation order: Betula nigra (black birch) is the largest in the country. TEA. *Adm 60p Chd 25p. Sun April 26 (2.30-6)*

Brook Lodge Farm Cottage ⚘⊛ (Mrs Basil Kingham) Blackbrook, 3m S of Dorking. Off A24 at sign Chart Lane South and Stonebridge, 150 yds past Plough Inn. 3-acre 40 year old plantsman's garden with wide selection of flowering trees, shrubs, herbaceous plants; large greenhouse, kitchen garden. TEA. *Adm £1 Chd 50p. Suns April 26, June 7, Sept 6 (2-6)*

Calluna ⚘⊛ (Mr & Mrs Phil Knox) Whitmoor Vale Rd, Hindhead, 5m N of Haslemere. From Hindhead A3 Xrds take A287 sign-posted Farnham. After 2½m turn left into Whitmoor Vale Rd. 1st house on left. Bus: 119 Aldershot-Midhurst; alight Whitmoor Vale Rd. ½-acre planted for all-yr-round colour with diversity of plants carefully combined for small setting; large rock garden with fine collection of alpines; island beds of herbaceous plants; shrub borders with bulbs and ground cover; wall shrubs and climbers; peat garden. Featured BBC TV's Exploring Gardens 1985. TEA. *Adm 60p Chd 10p. Suns April 26, May 10, 24, June 7, 28, July 12, 26, Aug 9, 30 (2-6); also by appt*

Chilworth Manor & (Lady Heald) 3½m SE of Guildford. From A248, in centre of Chilworth village, turn up Blacksmith Lane. Bus: LC 425 Guildford-Dorking; alight Blacksmith Lane. Station: Chilworth. Garden laid out in C17; C18 walled garden added by Sarah, Duchess of Marlborough; spring flowers; flowering shrubs; herbaceous border. House C17 with C18 wing on site of C11 monastery recorded in Domesday Book; stewponds in garden date from monastic period. Flower Decorations in house (Sats, Suns and May 25): April by Michael Kemp, Chilworth Manor, May by Horsley Floral Decoration Group, June by Ash Flower Ladies, July by Dorking FA Group, Aug by St Catherine's FA Club. Free car park in attractive surroundings open from 12.30 for picnicking. TEAS (Sats, Suns, and May 25 ONLY). *Adm to garden 60p Chd free. House 60p extra. Open Sats to Weds April 11-15, May 23-27, June 20-24, July 18-29, Aug 1-5 (2-6); also by appt*

Chobham Place ⚘⊛ (Sir William & Lady Atkins) Chobham. 4m NW of Woking. Take B383 Windsor rd from Chobham to Sunningdale; about 1m from Chobham turn left at signpost 'Valley End' & 'Chobham Place' Bus: AV55, 55A. Woking-Chobham; alight Burrow Hill. Collection of rhododendrons, azaleas, other flowering shrubs and trees; fine trees in park adjacent (about 36 acres); landscaping. *Adm 75p Chd 30p. Suns May 10 & 17 (2-5)*

Claremont Landscape Garden & (The National Trust) ½m SE of Esher; on E side of A307 (No access from new A3 by-pass). Station: Esher. Bus GL 715, alight at entrance gates. Earliest surviving English landscape garden; recently restored; begun by Vanbrugh and Bridgeman before 1720; extended and naturalized by Kent; lake; island with pavilion; grotto and turf amphitheatre; viewpoints and avenues. Refreshments available. *Sat adm 80p Chd 40p, Sun adm £1 Chd 50p.* △ *Sat May 16, Sun Sept 27 (9-7; last Adm 6.30)*

Coverwood Lakes &⚘❀ (Mr & Mrs C.G. Metson) Peaslake Rd, Ewhurst. 7m SW of Dorking. From A25 follow signs for Peaslake; garden ½m beyond Peaslake. Landscaped water and cottage gardens in lovely setting between Holmbury Hill and Pitch Hill; rhododendrons, azaleas, primulas, fine trees, both mature and young. Herd of pedigree Poll Hereford cattle and flock of mule sheep. (Mr Nigel Metson). TEAS. *Adm £1 Chd 50p carpark and Chd under 5 free. Farm & gardens. Suns June 7, 14, 21, Wed 17, Thurs 18. For NGS Suns May 24 & 31 (2-6.30)*

Cutt Mill House ⚘ (R.A. Skinner Esq) Puttenham, 6m W of Guildford. From Guildford via A31, after 4m take B3000; turn into Puttenham village; turn 1st left signed Cutt Mill and Elstead; 2m on left sign to House. 12 acres inc 6-acre lake; small water garden and streams, waterfall; many varieties daffodils, spring bulbs, fine trees; various ornamental duck in special enclosures. TEAS. Car Park Lower Puttenham Common. *Adm 50p Chd 20p (Share to St Edwards Church, Sutton Park). Sun April 26 (2-5)*

Dunsborough Park & (C.F.Hughesdon Esq) Ripley; entrance across Ripley Green. Bus: GL 715 alight Ripley village. Spring flowers, extensive rose gardens, herbaceous borders, greenhouses with tropical plants, water garden. *Adm 50p Chd 25p. Suns May 17, July 19, (2-6)*

Fairway Lodge ⚘❀ (Cdr & Mrs Innes Hamilton) South Drive, Virginia Water. From A30 at Virginia Water opp Wheatsheaf Restnt, turn down B389; right at roundabout; follow yellow signs. National Award garden celebrating year 20 from scratch. TEAS. *Adm 50p Chd 10p (Share to GRBS & RGOF). Suns May 24, 31 (2-7)*

Feathercombe &❀ (Miss Parker) nr Hambledon, S of Godalming. 2m from Milford Station on Hambledon Rd, turn to Feathercombe off rd between Hydestile Xrds and 'Merry Harriers' pub. Fine view; flowering shrubs, trees; heathers. Garden designed and made by Eric Parker. Picnic area at garden. Tea Winkworth Arboretum. *Adm 50p Chd 10p (Share to Order of St John). Suns, Mons May 3, 4, 24 & 25 (2-6)*

Gorse Hill Manor ⚘ (Mrs E. Barbour Paton) Gorse Hill Rd: Virginia Water. A30 turn opp Wheatsheaf Hotel into Christchurch Rd, phone box on right, turn 1st left into Gorse Hill Rd, house at end. Station: Virginia Water (15 mins walk). 3 acres; over 450 different varieties of trees and shrubs, all identified, which are a speciality. 2 donkeys and 1 pony. Croquet and putting. NO very young children. *Collecting box. By previous appt only; individuals & parties up to 40 are very welcome. (Tel Wentworth 2101)*

Hascombe Court ❀ (Mr & Mrs M.E. Pinto) 3½m SE of Godalming. Off A2130 between Hascombe and Godalming. Large garden with Jekyll influences, mostly designed by Percy Cane: Woodlands, rhododendrons, views. Herbaceous border, terrace and rose garden. Japanese, rock, water garden now restored, walled garden redesigned. Tea Winkworth Arboretum. *Adm 60p Chd 10p. Mons April 20, May 25, Aug 31. Sun July 26 (2-6)*

Haslehurst &⚘ (Mrs W.H. Whitbread) Bunch Lane, Haslemere. Turn off High St into Church Lane, leave church on left, carry on to T-junc Hazelhurst, 2nd on left. 2½ acres; lawns, superb trees, rhododendrons, azaleas; various shrubs; paved rose garden, double herbaceous border. C15 Barn. TEA. *Adm £1 Chd 50p (Share to Queen Mary's London Needlework Guild). Suns June 14, Sept 20 (2.30-6)*

Lime Tree Cottage ⚘❀ (Mr & Mrs P. Sinclair) 25 Ellesmere Rd; 1½m from Weybridge; Ellesmere Rd; turn off Queens Rd. A317 immediately W of junc with Severn Hills Rd. B365. Garden is at top of Ellesmere Rd. Design and planting combine to make this small (70'x70' inc house) cottage garden. TEA. *Adm 40p Chd free. Suns April 26, June 14; Wed May 27 (10.30-4.00). Also by appt.*

Little Mynthurst Farm &❀ (Mr & Mrs M. Stone) Norwood Hill. Between Leigh (2m) and Charlwood (3m); from Reigate take A217 to Horley; after 2m turn right just after R. Bridge at Sidlowbridge; 1st right signed 'Leigh'. Walled garden; old fashioned roses, herbaceous borders and shrubs around old farm house (not open). Kitchen garden with greenhouses. TEAS. *Adm £1 Chd 25p (Share to St Catherine's Hospice, Crawley). Sat & Sun July 11 & 12 (2-6.30)*

¶25 Little Woodcote Estate &⚘❀ (Mr & Mrs Brian Hiley) Wallington. Private Rd off Woodmansterne Lane. Signed SCC Smallholdings. Woodmansterne Lane joins B278 and A237. ½-acre exposed plantsmans garden overlaying chalk, built over last 6 years. Rock garden; herbaceous and annual borders; alpine greehouse; sink garden; interesting collection of old containers and garden bygones. *Adm 50p Chd 25p. Suns June 21, Sept 6 (2-7)*

Lodkin ❀ (Mr & Mrs W.N. Bolt) Lodkin Hill, Hascombe, 3m S of Godalming. Just off B2130 Godalming-Cranleigh, on outskirts of Hascombe; take narrow lane off signposted 'Thorncombe Street & Arboretum'. 2 acres; daffodils, cherries, pool formed by widening a stream developed naturally with small weirs, much wildlife inc. trout, crayfish and waterside plants etc. TEA. *Adm 60p Chd free. Suns April 19, June 21 (2-6)*

Loxhill ♿✂❀ 6m E of Godalming, 3m W Cranleigh on south-side of B2130. TEAS. *Combined adm £1 Chd 10p (Share to RDA) Sat & Sun June 6 & 7 (2.30-6)*

¶**Park Hatch** (Cdr & Mrs P. Corson) 15-acre flower arrangers garden. Rhododendrons, azaleas; lake; magnificent views on site of old mansion

¶**Coach House** (Mr & Mrs P. Turton) 2-acre small pretty garden on site of old stables

The Round House (Mr & Mrs V. Taylor) 4-acre market garden on site of old kitchen garden. Many old and forgotten types of apples, soft fruits and flowers.

Malthouse Farm (Mr & Mrs George Pitt) Hambledon, 3½m S of Godalming. Take A283 through Witley; after 1m at bottom of long downhill straight turn left to Hambledon; house ⅝m on right. 2-3 acres; overlooking fields with views to S Downs; rhododendrons, azaleas, flowering trees and shrubs; spring bulbs; roses; small water garden. House (not open) C17 with later additions. C18 granary on straddle stones. Small collection of Edwardian and vintage cars. Home-made TEAS (Sun, Mon only). *Adm 75p Chd 20p (honesty box Tues-Fri) (Share to Hambledon Nursery School). Sun-Fri May 3-8 (2-6)*

Merrist Wood Agricultural College ♿✂❀ Worplesdon. 4m NW of Guildford. 40-acres of amenity areas; landscape demonstration gardens; 15-acres nursery stock. House a listed building (Norman Shaw 1877). Second largest college of Agriculture and Horticulture in UK with students from many countries. TEA. *Adm £1 Chd 50p*

The Moorings ♿❀ (Dr & Mrs C.J.F.L. Williamson) Russells Cresc. Horley. Nr town centre between A23 and B2036; 400yds from the railway station. 1-acre secluded country garden in centre of small town; contains all sorts of rare plants, interesting trees, many roses, pleasant vistas. An escapist's garden! TEA. *Adm 60p Chd 20p. Sat, Sun, Mon June 27, 28, 29 (2-6)*

Pinewood House ♿✂❀ (Mr & Mrs J Van Zwanenberg), Heath House Rd, Worplesdon Hill. 3m Woking, 5m Guildford off A322 opp Brookwood Cemetery Wall. 4-acres. New walled garden and arboretum; water garden; bulbs in April. Interesting new house finished in Dec '86 with indoor plants. TEAS. *Adm £1 Chd 50p. Suns Apr 19, May 31, June 14 (2-5)*

Polesden Lacey ♿ (The National Trust) Bookham, nr Dorking. 1½m S of Great Bookham off A246 Leatherhead-Guildford rd. 60 acres formal gardens; extensive grounds, walled rose garden, winter garden, lavender garden, iris garden, lawns, good views. House originally a Regency villa dating early 1820's, remodelled after 1906 by the Hon Mrs Ronald Greville, well-known Edwardian hostess; fine paintings, furniture, porcelain and silver, also many photographs from Mrs Greville's albums on display. King George VI and Queen Elizabeth (now the Queen Mother) spent part of their honeymoon here. For wheelchair details contact Administrator (Tel Bookham 58203). Gift shop. Lunch and TEAS in licensed restaurant in grounds (11-6). *Adm garden £1, house £1.20 extra; Chd half price. Parties 15 or more must book (party rates £1.60, Chd £1.20, Wed, Thurs, Fri). Garden open daily 11-dusk; house 2-6. For NGS Sat July 18*

Postford House ♿❀ (Mrs R. Litler-Jones) Chilworth, 4m SE of Guildford. Route A248. Bus: LC 425 Guildford-Dorking; alight nr entrance. 25 acres; stream, rhododendrons, azaleas and shrubs. Swimming pool open (collecting box). TEAS. *Adm 40p Chd 10p. Sun May 24 (2-6), also by appt*

Pyrford Court ♿ (Mr & Mrs Cyril Laikin) Pyrford Common Rd, 2m E of Woking. B367 junc with Upshot Lane; off A3 to Ripley signed Pyrford. 20 acres; wild gardens, extensive lawns, azaleas, rhododendrons, wistarias, autumn colour. TEAS (May/June). *Adm 80p Chd 40p (Share to GRBS/RGOF and Sir William Perkins' School-Sports Hall Appeal). Suns May 31, June 7, (2-6.30), Oct 25 (12-4)*

♦**Ramster** ♿❀ (Mr & Mrs Paul Gunn) Chiddingfold. On A283, 1½m S of Chiddingfold; large iron gates on right. Mature 20 acre woodland garden of exceptional interest. Laid out by Gauntlett Nurseries of Chiddingfold in early 1900s. Fine rhododendrons, azaleas, camellias, magnolias, trees and shrubs. Picnic area. TEAS (Sats, Suns, Bank Hols May only). *Adm £1 Chd 20p. April 25 to June 14 daily (2-6). Parties by appt. (Tel. 0428 4422) For NGS each of the Suns in May*

St Mary's Homes ♿❀ Church Lane, Godstone. 6m E of Redhill. Parish church and old area of Godstone village, preservation area; Bay Pond (Surrey Naturalists Trust) 5 mins walk. A22 or A25(M25) to Godstone; Church Lane connects both, garden next to Church. Old people's almshouses with Chapel (open) all of architectural interest. Attractive gardens of traditional type; wide variety of annual and perennial plants. TEA. *Adm 40p Chd 10p. Sun July 19 (2-6)*

Santerre ♿❀ (Dr & Mrs Julian Edwards) Hamm Court, Weybridge. Hamm Court is a narrow lane off A317. From Weybridge take 1st right after crossing R. Wey. ¾-acre garden; borders of shrubs interplanted with herbaceous and lilies; woodland area with marsh garden of primulas etc; peat banks, raised beds, wall shrubs, alpines; butterfly corner; foliage plants a feature of garden which attempts to combine the needs of a family with a plantsman's love of variety (over 1700 varieties). Featured in The Garden, June 1982. By appt only (Tel. Weybridge 49057)

South Park Farm ♿ (Mr & Mrs E.B. Stewart-Smith) South Godstone, 1m S of railway bridge over A22 at South Godstone; turn right into Private Rd opp. Walker's Garden Centre; follow signs for 1m. Medium-sized garden; wide variety of roses, herbaceous border, fine trees and landscape, small lake. C17 (listed) farm house (not open). Peacocks. Home-made TEAS till 6 in large C17 barn. *Adm £1 Chd free. (Share to RNLI). Sat, Sun & Mon July 4, 5, 6 (2-7)*

Surrey End Cottage ❀ (Dr & Mrs W.R. Trotter) Tennyson's Lane. From Haslemere High Street (A286) take Petworth rd (B2131) then 2nd right. At next 2 Xrds follow signs for Tennyson's Lane. Park in lane. 1½-acre informal garden, created out of scrubland on upper slopes of beautiful wooded valley; variety of trees and shrubs, inc many with ornamental fruit or autumn colour; heathers and rhododendrons. Tea Haslemere. *Adm 50p Chd free. Sun Sept 13 (2-6)*

Vale End ❀ (Mr & Mrs John Foulsham) Albury, 4½m SE of Guildford. From Albury take A248 W for ¼m. 1-acre walled old-world cottage garden surrounding C18-C20 house (not open) in beautiful setting; views from terrace across sloping lawns to mill pond and woodlands; wide variety herbaceous plants, old roses, ornamental pond, attractive court yard; entirely maintained by owners. Home-made TEAS. *Adm 50p Chd 10p. Sun June 21 (2-6)*

Vann ❀ (Mr & Mrs M.B.Caröe) Hambledon, 6m S of Godalming. A283 to Chiddingfold; turn off at head of green. 1st left past P.O. signed 'Vann Lane'; house 2m on right: post box on gate. 4½ acres surrounding Tudor and William and Mary house; later additions and alterations incorporating old farm buildings by W.D. Caröe 1907-1909. Formal yew walk, ¼ acre pond. Gertrude Jekyll water garden, pergola, woodland, old cottage garden; spring bulbs, azaleas, roses. Featured in *Country Life 26 July 1986 and 1976, The Field, Surrey Magazine, Mon Jardin Ma Maison 1983-5 Feb 86.* Maintained by family with 12 hrs assistance per week. Home-made TEAS; April 20, May 4, 17, June 21. *Adm 85p Chd*

10p *(Share to Hambledon Nursery School Trust & Save the Children Fund). Mons April 20, May 4, Suns May 17, June 21, Tues-Sat Apr 21-25, May 5-9, Mon-Sat May 18-23, June 22-27 (10-6); also open by appt Easter; parties welcome (£1) (Tel Wormley 3413)*

22 West Hill Avenue ♿❀ (Dr & Mrs A. Hayward) Epsom. From Epsom High St (A24) take B280, West Hill, ⅓m, right into Meadway then 1st right. ¼-acre plantsman's garden; ponds, alpine houses, bulbs in pots. TEA. *Adm 50p Chd 25p. Suns April 26, May 31, July 5 (11-6); also by appt (Tel Epsom 22351)*

¶**The White House** ❀ (Mr & Mrs Henk Gentis) Sandy Way, Cobham. ½m from Oxshott. A244 (Esher-Leatherhead) 500 yds off A3 roundabout Leatherhead direction. 1st right Sandy Lane, 1st left Sandy Way. ½-acre flower arrangers garden with wide variety of annual and perennial cutting plants. TEA. *Adm 40p Chd 10p. Sun July 12 (2-6)*

¶**Windlesham Park** ♿❀ (Mr & Mrs James Scott) Woodlands Lane. 2m E of Bagshot. S of Sunningdale, NW of Chobham; from Windlesham Church S to T-junc, turn left into Thorndown Lane becoming Woodlands Lane over M3; entrance 100yds on right, white pillars. 9-acre parkland setting with many and varied well established azaleas and rhododendrons. Fine cedars and mature trees; wet areas. TEAS. *Adm £1 Chd 25p (Share to St John the Baptist Church). Sun May 24 (2-6)*

Winkworth Arboretum (The National Trust) Hascombe, Godalming. Entrances with car parks; Upper 3m SE of Godalming on E side of B2130; Lower 2¼m S of Bramley on Bramley-Hascombe rd, turn right off A281 from Guildford by Bramley Grange Hotel, up Snowdenham Lane. Coaches (by arrangement) should use Upper car park on B2130. Station: Godalming 3m. 95 acres of hillside planted with rare trees and shrubs; 2 lakes; many wild birds; view over N Downs. TEAS 2-6. *Adm £1 Chd 50p. △Sun July 12 (dawn-dusk)*

Wintershall ♿ (Mr & Mrs Peter Hutley) 2½m S of Bramley village on A281 turn right, then next right. Wintershall drive next on left. Bus: AV 33 Guildford-Horsham; alight Palmers Cross, 1m. 2½ acre garden and 100 acres of park and woodland; bluebell walks in spring; banks of wild daffodils; rhododendrons; pheasantry, specimen trees, ornamental pools and ponds; several acres of lakes and flight ponds; Domesday yew tree. TEAS served in Art Gallery with spring exhibition of paintings, prints, taxidermy and sculptures. Picnic area. *Adm £1 OAP/Chd Donations only. Suns May 10, 17 (11-6)*

Woodside ❀❀ (Mr & Mrs J.A. Colmer) Send Barns Lane, Send, nr Ripley, 4m NE of Guildford. 200 yds W of Roundabout at junc of

A247 and old A3 Ripley-Guildford rd. From London leave main rd at signs for Ripley; follow old A3 through Ripley village to roundabout. From Guildford after 2½m turn left off main rd at signs for Send and Woking. From Dorking via A247 through West Clandon. From Woking via A247 through Send village. ⅓-acre garden; main feature rock garden; many shrubs inc rhododendrons, ericaceous species etc; herbaceous planting; specialist collection of alpines. *Adm 50p Chd free. Sun April 26 (2-5)*

1 Yew Tree Cottages ⚬⊛ (Mr & Mrs G.A. Sinfield) Portsmouth Rd (Scilly Isles), Esher. ½m from Esher town centre on London side, close to Scilly Isles roundabout. Cars must park at 'Marquis of Granby' close to garden. Stations: Esher (main line), 1 min walk; Suns Hinchley Wood. Bus: Green Line 715, alight 'Orleans Arms'. Small, charming old-world cottage garden, designed and maintained entirely by owners; lawns and herbaceous borders set off by clipped yews, box edging, beautiful trees; spring garden with peonies, iris; Italian-style walled garden, with pool and fine old stonework, small courtyard garden; interesting stonework. TEA. (Meals & refreshments 'Marquis of Granby'). *Adm 50p Chd 25p. Suns May 31, June 21 (11-6); also by appt for parties (Tel 01-398 3871)*

SUSSEX

Hon County Organisers:
(East & Mid-Sussex) MRS MICHAEL TOYNBEE, Westerleigh, Mayfield Lane, Wadhurst TN5 6JE
(West Sussex) MRS NIGEL AZIS, Coke's Barn, West Burton, Pulborough RH20 1HD
Assistant Hon County Organisers:
MRS J. CHARLESWORTH, Snape Cottage Snape Lane, Wadhurst
MRS JANE NEWDICK, Dale House, West Burton, Pulborough
MRS A. TUCK, New Barn, Egdean, Pulborough
Hon County Treasurers:
(East & Mid-Sussex)
A.C.W. HUNTER ESQ, Cottenden Oast, Stonegate, Wadhurst
(West Sussex)
T. SANDEMAN ESQ, Littlehill, Hill Farm Lane, Pulborough

DATES OF OPENING

REGULAR OPENINGS for dates see text:
BORDE HILL, nr Haywards Heath
DENMANS, nr Arundel
GREAT DIXTER, Northiam
NEWICK PARK, Newick
PARHAM HOUSE GARDENS, nr Pulborough
SHEFFIELD PARK GARDENS, nr Lewes
WEST DEAN GARDENS, West Dean

MARCH Sun 15
POLLARDS NURSERY & SOUTHDOWN FLOWERS LTD., Walberton
MARCH Sat 28, Sun 29 & Mon 30
THE MANOR OF DEAN, nr Petworth
APRIL Friday 3
WEST DEAN GARDENS, nr Chichester
APRIL Sunday 5
RYMANS, Apuldram, nr Chichester
APRIL Tuesday 7
BATEMAN'S GARDEN, Burwash
APRIL Thursday 9
DENMANS, Fontwell, nr Chichester
APRIL Sunday 12
BERRI COURT, Yapton
DUCKYLS, Sharpthorne
FLORALDENE, Worthing
IMBERLEY, East Grinstead
THE UPPER LODGE, Stopham, nr Pulborough
APRIL Monday 13
BERRI COURT, Yapton
APRIL Friday 17
‡HOUGHTON FARM, nr Arundel
‡THE UPPER LODGE, Stopham, nr Pulborough
APRIL Easter Sunday 19
BIRCH GROVE HOUSE, Chelwood Gate
CHIDMERE, Chidham
THE UPPER LODGE, Stopham, nr Pulborough
APRIL Easter Monday 20
CHIDMERE, Chidham
THE FOX & HOUNDS FARM, Bolney
THE HIGH BEECHES, Handcross
HIGHDOWN, Goring-by-Sea
IMBERLEY, East Grinstead
APRIL Saturday 25
THE MANOR OF DEAN, nr Petworth
APRIL Sunday 26
BIRCH GROVE HOUSE, Chelwood Gate
COOKE'S HOUSE, West Burton
HORNBEAMS, Brede
LEGH MANOR, Ansty
MALT HOUSE, Chithurst, nr Rogate
THE MANOR OF DEAN, nr Petworth
NEWTIMBER PLACE, nr Pyecombe
PENNS IN THE ROCKS, Groombridge
RYMANS, Apuldram, nr Chichester
APRIL Monday 27
COOKE'S HOUSE, West Burton
ST ROCHE'S ARBORETUM
THE MANOR OF DEAN, nr Petworth
APRIL Tuesday 28
ST ROCHE'S ARBORETUM
APRIL Wednesday 29
ST ROCHE'S ARBORETUM

APRIL Thursday 30
 ST ROCHE'S ARBORETUM
MAY Friday 1
 ST ROCHE'S ARBORETUM
MAY Saturday 2
 ST ROCHE'S ARBORETUM
MAY Sunday 3
 BEECHES FARM, nr Uckfield
 ‡COOKE'S HOUSE, West Burton
 FITZHALL, Iping, nr Midhurst
 ‡THE HAZELS, Fittleworth
 HIGHDOWN, nr Goring-by-Sea
 MALT HOUSE, Chithurst, nr Rogate
 OFFHAM HOUSE, nr Lewes
 ST. ROCHES ARBORETUM
 ‡‡STILE HOUSE, Gay Street, nr
   Pulborough
 ‡‡THE UPPER LODGE, Stopham, nr.
   Pulborough
 ‡WATTS FARM COTTAGE, Watersfield
 WEDDERLIE HOUSE, Hastings
 WORTHING BOROUGH COUNCIL
   NURSERIES, nr Goring-on-Sea
MAY Monday 4 (Bank Hol)
 ‡COOKE'S HOUSE, West Burton
 THE FOX & HOUNDS FARM, Bolney
 ‡THE HAZELS, Fittleworth
 THE HIGH BEECHES, Handcross
 MALT HOUSE, Chithurst, nr Rogate
 ‡WATTS FARM COTTAGE, Watersfield
MAY Tuesday 5
 NYMANS, Handcross
MAY Saturday 9
 JOAN NIGHTINGALE HOUSE, Haywards
   Heath
 WEST RIDDENS, Ansty
MAY Sunday 10
 BERRI COURT, Yapton
 MALT HOUSE, Chithurst, nr Rogate
 PYRAMIDS, Harting
 RYSTWOOD HOUSE, Forest Row
 ‡STILE HOUSE, Gay Street, nr Pulborough
 ‡THE UPPER LODGE, Stopham
MAY Monday 11
 BERRI COURT, Yapton
 ST ROCHE'S ARBORETUM
MAY Tuesday 12
 ST ROCHE'S ARBORETUM
MAY Wednesday 13
 CHAMPS HILL, Coldwaltham, nr
   Pulborough
 HEASELANDS, nr Haywards Heath
 SHEFFIELD PARK GARDENS, nr Lewes
 ST ROCHE'S ARBORETUM
MAY Thursday 14
 CHAMPS HILL, Coldwaltham, nr
   Pulborough
 ST ROCHE'S ARBORETUM
MAY Friday 15
 ST ROCHE'S ARBORETUM
MAY Saturday 16
 CEDAR COTTAGE, Washington
 DUCKYLS, Sharpthorne
 RICARDO'S, Graffham, nr Petworth
 ST ROCHE'S ARBORETUM

MAY Sunday 17
 BERRI COURT, Yapton
 CHELWOOD VACHERY, Nutley, nr Uckfield
 DUCKYLS, Sharpthorne
 ‡HAMMERWOOD HOUSE, Iping, nr
   Midhurst
 HEASELANDS, Haywards Heath
 MALT HOUSE, Chithurst, nr Rogate
 MOORLANDS, Friar's Gate
 RICARDO'S, Graffam, nr Petworth
 ‡‡STILE HOUSE, Gay Street, nr
   Pulborough
 ST ROCHE'S ARBORETUM
 ‡TROTTON OLD RECTORY, nr Midhurst
 ‡‡THE UPPER LODGE, Stopham, nr
   Pulborough
 WEDDERLIE HOUSE, Hastings
MAY Wednesday 20
 HEASELANDS, Haywards Heath
 REACHWOOD, Northaim
MAY Saturday 23
 LANE END, Midhurst
 THE MANOR OF DEAN, nr Petworth
MAY Sunday 24
 BAKER'S FARM, Shipley
 CHIDMERE, Chidham
 COBBLERS, Crowborough
 ‡COWDRAY PARK GARDENS, nr Midhurst
 ‡HAMMERWOOD HOUSE, Iping, nr
   Midhurst
 HEASELANDS, Haywards Heath
 IMBERLEY, East Grinstead
 ‡LANE END, Midhurst
 ‡LITTLE PEANS, Robertsbridge
 MALT HOUSE, Chithurst, nr Rogate
 THE MANOR OF DEAN, nr Petworth
 MANVILLES FIELD, Fittleworth
 ‡MOUNTFIELD COURT, nr Robertsbridge
 SELEHURST, Lower Beeding
 ‡‡STILE HOUSE, Gay Street, nr
   Pulborough
 ‡‡THE UPPER LODGE, Stopham
MAY Monday 25 (Bank Hol)
 CHIDMERE, Chidham
 COPLANDS, Northiam
 THE HIGH BEECHES, Handcross
 HIGHDOWN, nr Goring-by-Sea
 LANE END, Midhurst
 MALT HOUSE, Chithurst, nr Rogate
 THE MANOR OF DEAN, nr Petworth
 MANVILLES FIELD, Fittleworth
 SELEHURST, Lower Beeding
MAY Wednesday 27
 HEASELANDS, Haywards Heath
MAY Saturday 30
 BIGNOR PARK, nr Pulborough
 KING EDWARD VII HOSPITAL, nr Midhurst
 LANE END, Midhurst
 NEWICK PARK, Newick
 WHITEHOUSE COTTAGE, Staplefield
   Lane, nr Haywards Heath
MAY Sunday 31
 ‡BIGNOR PARK, nr Pulborough
 COPYHOLD, Fernhurst

†COWBEECH, Hailsham
‡FITTLEWORTH GARDENS, nr
 Pulborough
HEASELANDS, Haywards Heath
HOLLYCOMBE, Liphook
LANE END, Midhurst
†LITTLE BUCKSTEEP, Dallington, nr
 Heathfield
MALT HOUSE, Chithurst, nr Rogate
NEWICK PARK, Newick
REACHWOOD, Northam
STANDEN, East Grinstead
‡THE UPPER LODGE, Stopham, nr
 Pulborough
WHITEHOUSE COTTAGE, Haywards
 Heath
JUNE Monday 1
 LANE END, Midhurst
 ST ROCHE'S ARBORETUM
JUNE Tuesday 2
 ST ROCHE'S ARBORETUM
JUNE Wednesday 3
 ST ROCHE'S ARBORETUM
JUNE Thursday 4
 ST ROCHE'S ARBORETUM
JUNE Friday 5
 ST ROCHE'S ARBORETUM
JUNE Saturday 6
 ST ROCHE'S ARBORETUM
 UPPARK, South Harting
JUNE Sunday 7
 COWBEECH, Hailsham
 ‡COBBLERS, Crowborough
 ‡COKE'S BARN, West Burton
 ‡DALE HOUSE, West Burton
 HOLLYCOMBE, Liphook
 KINGSTON GARDENS, nr Lewes
 LEGSHEATH FARM, East Grinstead
 MALT HOUSE, Chithurst, nr Rogate
 ‡MOORLANDS, Friar's Gate
 ST ROCHE'S ARBORETUM
 WEDDERLIE HOUSE, Hastings
JUNE Monday 8
 ‡COKE'S BARN, West Burton
 ‡DALE HOUSE, West Burton
JUNE Tuesday 9
 NYMANS, Handcross
JUNE Sunday 14
 CLAPHAM HOUSE, Litlington
 TROTTON OLD RECTORY, nr Midhurst
JUNE Monday 15
 ST ROCHE'S ARBORETUM
JUNE Tuesday 16
 ST ROCHE'S ARBORETUM
JUNE Wednesday 17
 REACHWOOD, Northiam
 ST ROCHE'S ARBORETUM
JUNE Thursday 18
 ST ROCHE'S ARBORETUM
JUNE Friday 19
 ST ROCHE'S ARBORETUM
JUNE Saturday 20
 HURST HOUSE, Sedlescombe
 THE MANOR OF DEAN, nr Petworth

ST ROCHE'S ARBORETUM
TELEGRAPH HOUSE, North Marden, nr
 Chichester
JUNE Sunday 21
 ‡BARCOMBE OLD RECTORY, nr Lewes
 BERRI COURT, Yapton
 ‡CLINTON LODGE, Fletching
 ‡‡COATES MANOR, Fittleworth
 COBBLERS, Crowborough
 ‡‡THE GARDEN HOUSE, Coates,
 Fittleworth
 ‡KNABBS FARMHOUSE, Fletching
 LITTLE HUTCHINGS, Etchingham
 ‡THE MANOR OF DEAN, nr Petworth
 ‡ORCHARD HOUSE, Lewes
 RYE GARDENS
 ROGATE GARDENS, nr Petersfield
 RYMANS, Apuldram, nr Chichester
 ST ROCHE'S ARBORETUM
 TELEGRAPH HOUSE, North Marden, nr
 Chichester
JUNE Monday 22
 BERRI COURT, Yapton
 ‡COATE'S MANOR, Fittleworth
 ‡THE GARDEN HOUSE, Coates,
 Fittleworth
 THE MANOR OF DEAN, nr Petworth
JUNE Tuesday 23
 ‡COATE'S MANOR, Fittleworth
 ‡THE GARDEN HOUSE, Coates,
 Fittleworth
JUNE Sunday 28
 AMBROSE PLACE BACK GARDENS,
 Worthing
 ‡BANKS FARM, Barcombe, nr Lewes
 CASTERS BROOK, Cocking, nr Midhurst
 CHIDMERE, Chidham
 CHILSHAM HOUSE, nr Hailsham
 COBBLERS, Crowborough
 HURSTON PLACE, Storrington
 ‡KETCHES, Newick
 ‡PHEASANTS HATCH, Piltdown
 ROGATE GARDENS, nr Petersfield
 TODDINGTON HOUSE, Littlehampton
 WINCHELSEA GARDENS, nr Rye
JUNE Monday 29
 CHIDMERE, Chidham
 HURSTON PLACE, Storrington
JULY Saturday 4
 CRAWLEY DOWN GARDENS, nr
 Haywards Heath
 FOLKINGTON PLACE, Polegate
JULY Sunday 5
 BARCOMBE OLD RECTORY, nr Lewes
 CASTERS BROOK, Cocking
 ‡COKE'S BARN, West Burton
 CRAWLEY DOWN GARDENS, nr
 Haywards Heath
 ‡DALE HOUSE, West Burton
 ‡‡FITZHALL, Iping, nr Midhurst
 FOLKINGTON PLACE, Polegate
 HARVEST HILL, Ansty
 NUTBOURNE GARDENS, nr Pulborough
 ‡‡THE PRIORY & 5 GARDENS,
 Eastbourne, nr Midhurst

PYRAMIDS, Harting
TODDINGTON HOUSE, Littlehampton

JULY Monday 6
COKE'S BARN, West Burton
DALE HOUSE, West Burton
NUTBOURNE GARDENS, nr Pulborough

JULY Saturday 11
COOKSBRIDGE, Fernhurst
THE MANOR OF DEAN, nr Petworth
TELEGRAPH HOUSE, North Marden, nr Chichester
UPPER HOUSE, West Burton

JULY Sunday 12
‡BAKER'S FARM, Shipley
BEECHES FARM, nr Uckfield
†BRICKWALL, Northam
‡BROOKFIELDS, River, nr Petworth
CARRIERS OAST, Northiam
COBBLERS, Crowborough
COOKSBRIDGE, Fernhurst
HORNBEAMS, Brede
‡THE MANOR OF DEAN, nr Petworth
‡NORMAN PLACE, Petworth
OFFHAM HOUSE, nr Lewes
‡PANNETTS, Shipley, nr Horsham
RYMANS, Apuldram, nr Chichester
TELEGRAPH HOUSE, North Marden, nr Chichester
UPPER HOUSE, West Burton
WEST STOKE HOUSE, nr Chichester

JULY Monday 13
‡BROOKFIELDS, River, nr Petworth
‡THE MANOR OF DEAN, nr Petworth
‡NORMAN PLACE, Petworth
WEST STOKE HOUSE, nr Chichester

JULY Tuesday 14
NORMAN PLACE, Petworth

JULY Wednesday 15
ALFRISTON GARDENS
NORMAN PLACE, Petworth

JULY Thursday 16 & Friday 17
NORMAN PLACE, Petworth

JULY Saturday 18
‡NORMAN PLACE, Petworth
‡SOUTH CORNER HOUSE, Duncton, nr Petworth

JULY Sunday 19
COBBLERS, Crowborough
COPLANDS, Northiam
DUCKYLS, Sharpthorne
HEASELANDS, Haywards Heath
‡SOUTH CORNER HOUSE, Duncton
‡WORMAN PLACE, Petworth

JULY Saturday 25
CROWN HOUSE, Eridge

JULY Sunday 26
CHILSHAM HOUSE, nr Hailsham
COBBLERS, Crowborough
CROWN HOUSE, Eridge
KINGSTON GARDENS, nr Lewes
STANDEN, East Grinstead

AUGUST Sunday 2
COBBLERS, Crowborough
COPYHOLD, Fernhurst
LEGH MANOR, Ansty
‡MILLSTONES, Wadhurst

‡SAXONBURY HOUSE, Frant

AUGUST Wednesday 5 & Thursday 6
PARHAM HOUSE & GARDENS, Pulborough

AUGUST Saturday 8
UPPARK, South Harting

AUGUST Wednesday 12 & Thursday 13
CHAMPS HILL, Coldwaltham, nr Pulborough

AUGUST Saturday 15
COOKSBRIDGE, Fernhurst
THE MANOR OF DEAN, nr Petworth

AUGUST Sunday 16
COBBLERS, Crowborough
‡COKE'S BARN, West Burton
COOKSBRIDGE, Fernhurst
‡DALE HOUSE, West Burton
FITZHALL, Iping, nr Midhurst
‡HOUGHTON FARM, nr Arundel
THE MANOR OF DEAN, nr Petworth

AUGUST Monday 17
‡COKE'S BARN, West Burton
‡DALE HOUSE, West Burton
‡HOUGHTON FARM, nr Arundel
THE MANOR OF DEAN, nr Petworth

AUGUST Sunday 23
FLORALDENE, Worthing
MEREWORTH, West Chiltington

AUGUST Monday 24
RYMANS, Apuldram, nr Chichester

AUGUST Friday 28
WAKEHURST PLACE, Ardingly

AUGUST Sunday 30
CHIDMERE, Chidham
NEWTIMBER PLACE, nr Pyecombe
TAPPINGTON GRANGE, Wadhurst

AUGUST Monday 31 (Bank Hol)
CHIDHERE, Chidham
PENNS IN THE ROCKS, Groombridge

SEPTEMBER Thursday 3
WEST DEAN GARDENS, nr Chichester

SEPTEMBER Saturday 5 & Sunday 6
THE MANOR OF DEAN, nr Petworth
NUTBOURNE MANOR VINEYARD, nr Pulborough

SEPTEMBER Monday 7
THE MANOR OF DEAN, nr Petworth

SEPTEMBER Saturday 12
BIGNOR PARK, nr Pulborough

SEPTEMBER Sunday 13
BIGNOR PARK, nr Pulborough
FITZHALL, Iping, nr Midhurst

SEPTEMBER Thursday 17
CHAMPS HILL, Coldwaltham, nr Pulborough

SEPTEMBER Sunday 20
MEREWORTH, West Chiltington
WADHURST PARK, Wadhurst

SEPTEMBER Sunday 27
COMBEHURST, Frant
MEREWORTH, West Chiltington

OCTOBER Saturday 3
MANOR OF DEAN, nr Petworth

OCTOBER Sunday 4
MANOR OF DEAN, nr Petworth

OCTOBER Monday 5
MANOR OF DEAN, nr Petworth
OCTOBER Sunday 11
ST ROCHES ARBORETUM, West Dean
OCTOBER Wednesday 14
SHEFFIELD PARK GARDENS, nr Lewes
OCTOBER Thursday 15
DENMANS, Fontwell, nr Arundell
OCTOBER Sunday 18 & Monday 19
BERRI COURT, Yapton
OCTOBER Sunday 25
THE HIGH BEECHES, Handcross
ST ROCHES ARBORETUM, West Dean
NOVEMBER Sunday 29
BEECHES FARM, nr Uckfield

DESCRIPTIONS OF GARDENS

¶**Alfriston Gardens** ⊛ 2m S of A27. TEAS
Cedar Cottage. *Combined adm £1 Chd 25p.*
Wed July 15 (2-5.30)
    Cedar Cottage (Mr & Mrs A.S.Crawley)
½-acre varied and colourful garden
    The Chaise House (Mrs Hyslop) small
walled garden full of colour; interesting
plants
    Walcot (Miss M. Turner) Sloe Lane.
Beautiful view and colourful garden

Ambrose Place Back Gardens, Richmond Rd
&⅍⊛ Worthing 10m E of Bognor, 7m W of
Brighton. Take Broadwater Rd into town centre, turn right at traffic lights into Richmond
Rd opposite Library; small town. Gardens
entrances on left; parking in rds. TEAS No 1 &
14. *Combined adm £1 Chd 25p (Share to*
Worthing Samaritans). Sun June 28 (2-6)
    No 1 (Mrs M.M. Rosenberg) Recently laid
out garden; shrubs, pond
    No 3 (Mr M. Smythe) Paved garden with
climbing plants and lawn
    No 4 (Mr & Mrs T.J. Worley) Small, newly
laid-out garden
    No 5 (Mrs A. White) Summer flowering
plants
    No 6 (Mr & Mrs Leslie Roberts) Recently
laid-out garden with conservatory
    No 11 (Mrs M. Stewart) Roses, summer
flowering plants
    No 14 (Mr & Mrs A.H.P. Humphrey)
Roses, summer flowering plants, greenhouse
    Ambrose Villa (Mr & Mrs Frank Leocardi)
Italian style small town garden

Baker's Farm ⅍⊛ (Mr & Mrs Mark Burrell)
Shipley, 5m S of Horsham. Take A24 then
A272 W, 2nd turn to Dragon's Green, left at
George & Dragon then 300 yds on left. Large
Wealdon garden; lake; laburnum tunnel;
shrubs, trees, rose walk; old fashioned roses;
new scented knot garden. TEAS. *Adm 75p*
Chd 20p (Share to St Mary the Virgin, Ship-
ley). Suns May 24, July 12 (2-6)

Banks Farm ⊛ (Michael Warren Esq) Barcombe 4m N of Lewes. Between A275 & A26,
well signposted. 7½ acres; shrubs, roses,
lawns; 2 ponds, water gardens; walled pool
garden. Picture exhibition in restored C18
barn. TEAS. *Adm 75p Chd 40p. Sun June 28*
(2-6)

Barcombe Old Rectory &⅍ (The Hon Mrs
Edmonstone) Barcombe. 4½m NE of Lewes.
Opp Church. 2 acres; herbaceous borders,
shrubs; typical country house garden; good
views of Downs. TEAS. *Adm 60p Chd 25p*
(Share to Distressed Gentlefolk Aid Associa-
tion. Suns June 21, July 5 (2-6)

¶**Bateman's** &⅍ (The National Trust) Burwash ½m S (A265). From rd leading S from W
end of village. Home of Rudyard Kipling from
1902-1936. Formal garden with lawns, yew
hedges, large pond in rose garden; wilder
part of garden with terraces, paths and borders. Bridge to Mill which grinds local wheat
into flour. Garden laid out before Kipling
lived in house, he planted yew hedges, rose
garden laid paths and made pond. TEAS.
Adm £2.20 Chd £1.10. △ *Tues Apr 7 (11-6)*

Beeches Farm &⅍⊛ (Mrs Vera Thomas)
Buckham Hill, Uckfield; Uckfield-Isfield rd.
Sunken garden; roses, borders; planted for
winter colour. TEA. *Adm 30p Chd 15p (Share*
to Royal Agricultural Benevolent Institution).
△*Suns May 3 & July 12 (2-5) Nov 29 (12-3)*

Berri Court & (Mr & Mrs J.C.Turner) Yapton,
5m SW of Arundel. In centre of village between PO & Black Dog pub. A2024 Little-
hampton-Chichester rd passes. 3-acre garden of wide interest; trees, flowering shrubs,
heathers, eucalyptus, daffodils, shrub roses,
hydrangeas. *Adm 60p Chd 25p. Suns, Mons*
April 12, 13; May 10, 11; June 21, 22 (2-5) Oct
18, 19 (12-4)

Bignor Park & (The Viscount & Viscountess
Mersey) Pulborough, 5m from Petworth on
West Burton rd. Nearest village Sutton (Sus-
sex). Medium-sized garden; walled her-
baceous garden; rhododendrons, azaleas.
Fine views to S Downs. TEAS in aid of Pet-
worth Cottage Hospital. *Adm 60p Chd 20p*
(Share to Village Hall, Sutton). Sats, Suns
May 30, 31 Sept 12, 13 (2-6)

Birch Grove House &⊛ (Birch Grove Estates
Ltd) Chelwood Gate. Station: East Grinstead
7m. Haywards Heath 8m. Daffodils in spring
woodland. *Adm 80p Chd 40p. Suns April 19,*
26 (2-6)

♦•**Borde Hill Garden** &⊛ (R.N.S.Clarke Esq)
1½m. N of Haywards Heath on Balcombe Rd.
Large garden of great botanical interest and
beauty; rare trees and shrubs; extensive
views; woodland walks, rhododendrons,
azaleas, camellias, magnolias, a wide variety
of other plants make this a delightful garden

to visit all year. New developments inc newly planted W bank terrace and water feature. Free car park. Picnic area. TEAS, snacks, luncheons, licensed rest. *Adm £1.50 Chd 50p parties of 20 or more £1. March 28 - Oct 31 Tues, Weds, Thurs, Sats, Suns & Bank Hols, inc Good Fri (10-6)*

♦¶**Brickwall** (Frewen Charitable Trust), Northiam. 8m NW of Rye on 2088. Tudor home of Trewen family since 1666. Gardens and walls built and laid out by Jane Frewen c.1680; chess and lavender gardens; arboretum. *Adm 50p. Sun July 12 (2-5)*

·¶**Brookfields** ✗ (R. Hodgson Esq) River, 3m W of Petworth; turn off A272 N signed River; follow NGS signs. Small cottage garden; herbaceous borders; lovely view to S. Downs. *Adm 50p Chd 20p. Sun, Mon July 12, 13 (2-6)*

¶**Carriers Oast** ✗ (Mr & Mrs John Andrews) Hastings Rd, Northiam. 8m NW of Rye; just out of Northiam on Hastings Rd (A28). ½-acre young attractive garden, started 1978, new pond and summer house. *Adm 50p Chd 25p. Sun July 12 (2-5)*

Casters Brook ✗❀ (Mr & Mrs John Whitehorn) Cocking; 3m S of Midhurst at Cocking PO on A286 take sharp turn E; garden is 100 yds on right, through farm-yard. 2-acre chalk garden made from old orchard since 1963; slopes to old mill pond, interesting corners; good collection of old roses; fine downland setting. TEA. *Adm 60p Chd 25p (Share to Cocking PCC). Sun June 28, Sun July 5 (2-6)*

Cedar Cottage ♿✗❀ (Mr & Mrs G. Goatcher) Rock Rd, Washington. S of Ashington turn W off A24 at Rock Xrds for ½m. Park in Nursery Car Park. 'Mixed' borders with plants for the connoisseur; mature and rare specimens in adjoining Nursery borders. *Adm 50p Chd 15p. Sat May 16 (2-6)*

Champs Hill ✗❀ (Mr & Mrs David Bowerman) Coldwaltham, S of Pulborough. From Pulborough on A29, in Coldwaltham turn right to Fittleworth Rd; garden 300 yds on right. 27-acre wild garden on old sandpits; woodland walks; heathers; views of Arun Valley and S Downs. *Adm 75p Chd free. Weds, Thurs May 13, 14; Aug 12, 13; Thurs Sept 17 (11-6)*

Chelwood Vachery ✗❀ (BAT Industries plc) Nutley, nr Uckfield on A22 3m S of Forest Row. 108 acres; woodland; paddocks; 24 acres formal gardens of great charm and much interest; ponds; rock pools, etc; bird sanctuary. TEA. *Adm £1.50 Chd 60p. Sun May 17 (2-6)*

Chidmere ♿ (Thomas Baxendale Esq) Chidham, 6m W of Chichester. A27 1m Bus: SD276/200 Chichester-Emsworth. Interesting garden; subject of article in *Country Life*; yew and hornbeam hedges; bulbs, rock garden and flowering shrubs bounded by large mere, now a private nature reserve. C15 house (not shown). *Adm 60p Chd 20p. Suns & Mons April 19, 20; May 24, 25; June 28, 29; Aug 30, 31 (2-7); also by appt for parties only (Tel Bosham 573096)*

Chilsham House ♿✗ (Mr & Mrs P. Cutler) Herstmonceux, 5m NE of Hailsham. From A271 in Hertsmonceux turn by Woolpack Inn towards Cowbeech; after ¾m turn right into Chilsham Lane; house ¾m on left. 1½ acres; herbaceous border; water garden; old-fashioned roses; small enclosures in colour harmony. TEAS. *Adm 70p Chd 20p. Suns June 28 July 26 (2-5.30)*

¶**Clapham House** ♿❀ (Mrs P.Brassart) Litlington W of Eastbourne. Garden of 24 acres; ponds with ducks and waterlilies; 1-acre of walled vegetable gardens, rose gardens. TEAS. *Adm 70p Chd 25p. Sun June 14 (2-6)*

Clinton Lodge ♿ (Mr & Mrs H. Collum) Fletching, 4m NW of Uckfield; from A272 turn N at Piltdown for Fletching, 1½m. 4-acre semi-formal romantic garden, with rose garden, herbaceous borders, walled garden; newly constructed copy of C17 scented herb garden. Queen Anne & Georgian house (not open). TEAS. *Adm 70p Chd 30p (Share to Fletching Church Fabric Fund). Sun June 21 (2-6.30)*

Coates Manor ♿✗ (Mrs G.H.Thorp) nr Fittleworth. ½m S of Fittleworth; turn off B2138 at signpost marked 'Coates'. 1 acre, mainly shrubs and foliage of special interest. Elizabethan house (not shown) scheduled of historic interest. TEAS. *Adm 75p Chd 20p. Sun, Mon, Tues June 21, 22, 23 (ll-6); also by appt*

Cobblers ✗ (Mr & Mrs Martin Furniss) Mount Pleasant, Jarvis Brook, Crowborough. A26; at Crowborough Cross take B2100 to Crowborough Station. at 2nd Xrds turn into Tollwood Rd for ¼m. Parking behind The Wheatsheaf Inn. 2-acre sloping site designed by present owners since 1968 to display outstanding range of herbaceous and shrub species and water garden, giving all-season colour. Subject of articles in RHS Journal Country Life, Homes and Gardens and BBC2 gardening programmes. TEAS. *Adm £1 Chd 50p. (Share to The National Trust). Suns May 24, June 7, 21, 28, July 12, 19, 26, Aug 2, 16 (2.30-6)*

Coke's Barn ♿✗ (Mr & Mrs Nigel Azis) West Burton 5m SW of Pulborough/Petworth. At foot of Bury Hill turn W off A29 to W. Burton for 1m then follow signs. Major part of existing garden redesigned surrounding converted stone barn. S facing conservatory with gravelled courtyard garden; old roses, herbaceous, shrubs; water area. TEA (Suns). *Adm 50p Chd 20p. Suns, Mons June 7, 8 July 5, 6 Aug 16, 17 (2-6)*

Cooke's House ✿ (Miss J.B. Courtauld) West Burton, 5m SW of Pulborough. 1m from Roman Villa, Bignor. Turn off A29 at White Horse, Bury, ¾m. Medium-sized garden under the Downs, round Elizabethan house (not open); varied interest inc spring flowers, topiary, old roses, herbs. Free car park. *Adm 50p Chd 10p. Suns, Mons April 26, 27 May 3, 4 (2-6)*

Cooksbridge ✗ (Mr & Mrs N.Tonkin) Fernhurst. On A286 between Haslemere & Midhurst, ¾m S of Fernhurst Xrds. 6 acres with many secluded corners; large variety of plants; lake; woodland; vegetable garden; greenhouses. TEAS. *Adm 75p Chd 30p. Sats, Suns July 11, 12 Aug 15, 16 (2-6)*

Combehurst ❀ (Mrs E.E Roberts) 3m S of Tunbridge Wells off A267, 400 yds S of B2099. 2½-acre beautifully laid out garden; shrubs trees, plants. *Adm 60p Chd 20p. Sun Sept 27 (2-6)*

Coplands ✿✗❀ (Mr & Mrs Hugh Saunders) Dixter Lane (nr Great Dixter) Northiam. 1 acre; established garden recently redesigned; rhododendrons, azaleas, flowering shrubs and roses, bulbs, mature trees, many rare plants. *Adm 50p Chd 30p. Mon May 25, Sun July 19 (2.30-6); also by appt (Tel Northiam 2598)*

Copyhold ✗ (Mr & Mrs P.B.L. Coghlan) Fernhurst, 3m S of Haslemere. Take A286 S towards Midhurst, before descending to Fernhurst, turn left into Copyhold Lane. 3-acre sloping garden; fine shrubs, rhododendrons, azaleas, camellias, hydrangeas; ornamental ponds; magnificent view to Blackdown and South Downs; woodland walk to lakes. *Adm 80p Chd 20p. Suns May 31, Aug 2 (2-6)*

Cowbeech Farm ✗❀ (Mrs M. Huiskamp) Cowbeech, 4m NE of Hailsham. A271 to Amerstone; then turn off N for Cowbeech. 5-acre garden; natural dell with waterfall; woodland walk; bog and herb garden, choice shrubs and trees. Farmhouse TEAS. *Adm 75p Chd 35p (Share to The Russian Church in Exile). Suns May 31, June 7 (2-6)*

Cowdray Park Gardens ✿ (The Viscount Cowdray) Midhurst. Bus:201, 261, Midhurst-Petworth-Worthing, alight Cowdray Park. Entrance by East Front. Avenue of Wellingtonias; rhododendrons, azaleas; sunken garden with large variety trees and shrubs; lebanon cedar 300 yrs old; pleasure garden surrounded by ha-ha. *Adm 50p. Sun May 24 (2-7)*

¶**Crawley Down Gardens** ✗❀ (Mr & Mrs R Lloyd) 8 m N of Haywards Heath on B2028. TEAS at Bankton Cottage. *Adm £1 Chd 20p. (Share to Birthright) Sat, Sun July 4, 5 (2-6)*

Bawkton Cottage (Mr & Mrs R.Lloyd) 3½-acre walled herbaceous, rose garden and woodland walk around lake.
Yew Tree Cottage (Mrs J.Hudson) ¼-acre cottage garden with all year round interest.

Crown House ✿✗❀ (Maj & Mrs L. Cave) Eridge, 3m SW of Tunbridge Wells. A26 Tunbridge Wells-Crowborough rd; in Eridge take Rotherfield turn S; house 1st on right. 1½ acres with pools; alpine garden; herbaceous border; herb garden; aviary. Full size croquet lawn. Large greenhouse. Plant, cake, etc stalls. Ample parking. Home-made TEAS. *Adm 60p Chd 25p (Share to MS). Sat, Sun July 25, 26 (2-7)*

Dale House (Mr & Mrs Jonathan Newdick) West Burton, 5m SW of Pulborough. At foot of Bury Hill turn W off A29 to W. Burton for 1m then follow signs. Small cottage garden; old roses, hardy perennials, shade plants, alpines in paved area. Large decorative vegetable garden, herbs, flowers; orchard; butterfly garden. *Adm 50p Chd free. Suns, Mons June 7, 8 July 5, 6 Aug 16, 17 (2-6)*

Denmans ✿✗❀ (Mrs J.H. Robinson) Denmans Lane, Fontwell. Chichester/Arundel 5m. Turn S on A27 at Denmans Lane, W of Fontwell Racecourse. Renowned gardens extravagantly planted for overall, all-year interest in form, colour and texture; areas of glass for tender species. John Brookes School of Garden Design at Clock House. Plant Centre. TEAS. *Adm £1.50 OAPs £1.40. Groups over 15 persons £1.30 Chd 75p. April 1 to Nov 1 daily except Mons, Tues; parties by appt. For NGS Thurs April 9 Oct 15 (1-6)*

Duckyls ✿✗ (Mr & Mrs Michael Taylor) Sharpthorne. 4m SW of E Grinstead. 6m E of Crawley. At Turners Hill take B2028 S 1m fork left to W Hoathly, turn left signed Gravetye Manor, garden on right. 12-acre large terraced garden being gradually restored with collection of azaleas, rhododendrons, camellias, woodland walk, good trees, fine views. Interesting primrose collection. TEAS. *Adm £1 Chd 25p (Share to British Butterfly Conservation Society) Sats April 12, May 16; Suns May 17, July 19 (2-6)*

Easebourne Gardens ✗❀ E of Midhurst on A272 towards Petworth. *Combined adm £1 Chd 50p (Share to Friends of St. Mary's Easebourne Restoration Fund). TEAS in Refectory. Sun July 5 (2-6)*
Easebourne Priory (The Rev & Mrs David Evans) C13 Priory
5 other village gardens Partly walled; mixed borders, roses, shrubs

Fittleworth Gardens ✗❀ A282 midway Petworth-Pulborough; in Fittleworth turn on to B2138 then W at Swan. TEAS in aid of NSPCC. *Combined adm £1 Chd 20p. Sun May 31 (2.6)*

¶**The Grange**Mr & Mrs W.M. Caldwell) 3-acre well planted island beds, interesting shrubs, lawns leading down to river with fine views of S. Downs

The Hazells (M.C. Pratt Esq.)

¶**The Hermitage** Mr & Mrs P. F. Dutton) Charming informal garden, lovely views to river to S. Downs

Lowerstreet House L. J. Holloway Esq) Small garden with shrubs, bulbs, herbaceous, greenhouse

Fitzhall ⚘ (Mr & Mrs G.F. Bridger) Iping, 3m W of Midhurst. 1m off A272, signposted Harting Elsted. 9 acres; herb garden; herbaceous and shrub borders; vegetable garden. Farm adjoining with poultry. House (not open) originally built 1550. TEAS (if fine). *Adm 60p Chd 25p. Suns May 3, July 5, Aug 16, Sept 13 (2-6)*

Floraldene ⚘❀ (Mr J.R. Tucker) Findon Rd. 2½m N of Worthing, 400 yds N of A24/A27 junc (Offington Corner) on W side of Findon rd; garden next to No 55. Park in Mayfield Close opp. Small all year round garden on chalk subsoil with approx 200 labelled varieties of heather set in a background of conifers and mainly evergreen shrubs. TEAS. *Adm 50p Chd 25p. Suns April 12, Aug 23 (2-5.30)*

Folkington Place ⚘ (Mrs H. Voorspuy) Polegate, 5m NW of Eastbourne. Turn left towards Lewes, signed Folkington "No Through Road". Unusual plants in beautiful walled setting. TEA. *Adm 60p Chd 30p. Sat, Sun July 4, 5 (2-6)*

The Fox & Hounds Farm ⚘❀ (Mrs C.W.Reed) Bolney. Turn at Bolney Stage, main Brighton Rd, Broxmead Lane. Haywards Heath, 5m Daffodils, flowering shrubs, rhododendrons, azaleas. C16 house. TEAS. *Adm 50p Chd 10p. Mons Apr 20, May 4 (2-5.30)*

The Garden House ⚘ (Sir Geoffrey & Lady Hardy-Roberts) Coates; SE of Petworth; ½m S of Fittleworth turn off B2138 signed 'Coates'. Small garden with shrubs and conservatory, featured in *Vogue* June 1979. Formerly the head gardener's house to Coates Castle. TEAS at Coates Manor. *Collecting box (Share to NSPCC). Sun, Mon, Tues June 21, 22, 23 (11-6)*

●**Great Dixter** ⚘ (The Lloyd Family) Northiam, ½m N of Northiam, 8m NW of Rye. Bus: MD 400 Hastings-Tenterden; 408 Rye-Northiam-Hastings, alight Northiam PO 500yds. Topiary; wide variety of plants. Historical house shown (2-5). Teas locally. *Adm house & garden £2 Chd 50p OAPs & NT members (Fris only) £1.50; garden only £1.20 Chd 25p. April 1 to Oct 11 daily except Mons but open on Bank Hols; Sats, Suns Oct 17, 18, 24, 25 (2-5); garden only open May 24, 25; also Suns in July & Aug, Aug Mon 31 (11-5)*

Hammerwood House ⚘❀ (Mr & Mrs John Lakin) Iping, 2½m W of Midhurst on A272 at Iping Xrds, turn right for ¾m; turn right signed Hammerwood, garden on right. Large informal garden; fine trees, rhododendrons, azaleas; acers, cornus, magnolias; wild garden (¼m away), bluebells, stream. TEAS. *Adm 70p Chd 30p. Suns May 17, 24 (2-7)*

Harvest Hill ⚘⚘ (Mr & Mrs John Fairbairn) Ansty 3m W of Haywards Heath on B2036. 1½m from A272/A23 intersection at Bolney. Informal garden; specimen trees, shrubs, old fashioned roses, herbaceous borders; downland views; small flock of black sheep. TEAS. *Adm 50p Chd 25p (Share to Elizabeth FitzRoy Homes, Sussex). Sun July 5 (2-5.30)*

The Hazels (M.C.Pratt Esq.) Fittleworth. A282 midway Petworth-Pulborough; in Fittleworth turn on to B2138. Turn right at the Swan, Fittleworth. 1-acre; collection of trees and shrubs planted since 1970; unique collection of azalea seedlings; small heather garden; a few rhododendrons; plantsman's garden. TEA (3, 4 at Watts Cottage; 24, 25 at Hanvilles Field). *Adm 50p Chd 20p (Combined with Lowerstreet House adm 60p Chd 20p). Sun, Mon May 3, 4; Sun 31 (2-6)*

Heaselands ⚘⚘ (Mrs Ernest Kleinwort). 1m SW of Haywards Heath on A273 to Burgess Hill. 30 acres; trees, shrubs, rhododendrons, azaleas, woodland, water garden; roses, aviaries, waterfowl. Coaches/parties by appt inc Oct for autumn colour. TEAS. *Adm £1 Chd 25p (Share to World Wildlife Fund UK). Suns May 17, 24, 31, July 19; Weds May 13, 20, 27 (2-6)*

●**The High Beeches** ⚘❀ (The Hon H.E. Boscawen) On B2110 1m E of Handcross. 16 acres; woodland garden; great botanical interest; see Country Life March 1983; one of the three famous gardens in Sussex designed by members of the Loder family who later created Leonardslee and Wakehurst Place. Picnic area. TEAS. *Adm £1.50 Chd free (Share to Slaugham Parish Church). Mons April 20 May 4, 25 (10.30-6) & Sun Oct 25 (10.30-5) also by appt for organised parties*

◆**Highdown, Goring-by-Sea** ⚘ (Worthing Borough Council) Littlehampton Rd (A259), 3m W of Worthing. Station: Goring-by-Sea, 1m. Famous garden in chalk-pit. TEAS. *Collecting box. △ Mons April 20 May 25 & Sun May 3 (2-6)*

Hollycombe ⚘⚘ (Mr & Mrs John Baldock) Liphook. A3, at Liphook take Haslemere rd, then first right on to Midhurst Rd for 1½m. Garden on right before stone bridge. 20 acres of original garden laid out by J. C. Hawkshaw, over one million trees, many rare. Considered to be most important small arboretum. Many very large rare trees, Beeches over 126 ft; ¼m azalea walk; interesting shrubs, inc many tender varieties, planted over last 30 yrs. Walled and terraced gardens. House (not shown) built 1800 by John Nash. Outstanding views to Goodwood. Coaches welcome; car park. TEAS. *Adm £1 Chd 50p. Suns May 31, June 7 (2-6)*

Hornbeams ✂❁ (Mr & Mrs D.J. Cater) Brede, 5½m W of Rye on B2089. 1½ acres; wide variety of bulbs, plants, shrubs, and trees; 'Bonsai'. Views of Tillingham Valley. TEAS. *Adm 60p Chd 20p (Share to St Michael's Hospice). Suns April 26 July 12 (2-6)*

Houghton Farm ✂❁ (Mr & Mrs Michael Lock) Arundel off B2139. 1 acre with shrubs. Good views. Tea Houghton Bridge Tea Gardens. *Adm 50p. Fri April 17, Sun, Mon Aug 16, 17 (2-5)*

Hurst House ♿❁ (Mr & Mrs Keeling) Hurst Lane. From Sedlescombe, take lane towards Brede; take 1st lane on left, 600 yds, garden on right. 6 acres; rhododendrons, azaleas, camellias, bulbs; herbaceous borders; rose garden; greenhouses with houseplants. TEAS. *Adm 50p Chd 10p (Share to Arthritis Care Hastings Branch). Sat June 20 (2-6)*

Hurston Place ✂ (Mr & Mrs David Bigham) Pulborough. 1½m W of Storrington. Turn N off A283 Storrington/Pulborough into Hurston Lane for 1½m. 2 acres with lawns, herbaceous border, shrubs, orchard with old fashioned roses, fine yew hedges, areas of interesting planting surrounding stone farmhouse. TEA. *Adm 50p Chd 25p (Share to West Sussex Association for the Disabled). Sun, Mon June 28, 29 (2-6)*

¶Imberley ✂❁ (Mr & Mrs J.K. Beney) Coombe Hill Rd, 1m SW of East Grinstead. Turn off B2110 nr Bus Stop. Garden 300 yrds on right. Daffodils, spring bulbs, bluebells, rhododendrons, azaleas in 6 acres of garden and woodland; ponds, meadow. Fine views. Some clearing and replanting in progress. TEAS. *Adm 60p Chd 30p (Share to TEAR Fund). Suns April 12 May 24 & Mon April 20 (2-6)*

Joan Nightingale House ♿ (The Little Black Bag Housing Assn Ltd) Bolnore Rd, Haywards Heath, ½ m. W of Haywards Heath, off A272 to Cuckfield, nr Munster Green. Bus stop 300 yds through Beechhurst. Small new formal garden; roses with mixed shrub borders. Part house shown (flatlets/accommodation for district & other nurses). TEAS. *Silver collection. Sat May 9 (2-6)*

Ketches ♿✂ (David Manwaring Robertson Esq) Newick, 5m W of Uckfield on A272. Take Barcombe Rd S out of Newick, house is on right opp turning to Newick Church. 3-acres; old-fashioned roses; specimen trees; shrub and herbaceous borders. TEAS. *Adm 75p Chd 10p. Sun June 28 (2-6)*

King Edward VII Hospital ❁ 3m NW of Midhurst. Bus: Alder Valley 219 Aldershot-Midhurst, alight at Hospital Drive, 1m. Transport direct to Hospital leaves Haslemere Station at 1.45 & Midhurst Bus Station at 2.30. Hospital, built early this century, stands in grounds of 152 acres; elevated position of great natural beauty; extensive views across Downs. Gardens by Gertrude Jekyll. Aspect over gardens and pine woods little changed. TEA. *Collecting box. Sat May 30 (2-5.30)*

Kingston Gardens ❁ 2½m SW of Lewes. Turn off A27 signposted Kingston at roundabout; at 30 mph sign turn right. Home-made TEAS Nightingales. *Combined adm (payable at Nightingales only) £1 Chd free. Suns June 7, July 26 (2-6)*

Nightingales (Mr & Mrs G. Hudson) The Avenue. Informal sloping ½-acre garden for all-year interest; wide range of plants including shrub roses, hardy geraniums, perennials, ground cover. Mediterranean plants in pots on terrace; tender wall plants. Childrens play area. Short pleasant walk to:-

Ridge House (Mr & Mrs K. Bloomfield) Kingston Ridge. Small garden on slope of S Downs with magnificent view along Ouse Valley; includes alpines and greenhouse of rare plants

Knabbs Farmhouse ♿❁ (Mr & Mrs W.G. Graham) 4m NW of Uckfield; from A272 turn N at Piltdown for Fletching, 1½m. Garden at N-end of village and farm. ½-acre informal garden; mixed beds and borders; shrubs, roses, perennials, foliage plants. Good views over ha-ha. Teas Clinton Lodge. *Adm 60p Chd 20p. Sun June 21 (2-6)*

Lane End ✂ (Mrs C.J. Epril) Sheep Lane, Midhurst. In North St turn left at Knockhundred Row, left into Sheep lane, left to garden. Park at church or in lane. 2 acres inc wild garden; alpine rockery with pools; rhododendrons, azaleas, heath border. Below ramparts of original castle with fine views over water meadows to ruins of Cowdray House. Tea Midhurst. *Adm 50p Chd 25p. Sats Suns, Mons May 23, 24, 25; 30, 31; June 1 (11-6)*

Legh Manor ✂ (Mr & Mrs N.J. Teale & The Archaeological Society) Cuckfield Rd, Ansty, 2½m SW of Cuckfield. From A23 London-Brighton Rd, turn off at Bolney; take A272 to Ansty; turn right, fork right; garden ½m on right. 5 acres; part designed by Gertrude Jekyll. Tudor house (not open) with later additions. *Adm 50p Chd 20p. Suns April 26, Aug 2 (2-5.30)*

Legsheath Farm ♿❁ (Miss M. Neal) Legsheath Lane. 4m S of East Grinstead nr Sharpthorne. Garden signposted. 1930s designed garden on 3 levels adjoining

Ashdown Forest. Spring shrubberies; azalea walk; herbaceous border, ponds. TEAS. *Adm £1 Chd free. Sun June 7 (2-5.30)*

Little Bucksteep &⚘ (Mr & Mrs D.A. Cameron) Dallington. 6m E of Heathfield off B2096. Through Dallington, 2nd right. ¼m on left. Rhododendrons, azaleas, shrubs, etc. TEAS. *Adm 50p Chd 20p (Share to Dallington PCC). Sun May 31 (2-6)*

Little Hutchings ⚘ (Mr & Mrs P. Hayes) Fontridge Lane, 1½m SW of Etchingham. 1½ acres; laid out over 10 yrs; shrub roses, herbaceous borders. TEAS. *Adm 75p Chd 25p. Sun June 21 (2-6)*

Little Peans & (Mr & Mrs Stuart Oddy) Robertsbridge. Turn off A2I in centre of Robertsbridge on rd to Brightling 1m. 9 acres with rhododendrons and azaleas. Garden suitable for wheelchairs if dry. *Adm 50p Chd 20p. Sun May 24 (2-6)*

Malt House ⚙ (Mr & Mrs Graham Ferguson) Chithurst, Rogate. From A272, 3½m W of Midhurst turn N signposted Chithurst then 1½m; or from A3 2m S of Liphook, turn SE to Milland, then follow signs to Chithurst for 1½m. 4 acres; flowering shrubs inc exceptional rhododendrons and azaleas, leading to 50 acres of lovely woodland walks. TEA. *Adm 70p Chd 30p. Every Sun April 26 to June 7 & Mons May 4, 25 (2-6); also by appt for parties only or plant sales (Tel Rogate 433)*

The Manor of Dean &⚘ (Miss S.M. Mitford) Tillington, 2m W of Petworth. Turn off A272 N at NGS sign. Flowers, shrubs, specimen trees, bulbs in all seasons. House (not open) 1400-1613. TEA *Adm 50p Chd 20p. Sats Suns Mons March 28, 29, 30 April 25, 26, 27 May 23, 24, 25 June 20, 21, 22 July 11, 12, 13 Aug 15, 16, 17 Sept 5, 6, 7 Oct 3, 4, 5, (2-6)*

Manvilles Field &⚘ (Mrs P. J. Aschan & Mrs J.M. Wilson) 2m W of Pulborough take A283 to Fittleworth, turn right on double bend. 1½ acres with many interesting shrubs, clematis, roses, other herbaceous plants. Beautiful views surrounding garden. TEAS. *Adm 50p Chd 20p. Sun, Mon, May 24, 25 (2-6)*

Mereworth &⚘ (Mr & Mrs H.C. Wiffen) Silverwood, Nyetimber Lane, West Chiltington, 3m E of Pulborough. From A283 turn N to Nutbourne & West Chiltington; cross junc; stay on lower road, 2nd left; 1st left. 1 acre made by owners since 1967; trees, conifers, heathers; small herbaceous and dahlia garden; shrub borders. TEA. *Adm 75p Chd 40p. Suns Aug 23, Sep 20, 27 (11-5.30)*

Millstones ⚘⚙ (Mr & Mrs Johnson) Wadhurst. 5m SE of Tunbridge Wells. Tapsells Lane is off B2099 at NW end of Wadhurst. ½-acre beautifully designed plantsman's garden. *Adm 70p. Sun Aug 2 (2-6)*

Moorlands (Dr & Mrs Steven Smith) Friar's Gate, 2m N of Crowborough. Approach via B2188; at Friar's Gate take left fork signposted 'Crowborough Narrow Road' entrance 100 yds on left; from Crowborough Xrds take St Johns Rd to Friar's Gate. 3 acres set in lush valley adjoining Ashdown forest; water garden with ponds and streams; primulas, rhododendrons, azaleas, many unusual trees and shrubs. TEAS. *Adm 60p Chd 30p. Suns May 17 & June 7 (2-6)*

Mountfield Court & (T. Egerton Esq) 2m S of Robertsbridge. On A21 London-Hastings; ½m from Johns Cross. Bus: MD 5, 5A Hastings-Maidstone, alight Johns Cross. 2-3 acre wild garden; flowering shrubs, rhododendrons, azaleas and camellias; fine trees. Tea Johns Cross Inn. *Adm £1 Chd 30p. Sun May 24 (2-6)*

•Newick Park ⚙ (Viscount & Viscountess Brentford) A272 signposted from Newick village green. Wild shrub garden featuring rhododendrons and azaleas; fine trees; snowdrops, daffodils, bluebells, National Collection of Primula Candelabra. Farmland walk. Herb and wild flower nursery in walled garden (not Suns). Home-made TEAS for parties by prior arrangement. *Adm £1 Chd 50p Groups 75p. March 1 to Oct 31 every day (10.30-6). For NGS Sat, Sun May 30, 31 (TEAS) (Share to Newick Church Barn Fund)*

Newtimber Place & (H. H. Judge Clay & Mrs Clay) Newtimber. 1m N of Pyecombe, turn W from A23 in dual carriageway. 7m N of Brighton. Medium-sized garden. Old moated house. TEAS in aid of Newtimber Church. *Adm 50p Chd 25p. △ Suns April 26, Aug 30 (2-6)*

Norman Place ⚘ (Mrs M. Parry) East Street, Petworth. 7m S of Northchapel on A283; 15m N of Chichester on A285; garden in centre of town on one-way st (heading S) nr PO. Small town garden recently redesigned to include flowering shrubs, herbaceous plants, especially lilies, is surprisingly set in midst of busy interesting old town; car parking in rds or town car park. *Adm 50p Chd 25p. Sun July 12 to Sun July 19 daily (11-6)*

Nutbourne Gardens nr Pulborough. Take A283 E then turn N to Nutbourne, next left and follow lane to gardens. TEAS (in aid of "Help a Child to See"). *Combined adm £1 Chd 50p. Sun, Mon July 5, 6 (2-5.30)*
> **Ebbsworth** ⚘ (Mr & Mrs F. Lambert) Charming, well-planted, cottage garden, designed and maintained by owner
> **Manor Farm** ⚙ (Mrs A.M. Rhys Jones) Pleasant ½-acre garden with interesting roses surrounding modern house
> **Mill House** ⚙ (Sir Francis & Lady Avery Jones) ¾-acre surrounding old miller's house, herb garden, cottage frontage

with sloping garden, ponds and stream
Old Manor Cottage ⚘⚙ (Mr & Mrs J.H.A. Lang) Steeply terraced small garden, alpines and trees

¶**Nutbourne Manor Vineyard** ⚙ (Mr & Mrs J.Sanger) Nutbourne. From Pulborough take A283 E, turn L to W Chiltington and Nutbourne; then N to Nutbourne. Fine Gerogian house, the site of which is recorded in the Doomsday Book (not open). The vineyard consists of 4 acres producing since 1980 and 10 acres on different tressling system due to produce soon. The vines grown have all been imported from Germany and are: Muller Thurgau, Reichensteiner, Huxelrede and Schonburger. *Adm £1 Chd 50p. Sat, Sun Sept 5, 6 (2-6)*

Nymans ⚘⚘⚙ (Anne, Countess of Rosse; The National Trust) Handcross. On B2ll4 at Handcross signposted off M23/A23 London-Brighton Rd, SE of Handcross. Bus: SD 771 from Crawley & Haywards Heath. Rare trees and shrubs. Botanical interest. Wheelchairs available at the garden. Car park free. TEAS. *Adm £1.40 Chd 70p organised parties £1 each.* △ *Tues May 5, June 9 (11-7)*

Offham House ⚘⚙ (Mrs H.S. Taylor; Mrs H.N.A. Goodman) Offham, 2m N of Lewes on A275. Cooksbridge station ½m. Fountains; flowering trees; double herbaceous border; long peony bed. Queen Anne house (not open) 1676 with well-knapped flint facade. Featured in George Pumptre's Guide to 200 Gardens in Britain. Home-made TEAS. *Adm £1 Chd 25p. Suns May 3, July 12 (2 6)*

Orchard House ⚘ (Mrs Kirwan Taylor) 59 Southover High St, Lewes; 5 mins from station opp Southover Church. Small town garden on two levels; old apple trees, old fashioned roses, mixed border; small white garden. *Adm 50p Chd 20p. Sun June 21 (2-6)*

¶**Pannetts** ⚘⚘ (Maj & Mrs J.N.P.Watson) Shipley, 5m S of Horsham. W from A24/A272 junction 2nd left 1m then right. 1¾ acres, lawns, oaks, mixed borders, shrubs; waterfowl collection. Part recently reclaimed from field, maintained by owners. TEA at Bakers Farm. *Adm 45p Chd 10p. Sun July 12 (2-6)*

Parham House and Gardens ⚘(gdns)⚘ (Hse)⚙ 4m SE of Pulborough on A283 Pulborough-Storrington Rd. Beautiful Elizabethan House with fine collection of portraits, furniture, rare needlework. 4 acres of walled garden; 7 acres pleasure grounds with lake. Picnic area. Light refreshments in Big Kitchen. Shop. St Peter's Church nearby. *Open April 19 to Oct 4; Weds, Thurs, Suns & Bank Hols. Adm House & garden £2.50 OAPs £2 Chd £1.50. Garden £1 Chd 75p. For NGS. Wed, Thurs Aug 5, 6 (Garden & picnic area 1-6, House 2-6 last adm 5.30)*

Penns in the Rocks ⚘ (Lord & Lady Gibson) Groombridge. 7m SW of Tunbridge Wells on Groombridge-Crowborough Rd just S of Plumeyfeather corner. Bus: MD 291 Tunbridge Wells-East Grinstead, alight Plumeyfeather corner, ¾m. Large wild garden with rocks; lake; C18 temple; old walled garden. House (not shown) part C18. Home-made TEAS. *Adm £1 Chd 50p family of 4 or more £3. Sun April 26, Mon Aug 31 (2.30-5.30)*

Pheasants Hatch ⚘ (Brig & Mrs Thubron) Piltdown, W of Uckfield. Medium-sized garden; mixed borders; foliage border; rose garden. Peacocks. Home-made TEAS. *Adm 50p Chd 20p. Sun June 28 (2-7)*

Pollards Nursery ⚘ Lake Lane, Barnham. Lake Lane is N and parallel to railway running from Barnham to B2132 Yapton Lane. Flowers and pot plants in 7 acres of glasshouses; roses, alstromerias, lilies, hydrangeas. **Southdown Flowers Ltd** ⚘⚙ Yapton Lane Walburton, just N of Yapton level X-ing. 16 acres, commercial flower and pot plant nursery growing all-year-round chrysanthemums, iris, lilies, roses, carnations, alstromeria, begonias, saintpaulias, impatiens. TEA Southdown Flowers. *Combined adm £1 or 45p each Chd 20p. Sun March 15 (2-6)*

The Priory ⚙ (Canon E.M.Youens) Easebourne, E of Midhurst on A272. Combined with 5 other village gardens, partly walled, mixed borders, roses, shrubs, vegetables and conversation areas. TEA. *Combined adm £1 Chd 50p (Share to The Macmillan Service, King Edward VII Hospital, Midhurst). Sun July 5 (2-7)*

Pyramids ⚘⚙ (Gillian Jacomb-Hood) South Harting. 4m SE of Petersfield, from B2146 take turning signed Nyewood/Rogate; 200 yds on right after Harting Stores. ½ acre with mainly chalk-loving plants; interesting modern house (designed by Stout & Lichfield) linked to garden by paved areas; pool, spring bulbs, old-fashioned roses, shrubs, trees. Fine views of Downs. TEA (May) TEAS (July). *Adm 50p Chd 25p. Suns May 10 July 5 (2-6)*

Reachwood (Mr & Mrs P Talbot-Smith) Ewhurst Lane, Northiam. 8m NW of Rye off A28 to Ewhurst. 1½-acre garden made by owners with large variety of trees and plants. Fine views. TEAS. *Adm 75p Chd 30p (Share to Macmillan Nursing). Weds May 20, June 17, Sun May 31 (2-6)*

Ricardo's ⚘ (Drs Kate & Colin Bertram) Graffham, 6m Midhurst/Petworth. On Selham Rd N of Graffham Village, signed S from A272, and from A286 and A285. 11 acres; partly-terraced from sandy ridge. Scots pines towering above mature arbutus over carpet of bluebells. House (not open) built by architect Halsey Ricardo in 1905 now occupied by his grand-daughter. TEA. *Adm £1 Chd 50p (Share to International Planned Parenthood Federation). Sat, Sun May 16, 17 (2-5.30)*

Rogate Gardens ⚹ 5m W of Midhurst on A272. WI TEAS at Village Hall North St where map available. *Combined adm £1 Chd 20p (Share to Rogate and Terwick Village Hall). Suns June 21, 28 (2-6)*

  Hunters Lodge (Mr & Mrs S. Rimmer) Small garden of shrubs, conifers, heathers

  Lower Lodge (Mrs G. M. Bodkin) Small attractive garden

  ¶**The Old Stable Cottage**, Fyning House (Capt & Mrs P G J Murison) 2-acre landscaped garden; wisteria-clad orangery, borders, fine trees and shrubs, old roses

  Slade Lane Cottage (H.H. Judge Broderick & Mrs Broderick) ¾ acre garden, scented plants, shrub roses. Outstanding views

  ¶**The Vicarage** (The Rev F H B & Mrs Leese). Amateur's organic garden ⅓-acre; made from building site since 1981. Herbaceous border, soft fruits and vegetables

Rye Gardens ⚹ Adjacent to Church & Town Hall. Cars must be left in nearby town car parks. TEA 11, High Street. *Combined adm 75p Chd 25p. Sun June 21 (2-6)*

  ¶**11, High Street** (Mr & Mrs C Festing) 1-way street, on righthand side, nextdoor to Midland Bank. ⅓-acre old walled garden; many flowering shrubs and trees inc Ginkgo tree by Fish Pond. Vinery; herbaceous borders, rose trees

  18 Church Square (Robert Banks Esq) Sloping garden with old fruit trees and interesting shrubs. Views of the Marsh and sea: ground cover predominating

Rymans ⚹ (The Hon Claud & Mrs Phillimore) Apuldram, 1½m SW of Chichester. Witterings Rd out of Chichester; at 1½m SW turn right signposted Apuldram; garden down rd on left. Walled and other gardens surrounding lovely C15 stone house (not open); bulbs, flowering shrubs, roses. Tea shops in Chichester. *Adm 60p Chd 20p. Suns April 5, 26, June 21, July 12, Mon Aug 24 (2-5.30)*

Rystwood House (Mrs George Pollitzer) Forest Row. 4m SE East Grinstead. Take A22 to Forest Row Church then B2110 for 1m. Turn right up Forest Road. House on left. 10 acres; lovely spring garden with views of Ashdown Forest. TEA. *Adm 50p Chd 25p. Sun May 10 (2-7)*

St Roche's Arboretum ⚹ (The Edward James Foundation) Singleton Hill, West Dean, 6m N of Chichester on A286, then ½m up hill from Weald and Downland Open Air Museum. Entrance nr Trundle and Goodwood Racecourse. Bus 260 to Singleton. An extensive arboretum begun in C19 notable for outstanding specimens of Douglas Fir 138', Incense Cedar 100; Lawson's Cypress 100', Western Red Cedar 124', Norway Spruce 117', Lucomb Oak 124', Red Oak 108' and good examples of Turkey Oak, Redwoods, Pines and many others grown on chalky soil. Rhododendrons/azaleas grow well on acid litter. *Adm 75p Chd 50p. Mon 27 April-Sun 3 May, Mon 11 May-Sun 17 May, Mon 1 June-Sun 7 June, Mon 15 June-Sun 21 June, Suns Oct 11, 25 (12-5)*

¶**Saxonbury House** (Lord & Lady Roderick Pratt) Frant. Entrance on Tunbridge Wells/Eastbourne Rd, ¼m S of Frant. 10-acre garden created from wilderness. Collection of trees and shrubs, woodland garden; extensive views over Eridge Park. *Adm 60p Chd 20p. Sun Aug 2 (2.30-6)*

¶**Selehurst** ⚹ (Mr & Mrs M.Prideaux) Lower Beeding, 4½m SE of Horsham on A28 opp Leonardslee. Large woodland garden, ponds, fine collection of camellia, azaleas, rhododendrons; walled gardenn, newly planted laburnum walk underplanted with azaleas; fine views. Refreshments. *Adm £1 (Share to Church of The Holy Trinity, Lower Beeding). Sun, May 24,(2-6) Mon, May 25 (11-5)*

Sheffield Park Garden ⚹ (The National Trust) Midway between E Grinstead and Lewes, 5m NW of Uckfield; E of A275. The garden, with 5 lakes, was laid out by Capability Brown in C18, greatly modified early in the C20. Many rare trees, shrubs and fine waterlilies; the garden is beautiful at all times of year. Teas Oak Hall (not NT). *Adm £2 Chd £1 parties £1.50 (April, June, Aug, Sept); £2.60 Chd £1.30 parties £2 (May to Oct, Nov). △ For NGS Wed May 13 Oct 14 (11-6)*

Southdown Flowers, see under Pollards Nursery.

South Corner House ⚹ (Maj & Mrs Shane Blewitt) Duncton, 3½m S of Petworth. On A285, 200 yds N of Duncton Hill. 1 acre on alkaline soil set beneath South Downs; substantial old fashioned herbaceous border, also shrub borders, roses and interesting greenhouse plants. Not suitable for wheelchairs. TEA. *Adm 50p Chd free. Sat, Sun July 18, 19 (2.30-6)*

Standen ⚹ (The National Trust) 1½m from East Grinstead. Signed from B2110 and A22 at Felbridge. Hillside garden of 10½ acres with beautiful views over the Medway Valley. New rose garden opening 1987. TEAS. *Adm £1 Chd 50p. △ Suns May 31, July 26 (2-5.30)*

Stile House ⚹⚘ (Mr & Mrs A. Archer-Wills) Gay St, 2m E of Pulborough; take A283 signposted to Storrington; turn left to West Chiltington & Nutbourne; then 1st left to Nutbourne, right into Stream Lane; left into Gay St. 1¾ acres; water plants, ponds, streams and waterfalls. TEAS. *Adm 50p Chd 25p. Suns May 3, 10, 17, 24 (2-5.30)*

Tappington Grange ⚘ (Mr & Mrs Peter Kininmonth) Wadhurst. 4m SE Tunbridge Wells. Sharp turning almost opp Wadhurst Station. 3 acres; herbaceous and shrub borders; ornamental wildfowl; newly planned water garden under construction. TEAS. *Adm 60p Chd 25p. Sun Aug 30 (2-6)*

Telegraph House ⚘ (Mr & Mrs David Gault) North Marden, 9 m. NW of Chichester. Entrance on B2141. From Petersfield to South Harting for 2m From Chichester via A286 for 4m N of Lavant turn W on to B2141. 1-acre enclosed chalk garden 700 ft asl; chalk-tolerant shrubs, shrub roses, herbaceous plants; 1m avenue of copper beeches; walks through 150-acre yew wood; lovely views. House (not shown) in small park, built on site of semaphore keeper's cottage. TEAS. *Adm 75p Chd 35p. Sats, Suns June 20, 21 July 11, 12 (2-6); also by appt May to Aug (2-5) (Tel Harting 206)*

Toddington House ⚘ (Mr & Mrs P.F. Holland) Toddington Lane, 2m N of Littlehampton. From A27 at Crossbush take A284 towards Littlehampton; through Lyminster, turn left (E) into Mill Lane; garden immediately S of Toddington level Xing. Or from A259 Worthing rd turn N into Toddington Lane. 1-acre garden designed by John Brookes; well-matured areas with herb, red-mauve, silver-white, blue gardens, mixed borders, rockery, pergola with paved areas, ponds; further alterations proposed 86/87, interesting garden within barn and outbuilding areas. TEAS. *Adm 75p Chd free (Share to Cystic Fibrosis Research Trust). Suns June 28 July 5 (2-6)*

Trotton Old Rectory ⚘ (Mr & Mrs John Pilley) Trotton. 3½m W of Midhurst. Turn of A272 opp Church. Medium-sized garden; azaleas, interesting shrubs, herbaceous borders, hardy lilies; lake; water and vegetable gardens. *Adm 50p Chd 25p. Suns May 17 June 14 (2-6)*

Upper House ⚘⚘ (Mr & Mrs C.M. Humber) West Burton, 5m SW of Pulborough, right off A29 at Bury/West Burton Xrds; garden is ½m from Roman Villa at Bignor. Large garden, formal yew lawn, walled garden inc herb garden and raised beds, many unusual plants, shrubs, large greenhouse; rose-garden being re-designed. Extensive re-planting. TEAS. *Adm 50p Chd 20p. Sat, Sun July 11, 12 (2-7)*

The Upper Lodge ⚘⚘ (J.W. Harrington Esq) Stopham, 1m W of Pulborough; via A283 towards Petworth; Lodge is on left by telephone kiosk at Stopham. Mainly rhododendrons and azaleas; wide selection of shrubs for acid soil. *Adm 50p Chd 20p. Fri, April 17 & Suns April 12, 19, May 3, 10, 17, 24, 31 (2-5)*

Uppark ⚘⚘ (The National Trust) South Harting. 5m SE of Petersfield; via B2141/B2146. Medium size garden, mostly lawns, shrubs, large yews, beech and cedar trees; some flower beds. House built in 1690; redecorated and embellished interior in 1750s; little change since then. Chippendale furniture; original carpets and curtains; collection of porcelain; domestic quarters also shown. Magnificent views of Solent and Isle of Wight. TEAS. *Adm house and gardens £2.20 Chd £1.10 (Collection for NGS).* △ *Sats June 6, Aug 8 (2-6)*

¶**Wadhurst Park** ⚘ (Dr & Mrs H.Rausing) Wadhurst. 6m SE of Tunbridge Wells. Turn R down Mayfield Lane off B2099 at NW end of Wadhurst. L by pub to Mayfield. 600 acres, re-created garden on C19 site overlooking parkland with deer. TEAS. *Adm £1 Chd 30p. Sun Sept 20 (2-5.30)*

Wakehurst Place ⚘ (National Trust Royal Botanic Gardens, Kew) Ardingly, 5m N of Haywards Heath on B2028. National botanic garden noted for one of the finest collections of rare trees and flowering shrubs amidst exceptional natural beauty. Walled gardens and impressive herbaceous borders, heath garden, Pinetum, scenic walks through steep and wooded valley; Himalayan Glade and major collections of rhododendrons. An extensive water feature of lakes, attractive water courses and a large bog garden. A garden for all seasons. Restaurant, Bookshop and exhibition rooms in Elizabethan mansion. *Adm £1.50 Chd 60p* △ *Fri Aug 28 (10-7)*

Watts Farm Cottage ⚘⚘ (Mrs Peggy Clark) Watersfield, 3m S of Pulborough. On A29 in Watersfield; turn left at Watersfield Garage; garden lies at end of lane. ⅓-acre, owner-maintained, with borders, roses and shrubs. TEAS. *Adm 45p Chd free. Sun, Mon May 3, 4 (2-6)*

Wedderlie House ⚘ (Mr & Mrs L.A. Edgar) St Helen's Avenue, Hastings. Adjacent St. Helens Woods. Turn off A21 at mini-roundabout into St Helen's Rd; after 1½m, left into St Helen's Park Rd; left into Hillside Rd, right into St Helen's Ave. 4-acre woodland garden; camellias, rhododendrons, azaleas. Shrubs for sale. *Adm 50p Chd 20p. Suns May 3, 17, June 7 (2-6)*

West Dean Gardens ⚘⚘⚘ (Edward James Foundation) On A286, 5m. N of Chichester, nr Weald & Downland Open Air Museum. 35 acres; informal gardens, fine specimen trees, 300ft pergola; gazebo; borders; wild garden; picnic and play area; walled garden with Victorian glasshouses containing large collection lawnmowers and Garden History Exhibition. Garden shop. TEAS. *Adm £1.10*

OAPs 95p Chd 50p; parties by appt at 85p per person. April 1 to Sept 30 daily (11-6, last adm 5). For NGS Fri April 3 & Thurs Sept 3 (11-6)

West Riddens ⚘ (Mr & Mrs Charles Keyser) Ansty, 2m SW of Cuckfield. From A23 London-Brighton Rd turn off at Bolney; take A272 to Ansty; at 'T' junc opp Ansty Cross turn right; then fork right to Hurstpierpoint Rd; 1st entrance on left. 30 acres garden and woodland; greenhouses, vegetable garden. Home-made TEAS. *Adm 60p Chd 20p. Sat May 9 (2-6)*

West Stoke House ⚘❀ (Mr & Mrs R.C. Elwes) 4m W of Chichester; from Lavant on A286 turn W for West Stoke. Large garden in lovely situation at foot of downs; fine trees, bulbs and shrubs; market garden shop. House 1760 (not open). Downland church next door. Kingley Vale Nature Conservancy, 1m walk. TEAS. *Adm 50p Chd 25p (Share to West Stoke Church). Sun, Mon July 12, 13 (2-6.30)*

Whitehouse Cottage (Barry Gray Esq) Staplefield Lane, 5m NW of Haywards Heath. Garden is ⅓m. E of A23; turn off main rd at Warninglid flyover; take the lane to Staplefield (not the B2115 to Haywards Heath & Cuckfield). Large garden with mixed shrubs, old roses; woodland path beside stream linked by ponds; interesting paved and planted areas around house. TEAS. *Adm 50p Chd 10p (Share to Woodland Trust). Sat, Sun May 30, 31 (2-7)*

Winchelsea Gardens ⚘ S of Rye. TEAS The Mount. *Combined adm £1 Chd 25p. Sun June 28 (2-6)*
   Cleveland House (Mr & Mrs J. Jempson) 1⅓-acre semi-formal walled garden; many varied plants, ornamental trees; water feature; beautiful views; swimming in heated pool
   The Old Post Office (Mr & Mrs A. Sandeman) Very small walled garden; full of colour, interesting plants
   Nesbit (Mr & Mrs G. Botterell) Formal enclosed ¼-acre garden; many and varied plants
   The Mount (Mr & Mrs A. Cox) Informal ⅔-acre garden; magnificent views

Worthing Borough Council Nurseries ♿⚘ Titnore Way, Worthing. On A259 1m N of Goring roundabout. 13 glasshouses; largest is palm house with large selection of foliage plants; others contain flowering plants for arrangements. No plants for sale. *Collection box. Sun May 3 (10-4.30)*

WARWICKSHIRE & WEST MIDLANDS

Hon County Organiser:
DENNIS L. FLOWER ESQ, Ilmington Manor, Shipston-on-Stour CV36 4LA
Assistant Hon County Organiser:
MISS HELEN SYME, Puddocks, Frog Lane, Ilmington, Shipston-on-Stour CV36 4LQ

DATES OF OPENING

REGULAR OPENINGS for dates see text:
THE MILL GARDEN, Warwick
PACKWOOD HOUSE, nr Hockley Heath
RYTON GARDENS, nr Coventry

APRIL Sunday 5
  ELM CLOSE, Welford-on-Avon
  THE MILL GARDEN, Warwick
  86, WOODLAND ROAD, Northfield
APRIL Saturday 18
  THE MILL GARDEN, Warwick
APRIL Easter Sunday 19
  ILMINGTON MANOR, nr Shipston-on-Stour
  PUDDOCKS, Ilmington
  STRETTON-ON-FOSSE GARDENS, nr Shipston-on-Stour
APRIL Easter Monday 20
  WOODPECKERS, Bidford-on-Avon
APRIL Sunday 26
  PARHAM LODGE, Alveston
MAY Sunday 3
  SHERBOURNE PARK, nr Warwick
MAY Sunday 10
  DORSINGTON GARDENS, nr Stratford-on-Avon
  ELM CLOSE, Welford-on-Avon
  IVY LODGE, Radway
  86, WOODLAND ROAD, Northfield
MAY Sunday 24
  ‡ILMINGTON MANOR, nr Shipston-on-Stour
  ‡ILMINGTON OLD RECTORY
  ‡PUDDOCKS, Ilmington
MAY Sunday 31
  LOXLEY HALL, nr Stratford-on-Avon
  ROTHERWOOD, Warmington
JUNE Sunday 7
  BICKMARSH HALL, nr Bidford-on-Avon
  ELM CLOSE, Welford-on-Avon
  PACKWOD HOUSE, nr Hockley Heath
  THE SPRING, Kenilworth
  86, WOODLAND ROAD, Northfield
  WROXALL ABBEY SCHOOL, nr Warwick
JUNE Saturday 13
  BARTON HOUSE, Barton-on-the-Heath
JUNE Sunday 14
  BARTON HOUSE, Barton-on-the-Heath
  CEDAR HOUSE, Wasperton
  FOXCOTE, nr Shipston-on-Stour

SHERBOURNE PARK, nr Warwick
UPTON HOUSE GARDENS, nr Banbury
WHICHFORD & ASCOTT GARDENS,
WOOLSCOTT MANOR, nr Grandborough
WROXALL ABBEY SCHOOL, nr Warwick
JUNE Saturday 20
17 GERRARD STREET, Warwick
THE MILL GARDEN, Warwick
JUNE Sunday 21
ALSCOT PARK, nr Stratford-on-Avon
17 GERRARD STREET, Warwick
ILMINGTON MANOR, nr
Shipston-on-Stour
MAXSTOKE CASTLE, nr Coleshill
THE MILL GARDEN, Warwick
PUDDOCKS, Ilmington
UPTON HOUSE GARDENS, nr Banbury
JUNE Saturday 27
ADMINGTON HALL, nr Stratford-on-Avon
HICKECROFT, Rowington
JUNE Sunday 28
ADMINGTON HALL, nr Stratford-on-Avon
BRAILES HOUSE, nr Banbury
THE BUTCHERS ARMS, Rugby
HICKECROFT, Rowington
HONINGTON GARDENS, nr
Shipston-on-Stour
LOXLEY HALL, nr Stratford-on-Avon
SHERBOURNE PARK, nr Warwick
STRETTON-ON-FOSSE GARDENS, nr
Shipston-on-Stour
JULY Sunday 5
‡BROOK COTTAGE & ALKERTON HOUSE
(see Oxon)
ELM CLOSE, Welford-on-Avon
FOXCOTE, nr Shipston-on-Stour
‡IVY LODGE, Radway
86 WOODLAND ROAD, Northfield
JULY Sunday 12
ALSCOT PARK, nr Stratford-on-Avon
ASHBORNE HOUSE, nr Warwick
HOLYWELL FARM, nr Shrewley
ILMINGTON GARDENS, nr
Shipston-on-Stour
REDLANDS, Four Oaks
THE SPRING, Kenilworth
JULY Monday 13
ASHBOURNE HOUSE, nr Warwick
JULY Sunday 19
AVON DASSETT GARDENS, nr Banbury
CLIFTON ON DUNSMORE GARDENS
DORSINSGTON MANOR & LODGE, nr
Stratford-on-Avon
MARTINEAU CENTRE GARDENS,
Egbaston
JULY Sunday 26
IDLICOTE GARDENS, nr
Shipston-on-Stour
AUGUST Sunday 2
ALVESTON GARDENS, nr
Stratford-on-Avon
86 WOODLAND ROAD, Northfield
WOOLSCOTT MANOR, nr Grandborough
AUGUST Sunday 16
17 GERRARD STREET, Warwick
THE MILL GARDEN, Warwick

SEPTEMBER Sunday 6
CEDAR HOUSE, Wasperton
RYTON GARDENS, nr Coventry
SHERBOURNE PARK, nr Warwick
86, WOODLANDS ROAD, Northfield
OCTOBER Sunday 11
THE MILL GARDEN, Warwick

DESCRIPTIONS OF GARDENS

Admington Hall &⊛ (Mr & Mrs J.P. Wilkerson) 6½m S of Stratford-on-Avon. Between A34 and A46 nr Quinton. Large garden, interesting water garden, mixed borders, extensive kitchen garden, greenhouses. TEA. *Adm 70p Chd 30p (Share to St Swithin's Church). Sat & Sun June 27 & 28 (2-7)*

Alscot Park &⊛ (Capt & Mrs James West) 2½m S of Stratford-on-Avon via A34. Fairly large garden; extensive lawns, shrub roses, fine trees, orangery, with C18 Gothic house (not open), river, deer park, lakes. Coach parties by appt. Home-made TEAS. *Adm 60p Chd 20p (Share to Cancer Research). Suns June 21, July 12 (2-6)*

Alveston Gardens ⚘⊛ 2m NE of Stratford-upon-Avon. Turn left at War Memorial off B4086 Stratford-Wellesbourne rd; Alveston ¼m. TEAS Parham Lodge. *Combined adm £1 Chd 20p (Share to Alveston Village Assoc). Sun Aug 2 (2-6)*

 Parham Lodge & (Mr & Mrs K.C.Edwards) 1-acre; designed and maintained by owners. Old cedars, copper beech, hornbeam, small woodland; variety of choice shrubs, trees, plants, bulbs. Island beds with heathers, large pond, patios and tubs. New rose garden. Flower arrangers garden
 The Bower House & (Mr & Mrs P.S.Hart) 1-acre, owner-designed. unusual trees, water garden and rockeries. Pergolas, alpine sinks, choice shrubs
 ¶**Court Leys** (Mr & Mrs E. Barnard) 1-acre. Interesting shrubs and trees, enclosed courtyards, ponds. Beautiful conservatory

Ashorne House &⊛ (Mr & Mrs A. J. Sidwell) Ashorne 5m S of Warwick. 1½m W of junc of A4l Warwick-Banbury, signed Ashorne. Entrance & carpark in adjacent cricket pitch. 8 acres; typical English country garden TEAS (Share to Village Hall Fund). *Adm 80p Chd 30p. Sun, Mon July 12, 13 (2-7)*

¶**Avon Dassett Gardens** 7m N Banbury off A41. TEAS. *Adm £1 Chd 50p. Sun July 19 (2-6)*

 Hill Top Farm (Mr & Mrs R. Hicks) ½-acre garden. Fine show of bedding plants, perennials and roses. Large kitchen garden. Greenhouses
 Old Mill Cottage (Mr & Mrs M. Lewis) Conservation garden of ½ acre with

shrub, perennial borders and rockeries. Collection alpines and herbs. Two ponds and kitchen garden

The Old Rectory (Mr & Mrs T. Hope-Frost) 2-acre garden surrounding listed building mentioned in Doomsday Book (not open). Large variety of fine trees and shrubs. Small wood

Dassett House (Mrs P.G. Kelsey) Colourful borders of perennials, shrubs and roses. Lawns and kitchen garden

1, The Drive (Mrs Herburt) Cottage style garden with herbaceous borders. Wide variety of plants. Kitchen garden

The Old Pumphouse (Mr & Mrs W. Wormell) Cottage garden with mixed borders featuring varieties of pinks and shrub roses. Kitchen garden and greenhouse

Barton House & (Dr I.A. Bewley-Cathie) Barton-on-the-Heath, 3m E of Moreton-in-Marsh. 2m W of A34 at Long Compton; 1m N of A44 at Kitebrook. 5-acres; lawns, trees, flowering shrubs, particularly rhododendrons. TEA. *Adm £1 Chd 25p (Share to Leukaemia Research Fund). Sat, Sun June 13, 14 (2-6)*

Bickmarsh Hall &✗ (Mr & Mrs Jeremy Green) Bidford-on-Avon. 3m S of Alcester. Turn S off A439 Evesham/Stratford-upon-Avon rd at Bidford. Bickmarsh Hall 1½m. Medium-sized garden; lawns, shrubs, roses, clematis, wisterias on walls, flowering cherry trees; walled garden with swimming pool. TEA. *Adm 50p Chd 20p. Sun June 7 (2.30-6)*

Brailes House ✗ (Mrs P.M. Laing) nr Banbury 4m E of Shipston-on-Stour via B4035; gates opp George Hotel, Lower Brailes. 3 acres recently reconstructed; old fashioned roses, shrubs. TEAS. *Adm 50p Chd 25p. Sun June 28 (2-6)*

The Butchers Arms (Mr & Mrs L. Pires) Priors Hardwick, S of Rugby. 6m SE of Southam. From Southam turn right off Daventry rd. 4-acre garden started 1977 (parts very new) informal garden made from S sloping field; island beds with shrubs, trees, old-fashioned shrub roses, hedges, conifers, natural stream and pond. Swimming pool, patio, pergola. C15 stone-built cottage (not open). TEAS. *Adm 50p Chd 20p. Sun June 28 (2-5)*

Cedar House & (Mr & Mrs D. L. Burbidge) Wasperton. 4m S of Warwick on A429, turn right between Barford and Wellesbourne, Cedar House at end of village. 3-acre mixed garden; woodland, shrubs, herbaceous borders, ornamental trees. TEAS. *Adm 60p Chd 20p (Share to St John's Church, Wasperton). Suns June 14, Sept 6 (2.30-6)*

¶**Clifton-on-Dunsmore Gardens** ✗❀ 2m E of Rugby on Market Harborough Rd. TEAS. *Combined adm £1 Chd free. Sun July 19 (2-7)*

Haslemere Cottage, Lilbourne Lane. Small garden; some rare plants

Hall Farm, Lilbourne Lane. Over an acre

Dunsmore House, Lilbourne Lane. 6-acres woodland walk

32 North Rd. ½-acre. TEAS

50 North Rd. Small nice garden; pool

20 North Rd. ½-acre large pool

36 Shuttleworth Rd. Pretty, small pool

30 Shuttleworth Rd. Close planting; lots of colour

Dorsington Gardens & 7m SW of Stratford-upon-Avon. On A439 from Stratford turn left to Welford-on-Avon, then right to Dorsington. TEAS Aberfoyle. *Combined adm £1.30 Chd 30p (Share to St Peter's Church, Dorsington). Sun May 10 (2-6)*

Aberfoyle (Mr & Mrs P.J. Lovell)

Knowle Thatch (Mrs E. Turner)

Manor Farm (Mrs D. Walton)

The Old Rectory (Mr & Mrs N. Phillips)

White Gates (Mr & Mrs G.I. Turner)

Windrush (Mrs M.B. Mills)

¶**Dorsington Manor** ❀ (Mr & Mrs John Shenton) 7m SW Stratford-Upon-Avon. A439. Turn left for Welford second right in Welford, then second left. 28-acres. Large lawn with mixed borders flanked by river with bridges. (Share to St Peters Church, Dorsington) Also open **Dorsington Lodge** (Mr & Mrs R.W. Roberts) New cottage garden graced by large walnut trees. TEAS. *Combined adm 60p Chd 25p. Also open Sun July 19 (2-6)*

Elm Close &❀ (Mr & Mrs E. W. Dyer) Binton rd, Welford on Avon 5m W of Stratford on Avon on A439; turn left after 4½m signed to Welford. Elm Close is ½m on right. ⅔-acre created over last 5 yrs. Large rock garden with many bulbs; azaleas, rhododendrons, hostas, hellebores, peonies, many dwarf conifers, well-established clematis; alpines in troughs. TEAS. *Adm 40p Chd 20p. Suns April 5, May 10; June 7; July 5 (2.30-6)*

Foxcote ❀ (Mr C.B. & the Hon Mrs Holman) 4½m W of Shipston-on-Stour. From A429 Fosse Way, 4m N of Moreton-in-Marsh, turn W, follow signs for Ilmington. Medium-sized terraced garden. Lake walk with magnificent mature trees. TEAS. *Adm 75p Chd free Suns June 14; July 5 (2-6)*

17 Gerrard Street (Miss P.M. & Mr T.K. Meredith) Warwick. 100yds from Castle main gate. Car park at St Nicholas. Small town garden with interesting plants. *Adm 30p Chd 10p. Sat, Suns June 20, 21, Aug 16 (11-1 & 2-6)*

Hickecroft &✗❀ (Mr & Mrs J.M. Pitts) Mill Lane, Rowington, 6m NW of Warwick. 15m SE of Birmingham on B4439 between Hockley Heath and Hatton. Turn into Finwood Rd. (Signed Lowsonford) at Rowington Xrds 1st left into Mill Lane. Re-designed 2-acre garden beginning to mature; unusual plants; mixed borders; lily pond. TEA. *Adm 60p Chd 20p (Share to The Margaret Wharam Choir). Sat & Sun June 27 & 28 (2-6) also by appt (Tel Lapworth 2384)*

¶**Holywell Farm** ♿❀ (Mr & Mrs Ian Harper) Holywell, Nr Shrewley. Henley-in-Arden 5m W. Nearest village Claverdon. 2¼-acre natural garden; lawn, trees and shrubs. Laid out in 1963 for easy maintenance surrounding C16 half-timbered house. *Adm 60p Chd 25p. Sun July 12 (11-6)*

Honington Gardens ✄ 1½m N of Shipston-on-Stour. Take A34 then right ½m signed Honington. TEAS Honington Hall. *Combined adm £1.50 Chd free (Share to Honington Church Restoration Fund). Sun June 28 (2-6)*
8 gardens open including
Honington Glebe(Mr & Mrs J.C.J. Orchard) large informal garden; good collection interesting trees and shrubs
Honington Hall (Sir John Wiggin Bt) Extensive lawns; fine trees. Carolean house (not open); Church adjoining house (open)

¶**Idlecote Gardens** ❀ 3m E of Shipston-on-Stour. TEAS. *Combined adm £1 Chd 30p (Share to Parish Church of St James the Great). Sun July 26 (2-6)*
Idlicote House (Maj & Mrs R.P.G. Dill) About 4-acres. Fine views. Small Norman Church in grounds also statuary and follies. Garden being improved each year. House C18 (not open) listed Grade II partly attributed to Sir John Soane
Home Farm (Mr & Mrs L. Gleed)
Mews Cottage (Mr & Mrs D. Colton)
The Old Rectory (Mr & Mrs D. Higgs)
Woodlands (Capt & Mrs P.J. Doyne) and others

Ilmington Gardens ❀ 8m S of Stratford-on-Avon, 4m NW of Shipston-on-Stour. Ilmington Morris dancers. TEAS Village Hall. *Combined adm £1.50 Chd free (Share to St Mary's Ilmington. Sun July 12 (2-7)*
The Bevingtons Mr & Mrs W. Jones)
Crab Mill (Prof D.C. Hodgkin)
Foxcote Hill (Mr & Mrs M. Dingley)
Foxcote Hill Cottage (Miss A. Terry)
Frog Orchard (Mrs C. Naish)
Grey Cottage (The Misses Parker)
Loreto (Mrs E. Bladon)
The Manor (Mr D. & Lady Flower)
Pear Tree Cottage (Dr & Mrs A. Hobson)
Puddocks (Miss H. Syme)
Rose Cottage (Miss M. James)
1 Washbrook Place (Mrs J.T. Tilley)

Ilmington Manor♿❀ (Dennis L. Flower Esq) 4m NW of Shipston-on-Stour, 8m S of Stratford-on-Avon. Daffodils in profusion; orchard with ornamental trees, shrub and herbaceous borders, topiary, pond garden; fish ponds with Canada geese, ducks etc.

House (not open) built 1600. TEAS. *Adm 80p Chd 30p. Suns April 19, May 24 (2-6), June 21 (2-7)*

Ilmington Old Rectory ♿ (Mr & Mrs David Marland) 4½m NW of Shipston-on-Stour. 4½-acre old established garden with interesting trees, climbing roses and walled kitchen garden. *Adm 40p Chd 20p. Sun May 24 (2-6)*

Ivy Lodge ♿ (Mrs M.A. Willis) Radway 7m NW of Banbury via A41 and B4086 right down Edgehill; 14m SE of Stratford via A422. Left below Edgehill. 4-acres; spring bulbs and blossom; new wildflower area; midsummer roses in trees; shrub roses, site Battle of Edgehill. TEAS. *Adm 60p Chd 30p (Share to Radway Church). Suns May 10 (2-6), July 5 (2-7)*

Loxley Hall ♿ (Col A. Gregory-Hood) 4m SE of Stratford-on-Avon. Turn N off A422 or W off A429 1½m SW of Wellesbourne. Modern sculpture, iris, shrubs, roses, herbaceous, trees. Old Church adjacent can be visited. TEAS. *Adm 80p Chd 20p. Suns May 31 & June 28 (2-7)*

Martineau Centre Gardens ♿❀ (City of Birmingham Education dept) Priory Rd, Edgbaston. From Birmingham S via A38; right at Priory Rd (lights and box junc); entrance 100yds on right opp Priory Hospital. 2-acre demonstration gardens of City Education Dept; hardy ornamentals, vegetables, small orchard; glasshouses; nature reserve/wild garden. Mown field for picnics. *Adm 80p Chd 50p. Sun July 19 (10.30-5)*

Maxstoke Castle ♿✄❀ (Capt & Mrs C.B. Fetherston-Dilke) nr Coleshill, E of Birmingham, 2½m E of Coleshill on B4114 take right turn down Castle Lane; Castle drive 1¼m on right. 4-5 acres of garden and pleasure grounds with flowers, shrubs and trees in the immediate surroundings of the Castle and inside courtyard; water-filled moat round Castle. *Adm 70p, Chd 30p (Share to RNLI). Sun June 21 (2-7)*

The Mill Garden ♿✄❀ (A. B. Measures Esq) Mill St Warwick off A425 beside castle gate. 1-acre; series of informal, partially enclosed areas, on river next to Castle. Superb setting; herb garden; raised alpine beds; small trees, shrubs, herbaceous, unusual and annual cottage plants. Use St Nicholas Car Park. Tea in Warwick. *Collecting box. Every Sun Easter to mid-Oct & other times when possible. For NGS Sats, Suns April 5, 18; June 20, 21; Aug 16; Oct 11 (2-6)*

Packwood House ♿✄ (The National Trust) 11m SE of Birmingham. 1½m E of Hockley Heath on A34. Carolean yew garden representing the Sermon on the Mount. Tudor house with tapestries, needlework and furniture of the period. Tea Baddesley Clinton (NT) Henley in Arden or Knowle. *Adm garden only £1.10; house & garden £1.60 Chd 80p. April - end Sept Wed - Sun & Bank Hol Mons (2-6). (closed Good Friday). Oct Sat & Sun (12.30-4). For NGS. Sun June 7 (2-6)*

Parham Lodge *⚘* (Mr & Mrs K.C. Edwards) Alverston, 2m NE of Stratford-upon-Avon. See directions and description under Alverston Gardens. TEAS. *Adm 50p Chd 10p (Share to Alverston Village Association). Sun April 26 (2-5)*

Puddocks (Miss Helen Syme) Frog Lane, Ilmington 4 m NW of Shipston-on-Stour. Small owner-designed garden with village stream; rockeries, shrubs. Tea Ilmington Manor. *Adm 30p Chd 10p. Suns April 19; May 24 (2-6), June 21 (2-7)*

Redlands &⚘ (Mr & Mrs G.W. Colman) 1 Hartopp Rd, Four Oaks. 2m N of Sutton Coldfield on A5127, fork left onto A454 (Walsall) turn left into Hartopp Rd after ½m. 2-acre garden, rhododendrons, herbaceous, shrubs, clematis, roses. *Adm 60p Chd 25p. Sun July 12 (2-6)*

Rotherwood &⚘❀ (Miss E. M. Kirkpatrick & Miss M. R. Goodison) Warmington. 7m NW of Banbury off A41. ⅓-acre on slope. Terraced beds of foliage, flowering shrubs, heathers, planned for all-year-round interest; some unusual plants. TEAS. *Adm 60p Chd 30p. Sun May 31 (2-6)*

¶**Ryton Gardens** &⚘❀ (The Nat Centre for Organic Gardening) 5m SE of Coventry on B4029 (off A45 to Wolston). 6-acre site demonstrating organic gardening methods: composting display, herb, rose and bee garden; shrub borders; vegetable plots and fruit; conservation area with pond and wild flowers meadow. Shop; childrens play area; cafe serving organically grown food. *Adm £1.20 Chd 75p. Open daily except Christmas and Boxing Day. Apr-Sept (10-6); Oct-Mar (10-4). For NGS Sun Sept 6 (10-6)*

Sherbourne Park &❀ (The Hon Mrs Smith-Ryland) 3m S of Warwick off A49; ½m N of Barford. Medium-sized garden; lawns, shrubs, borders, roses, lilies; lake; temple; church by Gilbert Scott adjacent to house (early Georgian, 1730). TEAS. Free car park. *Adm 80p Chd free (Share to All Saints Church, Sherbourne). Suns May 3, June 14, 28 (2.30-6); Sept 6 (2-6.30); also by appt (Tel 0926 624255)*

The Spring &❀ (Miss H. Martin) Upper Spring Lane, Kenilworth. Off A46 or A452. Bus 518 Leamington-Coventry, alight Water Tower, Kenilworth ½m. Medium-sized garden; azaleas, rhododendrons; herbacous border, rose garden; walled kitchen garden, large lawns. Dogs welcome. *Adm 50p Chd 10p Suns June 7 & July 12 (2-7)*

Stretton-on-Fosse Gardens ⚘ 4m N of More-ton-in-Marsh on A429 (Fosse Way). TEAS The Rectory. *Combined adm 60p Chd 30p (Share to Foundation for Study of Infant Deaths). Suns April 19 & June 28 (2-6)*
Court House & (Mr & Mrs C. J. V. White) 3-acres; rose garden with old shrub roses; herbaceous borders, shrubbery
The Rectory (Mr & Mrs R. Graham) Shrubs, borders, large lawn

Upton House Gardens (The National Trust) 7m NW of Banbury on A422; 2m S of Edgehill. Terraced garden, rockeries, herbaceous borders, roses, water gardens, lawns. TEAS. Coaches by appt. *Adm 50p Chd 20p. △ Suns June 14, 21 (2-6)*

Whichford & Ascott Gardens 6m SE of Shipston-on-Stour. Turn E off A34 at Long Compton for Whichford. Cream TEAS. *Combined adm £1.50 Chd 50p (Share to Leukaemia Research Fund). Sun June 14 (2-7)*
Brook Hollow (Mr & Mrs J.A. Round) Garden on a bank, recently planted; stream and water garden
Combe House (Mr & Mrs D.C. Seel) Hidden, garden surrounding house; mature fine trees
The Gateway (Mrs M.W. Thorne) Large garden; old apple trees; fine views
The Old Rectory (Mr & Mrs R.M. Spitzley) Medium garden with pond, water garden; paved rose garden
Rightons Cottage (Col & Mrs C.R. Bourne) Small garden very well planted; some interesting plants
Stone Walls (Mrs Scott-Cockburn) Walled garden; natural rock garden in old stable. TEA
Whichford House (Mr & Mrs Oakes) Large garden with extensive views. Cream TEAS

¶**86, Woodland Road** ⚘❀ (N.T.L. Jones Esq) Northfield, Birmingham. 7m SW of city centre. Very small garden; varied and interesting plant collection; climbers, shrubs, roses and herbaceous plants. *Adm 30p Chd 10p. Suns Apr 5, May 10, June 7, July 5, Aug 2, Sep 6 (11-5)*

Woodpeckers &⚘❀ (Dr & Mrs A.J. Cox) Marlcliff, nr Bidford-on-Avon 7m SW of Stratford-upon-Avon. Between Bidford-on-Avon and Cleeve Prior on B4085. 2½-acre informal garden designed and maintained by owners; meadow garden; alpines in troughs; pool and bog garden; shrub roses, clematis, white garden. *Adm 50p Chd 10p (Share to NCCPG). Mon April 20 (2.30-6); also by appt March 1 to Sept 30 (Tel Bidford-on-Avon 773416)*

¶**Woolscott Manor** ❀ (Mrs Carolynn Harrison) Nr Grandborough, Rugby. 2m S of Dunchurch. 2-acre flower arrangers garden with many unusual shrubs and plants. Secret patio, herb border, pond. Brick features in garden complement Georgian Farmhouse open for home-made TEAS. Herbs for sale. *Adm 75p Chd 25p. Suns June 14, Aug 2 (2-5.30); also by appt 0788 810275*

Wroxall Abbey School ප්‍රර🌐 (Mrs I.D.M. Iles, Principal) Wroxall 6m NW of Warwick. Nr Fiveways junc on A41. 27 acres; spring flowers, shrubs, rhododendrons, small enclosed flower garden. 'Nature trail' inc comments on plants, flowers, etc. Evensong in Chapel 5pm. TEAS. *Adm 60p Chd 20p (Share to St Leonard's Church, Wroxall). Suns June 7, 14 (2-5)*

WILTSHIRE

Hon County Organiser:
BRIGADIER G.R. FLOOD, Cheverell Mill, Little Cheverell, Devizes SN10 5UP
Assistant Hon County Organisers:
MRS DAVID ARMYTAGE, Sharcott Manor, Pewsey
MRS ANTHONY HEYWOOD, Monkton House, Monkton, Deverell

DATES OF OPENING

BY APPOINTMENT ONLY for dates see text:
THE HALL, Bradford-on-Avon
HOME COVERT, nr Devizes
WESTFIELD PLANTS, Melksham
REGULAR OPENINGS for dates see text:
BROADLEAS, nr Devizes
CHISENBURY PRIORY, nr Pewsey
CORSHAM COURT, nr Chippenham
THE COURTS, Bradford-on-Avon
FITZ HOUSE, Teffont Magna
GREAT CHALFIELD MANOR, nr Melksham
HEALE GARDENS & NURSERY, Middle Woodford
IFORD MANOR, nr Bradford-on-Avon
LITTLECOTE HOUSE, nr Hungerford
SHELDON MANOR, nr Chippenham
STOURHEAD GARDEN, Stourton, nr Mere
STOURTON HOUSE, nr Mere
WANSDYKE NURSERY & PIGMY PINETUM, Devizes

MARCH Sunday 22
THE OLD RIDE, Bradford-on-Avon
APRIL Saturday 11
WANSDYKE NURSERY & PIGMY PINETUM, Devizes
APRIL Sunday 12
BROADLEAS, nr Devizes
FONTHILL HOUSE, nr Tisbury
MANOR HOUSE, Lower Woodford
APRIL Easter Sunday 19
EASTON GREY HOUSE, nr Malmesbury
‡LONG HALL, Stockton, nr Warminster
‡STOCKTON HOUSE, Stockton, nr Warminster
WEDHAMPTON MANOR, nr Devizes

APRIL Easter Monday 20
THE COURTS, nr Bradford-on-Avon
APRIL Wednesday 22
CORSLEY MILL, Corsley
APRIL Sunday 26
ANDOVER HOUSE, Charlton Park, nr Malmesbury
BAYNTON HOUSE, Coulston
CORSLEY MILL, Corsley
‡DRAYTON FITZPAYNE MANOR, nr Pewsey
GREAT CHALFIELD MANOR, Melksham
IFORD MANOR, nr Bradford-on-Avon
‡OARE HOUSE, nr Pewsey
SNARLTON HOUSE, nr Trowbridge
WYLYE VALLEY GARDENS, nr Salisbury
MAY Sunday 3
HAZELBURY MANOR, Box, nr Chippenham
LACKHAM COLLEGE OF AGRICULTURE, nr Chippenham
‡LAKE HOUSE, Lake, nr Salisbury
‡LITTLE DURNFORD MANOR, nr Salisbury
THE OLD RIDE, Bradford-on-Avon
SHARCOTT MANOR, nr Pewsey
MAY Monday 4 (Bank Hol)
HAZELBURY MANOR, Box, nr Chippenham
MAY Saturday 9
HEALE GARDENS & NURSERY, Middle Woodford
‡STOURHEAD GARDEN, Stourton, Mere
‡STOURTON HOUSE, nr Mere
MAY Sunday 10
‡STOURHEAD GARDEN, Stourton, Mere
‡STOURTON HOUSE, nr Mere
MAY Sunday 17
ALDERBURY HOUSE, Alderbury
CORSHAM COURT, nr Chippenham
INWOODS, Farleigh Wick
LONG HALL, Stockton, nr Warminster
MAY Sunday 24
CONOCK MANOR, nr Devizes
LUCKINGTON COURT, nr Chippenham
MAY Monday 25 (Bank Hol)
THE COURTS, nr Bradford-on-Avon
MAY Sunday 31
‡BLAGDEN HOUSE, nr Trowbridge
BOWDEN PARK, Lacock, nr Chippenham
LANDFORD LODGE, Salisbury
‡THE OLD VICARAGE, Edington, nr Westbury
JUNE Saturday 6
‡STOURHEAD GARDEN, Stourton, nr Mere
‡STOURHEAD HOUSE, nr Mere
JUNE Sunday 7
CHISENBURY PRIORY, nr Pewsey
CLARENDON PARK, nr Salisbury
‡STOURHEAD GARDEN, Stourton, nr Mere
‡STOURTON, nr Mere
JUNE Sunday 14
‡KELLAWAYS, nr Chippenham
‡LANGLEY HOUSE, Langley Burrell
THE MILL HOUSE, Calstone Wellington

JUNE Thursday 18
SHELDON MANOR, nr Chippenham
JUNE Sunday 21
FARLEIGH HUNGERFORD GARDENS, nr
Trowbridge
FITZ HOUSE, nr Wilton
LONG HALL, Stockton, nr Warminster
‡MANNINGFORD BRUCE HOUSE, Pewsey
MANOR FARM, West Kington
MANOR HOUSE, Lower Woodford
‡SHARCOTT MANOR, nr Pewsey
JUNE Wednesday 24
CORSLEY MILL, Corsley
JUNE Sunday 28
ANDOVER HOUSE, Charlton Park, nr
Malmesbury
‡BALCONY HOUSE, Sherston
BELCOMBE COURT, Bradford-on-Avon
CHEVERELL GARDENS, nr Devizes
CORSLEY MILL, Corsley
FITZ HOUSE, nr Wilton
‡FOSCOTE GARDENS, Grittleton
HILLBARN HOUSE, Great Bedwyn
LAKE HOUSE, Lake, nr Salisbury
‡THOMPSON'S HILL, Sherston
JULY Wednesday 1
CORSLEY MILL, Corsley
JULY Sunday 5
‡CHISENBURY PRIORY, nr Pewsey
CORSLEY MILL, Corsley
‡THE GRANGE ENFORD, nr Pewsey
THE OLD RIDE, Bradford-on-Avon
JULY Saturday 11
THE MOUNT HOUSE, Great Somerford
JULY Sunday 12
BIDDESTONE MANOR, nr Corsham
CASTLE COMBE GARDENS, nr
Chippenham
‡EAST KENNET MANOR, nr Marlborough
HANNINGTON HALL, nr Swindon
LACKHAM COLLEGE OF AGRICULTURE,
nr Chippenham
‡LOCKERIDGE HOUSE, nr Marlborough
MIDDLEHILL HOUSE, Box
THE MOUNT HOUSE, Great Somerford
JULY Saturday 18
HAZELBURY MANOR, Box, nr
Chippenham
JULY Sunday 19
BAYNTON HOUSE, Coulston
HAZELBURY MANOR, Box, nr
Chippenham
JULY Sunday 26
CORSHAM COURT, nr Chippenham
‡DRAYTON PITZPAYNE MANOR, nr
Pewsey
LITTLE DURNFORD MANOR, nr Salisbury
LUCKINGTON MANOR, nr Chippenham
‡OARE HOUSE, nr Pewsey
WEDHAMPTON MANOR, nr Devizes
AUGUST Sunday 2
‡CHISENBURY PRIORY, nr Pewsey
JOB'S MILL, Crockerton, nr Warminster
‡THE OLD BAKERY, Milton Lilbourne
AUGUST Sunday 9
BROADLEAS, nr Devizes

SEPTEMBER Sunday 27
HILLBARN HOUSE, Great Bedwyn
THE OLD RIDE, Bradford-on-Avon
OCTOBER Sunday 4
LACKHAM COLLEGE OF AGRICULTURE,
nr Chippenham

DESCRIPTIONS OF GARDENS

Alderbury House ⅍⚘ (Mr & Mrs R. Cookson)
Alderbury. 3m SE of Salisbury via A36; turn
W to Alderbury. After 1m Green Dragon on
left; right at Xrds, down Folly Lane; right at
T-junc; house on left opp church. 10 acres
garden and park laid out by Peter Coats. Park
runs down to lake; many fine specimen
trees; bog garden with azaleas; rhododendrons and flowering shrub borders.
Walled garden with herbaceous, well laid out
fruit and vegetables also swimming pool and
good play area for children (both can be
used). C18 listed house (not open) built by
James Wyatt for Fort family of stone from
bell tower of Salisbury Cathedral which
Wyatt demolished. Floral display in Church
(opp). TEAS in aid of St Mary's Church. *Adm
£1 Chd 30p. Sun May 17 (2-6)*

¶**Andover House** ⅍⚘⊛ (Earl & Countess of
Suffolk and Berkshire) Charlton Park. 2m
from Malmesbury on A429 take North Lodge
entrance to Charlton Park. 5-acre garden with
parkland and arboretum. A series of gardens
within the garden with about 500 climbing,
old fashioned and floribunda roses. Many
fine trees, shrubs, herbaceous and herb garden. Drifts of spring bulbs inc many varieties,
many newly planted. C18 Dower House (not
shown) with stable yard. TEA. *Adm £1 Chd
free (Share to NSPCC). Suns April 26, June 28
(2-6)*

¶**Balcony House** ⚘⊛ (Mrs E.M.J.Byrne) High
Street, Sherston, 5m from Malmesbury. Oldest house in Sherston. Small garden with old
fashioned roses, some topiary, small white
garden with yew hedge separating it from
coloured garden. Acid bed with azaleas, rhododendrons, acers etc. Some plants from
Turkey and Greece in conservatory. *Adm 50p
Chd free. Sun June 28 (2-6.30)*

Baynton House ⚘ (Viscount & Viscountess
Petersham) Coulston, 4m E of Westbury. On
B3098 between Edington and Erlestoke. 16
acres with spring bulbs, rock garden, wild
woodland, ornamental wildfowl and water
garden. TEA. *Adm £1 Chd 25p (Share to St
Thomas a Becket Church, Coulston). Suns
April 26; July 19 (2.30-6)*

Belcombe Court ⅍⊛ (Mrs A.J. Woodruff)
Bradford-on-Avon. On Bradford-on-Avon-
Turleigh rd; entrance by de-restriction sign.
2-acre Georgian garden with grotto, Doric
temple, serpentine pool with park and woodland. Fine C18 house by John Wood the Elder

(not shown). TEAS. *Adm 80p Chd 20p (Share to RAF Benevolent Fund). Sun June 28 (2-6)*

Biddestone Manor &⚘ (Princess R. Loewenstein) Biddestone, nr Corsham, 5m W of Chippenham, 3m N of Corsham. On A4 between Chippenham and Corsham turn N; or from A420, 5m W of Chippenham, turn S. Large garden with extensive lawns, small lake, topiary, many unusual shrubs. Fine C17 manor house (not open) with interesting older outbuildings. *Adm £1 Chd 50p. Sun July 12 (2-7)*

Blagden House & (Maj & Mrs Anthony Carr) 4m E of Trowbridge. Turn S off A361 between Devizes and Trowbridge. Medium-sized garden, kitchen garden of general interest. Queen Anne house (not open); stable block. Home-made TEAS. *Adm 60p Chd free. (Share to St John Ambulance). Sun May 31 (2-6.30)*

Bowden Park &⚘❀ (Bowden Park Estate) Lacock, 5m S of Chippenham. From Lacock village take rd to Bowden Hill, Sandy Lane and Devizes; proceed up hill; turn left opp church (entrance for parking top lodge opposite Spye Arch). 12 acres inc horticultural areas, shrubberies, borders, fountains, follies, woodland and water gardens. *Adm £1 Chd 20p OAPs 50p. Sun May 31 (2-6)*

Broadleas &❀ (Lady Anne Cowdray) S of Devizes. Bus: Devizes-Salisbury, alight Potterne Rd. Medium-sized garden; attractive dell planted with unusual trees, shrubs, azaleas and rhododendrons; many rare plants in secret and winter gardens. Home-made TEAS (for parties on NGS days or by prior arrangement). *Adm Suns £1; weekdays 80p; Chd ½-price. April 1 to Oct 30 every Sun, Wed & Thurs. For NGS (Share to Wilts Gardens Trust). Suns April 12, Aug 9 (2-6)*

Castle Combe Gardens &⚘ Chippenham 5m. M4 exit 17 S B4039 Chippenham-Burton. Large carpark clearly signed at top of hill. Originally Norman, now mostly C15, one of England's prettiest villages. Map of gardens available. TEAS in village. *Combined adm £1.50 Chd 25p (Share to RNLI). Sun July 12 (2-6)*

> **61 Whitegate** (Mr & Mrs C.J. Pratt) Small garden with all-year-round planting
> **Old Werretts** (Mr D. Briggs & Mr I. Dixon) ¾ acre with herbaceous border, summer bedding, old-fashioned roses, pond, orchard, young specimen trees
> **April Cottage** (Dr & Mrs W.J. Strang) ½ acre with something of everything
> **Dower House** (Dr & Mrs P.J. King) 1-acre terraced garden with trees, shrub roses, herbaceous border, small pool
> **Mead Cottage** (Mr & Mrs C. Richards) Rear entrance. Small shrub garden
> **Preedy's Cottage** (Mr & Mrs J.A.L. Timpson) Roses, herbaceous border, summer

bedding, lawns, swimming pool (not open)

Cheverell Gardens 5m S of Devizes; turn W off A360 Salisbury - Devizes Rd. Take any rd into Great Cheverell; follow signs to gardens. TEAS Cheverell Mill (in aid of Great & Little Cheverell Churches). *Combined adm £1 Chd 10p or 40p each. Sun June 28 (2-6.30)*

> **The Manor House** (Brigadier & Mrs Oliver Brooke) Great Cheverell, take lane beside Bell Inn. Medium-sized garden; herbaceous borders; roses; interesting very old yew and box hedges
> **Cheverell Mill** ⚘❀ (Brigadier & Mrs G.R. Flood) Little Cheverell; follow signs to Mill. 2 acres created from wilderness since 1972; based on original mill features; shrubs, shrub roses, waterplants beside stream running through garden. Courtyard, conservatory and restored barns. Iron water wheel
> **Hilliers Cottage** (Mrs M.L. Wort) Little Cheverell. Cottage garden planted by owner since 1964. Stream. Many shrubs, roses and unusual plants

Chisenbury Priory &⚘❀ (Mr & Mrs Alastair Robb) 6m SW of Pewsey, turn E from A345 at Enford then N to East Chisenbury, main gates 1m on right. Medieval Priory with Queen Anne face (not open) in middle of 5-acre garden on chalk; walled gardens; mature trees; shrubs; lawns; water; fine herbaceous borders; vineyard. Cream TEAS. Every Wed May to Sept. Adm 50p Chd 25p (Share to Enford Church, June; ARC, July; WGT, Aug). △ For NGS Suns June 7, July 5, Aug 2 (2-6)

Clarendon Park (Mr & Mrs A.W.M. Christie-Miller) 3m S of Salisbury. Via A36, 1½m S of Salisbury, right off dual carriageway at sign to Alderbury; in Alderbury left down Clarendon rd and follow signs for ½m. 12 acres; wild garden with interesting varieties of trees and shrubs, magnificent azaleas and rhododendrons in beautiful wooded setting. Fine Georgian mansion, now open as Conference and functions centre. *Adm £1 Chd free. Sun June 7 (2-6)*

Conock Manor &⚘❀ (Mr & Mrs Bonar Sykes) 5m SE of Devizes off A342. Lawns, borders, flowering shrubs; woodland walk. C18 house in Bath stone. Home-made TEAS. *Adm 50p Chd 20p (Share to Wilts Archaeological & Natural History Soc). Sun May 24 (2-6)*

Corsham Court &⚘❀ (The Lord Methuen) 4m W of Chippenham. S of A4. Bus: 23½ Bath-Chippenham, alight Newlands Rd. Park and gardens laid out by Capability Brown and Repton; trees, flowering shrubs; some rare specimens of flowering trees. Elizabethan mansion; famous Old Masters in C18 state rooms and C18 furniture by Adam etc shown. Tea Methuen Arms, Corsham, by arrangement. *Adm gardens £1.20 Chd 60p; house &*

garden £2.50 Chd £1.20 (parties £1.60 each) (Share to RNLI). △Suns May 17 (2-4) & July 26 (2-6)

Corsley Mill ⚭❀ (Mr & Mrs Charles Quest-Ritson) Corsley. Between Warminster, Westbury and Frome; turn S off B3098 in Chapmanslade. Young 4-acre plantsman's garden on open site with stream. Formal design and stylised planting; 2 rose gardens with 350 different old and species roses; young wood planted for autumn colour; bog garden; National European Primula collection. TEA 28 June, 5 July. *Adm 50p Chd free (Share to Mother Teresa). Suns April 26, June 28 & July 5; Weds April 22, June 24, July 1 (2-5); groups by appt (Tel Chapmanslade 270)*

The Courts ⚭⚯ (Miss E.M. Goff) Holt, 2m W of Bradford-on-Avon, S of B3107 to Melksham. In Holt follow National Trust signs, park at Village Hall. 3½ acres different formal gardens divided by yew hedges, raised terraces and shrubberies. Features inc conservatory, lily pond, herbaceous borders, pleached limes with interesting stone pillars, venetian gates and stone ornaments. 3½ acres wildflower and arboretum; many fine trees inc large Cornus Macrophylla. NT C15 House (not shown). TEA. *Adm £1 Chd free (Share to RSPCA). Mon-Fri April to Oct. For NGS Mons April 20, May 25 (2-6)*

¶**Drayton Fitzpaine Manor** ⚯ (Lady Mary Dunn) Oare, 2m N of Pewsey on A345. Turn left before Oare and follow signs for Stowell. Small 1-acre walled garden with herbaceous borders and climbing plants. Many spring bulbs, pleached limes, gazebo, C15/16 Manor House (not shown). *Adm 50p. Suns April 26, July 26 (2-6)*

¶**East Kennett Manor** ⚭⚯ (Dr & Mrs C.B. Cameron) 5m W of Marlborough; ½m S of A4, approach via West Overton. 3-acre sarsen stone walled garden, featuring long herbaceous border, shrubs, herbs and several small gardens divided by hedges. C18 house (not open) with stable block and dovecote. *Adm 50 Chd free. Sun July 12 (2-6)*

Easton Grey House ⚭❀ (Mrs Peter Saunders) 3½m W of Malmesbury on B4040. Intensively cultivated 9-acre garden of beautiful C18 house. Also contains Easton Grey Church with its interesting Norman tower, font etc. Superb situation overlooking R. Avon and surrounding countryside; lime-tolerant shrubs; tremendous display of spring bulbs; many roses, clematis. Home-made TEAS in garden; produce, cake, and other stalls (in aid of Easton Grey Parish Church). *Adm Cars (inc occupants) £1; adults on foot 25p Chd 10p. Sun April 19 (2-6)*

Farleigh Hungerford Gardens 3½m W of Trowbridge on A366. A36 from Bath and Warminster. TEAS Ravenscroft School in aid of Friends of St. Leonards Church, Farleigh Hungerford. *Combined adm £1 Chd und. 12 free. Sun June 21 (2-6)*

 Farleigh Cottage (Mr & Mrs Anthony May) Thatched house with recently planted garden; shrubs, herbaceous, roses and peonies a speciality. Lovely position with reaching views

 Ravenscroft School (Mr & Mrs J.F.R. Gillam) Extensive lawns with many fine old trees around house; rose and walled kitchen gardens; orchard; glass houses. House (not open)

 Rowley Grange ❀ (Mr & Mrs Arthur King) Parking available. 5-acre terraced garden leading to lawns; herbaceous borders; R. Frome forms boundary line, Farleigh Castle can be seen across it. The house was formerly 'Wiltshire Park Farm'; this side of river was the Wiltshire Park of Hungerford family. Plants for sale in aid of Friends of St Leonards

Fitz House ⚯ (Maj & Mrs Mordaunt-Hare) Teffont Magna village on B3089, 10m W of Salisbury. Hillside terraced gardens frame listed group of stone buildings in one of Wiltshire's prettiest villages. C16-C17 house (not open) admired by Nikolaus Pevsner in his Wiltshire Guide. The gardens, bordered by yew, beech hedges and stream, are haven of tranquillity planted with spring bulbs, blossom, azaleas, profusion of roses, clematis, honeysuckles, vines and mixed borders. Much new planting in last two years. Many scented plants. TEAS. *Adm £1 Chd 50p. Suns April; Weds & Suns May to Sept (2-6). For NGS Suns June 21, 28 (2-6)*

◆**Fonthill House** ⚭❀ (The Lord Margadale) 3m N of Tisbury. W of Salisbury via B3089 in Fonthill Bishop. Large woodland garden; rhododendrons, azaleas, shrubs, bulbs; magnificent views; formal garden. TEAS. *Adm 75p Chd 30p (Share to Wiltshire House). Sun April 12 (2-6)*

Foscote Gardens ⚭❀ Grittleton, 5m NW of Chippenham. A420 Chippenham-Bristol; after 2m turn right on B4039 to Yatton Keynell; fork right for Grittleton; in village for 2m; just over motorway turn right at Xrds; house on right. Home-made TEAS Foscote Stables. *Combined adm 70p Chd 20p. Sun June 28 (2-6)*

 Foscote Stables (Mr & Mrs Beresford Worswick). 2½ acres; many clematis; shrub roses; unusual shrubs, trees; small collection ornamental ducks; adjoining Victorian cottage garden

 Foscote House (Mr & Mrs John Lendrum) adjacent, C16 cotswold stone house visited by Cromwell during Civil War (not open) surrounded by compact 1½-acre garden; mainly lawns, shrubs and trees planted since 1970

The Grange Enford ♿🚫 (Maj & Mrs A.M. Everett) 6m S of Pewsey. From A345 at Enford across Avon bridge; turn right 300yds. Garden on R. Avon surrounding Queen Anne farmhouse; ornamental pool; trout stream; walled gardens; shrubs, water-loving plants; large conservatory, climbing plants and shrubs. TEAS in aid of local church. *Adm 50p Chd free. Sun July 5 (2-6)*

¶Great Chalfield Manor 🚫 (The National Trust) 4m from Melksham. Take B3107 from Melksham then first right to Broughton Gifford signed Atworth, turn left for 1m to Manor. Park on grass outside. Garden and grounds of 7-acres laid out 1905-12 by Robert Fuller and his wife; given to NT in 1943, it remains the home of his family. Garden paths, steps, dry walls relaid and rebuilt in 1985/6 by Manpower Services Commission (NT scheme); daffodils, spring flowers; topiary houses, borders, terraces, gazebo, orchard, fine mulberry tree. C15 moated manor (not open) and adjoining Church. *Adm £1 Chd free (Share to All Saints' Church, Great Chalfield). △Sun April 26 (2-6)*

The Hall 🚫 (Dr A.E. Moulton) Bradford-on-Avon; nr town centre, on B3107. Large garden beside R. Avon with lawns, fine trees; interesting acoustic baffle fence. Fine example of Jacobean house set on high terrace. *Collecting Box. Open by appt only*

Hannington Hall ♿ (Mrs A.F. Hussey-Freke) Hannington, 5m N of Swindon. 2m NW of Highworth; from B4019 Highworth-Blunsdon, at Freke Arms, turn N for Hannington. 3 acres. Well preserved ice house. Very interesting house built 1653 (not open). TEAS. *Adm 50p Chd free. Sun July 12 (2-6)*

Hazelbury Manor 🚫 (Mr & Mrs I.D. Pollard) nr Box. 5m SW of Chippenham; 3m NE of Bath; 3m N of Bradford on Avon. From A4 at Box, take A365 to Melksham, left onto B3109; left again at Chapel Plaister; drive immediately on right. 8 acres of formal gardens, shrubs, mixed and herbaceous borders, yew topiary, large rockery with waterfall, pond, beech and laburnum walks, mediaeval archery walk, designed and developed on very human scale. C15 fortified Manor House with Elizabethan additions; Great Hall with Minstrel Gallery and central cloistered courtyard. TEA. *Adm £1.50 Chd 75p. Sun, Mon May 3, 4 ; Sat, Sun July 18, 19 (2-6)*

Heale Gardens & Nursery ❀ (Maj David & Lady Anne Rasch) Middle Woodford, 4m N of Salisbury on Woodford Valley Rd between A360 and A345. 8 acres besides R Avon; interesting and varied collection of plants, shrubs; musk and other roses in formal setting of clipped hedges and mellow stonework; water garden with magnolia and acers around authentic Japanese Tea House and Nikki bridge. C16 House, largely unchanged since Charles II sheltered here after the battle of Worcester in 1651. TEA. Easter - Autumn Mon - Sat & 1st Sun of month. *Adm £1 Chd under 14 free. Sat May 9 (10-5). For NGS*

Hillbarn House 🚫❀ (Mr & Mrs A.J. Buchanan) Great Bedwyn, SW of Hungerford. S of A4 Hungerford-Marlborough. Medium-sized garden on chalk with hornbeam tunnel, pleached limes, herb garden; some planting by Lanning Roper; a series of gardens within a garden. Swimming pool may be used (under 12). TEA. *Adm 50p Chd 30p. Suns June 28 & Sept 27 (2-6)*

Home Covert (John & Sarah Phillips) Roundway, 2m N of Devizes. Off A361 to Swindon, signed to Roundway 1m. At trading estate fork left at tel kiosk, down steep hill, signed at crest. 33 acres of mixed woodland on upper greensand. 6-acre plateau and water garden at lower level. Plants more botanical than purely decorative nature. Wide range of species inc ericaceous. Mixture of trees, shrubs, plants and good autumn colour. *Collecting box (Share to Wilts Garden Trust). Small parties by appt (Tel Devizes 3407)*

Iford Manor (Mr & Mrs J.J.W Hignett) 2½m SW of Bradford-on-Avon. Entrance through gates at Iford Bridge by the lanes from Westwood or from A36. Medium-sized terraced garden with shrubs, plants and bulbs of interest. Italian marbles and bronze. Cloisters; many examples of archaeological interest. House not shown. TEAS Suns from 3.30pm. *Adm £1 OAPs/Chd 70p (Share to Christian Aid). May to August every Wed & Sun (2-5). For NGS Sun April 26 (2-5)*

Inwoods ♿🚫 (Mr & Mrs D.S. Whitehead) Farleigh Wick, 3m NW of Bradford-on-Avon. From Bath via A363 towards Bradford-on-Avon; at Farleigh Wick, 100yds past Fox & Hounds, right into drive. 5 acres with lawns, borders, flowering shrubs, wild garden, bluebell wood. TEAS. *Adm 50p Chd 20p. Sun May 17 (2-6)*

Job's Mill ❀ (The Marquess & Marchioness of Bath) Crockerton, 1½m S of Warminster. Bus: Salisbury-Bath, alight Warminster. Medium-sized garden; small terraced garden, through which R. Wylye flows; swimming pool; kitchen garden. TEA. *Adm 60p Chd 30p (Share to The WWF). Sun Aug 2 (2-6.30)*

Kellaways ♿🚫❀ (Mrs D. Hoskins) 3m N of Chippenham. A420 from Chippenham, 1st right through Langley Burrell on East Tytherton Rd. From M4, exit 17 (Chippenham/Cirencester) follow signs to Sutton Benger thence right to East Tytherton and Calne. 2 acres; early C17 Cotswold stone house; walled garden; herbaceous borders; irises, roses, shrubs; rock garden; collection old roses, many unusual plants. TEAS. *Adm 75p Chd 30p. Sun June 14 (2-7); also by appt March-Nov with Tea by arrangement (Tel Kellaways 203)*

Lackham College of Agriculture &⊛ (Wiltshire County Council: Principal Peter W. Morris Esq) Lacock, 4m S of Chippenham. Signposted N of Notton on A350. Few mins S of junc 17 on M4. Station: Chippenham. Bus: Chippenham-Trowbridge, alight drive entrance, 1m walk. Large gardens; walled garden with greenhouses, carnations, alstroemeria, pot plants, warm greenhouse plants, propagating house, fuchsias, begonias; lawn paths separating plots well laid out, labelled with great variety of interesting shrubs, usual and unusual vegetables, herbaceous plants, fruit. Pleasure gardens, mixed borders, herbs, shrubs, lawns; woodland down to river; large bird viewing hide. Raffle drawn shortly after demonstrations at 3.30pm; lawn care (May), ground cover (July), outdoor chrysanthamums (Oct). Particulars of Lackham full and part-time courses available. Light refreshments. Teas for coach parties by arrangement in advance. *Adm £1 Chd free (Share to Great House Cheshire Home, Kington Langley). Suns May 3, July 12, Oct 4 (2-6)*

Lake House &⊛ (Capt. O.N. Bailey, RN) Lake, 7m N of Salisbury; S of Amesbury on Woodford Valley Rd. Station: Salisbury. Large, mainly informal grounds; rose and herbaceous gardens; water; old yew hedges; pleached lime alley; peacocks. Jacobean gabled and flint house (not shown). TEAS. *Adm 50p Chd free. Suns May 3, June 28 (2-7)*

Landford Lodge ⊛ (Mr & Mrs Christopher Pilkington) 9m SE of Salisbury turn W off A36; garden ½m N of Landford. C18 House (not open) in lovely parkland overlooking lake; many fine trees. Special feature 3-acre wood with rhododendrons and azaleas. Herbaceous; ornamental terrace and swimming pool (open). Tree nursery. TEAS. *Adm 75p Chd free. Sun May 31 (2-6)*

Langley House &⊗⊛ (Mr & Mrs A.L. Scott-Ashe) Langley Burrell. 2m NE of Chippenham on A420; 300yds from Langley Burrell rd junc. 5-acre formal garden and parkland; magnificent old trees; mainly herbaceous with shrubs, old fashioned roses and lily pool. Lovely old coach house and stabling. C18 Georgian Manor (not open); C12 Saxon Church with Kilvert the diarist connections (open). TEA. *Adm 50p Chd 20p (Share to Wilts Gardens Trust). Sun June 14 (2-7)*

Littlecote House &⊛ (Peter de Savary Esq) 3m W of Hungerford. 1m off A4 and A419; good signposts. 6-acres lovely Tudor walled gardens; trout stream. Historic Tudor manor c. 1490-1520; Great Hall with unique Cromwellian armoury. In park Roman villa with mosaic floor. Jousting and falconry display

daily. Restaurant. *Adm not known on going to print.* △ *Collecting box for NGS*

Little Durnford Manor & (Earl & Countess of Chichester) 3m N of Salisbury, just beyond Stratford-sub-Castle. Extensive lawns with cedars; walled garden, fruit trees, vegetables; small knot and herb gardens, terraces, borders, water garden, lake with islands, river walks. TEA. *Adm 50p Chd free (Share to Wessex Medical School Trust). Suns May 3, July 26 (2-6.30)*

Lockeridge House &⊗ (Mr & Mrs P. Lowsley-Williams) Lockeridge. 2m W of Marlborough via A4 turn S, ¼m on right. 2 acres with R. Kennet running through; herbaceous, rose garden, shrub roses. TEAS. *Adm 50p Chd free. Sun July 12 (2-6)*

¶**Long Hall** ⊗⊛ (Mr & Mrs N.H. Yeatman-Biggs) Stockton 7m SE of Warminster. S of A36; W of A303 Wylye interchange. Follow signs to church in Stockton. Park in street. 4-acre mainly formal garden; a series of gardens within a garden; herbaceous gardens, shrub rose gardens; chipped yews; small vine walk; flowering shrubs, fine old trees; woodland walk with masses of spring bulbs; fine hellebore walk. C13 Hall with later additions (not open). *Adm 60p Chd free (Share to Wilts Trust for Nature Conservation). Suns April 19, May 17, June 21 (2-6)*

Luckington Court &⊛ (The Hon Mrs Trevor Horn) Luckington village, 10m NW of Chippenham; 6m W of Malmesbury. Turn S off B4040 Malmesbury-Bristol. Bus: Bristol-Swindon, alight Luckington. Medium-sized garden, mainly formal, well-designed, amid exquisite group of ancient buildings; fine collection of ornamental cherries; other flowering shrubs. House much altered in Queen Anne times but ancient origins evident; Queen Anne hall and drawing-room shown. TEAS in aid of Luckington Parish Church. *Collecting box. Sun May 24 (2.30-6)*

Luckington Manor & (W. Greville Collins Esq) NW of Chippenham. 7½m SW of Malmesbury on B4040 Malmesbury-Bristol. 4 acres; 3 walled flower gardens; shrubberies; young arboretum. TEA. *Adm 50p Chd 25p (Share to St John Ambulance). Sun July 26 (2-5)*

¶**Manningford Bruce House** &⊗ (Maj & Mrs Robert Ferguson) Manningford Bruce 2m SW of Pewsey on A345 on right after Manningford Bruce sign. From Upavon/Devizes 1m after Woodbridge Inn on left. 1½ acres; lawns, shrubbery and walled garden of C11/C18 Rectory (not open). Herbaceous borders with many unusual plants, shrubs and a folly. Small kitchen garden. Owner maintained. Picnics allowed in car park. *Adm 50p Chd 10p. Sun June 21 (2-6)*

Manor Farm ৬✗ (Sir Michael & Lady Farquhar) West Kington 8m NNW of Chippenham, 2m NE of Marshfield; exit 18 on M4. Take A420 Chippenham/Bristol road N signed West Kington; in village take No Through Rd at Xrds. 1-acre; roses, herbaceous plants, shrubs and trees planted since 1978. TEAS. *Adm 50p Chd 20p (Share to West Kington Church). Sun June 21 (2-6)*

¶**Manor House** ✗ (Major Sir Richard & Lady Rasche) Lower Woodford, 4m Salisbury on Salisbury/Amesbury lower rd, W of rd in middle of village. 3-acre garden surrounding small Queen Anne Manor House, spacious lawns, many fine trees with shrub and shrub rose borders. Drifts of spring bulbs;walled kitchen garden. TEA. *Adm 50p Chd free (Share to National Autistic Society). Suns April 12 (2-5), June 21 (2-6)*

¶**Middlehill House** ✗ (Mr & Mrs Ronald Banks) nr Box, turn W from A4 at Northey Arms, signed 'Middlehill, Ditteridge and Colerne'. Buses from Bath and Chippenham, alight Northey Arms, 5 mins. Intensive garden created around C18 Regency-fronted house with glass-covered Italian verandah. Cultivated herbaceous borders, lawns, many roses and shrubs leading to natural woodland with rare trees. Pools containing ornamental fish. TEAS. *Adm 50p Chd free. Sun July 12 (2-7)*

The Mill House ৬ (Mr & Mrs Richard C. Wheeler-Bennett) Calstone Wellington. 2m E of Calne on A4 turn S; left after ½m at Theobalds Green. 2 acres inc recent landscape design features of swimming pool with associated terracing and planting; new parterre in medieval style; hedges and woodland planting to give structure and interest. Also vineyards planted in 1982 with winery in restored tiled barns. Fine C18 Mill House (not open) with Malt House on R. Marden. TEAS in aid of Cancer Research. *Adm 50p Chd 30p. Sun June 14 (2-7)*

The Mount House ৬✗❀ (Maj & Mrs Peter Phillips) Great Somerford. 4m SE Malmesbury. M4 Exit 16/17 S of B4042 Malmesbury-Swindon; East of A429 Malmesbury-Chippenham to Gt Somerford. Follow signs to house beside Church. 2-acre informal garden recreated from wilderness from 1957 by owners with limited help; herbaceous and mixed borders inc shrubs and old fashioned roses; swimming pool a principal feature landscaped into a walled garden at different levels; kitchen garden enclosed by espaliers; many unusual plants. Small C16 manor house (not shown). TEAS. *Adm 50p Chd 10p. Sat, Sun July 11, 12 (10.30-6.30)*

Oare House (Henry Keswick Esq) 2m N of Pewsey on Marlborough Rd (A345). Fine house (not shown) in large garden with fine trees, hedges, spring flowers, woodlands;

extensive lawns and kitchen garden. TEAS. *Adm 40p Chd 10p (Share to The Order of St John). Suns April 26, July 26 (2-6)*

¶**The Old Bakery** ✗❀ (Joyce, Lady Crossley) Milton Lilbourne E of Pewsey on B3087. Turn down village street by garage at X-rds. The Old Bakery is opp churchyard. Fairly intensive 1-acre garden. Mixed shrub and herbaceous plantings. 3 small glasshouses; small rock garden; some rare plants. TEAS. *Adm 50p Chd free. Sun Aug 2 (2-6)*

The Old Ride ৬❀ (R.J. Willder Esq) Bradford-on-Avon via A363 to Bath, house on junc to Trowbridge, well signed. Many varieties mature trees in lovely setting; prolific spring flowers, particularly daffodils, rose garden; good autumn colours. TEA. *Adm 40p Chd 20p (Share to Save the Children Fund). Suns March 22; May 3; July 5; Sept 27 (2-6)*

The Old Vicarage ৬❀ (J.N. d'Arcy Esq) Edington. On B3098 beside turning to church and Steeple Ashton. 1½ acres with herbaceous borders, shrubs, trees and woodland plants. National Oenothera collection. TEAS Blagden House. *Adm 50p Chd 25p (Share to Wilts Gardens Trust). Sun May 31 (2-6)*

Sharcott Manor ৬✗❀ (Capt & Mrs David Armytage) 1m SW of Pewsey via A345. 5 acres with water; redesigned since 1977 with a lot of new planting for all-year interest; many young trees; shrubs, old roses, foliage plants. Small collection of ornamental waterfowl. TEAS. *Adm 50p Chd free (Share to IFAW). Suns May 3, June 21 (2-6); also by appt & parties welcome (Tel: 067 263485)*

Sheldon Manor ৬ (Maj M.A. Gibbs) 1½m W of Chippenham turn S off A420 at Allington Xrds. Eastbound traffic signed also from A4. Formal garden around C13 house (700yrs old); collection of old-fashioned roses in profusion; very old yew trees; many rare, interesting trees and shrubs. Buffet lunches and cream TEAS. *Adm house & garden £2; Garden only £1 Chd free. March 28 to Oct 4 every Sun, Thurs & Bank Hol. For NGS Thurs June 18 (12.30-6)*

Snarlton House ❀ (Mr & Mrs Adrian Butler) Wingfield. 2½m Trowbridge/Bradford. Midway between Wingfield Xrds and Farleigh Hungerford; opp pair of cottages, turn down farm track. 1½-acre newly created gardens with frontage on R. Frome. Large variety shrubs, herbaceous and spring bulbs; conservatory; interesting alpine garden sloping down to riverside walk. C16 farmhouse. Morning coffee and TEAS (in aid of Dorothy House). *Adm 50p Chd free (Share to Dorothy House, Bath). Sun April 26 (10-5)*

¶**Stockton House** ৬ (Mr & Mrs A.Bell) 8m from Warminster SW of junc off A303 and A36; from junc take Wylye, then Stockton directions. 20 acres of parkland with fine trees and drifts of spring bulbs. Herbaceous garden, roses, lawns; extensive views; exceptional C16 listed Elizabethan House (not shown) with listed outbuildings. TEA. *Adm 50p Chd free. Sun April 19 (2-6)*

Stourhead Garden ⅄⅍ (The National Trust) Stourton, 3m NW of Mere on B3092. One of earliest and greatest landscape gardens in the world; creation of banker Henry Hoare in 1740s on his return from the Grand Tour, inspired by paintings of Claude and Poussin; planted with rare trees, rhododendrons and azaleas over last 240yrs. Open every day of year. Lunch, tea and supper Spread Eagle Inn at entrance. NT shop. *Adm March 1 to May 14 & July 1 to Nov 30; £1.50 Chd 80p; parties of 15 & over £1.20 each; May 15 to June 30 £2 Chd £1; parties of 15 & over £1.50 each. △ For NGS Sats, Suns May 9, 10 June 6, 7 (8-7) (Buffet service Village Hall)*

Stourton House ⅄⅍⅊ (Anthony & Elizabeth Bullivant) Stourton, 2m NW of Mere (A303) on rd to Stourhead, park in Nat Trust car park. 4-acres informal gardens; much to attract plantsmen and idea seekers. Interesting bulbs, plants and shrubs through all seasons. Speciality daffodils and hydrangeas. Well known for 'Stourton Dried Flowers' whose production interests visitors (BBC Gardeners World '81). Tea Village. *April 1 to Nov 29 every Sun, Wed, Thurs & Bank Hol. For NGS Adm £1 Chd 25p (Share to St John Ambulance). Sats, Suns May 9, 10; June 6, 7 (11-6)*

Thompson's Hill ⅍⅊ (Mr & Mrs J.C. Cooper) Sherston. 5m Malmesbury/Tetbury. In Sherston village turn left at Church down hill, bear right up Thompson's Hill. ½-acre fully planted, interestingly designed garden made since 1980. Illustrated in House & Garden Magazine and next issue The Englishwoman's Garden. *Adm £1 Chd free. (Share to Cancer Research). Sun June 28 (2-6.30)*

Wansdyke Nursery & Pygmy Pinetum ⅄ (Mr & Mrs D van Klaveren) Hillworth Rd, Devizes. At S end of Devizes, turn into Hillworth Rd; pinetum on left. Bus: Bath-Salisbury; alight; Market Place, Devizes 1m. Small specialist nursery and pinetum containing largest collection of dwarf and slowgrowing conifers in Britain; other interesting plants. TEA. *Adm 50p Chd free. All year Mon-Sat; Mon-Fri (8-5); Sats (9-12.30). For NGS Sat Apr 11 (10-5)*

Wedhampton Manor ⅍ (Mrs E.L. Harris) 5m SE of Devizes. Off N side of A342 (nr junc with B3098) Moderate-sized 'homely' garden; general mixed interest; a remarkable rare specimen cut-leaved lime. Fine Queen Anne house (not open). TEA. *Adm 40p Chd 20p (Share to Order of St John). Suns April 19 July 26 (2-6)*

Westfield Plants ⅍⅊ (Terence & Mary Baker) Westfield Cottage, Great Chalfield. 4m SW of Melksham. From Melksham take roundabout exit for Broughton Gifford. After village common turn left to Gt Chalfield Manor (NT), then right up private road 1m. ⅓-acre plantsman's garden devoted to cultivation and propagation of wide range of interesting and rare trees, shrubs, and border perennials planted for year-round effect. Small nursery offering largest range of choice and uncommon hardy plants in Wiltshire. TEA. *Adm 50 Chd free (Share to British Institute for Brain Damaged Children). Open all year by appt; coach parties by arrangement (Tel 02216 5133)*

¶**Wylye Valley Gardens** ⅍ 9-11m NW of Salisbury; S of A36 Salisbury/Warminster; 1-3m E of A303 Wylye interchange. Follow signs. TEAS Hanging Langford Village Hall in aid of Staple Langford Church. *Adm £2 or 50p each garden Chd free. Sun April 26 (2-6)*

Ballington Manor ⅄ (Mr & Mrs David McCormick) Wylye 1m E of A303 interchange. Lovely parkland down to R. Wylye with many old trees. Masses of spring bulbs. Elizabethan garden, pond, grange, mill house, kitchen garden. C16 Manor (not open) with unique dovecote

Corpus Christie House ⅄⅊ (Walter Dowa Esq) Steeple Langford 3m E of A303 interchange. Turn down Duck Street in village centre; park in street. C17 house (not open) in lovely walled garden with herbaceous, shrubs, old fashioned roses and naturalised bulbs. Brew house/dovecote, coach house, tythe barn, stableyard. Orchard; kitchen garden

Manor House Farm ⅄ (Miss Anne Dixon) Hanging Langford. Follow signs from Staple Langford. There is also a footpath through the meadows (10 mins), over R. Wylye between the two villages and gardens. Series of walled gardens with masses of bulbs, herbaceous, many shrubs, old fashined roses, collection of clematis and paeonies. Ornamental pond; secret garden in walls of old shearing barn; superb walnut. C14/16 Wiltshire manor house (not open)

Mill House (Mrs Robin Huntington) Steeple Langford. Short walk from Duck Street through churchyard. Lovely position on R. Wylye millstream with leat stream through garden; views of church and over watermeadows down Wylye valley. Spring bulbs in small garden; lawns, shrubs, trees

YORKSHIRE

Hon County Organisers:
(N Yorks - Districts of Hambleton, Richmond, Ryedale & Scarborough)

MRS WILLIAM BALDWIN, Riverside Farm,
Sinnington, York YO6 6RY
(West & South Yorks & North Yorks Districts
of Craven, Harrogate, Selby & York)
LADY VEALE, West House, Wetherby
LS22 4NH
Asst Hon County Organiser:
MISS MARY WELLBURN, 1 Caxton Street,
Wetherby

DATES OF OPENING

REGULAR OPENINGS for dates see text:
CONSTABLE BURTON HALL GARDENS,
nr Leyburn
GILLING CASTLE, Gilling East
LAND FARM, nr Hebdon Bridge
NEWBY HALL, Ripon

APRIL Easter Sunday 19
OLD SLENINGFORD, nr Ripon
ST NICHOLAS, Richmond
APRIL Easter Monday 20
OLD SLENINGFORD, nr Ripon
APRIL Sunday 26
THE DOWER HOUSE, Great Thirkleby
NETHERWOOD HOUSE, nr Ilkley
PARCEVAL HALL GARDENS, Skyreholme
MAY Sunday 3
THE GRANGE, West Burton
LING BEECHES, Scarcroft
MAY Monday 4 (Bank Hol)
THE GRANGE, West Burton
MAY Wednesday 6
WASS GARDENS, nr Helmsley
MAY Saturday 23
NAWTON TOWER, nr Helmsley
MAY Monday 25 (Bank Hol)
NAWTON TOWER, nr Helmsley
SHANDY HALL, Coxwold
MAY Sunday 31
ANDANTE, Bardsey
78, LEEDS ROAD, Selby
SILVER BIRCHES, Scarcroft
JUNE Thursday 4
BILTON BROW, York
JUNE Saturday 6
BROUGHTON HALL, Skipton
PENNYHOLME, nr Kirbymoorside
YORK GATE, Adel, Leeds 16
JUNE Sunday 7
BILTON BROW, York
LITTLE HILLA GREEN, Hackness
PENNYHOLME, nr Kirbymoorside
YORK GATE, Adel, Leeds 16
JUNE Saturday 13
PENNYHOLME, nr Kirbymoorside
JUNE Sunday 14
BRIERY WOOD, Ilkley
CROSLAND HALL, Netherton
78, LEEDS ROAD, Selby
NAWTON TOWER, nr Helmsley
THE OLD RECTORY, Wath
PENNYHOLME, nr Kirbymoorside

RYEDALE HOUSE, Helmsley
ST NICHOLAS, Richmond
YORK HOUSE, Claxton
JUNE Friday 19
NUNNINGTON HALL, Ryedale
JUNE Sunday 21
THE DOWER HOUSE, Great Thirkleby
JUNE Sunday 28
ARTHINGTON HALL, nr Otley
NORTON CONYERS, Wath
PARCEVAL HALL GARDENS, Skyreholme
WYTHERSTONE HOUSE, Pockley
JULY Saturday 4
SLEIGHTHOLME DALE LODGE, nr
Kirbymoorside
JULY Sunday 5
THE HEATH, Long Causeway
SLEIGHTHOLME DALE LODGE, nr
Kirbymoorside
YORK HOUSE, Claxton
JULY Wednesday 8
SHANDY HALL, Coxwold
JULY Sunday 12
COPT HEWICK HALL, nr Ripon
GALPHAY MANOR, Ripon
78 LEEDS ROAD, Selby
SHANDY HALL, Coxwold
SILVER BIRCHES, Scarcroft
SINNINGTON GARDENS, nr Pickering
SPRINGFIELD HOUSE, Tockwith
STOCKELD PARK, nr Wetherby
JULY Sunday 19
ASKHAM BRYAN COLLEGE, York
GRIMSTON MANOR FARM, Gilling East
HOVINGHAM HALL, nr Malton
30, LATCHMERE ROAD, Leeds 16
TAN COTTAGE, Cononley
JULY Sunday 26
HIGH DALBY HOUSE, Thornton Dale
30 LATCHMERE ROAD, Leeds 16
78 LEEDS ROAD, Selby
AUGUST Sunday 2
30 LATCHMERE ROAD, Leeds 16
AUGUST Sunday 9
NORTON CONYERS, Wath
AUGUST Sunday 16
SETTRINGTON HOUSE, Malton
SEPTEMBER Sunday 6
PARCEVAL HALL GARDENS, Skyreholme

DESCRIPTIONS OF GARDENS

Andante (Mrs J.L. Jackson & Miss V. A.
Pennington) Bardsey; A58 out of Leeds to
Wetherby, turn left into Church Lane (signed
Bardsey), through village centre; at top of
hill, right into Blackmoor lane; garden 4th on
right. Small rural garden in the making. Informal plan; lawns, rockeries, heather beds,
herb garden, maturing borders. 40m views to
Kilburn's White Horse. TEA. *Adm 30p Chd
10p. Sun May 31 (2-6)*

Arthington Hall ✗ (C.E.W. Sheepshanks Esq)
5m E of Otley, A659. Large garden; part wal-

led; fruit, vegetables; glasshouses, mixed borders, arboretum; heathers; woodland walks. Fine views. TEA. *Adm 75p Chd 10p (Share to Harlow Car NHS). Sun June 28 (2-7)*

¶**Askham Bryan College of Agriculture & Horticulture** &⚘ (North Yorkshire County Council). 4m W of York on A64. 15 acres, lawns, shrubs, herbaceous, woodland garden, small arboretum, demonstration beds, pond, display glasshouses. *Adm 75p Chd 20p. Sun July 19 (2-5)*

¶**Bilton Brow** (Mr & Mrs H.A. Schmidt) Bilton-in-Ainsty. 4m W of Wetherby on the B1224. Modest 1½-acre garden, maintained by owners. Water garden in the making. TEAS. *Adm 50p. Thurs, Sun June 4, 7 (2-6)*

Briery Wood &⚘ (Mrs M.B. Marshall) Hebers Ghyll Drive, Ilkley. Bear left at traffic lights in town centre; Brook St, turn right into The Grove; then bear up Hebers Ghyll Rd; Briery Wood last on right up Hebers Ghyll Drive. 4acres; fine rhododendrons, azaleas, spring shrubs, conifers. Fine views over Blue Bell woods up Wharfedale. TEAS. *Adm 60p Chd 30p (Share to Harlow Car) Sun June 14 (2-6)*

Broughton Hall (H.R.Tempest Esq) 3½m W of Skipton adjoining A59. 10 acres of pleasure grounds laid out by WA Nesfield in 1856 and now finest surviving example of his work. TEA. *Adm £1 Chd 50p. Sat June 6 (2-5)*

•**Constable Burton Hall Gardens** & (Charles Wyvill Esq) 3m E of Leyburn on A684, 6m W of A1. Bus: United No. 72 from Northallerton alight at gate. Large garden, woodland walks; something of interest all spring and summer; splendid display of daffodils; rockery with fine selection of alpines (some rare); extensive shrubs and roses. Beautiful John Carr house (not open) in C18 park; small lake with wildfowl. Beautiful countryside at entrance to Wensleydale. *Adm 50p; reduction for large parties (Tel Bedale 50428). April 1 to Aug 4 daily (9-6)*

Copt Hewick Hall &⚘⚘ (Earl & Countess of Ronaldshay) 2m E of Ripon. 1½m W of A1 at Dishforth roundabout. 3½ acres; old roses, shrubs, walled gardens, conservatory. Home-made TEAS. *Adm 50p OAPs/Chd 25p. Sun July 12 (2-5.30)*

Crosland Hall ⚘ (Mr & Mrs R.M. Brook) Netherton; A616 S from Huddersfield, continue on B6108 signed Meltham; then through Netherton; ¾m turn left signed Healey House. Garden on left; look for 'Auto Systems'. 6-acres; trees and spring flowering shrubs. TEA. *Adm 75p Chd 50p. Sun June 14 (2-6)*

The Dower House & (Mr & Mrs H. Coupe) Great Thirkleby. 4m from Thirsk on A19 on alternative route avoiding Sutton Bank. Cottage garden, bulbs and shrubs. Spring collec-

tion of shrub, species roses and clematis; two ponds with wildlife. TEA. *Adm 50p Chd free (Share to Ripon Choral Soc, April, St Leonards Hospice, June). Suns April 26 & June 21 (2-6)*

Elvington Hall & (Mrs Pontefract) 8m SE of York. From A1079, immediately after leaving York's outer ring rd, turn S on to B1228 for Elvington; entrance at far end of village. 3-4 acre garden being re-constructed for easier management; terrace overlooking lawn sloping down to Ings; fine trees, rockery, swimming pool and sanctuary with fishpond. Lawrence Sterne lived here at one time with his aunt. TEA. *Adm 60p Chd 30p. Sun June 7 (2-5)*

Galphay Manor & (Mr & Mrs David Hopkins) Ripon; take B6265 SW out of Ripon after 1m turn right. Formal garden: lawns, borders, rock garden; C17 house (not shown) TEA. Coaches by appt. *Adm 50p Chd 25p. Sun July 12 (3-5)*

Gilling Castle ⚘ (The Rt Revd the Abbot of Ampleforth) Gilling East, 18m N of York. Medium-sized garden. *Adm 50p Chd free. For NGS July & Aug daily (10-dusk)*

The Grange &⚘⚘ (Mr G. Wooler) West Burton. A1 to Bedale; A684 through Leyburn; 6m from Leyburn fork left on B6160 for 1m. Well-established small garden about 100yrs old; interesting conifers, rock garden and shrubs. Home-made TEAS (Suns only). *Adm 60p Chd 30p. Sun & Mon May 3 & 4 (2-6)*

Grimston Manor Farm &⚘ (Richard & Heather Kelsey) Gilling East: 17m N of York; 7m S of Helmsley on B1363, follow 'Kelseys Roses' sign 1m S of Gilling East. Medium-sized garden, profuse and varied plants suitable for dry soils. Coach parties by appt. *Adm 60p Chd 10p. Sun July 19 (2-6)*

The Heath & (Richard Wainwright Esq MP) Long Causeway, Adel, Leeds 16. From A660 Leeds-Otley, right at Ring Rd roundabout; then left at traffic lights. Buses from city centre. 6 acres; herbaceous and rose borders; over 100 varieties of exhibition delphiniums; lawns; trees; fine views. Picnicking in grounds. *Adm 70p Chd 10p (Share to NT). Sun July 5 (2-7)*

¶**High Dalby House** ⚘ (Lady Whittaker) 4m from Thornton Dale on Whitby Road. 1m right turn Forest Drive, past Dalby village, bear left, house 1m. Informal 5-acre garden in forest with stream, large shrub area, beautiful natural situation. TEAS. *Amd 60p Chd 10p. Sun July 26 (2-6)*

Hovingham Hall & (Sir Marcus & Lady Worsley) 8m W of Malton. House in Hovingham village, 20m N of York; on B1257 midway between Malton and Helmsley. Medium-sized garden; yew hedges, shrubs and herbaceous borders. C18 dovecote; Riding School; Cricket ground. Tea Worsley Arms Hotel, Hovingham. *Adm 60p Chd 30p (Share to York Area Appeals Committee for Mental Health). Sun July 19 (2-6)*

Land Farm ⚘⚭ (J. Williams Esq) Colden, nr Hebden Bridge. From H.B. follow rd to Burnley for 3m, by pass Heptonstall; right at edge Hey Green at some wooden garages; follow signs. 1acre inc alpine; herbaceous, formal, heather. Elevation 1000ft N facing. C17 house. *Collecting Box for NGS. April 1 to Sept 30 daily (10-6)*

30 Latchmere Rd ⚘⚭ (Mr & Mrs Joe Brown) Leeds, 16. A660 from City Centre to Lawnswood Ring Rd roundabout; turn sharp left on to ring rd A6120 for ¼m to 3rd opening on left Fillingfir Drive; right at top of hill then 1st left, 3rd house on left. Bus stop at gate (Bus every ½ hr); 74 & 76 from City Centre; 73 from Greenthorpe. A small garden full of interest; fern garden; herbaceous borders; alpine garden; glade; camomile lawn; 2 pools; patio built of local York stone; sink gardens; collection of 50 clematis. Small limestone garden. Featured Sunday Telegraph Magazine & TV with Yehudi Menuhin in 'Fiddling with Nature' 1985. *Adm 40p Chd 20p (Share to GRBS & RGOF). Suns July 19, 26, Aug 2 (2.30-6)*

78 Leeds Rd ⚭ (Mr & Mrs R. Marshall) Selby. 1 m from Selby on A63 Leeds rd (approachable from M62 or A1; Selby turn off). ½-acre suburban garden, of particular interest to plant lovers; mature clematis, conifers, roses, small shrubs, herbaceous border, several alpine troughs, small pool and rockery. TEA. *Adm 30p Chd free. Suns May 31, June 14, July 12, 26 (2-6)*

Ling Beeches ⚘⚭⚭ (Mrs Arnold Rakusen) Ling Lane, Scarcroft 7m NE of Leeds. A58 mid-way between Leeds and Wetherby; at Scarcroft turn W into Ling Lane, signed to Wike on brow of hill; garden ⅓m on right. 2-acre woodland garden designed by owner emphasis on labour-saving planting; unusual trees and shrubs; ericaceous plants, but some species roses, conifers, ferns and interesting climbers. Featured in The English Woman's Garden and Gardens of Yorkshire and Humberside (Batsford Series). TEA. *Adm 60p Chd 30p. Sun May 3 (2-6) also by appt (Leeds 892450)*

Little Hilla Green ⚭⚘⚭ (Mr & Mrs J. Guthrie) Hackness. 7m NW of Scarborough; Langdale End Rd out of Hackness; ½m left turn to Troutsdale; ½m 1st house on left. 1 acre garden in fine valley, alpines, pond, walled garden, herbs. TEAS. *Adm 60p Chd 30p. Sun June 7 (2-6)*

Nawton Tower ⚭⚘ (Mr & Mrs D. Ward) Nawton, 5m NE of Helmsley. From A170, between Helmsley and Nawton village, at Beadlam turn N 2½m to Nawton Tower. Large garden; heaths, rhododendrons, azaleas, shrubs. Tea Helmsley and Kirbymoorside. *Adm 60p Chd 30p. Sat, Mon May 23, 25; Sun June 14 (2-6). also open by appt*

Netherwood House ⚭ (Mr & Mrs Peter Marshall) 1m W of Ilkley on A65 towards Skipton; drive on left, clearly marked Netherwood House. Daffodils, spring flowering shrubs, duck pond. *Adm 60p Chd 30p (Share to Harlow Car). Sun April 26 (2-6)*

Newby Hall ⚘⚭ (R.E.J. Compton Esq) Ripon. 25 acres extensive gardens laid out in 1920s; small seasonal gardens reputed longest double herbaceous borders to R. Ure. C19 statue walk; woodland discovery walk. LUNCHES & TEAS in licensed restaurant. Gift shop. *Adm House & garden £2.50 OAPs £2.20 Disabled/ Chd £1.30; Garden only £1.60 OAPs £1.50 Chd £1.20. April 1 to Oct 25 daily (House closes Oct 4), ex Mons, but inc Bank Hols (11-5.30)*

Norton Conyers ⚭⚘ (Sir James Graham Bt) 3½m N of Ripon. Take Melmerby turn off A1, or Wath sign off A61 Ripon-Thirsk. Large C18 walled garden in full cultivation; interesting borders and orangery; old fashioned and unusual hardy plants a speciality, many for sale. TEAS (Aug only). *Adm 50p Chd free. Suns June 28; Aug 9 (2-5.30)*

¶**Nunnington Hall** ⚭⚘ (The National Trust) 4½m SE Helmsley, signed ½m from Helmsley on A170 Thirsk rd (Sproxton turn off). Signed at Welburn on A170 Scarborough to Helmsley rd. 8-acre garden and grounds in 5 distinct areas. Mature sycamores, underplanted with shrubs and bulbs in car park; woodland of ash and sycamore with riverside hybrid rhododendrons and blossom trees. West garden with lawns, beech hedge, specimen trees and shrub borders. Main walled garden with formal lawns, rose beds, mixed borders, apple/pear orchards, clematis collection, cherry avenue, specimen trees and terraced shrubberies. Large, old copper beech tree. Privy/Tea garden offers picnic facilities by river amongst clematis and aromatic plants. TEAS. *Adm 75p Chd 20p, Fri June 19 (2-6)*

¶**The Old Rectory** ⚘ (Mrs Bemrose) Wath. 5m from Ripon off the A61 Ripon-Thirsk rd, 1½m off the A1. 6½ acres of grounds inc lawns, unusual shrubs, walled garden and terrace. *Adm 50p Chd 25p. Sun June 14 (2.30-5.30)*

Old Sleningford ⚭ (Mr & Mrs Ramsden) 5m W of Ripon, off B6108. After North Stainley take 1st or 2nd left; follow sign to Mickley for 1m from main rd. Unusual, interesting 3-acre garden with extensive lawns, interesting trees; woodland walk; exceptionally lovely lake and islands; mediaeval mill; walled kitchen garden; herbaceous border, yew hedges, huge beech hedge, Victorian fernery; flowers and grasses grown for drying. Home-made TEAS. *Adm 70p Chd 30p (Share to Spennithorne, Home of Healing). Sun & Mon April 19 & 20 (2-6); also by appt*

Parceval Hall Gardens ❀ (Walsingham College) Skyreholme, 12m N of Skipton. From Grassington on B6265 turn S at Hebden Xrds, follow signs to Burnsall, through Appletreewick to Parceval Hall. 20 acres in Wharfedale; shelter belts of mixed woodland, fine trees; terraces; fishponds; rock garden; tender shrubs inc Eucryphia Crinodendron, camellia; bulbs; rhododendrons; orchard for picnics, old varieties of apples; autumn colour; birds in woodland; splendid views. *Adm 50p Chd 25p. △ Suns April 26, June 28, Sept 6 (10-6)*

Pennyholme (Mr C.J. Wills) Fadmoor, 5m NW of Kirbymoorside. From A170 between Kirbymoorside and Nawton, turn N, ½m before Fadmoor turn left, signed 'Sleightholmedale only' continue N up dale, across 3 cattlegrids, to garden. No Buses. Large, wild garden on edge of moor with rhododendrans, azaleas, primulas, shrubs. Tea Kirbymoorside. *Adm 60p Chd 10p (Share to York Area Appeals Committee for Mental Health). Sats, Suns June 6, 7, 13, 14 (11.30-5)*

Ryedale House ຝ (Dr & Mrs J.A. Storrow) 41 Bridge Street, Helmsley. On A170, 3rd house on right after bridge into Helmsley from Thirsk-York. ¼-acre walled garden; varieties of flowers, shrubs, trees, herbs. Teashops in Helmsley. *Adm 60p Chd 30p (Share to CPRE). Sun June 14 (2-6)*

♦**St Nicholas** ⚘ (The Lady Serena James) 1m S of Richmond. On Brompton Catterick Bridge rd, ½ way down hill after leaving Maison Dieu. Bus: Darlington-Richmond, alight The Avenue, 500yds. Medium-large garden of horticultural interest, shrubs, topiary work. TEA Terrace House Hotel, Richmond. *Adm 50p Chd 25p. Suns April 19 & June 14 (all day)*

¶**Settrington House** (Sir Richard Storey) 4m E of Malton. Turn off A64 at Scagglethorpe. Settrington House 2m, next to Settrington Church. Late C18 garden with herbaceous border; woodland and lakeside walks; herb garden. TEA. *Adm 60p Chd 20p (Share to Salvation Army, Malton Corps). Sun Aug 16 (2-6)*

Shandy Hall ⚘❀ (The Laurence Sterne Trust) Coxwold, N of York. From A19 7m from both Easingwold and Thirsk turn E signed Coxwold. C18 walled garden, 1-acre, with low-walled beds. Home of C18 author, Laurence Sterne, who made the house famous. Craft shop in grounds. Tea Coxwold (Schoolhouse Tea Room; home baking). *Adm 60p Chd 30p (Share to Laurence Sterne Trust). Mon May 25; Wed July 8; Sun July 12 (2-4.30)*

Silver Birches ຝ⚘❀ (Mr & Mrs S.C. Thomson) Ling Lane, Scarcroft, 7m NE of Leeds. A58 mid-way between Leeds/Wetherby; at Scarcroft turn W into Ling Lane, signed Wike; garden ½m up lane on S side. Bus: Leeds/ Wetherby, alight Ling Lane, ½m. 2½-acre woodland garden; foliage trees and shrubs; many conifers, rhododendrons, azaleas; good collection of heaths and heathers; pond, aquatic plants; climbers and roses. TEAS. *Adm 60p Chd 20p (Share to Harlow Car, NHS). Suns May 31, July 19 (2-6); also by appt June to Oct for parties*

Sinnington Gardens ຝ⚘ 4m W of Pickering on A170. A group of gardens. Tickets on village green. TEAS. *Combined adm 75p Chd 10p. Sun July 12 (2-6)*

Sleightholme Dale Lodge ❀ (Mrs Gordon Foster; Dr & Mrs O. James) Fadmoor, 3m N of Kirkymoorside. 1m from Fadmoor. Hillside garden; walled rose garden, rock garden, shrubs. *Not* suitable for wheelchairs. No coaches. TEAS. *Adm 60p Chd 30p. Sat, Sun July 4, 5 (2-7) also by appt*

¶**Springfield House** ⚘❀ (Mr & Mrs S.B. Milner) Tockwith. 5m E of Wetherby; 1m off B1224. Garden at west end of village. 1½-acres. Walled garden with herbaceous borders, water and rock gardens. Rose and conifer garden; shrub walk. Wide variety of plants. TEA. *Adm 50p Chd 25p. Sun July 12 (2-6)*

Stockeld Park ຝ❀ (Mrs Gough) 2m NW of Wetherby. On A661 Wetherby-Harrogate Rd; from Wetherby after 2m entrance 2nd lodge on left. Bus: Wetherby-Harrogate, alight Stockeld lodge gates (¼m drive). Listed grade 1 house and garden. 4 acres with lawns, grove and flowers, fine trees and roses. House built 1758 for Col Middleton by James Paine (listed Grade 1). C18 pigeon cote. Chapel 1890. TEAS. *Adm £1.25 Chd 50p. Sun July 12 (2.30-5.30)*

Tan Cottage ⚘ (Mr & Mrs D.L. Shaw) West Lane, Cononley. Take A629; turn off to Cononley 2½m out of Skipton; top of village turn right onto Skipton rd. ½-acre plantsman's garden adjoining C17 house (not open). Interesting plants, many old varieties; collection of primulas. TEA. *Adm 80p Chd 50p. Sun July 19 (2.30-5)*

Wass Gardens ⚘❀ ¼m from Byland Abbey on Coxwold-Ampleforth rd. 6m SW of Helmsley turning from A170. 9m E of Thirsk; turn from A19 signed Coxwold. Free parking and TEAS at Wass Village Hall. A group of gardens in the village may be visited. *Combined adm 75p Chd 20p obtainable at Car Park or under Lime tree at the Xrds. Wed May 6 (2-6)*

Wytherstone House ♿✗❀ (Lady Clarissa Collin) Pockley, 3m NE of Helmsley from A170 signpost. Medium-large garden; roses, rock garden, shrubs, lawns; lovely views, beech hedges; geraniums and pelargoniums a speciality. TEAS (Proceeds to Pockley Village Activities). *Adm 60p Chd 20p. Sun June 28 (2-6)*

York Gate ✗ (Mrs Sybil B. Spencer) Back Church Lane, Adel, Leeds 16. Behind Adel Church on Otley Rd out of Leeds (A660). Bus: WY 34 Leeds-Ilkley; alight Lawnswood Arms, ½m. An owner-made and maintained garden of particular interest to the plantsman, containing orchard with pool, an arbour, minia-ture pinetum, dell with stream, Folly, nut-walk, peony bed, iris borders, fern border, herb garden, summerhouse, alley, white and silver garden, vegetable garden, pavement maze, Sybil's garden, all within 1 acre. NO COACHES. *Adm 75p Chd 10p. Sat, Sun June 6, 7 (2-6)*

York House ♿❀ (Mr & Mrs W.H. Pridmore) Claxton, 8m E of York, off A64. 1-acre plantsman's garden, created by owners since 1975; old roses, herbaceous, shrubs, fruit. TEAS at shop. *Adm 60p Chd 20p (Share to Northern Horticultural Society). Sun June 14, July 5 (2-6); also by appt (Tel Flaxton Moor 360)*

Stop Press

See Hampshire, page 83

Pennington Chase♿✗ (J. B. M. Coates Esq) 2m SW Lymington on A337, behind Pennington Cross garage. 4 acres, flowering shrubs, azaleas and rhododendrons with some unusual trees in fine state of maturity. *Adm 50p Chd 25p. Suns April 12 & May 24 (2-7)*

See Kent, page 103

Hever Castle, Edenbridge, Kent. FESTIVAL OF FLOWERS 25th, 26th, 27th September 1987. Benefiting Charities, the National Gardens Scheme and Sandy Gall's Afghanistan Appeal. For further information telephone Edenbridge (0732) 865224. *For directions see page 103, normal opening times and admission rates will apply.*

The National Gardens Scheme hope you enjoy visiting some of the many gardens included in this book, for our Diamond Jubilee year. We feel sure that you would wish to join us in saying "Thank You" to the Owners for the great generosity they display in allowing us all to share their gardens.

THE CORNWALL GARDENS FESTIVAL

19 April to 4 May 1987
A glorious celebration for garden lovers everywhere

From 19 April to 4 May 1987. While the rest of Britain is still cold and wintry, over 40 beautiful Cornish gardens will be open to the public.

To celebrate the 75th Anniversary of the Cornish County Flower Show – always a magnificent spectacle – the Garden Festival will be centred at the world famous Trelissick Gardens – near Truro. A unique collection of trees, shrubs and plants on the theme 'The contribution of Cornish plant hunters and raisers to British Horticulture.' Plus archive material, video films and a plant clinic will be on view.

The Festival, however, extends to every corner of Cornwall. From westerly gardens – like Tresco at the Isles of Scilly to Ince Castle and Mount Edgcume in the East. The great valley gardens of Trebah, Glendurgan and Penjerrick are on view; and Caerhays, renowned for magnolias, rhododendrons and camellias. Private gardens, smaller wild flower gardens and examples of exoticas and rock plants are all there to be admired. Truly a dream opportunity for garden lovers everywhere.

Full colour brochure from: Cornwall Tourist Board, Station Road, Truro, Cornwall. Telephone: 0872 41313.

A legacy to be proud of

THE WILDFOWL TRUST
Registered Charity No. 204184

Started in 1946 by Sir Peter Scott to save wild swans, geese and ducks for future generations.

Seven Centres in Britain welcome visitors. They provide facilities for people to enjoy the world's wildfowl close at hand in pleasant surroundings.

This unique way of conservation needs help now and for the future.

Information on the Trust (including opening times), and a leaflet on legacies is available from The Wildfowl Trust (J), Slimbridge, Glos. GL2 7BT. Tel: (045389) 333 Ext. 239

CAERLAVEROCK
WASHINGTON
MARTIN MERE
PEAKIRK
WELNEY
SLIMBRIDGE
ARUNDEL

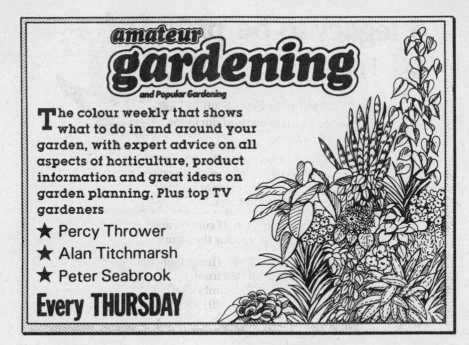
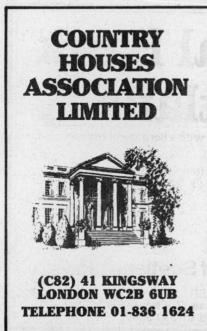

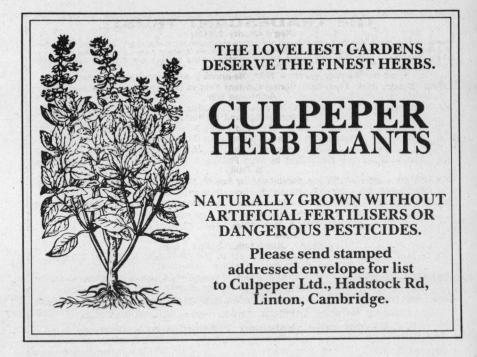

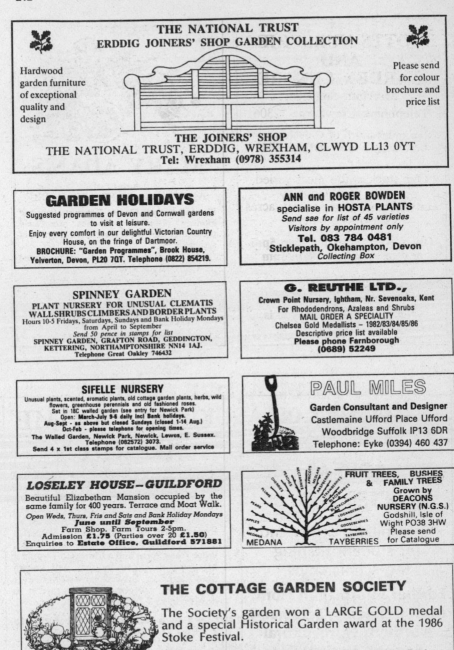

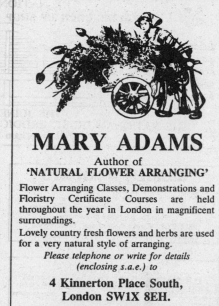

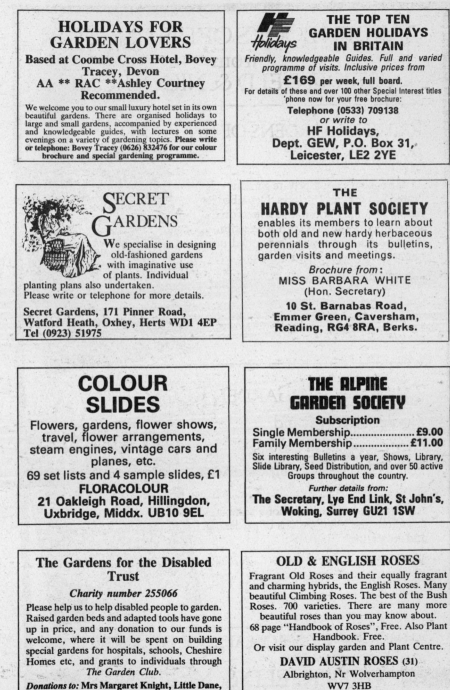

You are cordially invited to
a study day in aid of

The National Gardens Scheme Charitable Trust
and
The Gardens for the Disabled Trust

on
Thursday, 18th June 1987
at
The English Gardening School,
Chelsea Physic Garden, London SW3

For further details and costs please contact:
Mrs Heather Fooks
Dale Hill Farmhouse
Ticehurst
East Sussex   TN5 7DQ

Advertisers Index

Notes

Notes

THE COUNTIES OF ENGLAND

AND WALES

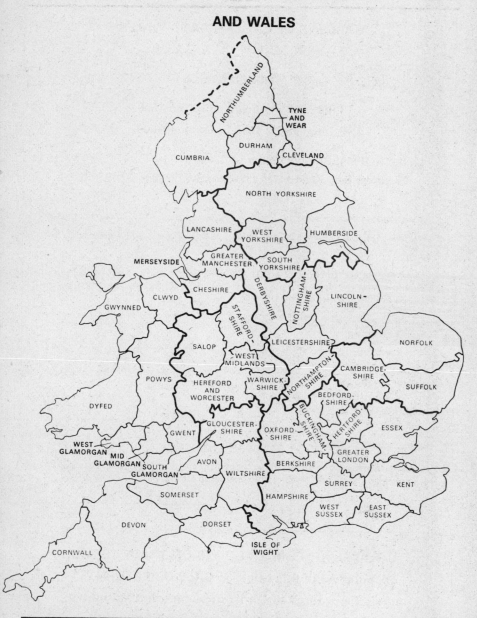

Map by courtesy of the Staples Printing Group

GARDENS OF ENGLAND AND WALES
OPEN TO THE PUBLIC 1988

PUBLISHED MARCH

PRICE: £2.25, including UK postage

(Europe £2.25; USA or Canada $8.00)

To: The National Gardens Scheme

57 Lower Belgrave Street, London, SW1W 0LR   01-730 0359

Please send to the address below ....copy/copies of

Gardens of England and Wales, for which I enclose Postal Order/Cheque

value..

(Postal Orders and Cheques should be made payable to The National Gardens Scheme and crossed. If sending money from abroad please use International Stamps or International Money Order).

Name (Mr/Mrs/Miss) ....
(BLOCK LETTERS)

....

Address ....
(BLOCK LETTERS)

....

....

Date ....

Note: The book/s will be posted on publication. If meantime you wish to receive an acknowledgement of your order, please enclose an s.a.e.

TO THOSE WHO ORDER BOOKS ON TRADE TERMS:
Supplies of this book on SALE OR RETURN
should be ordered direct from our trade distributors:
SEYMOUR

334 Brixton Road, London SW9 7AG

(Tel. 01-733 4444)